AIDS

BIOLOGICAL WARFARE

© T. E. Bearden 1988

All Rights Reserved

Cover Illustration by Patricia Pedersen

TESLA BOOK COMPANY
P.O. Box 1649
Greenville, Texas 75401

ISBN 0-914119-04-4
Copyright 1988 • All rights reserved
Printed in the United States

TESLA BOOK COMPANY
P. O. BOX 121873
CHULA VISTA, CA 91912

Dedication

This book is sincerely dedicated to the millions of persons who have died needlessly of cancer, leukemia, and AIDS in the last two and half decades. They were men, women, and children. Some were weak, some were strong. Some died in agony, some died silently. All of them were our fellow human beings. We remember them. They were important. Their anguish cries out to be heard. God willing, the new electromagnetic medicine so long suppressed will flower, and save the millions otherwise yet to die.

Special Acknowledgements

Mr. Christopher Bird's kind permission to print his summary of the Priore Affair is gratefully acknowledged, as is the contribution of his own extensive Priore research material to this effort. The author owes a great debt indeed to Chris Bird for his magnificent assistance.

Mr. Robert Whitney graciously contributed rare photographs of Antoine Priore's device and also translations of background papers by French scientific journals. His previous valiant though fruitless efforts to bring the Priore machine into the mainline of Western medical treatment are specifically recognized and commended.

Vital contributions by Drs. Robert B. and Theodore A. Strecker are particularly acknowledged. Their March 1986 alert to the federal government, that AIDS was a deliberate biological attack spawned by Soviet agents working in Western research laboratories, is specially pointed out.

Heroic efforts by Dr. John Seale and other scientists to alert the medical research community to the true source of AIDS is specifically recognized and gratefully acknowledged.

Continuing efforts by Dr. William C. Douglass to "tell it like it is" on the AIDS crisis is specially pointed out. His permission to extract and present an excerpt from his research, pointing out tested healing of viral infections by UV irradiation of the blood, is deeply appreciated.

The unyielding and continuing efforts of Dr. Eva Snead, to alert the national authorities to the fact that there is more to AIDS than meets the eye, is also particularly recognized and appreciated.

Decades of effort by John Crane to bring Royal R. Rife's work out of suppression are specifically recognized and appreciated.

Important scalar EM experiments by John Bedini and Frank Golden are fully recognized and deeply appreciated. Their experimental efforts over a period of years have profoundly influenced my own thinking and understanding.

As always, my great admiration and deep thanks go to my friend Hal Crawford, whose keen artistic vision and skilled hand have contributed key illustrations to my work for years.

Other important illustrations and artwork by Messrs. James Thomas Neumann and Lee Giles are gratefully acknowledged.

Photographs furnished by John Moray showing his father's pioneering free energy work are appreciated. T.H. Moray's genius and achievements will yet be recognized.

Support from the Association of Distinguished American Scientists and Mr. Richard J. Reynolds III is deeply appreciated. Without that support, this effort could not have been accomplished.

Important contributions from a host of other colleagues and persons are deeply appreciated. These persons include Frank Golden, John Bedini, Ken Moore, Tom McLaughlin, Joe Parrot, Randy Davidson, George Fencl, Andrew Michrowski, Stefan Possony, Tony Gideon, Electra Briggs, and many others too numerous to mention.

Finally, nothing that I have attempted could have been accomplished at all without the unflinching and loyal support of my beloved wife, Doris.

To all of you I owe a great deal. If this bizarre struggle to save humanity is ever won, it will largely be due to the significant contributions you have made.

Thomas E. Bearden
Jan. 17, 1988

TABLE OF CONTENTS

TABLE OF CONTENTS

TABLE OF CONTENTS

TABLE OF CONTENTS

TABLE OF CONTENTS

LIST OF FIGURES

LIST OF FIGURES

LIST OF FIGURES

LIST OF FIGURES

LIST OF TABLES

LIST OF TABLES

Chapters 4 and 5 contain complex scientific material and are suggested for those who are technically proficient.

FOREWORD

What This Book is About
In my book, "**Fer-de-Lance: A Briefing on Soviet Scalar Electromagnetic Weapons,**" (Tesla Book Co., P.O. Box 1649, Greenville, Texas 75401, 1986), I specifically pointed out that I was of necessity neglecting the biological warfare (BW) aspects. I intended to later write a second book covering the BW aspects.

This book contains the most important item of that planned second book, including the photobiology aspects of BW.

The material is put down in great haste, for it is meant to serve as an urgent warning. There is no time to do the six months additional research and compilation necessary to "flesh it out", sculpture it and meticulously document it , as should be done by a careful scholar.

I apologize to the reader for this lowered standard, but in this case the basic information is far more important than scholarship.

Further, I acknowledge the fundamental contributions of Dr. Robert B. Strecker, M. D., Ph. D., who together with his brother Ted, has for some time urgently called attention to the terrible threat posed by the AIDS epidemic.

I specifically acknowledge his important warning, "This is a Bio-Attack Alert," Mar. 28, 1986, which was sent to the U. S. President and Vice-President, Governors of the states, various federal agencies such as Departments of State, Defense, and Agriculture; National Security Agency, Federal Bureau of Investigation, Central Intelligence Agency; and three members of Congress.

Dr. Strecker has also strongly pointed out the covert involvement of Soviet and other communist agents in the epidemic, and the absolute necessity for an *electromagnetic* solution.

Also recognized are the efforts of the other medical scientists, such as Dr. John Seale, M.D., and Dr. Eva Snead, who have tried repeatedly to call attention to the nature of the AIDS initiation, only to have their submitted papers resoundingly rejected by important journals such as **New Scientist, The Lancet,** etc.

Work by Dr. William C. Douglass in alerting the public to the no-nonsense truth about aids is particularly recognized. His monthly newsletter, **The Cutting Edge**, is an oasis of clarity sharply standing out in a sea of misinformation. Permission to reproduce his published research article on UV irradiation of the blood to successfully heal viral infections is deeply appreciated.

The continuing efforts of Dr. Andrija Puharich and Dr. Robert Beck to assist in achieving an AIDS solution are pointed out and recognized. Important contributions by Ed Skilling are also recognized in this regard.

The vital and extensive contributions of Christopher Bird are particularly acknowledged. Chris has unstintingly and unselfishly shared with me the results of his enormous research on the Priore device and affair and the results of his translations from the French. He has most graciously permitted me to publish his important summary of the Priore affair, and I am greatly in his debt. The reader will find that material most illuminating, and well may be shocked at the depth and malevolence of the scientific and political suppression of Priore's rigorously demonstrated electromagnetic cure for cancer, leukemia, and other killer diseases.

Special acknowledgement is made to Robert Whitney, who so nobly labored to bring the Priore technology into the mainstream of medical treatment, only to be ruthlessly suppressed in his efforts. Photographs of the Priore machine were furnished by Bob from his collection.

My special thanks to colleagues John Bedini, Frank Golden, Andrew Michrowski, George Fencl, Ken Moore, Tom McLaughlin, Joe Parrott and Randy Davidson, without whose assistance this project could not have been accomplished.

The material in this present small book is intended to be of any assistance possible to certain brave colleagues who — with little or no funds or resources except what they can tear out with their bare hands — are already laboring around the clock to develop a permanent solution to the AIDS problem.

As a matter of discretion, I shall not mention the names of those colleagues. The solution sought is radical, by orthodox assessment. Yet it is the only possible approach that has any chance whatsoever of succeeding.

What they are doing, I cannot do. If they do not succeed, no one can. But I will say this, and most strongly: In my view, the only hope for humanity lies in the work they are doing, and they have my utmost admiration and support.

Their initial results are exciting and encouraging. Basic phase conjugated electromagnetic "mixed-modulations" signals lethal to bacteria, nematodes (hookworm-like organisms), various amoeba, viruses, etc. at very weak power levels have been synthesized and demonstrated.

In my best estimate/opinion, these researchers must succeed in *two years or less, certainly in no longer than three years,* else the AIDS incubation already accomplished by then, and the implementation time delay — even given a cure —together will insure a devastation of humanity unparalleled in all of history.

Let me accent that developing this AIDS cure is far more important than developing our entire arsenal of new military weapons. It is even more important than the development of defenses against the Soviet scalar electromagnetic weapons I detailed in **Fer-de-Lance.** Problems in the Middle East, Korea, and Nicaragua are insignificant compared to the AIDS problem.

Desperate Diseases, Desperate Remedies

Spurred by the looming holocaust of AIDS, and by the strong efforts of my colleagues, I have decided to release specific *information on how to develop electromagnetic healing, essentially against any and all of the "killer" diseases including cancer, leukemia, and AIDS.*

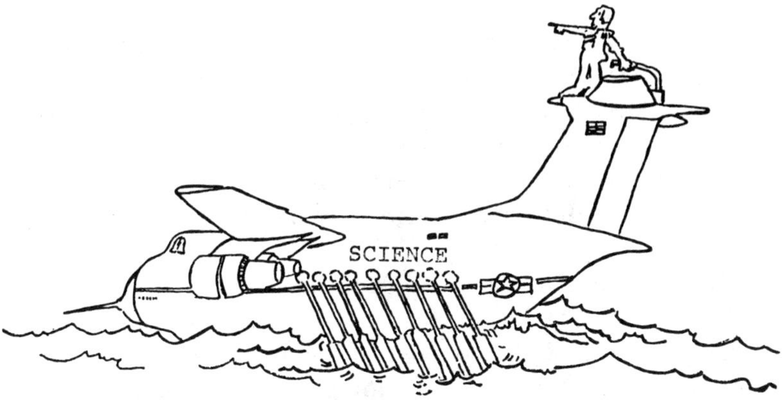

Figure 1. Conventional science cannot do the job.

Unavoidably this also releases a major principle of scalar electromagnetics: what is really going on in phase conjugation. If phase conjugation is truly understood and applied, all the Soviet weapons I have pointed out in **Fer-de-Lance** can be understood, designed and developed.

I'm also releasing specific information on mind and thought that will enable them to eventually be directly detected, measured, and investigated scientifically. Unfortunately, this also will enable them to be technologically manipulated for nefarious purposes.

However, the developing scalar EM technology for the AIDS cure must not be hamstrung. There is no time to apply the standard "Let's classify it!" response. If we do, we'll win the skirmish and lose the war.

As shocking as it sounds, I am convinced that the Soviets have already launched WW III, to the hilt. And it's not at all the kind of war we've been expecting.

There's no time to rail against the Soviets, who have cunningly and in great secret "struck our vitals with the mailed fist." We've been struck in such a way that, *unless we can solve the AIDS problem in two to three years or less, we are already finished.*

We have been preparing to fight a better World War II. The one we're preparing for is never going to be fought. The real World War III is already raging. Our death knell has been sounded, *and we've not yet even recognized that the battle is underway.*

A great Soviet "first strike to finish us" has already been accomplished. The new "Pearl Harbor" has already happened. The enemy has already overrun our Maginot Line; we are at our Dunkirk. There are no boats waiting, and there are none on the way.

The great Soviet first strike has been delivered with surreptitious biological warfare, not with nuclear weapons or ground forces.

As always in the past, we have almost no troops facing the brunt of the first strike and trying to turn it. This time we have far fewer than we've ever had. Just two or three unorthodox researchers. All the orthodox researchers are manning the wrong ramparts.

Ironically, this time our entire system—the government, the medical establishment, the scientific establishment, the universities — all are far too dogmatic, and have far too sluggish a response time, to offer any assistance at all. They are simply so "out of it" that they don't even know what's really happened.

The bureaucracy simply is so stagnated that, even with a giant paroxysm, it cannot change quickly enough to do the job in time.

The best response the orthodox system could theoretically make — if it immediately placed the nation under martial law, marshalled all the universities and scientists, everything — would require at least seven years to produce results. A more likely response time is 10 to 14 years. That won't do the job.

So the job has to be done from completely *outside* the system. It has to be done with *independent* financing. Financing without a lot of conventional, bureaucratic strings on it. Resources must be committed as needed, immediately, not with a several months' approval process.

Everything in the orthodox establishment simply has to be bypassed.

The government, the medical establishment, the scientific establishment, the universities, everything.

Otherwise, we're as good as finished *right now.*

The "Dirty Dozen"

In the West, there are only perhaps a dozen persons or so that I know of, who are qualified to work on the main task required. They are all unorthodox researchers and scientists.

There are thousands of fine orthodox scientists, of course, who can help with the peripherals — making and testing viral solutions, setting up and operating equipment, doing interminable tests, all the lab stuff, etc.

But only about 12 unorthodox guys are qualified and mentally and emotionally prepared to come to grips with the particular scalar EM technology required for rapid development of an AIDS cure.

Right now, there are just two or three of the 12 working on this, hammering away as best they can, at terrible cost to themselves and their normal endeavors.

Obviously immediate funds are needed for facilities, equipment, and marshalling that dozen unorthodox researchers and a team of scientists — along with support staff and personnel.

An Analogy

I'm reminded of a story from WW II.

On the beach at Anzio, in a battle lull some doughboys were briefly resting near their foxholes, eating lunch from C-ration cans.

A lone German Messerschmitt appeared, closing on them fast and low with machineguns blazing. They were forced to hastily jump into their foxholes as the Messerschmitt strafed their position.

The pilot continued to make strafing run after strafing run, low and "on the deck." Obviously lunch was rather totally disrupted.

Suddenly, in total disgust a soldier leaped up and flung his half-filled C-ration can into the air directly at the approaching aircraft, full in the teeth of the machinegun fire.

Incredibly, the can sailed straight up into the air intake of the hurtling aircraft, where it was sucked into the engine, which sputtered and died.

The surprised German pilot banked his plane upward and bailed out.

He was promptly captured by the very troops he had been strafing only moments before.

Those two or three colleagues of mine are literally "throwing their C-ration cans" in a desperate effort to ward off a monstrous threat.

Those two or three are striving to the limit of their endurance.

This book and the release of the material in it represent my own "C-ration can" hurled into the teeth of the actual Soviet threat as a last resort. Hopefully we can "hit the air intake" of the Soviet juggernaut, so to speak, and stop its progress.

The giant Soviet scalar electromagnetic weapons that I detailed in **Fer-de-Lance**, e.g., are easily countered — in six months or less. Primarily, it is necessary to make a pumped phase conjugate mirror adjunct (PPCMA) that operates at the frequency band of interest, and associate it with a receiver. Once a signal is received from the enemy weapon — say, from a Woodpecker transmitter — it is introduced to the PPCMA. A powerful phase conjugate replica energy pulse is returned into the distant hostile transmitter, totally destroying it.

To meet the viral biological warfare weapon, however, we must develop electromagnetic healing.

In an important article, "SDI vs. the plague," Mar. 8, 1988, p. 6, the **Washington Times** revealed a startling Pentagon conclusion that the Soviets may counter SDI with genetically engineered weapons.

Valentin Falin, Chief of the Soviets' Novasti Press Agency, is quoted as saying:

"We won't copy you anymore: We'll take asymmetrical means with new scientific principles... genetic engineering could be a hypothetical example. Things can be done for which neither side could find defenses or countermeasures, with very dangerous results. If you develop something in space, we could develop something on earth. These are not just words. I know what I'm saying."

The genetically engineered Soviet counterstrokes exist and are already being taken. This book tells you what the asymmetrical means, new scientific principles, and genetically engineered weapons are.

May God help us all. If we do not move immediately and correctly to augment the effort of my colleagues, the Free World and half of the peoples of the earth will perish before another decade passes.

CHAPTER 1

THE VACCINE CONNECTION

The following quote is from Don Rowe, **Wall Street Digest**, 214 Carnegie Center, Princeton, New Jersey 08540.

"The AIDS Plague will affect society in ways that you cannot now imagine. AIDS is 100% fatal. Scientists and medical research people are not optimistic about an immediate cure to [or] vaccine. They do not expect to develop an effective vaccine within the next two decades. Public health officials estimate that as many as 2.4 billion people (half the world's population) will die from AIDS within the next 15-20 years."

"Economically, the insurance and medical health systems could be devastated in the 1990's. Nothing short of a spectacular medical breakthrough will keep Western civilization from suffering the worst catastrophe in the history of the world."

The first official U. S. AIDS case was diagnosed in San Francisco in 1981. This followed the puzzling outbreak of the disease in Third World areas such as Africa and Haiti in the 1970's.

The U.S. AIDS outbreak at first seemed to be confined to the gay community, such as in San Francisco.

No one seemed to connect the apparently unrelated facts that, before the outbreak in the U.S. gay community, (1) the World Health Organization had accomplished substantial smallpox vaccination in Haiti, and (2) West Coast gays — particularly from San Francisco — had made Haiti a main playground and vacation spot.

Most orthodox medical scientists have not the foggiest notion why such a drastic "explosion" of the virus has occurred.

It has occurred because *AIDS was introduced by contaminated vaccine used by WHO in its smallpox eradication campaign.* A high correlation exists between WHO vaccination and subsequent outbreak of AIDS.

Figure 2. The "monkey-bite" theory.

The "Monkey-Bite" Theory

As the prevailing rationale goes, a naturally-mutated monkey AIDS virus derivative or strain is believed to be the cause of the monstrous plague looming to strike down half of all the humans on earth.

That is, a monkey is supposed to have bitten a man — an African —and transmitted the normally harmless monkey AIDS virus to him. The virus is then supposed to have naturally "recombined" its genetic material with other viral genetic material and the man's human genes, to produce the virulent new strain of AIDS.

Then this new strain, *from its single human host,* is supposed to have rapidly started spreading through Africa and around the world.

That is simply nonsense.

In Africa, for example, monkeys as well as other animals have had their viral diseases for thousands of years. If monkey virus were the culprit, African man would have been devastated by AIDS thousands of years ago. He either would have been dead or — as have the monkeys — he would have developed a certain resistance and tolerance for the disease, so that it is no more harmful than others.

Understand, the "monkey bite plus human cell modification" undoubtedly does occur in Africa with great rarity — once in several thousand years.

However, even if that rare natural recombination of the monkey AIDS virus were to occur in a single human, normal contact between other humans and the infected human is totally insufficient to provide any substantial infection rate *unless the rate of infection of new individuals is greatly assisted and vastly speeded up by some other outside mechanism — for example, by something like AIDS-contaminated vaccine and a mass inoculation program.*

Retroviruses and Recombinants

As Dr. John Seale has pointed out, "The AIDS virus (human immunodeficiency virus or HIV) is a lentivirus — a little-studied sub-family of the retroviruses. It is highly pathogenic to man but it differs profoundly from any other virus of humans. It is spreading rapidly in the general population of central Africa, and amongst homosexual men and drug addicts in the West. *It is the first virus to have appeared in mankind for many centuries which is entirely new, highly lethal, and spreading steadily from person-to-person world-wide."* [accent by the present author.]

Dr. Seale has courageously pointed out some other very disturbing facts:

(1) Retroviruses of animal origin, if repeatedly passed from human cell culture to human cell culture, will gain the ability to infect human cells *preferentially.* Indeed, they may then even cease to be infectious to their original animal hosts.

(2) In 1982 Robert Weiss pointed out that, in the laboratory, the genetic code of retroviruses commonly recombine if two of them infect the same cell simultaneously.

(3) In a 1984 article in the **Journal of Virology**, David Baltimore showed an efficient means of overcoming the cell's block against simultaneous infection by two or more retroviruses.

(4) Further, Baltimore reviewed how *this had widely been done during the preceding ten years!*

(5) Outside the laboratory, recombination of multiple simultaneous retroviruses has not been shown to occur naturally in humans.

(6) In animals, there is some evidence that it may occur naturally with extreme rarity — indeed, only once in many thousands of years.

(7) By the early 1970's, the technology to make new recombinant retroviruses virulent to humankind was already developed and had been widely published.

To the layman, the infection and reproduction by retroviruses is peculiar to say the least.

When a retrovirus infects a cell, from its own genetic material (RNA) it first makes a "template" or pattern (DNA) for forming other retroviruses just like it. It then inserts this "DNA template" into the DNA of a cell. The host cell itself is now a "sleeping factory", ready to start producing retroviruses.

When activated, the "template" in the cell causes the factory to go into production of retroviruses. Activation is varied. The "infection production factory" can just remain dormant, be slowed over years, take place almost immediately, or be slowed for years and then "explode" to rapidly increase the infective viruses.

Genetically, the cells of any person infected with AIDS or any other recombinant retrovirus have been permanently transformed. Literally that person has acquired a new set of genes. He or she has been converted into a "factory" for producing — and spreading — the virus.

Cancer Research Produced Ideal Biological Warfare Agents

In 1971 President Nixon signed into law the National Cancer Attack Act. Though certainly not intended by the President and the Congress, *the inadvertent result of this act was that taxpayer's funds were used to research and develop the precise things that constitute the most lethal kind of viral biological warfare.*

The on-going small effort in medical research laboratories to alter animal tumor viruses — including retroviruses —to replicate efficiently in human cells was drastically speeded up, as part of the new "war on cancer." In other words, whether intended or not, much of our cancer research money was converted into the precise kind of research that develops virulent biological retroviruses for potential use in biological warfare.

Not only was the research drastically accelerated, but also the direct participation by Communists and scientists sympathetic to the communist cause was accepted and encouraged.

Astoundingly, this open invitation to the communist scientists was issued at a time when one of the high KGB priorities was to infiltrate our recombinant DNA genetics laboratories! To the Soviets' utter astonishment, we simply opened our labs and invited them in.

The Soviets participated — and penetrated — with alacrity. It is an obvious conclusion that a number of the Iron Curtain scientists sent to help staff our laboratories were undercover KGB agents.

In the cancer laboratories, on a wide-spread scale, animal retroviruses were injected and reinjected into human cell cultures, until these retroviruses had become efficient, lethal recombinants favoring human cells as their hosts.

At that point, infection of one or more persons by one of these lethal new retroviruses could unleash a massive AIDS-like plague on all mankind.

A single laboratory accident (or a single act by one Communist agent) could unleash the Great Death Plague.

Weak and ineffective reference to this forthcoming danger was made in 1974 by the Committee on Recombinant DNA Molecules, which had been established by the U.S. National Academy of Sciences. According to **Science,** July 26, 1974, p. 303, the Committee made the following rather bland and ineffectual recommendation:

"Scientists throughout the world (should) join with the members of this committee in voluntarily deferring experiments (linking) segments of the DNA from (cancer-causing) animal viruses to... possibly increase the incidence of cancer or other diseases."

So much for the great scientific watchdogs.

U. S. "Cancer War" Labs Were Infiltrated

As we said, ironically we ourselves helped load and cock this potentially disastrous biological warfare cannon. Incomprehensibly, enemy fingers were permitted — even encouraged! — to be placed on the trigger. Many of our medical research facilities involved in this research contained known Communists, dissidents, etc.

For example, see page 106 in **Omni,** March 1986. Carlton Gajdusek, presently Chief of the National Institute of Health's Laboratory of Central Nervous System Studies and Laboratory of Slow, Latent and Temperate Virus Infections, was asked the question, "Isn't Fort Detrick in Maryland such a biological-warfare research facility?" He responded:

"No, emphatically no! There is no defensive or offensive warfare microbiology done at Fort Detrick today. It is the national cancer research facility of NIH. In this facility I have a building where more good and loyal Communist scientists from the USSR and mainland China work — with full passkeys to all the laboratories — than Americans. With night-working U. S. citizens and foreign Communist investigators here, obviously there is no "secret" bacterial warfare activity going on. Even the Army's infectious-disease unit is loaded with foreign workers — not always friendly nationals. It is a valid basic research unit on worldwide problems of infectious -diseases in which no classified or secret activities unfold."

The point is, what was being produced in these labs were viruses that would grow in human cells. Under tight control, these new lethal agents could be safely studied, and many things could be tried experimentally to see if they would slow, stop, or kill the viruses and heal or benefit the virally infected human cell cultures.

The viruses were being developed to benefit man by aiding in the war on cancer -- we accent this most strongly.

However, many of them were precisely the same things that would be developed in a biological warfare lab: lethal new viruses that preferred the human as a host, and against which humans have developed little or no immunity.

The Deed Was Easily Done

Now one can see the subtlety and irony in the Soviet Union accusing the U. S. of having made the AIDS virus at Ft. Detrick!

It's both true and false at the same time.

There is substantial information indicating that the AIDS disease is manmade, and has been deliberately unleashed on mankind by Soviet and other Communist agents, augmented by the international control groups and shockingly inept work by U. S. and European medical researchers.

Human cell cultures deliberately infected with animal viruses were carelessly handled in U. S. and European laboratories — carelessly handled in that far too great (essentially open) access to the new viral strains was permitted.

Our own scientists were apparently unwitting pawns, and Soviet agents performed the "final touchups" to insure release — whether intentional or inadvertent — of the lethal new agents against an unsuspecting world.

Viruses can infect bacteria, since a bacterium is a one-celled organism and the virus is a single molecule.

Cell cultures where vaccine is made from weakened bacteria could easily be contaminated with the desired recombinant viruses available in the cancer laboratories.

To insure worldwide release of the lethal virus, covert Communist agents apparently caused contamination of the smallpox vaccine that was prepared in quantity in Western laboratories.

This contaminated vaccine then was widely used to inoculate Third World peoples and others, in the successful international program to eradicate smallpox.

With only a few agents in key places, the Soviets could easily have taken advantage of the looseness of Western laboratory procedures to deliberately contaminate the animal cell cultures used to make the vaccines.

They had an abundance of agents in the key laboratories, for they were openly invited in and accepted!

The Soviets had their fingers in it, up to the elbow.

And at just exactly the right time, the answer to a Communist's biological warfare dream was available: The World Health Organi-

© Hal Crawford 1979

Figure 3. The Soviets have delivered an intended knock-out.

zation was already involved in its 13-year campaign of massive smallpox inoculation in the Third World, to eradicate smallpox.

All that was needed was to contaminate the WHO vaccine by one or more of the lethal new recombinant retroviruses that had been developed — and were continually being developed — in cancer research laboratories filled with Communists agents.

The opportunity was presented for a great Soviet "first strike" against the West, using biological warfare agents developed in U.S. and European laboratories and administered by an international agency .

The opportunity was ripe for the taking. It was irresistible. You can be sure the Soviets took it.

It's Actually Documented!

Virus-contaminated vaccines were then widely administered to Third World countries — particularly in Africa, South America, and Haiti. Administration of these vaccines by the World Health Organization is precisely correlated to the subsequent outbreak of the AIDS epidemics in those countries.

This strongly indicates that the vaccine itself was the "precursor" agent initiating the start of the AIDS infection.

In a shocking article, "Smallpox vaccine 'triggered Aids virus'," in the London **Times** of May 11, 1987, **Times** Science Editor Pearce Wright announced that the AIDS epidemic may have been caused by World Health Organization (WHO) smallpox inoculations in third-world countries.

In an important article in **Easy Reader,** June 4, Jon Rappoport reported the **Times** article and the results of an interview with Robert Matthews, technical correspondent of the **Times.**

According to Rappoport, Matthews informed him WHO itself had somehow suspected that its immunization program against smallpox might be connected to AIDS. An outside consultant was employed to perform an independent study, and the study confirmed that WHO vaccines were indeed — somehow — causing AIDS to evidence in inoculated persons.

Needless to say, WHO promptly buried that report — whose conclusion must have been the last thing WHO wanted to hear.

The consultant then came to the **Times.** The **Times** heard him out and printed the story.

This astounding story has almost startling correlations: *"The smallpox vaccine theory would account for the position of the Central African states as the most afflicted countries; why Brazil became the most afflicted Latin American country; and how Haiti became the route for the spread of AIDS, to the U.S.: Brazil, the only South American country covered in the eradication campaign, has the highest incidence of AIDS in that region."*

Rappoport confirms that the subject of contaminated vaccines — "vaccines which, made in tissue cultures of animal parts, contain 'extra' dangerous viruses" — has been of increasingly serious concern to medical scientists in recent years, and the WHO smallpox vaccines may have been contaminated in this fashion.

A documented U.S. Army incident is a case in point.

New U.S. Army recruits are routinely vaccinated against a

range of diseases. One of them is smallpox, in case an enemy should try to use smallpox as a biological warfare agent.

A healthy 19-year old Army recruit developed AIDS after vaccination, and was admitted to Walter Reed Army Medical Center, where he died.

In a paper published in the **New England Journal of Medicine,** Walter Reed medical team scientists reported their discovery of the connection between vaccination and stimulated AIDS disease.

They also warned against the WHO plan to use modified versions of the smallpox vaccine to combat other diseases in developing countries.

WHO's 13-year vaccination and eradication program ended in 1980. The program is credited with saving two million lives a year and preventing 15 million infections.

It may be inadvertently responsible for the ultimate death of billions.

In a meeting of 50 experts near Geneva in May, 1987, it was revealed that millions of new AIDS cases are about to hit Southern Africa. The experts believe that up to 75 million Southern Africans — about a third of the population — may have AIDS within the next five years.

From our previous statements above, it appears almost certain that Communist agents who had penetrated U.S. and European laboratories manipulated the contamination of the altered vaccines.

Further, the Soviets may be stimulating the disease and guiding it electromagnetically, by special implanted signals carried by the giant Soviet woodpecker "over-the-horizon radars" and other Soviet transmitters.

Or, the Soviets may be using their own transmitters and ours, including our own power lines and radio and TV stations, to broadcast signals that "precondition" and greatly amplify our population's vulnerability to certain selected diseases — AIDS and otherwise.

We will address these issues and Soviet subtle EM capabilities later.

Soviet Biological Warfare Background

In World War I, the Russians suffered half a million casualties to gas warfare, including 50,000 dead.

At 10,000 troops per light division, that's the equivalent of 5 divisions killed and 45 divisions incapacitated.

This made a deep and lasting impression on the Soviets. Lenin himself ordered a major effort mounted to develop and manufacture chemical and biological weapons, for he understood the implications of such mass-destruction weapons.

In 1919 the Soviets began work in earnest on BW weapons. Work on them has not stopped since then. It will not stop so long as the Communists remain in power.

To loyal Communists, Lenin's dictate to develop and lead the world in biological weapons is absolute and unquestioned.

By 1937, the Red Army was fully equipped and psychologically prepared to wage chemical and biological warfare.

Continuing today, the Soviet forces have the highest training in chemical warfare of any troops in the world. Red Army soldiers practice regularly, often using actual chemical agents. Decontamination is a standard measure and practiced as a matter of course.

Even though the Soviets, along with many other nations, signed the Geneva Protocol of 1925 which banned the use of deadly chemical and bacteriological weapons, the Soviets have never ceased development of such weapons.

In the 1930's, a secret Soviet bacteriological institute was set up at the town of Suzdal. Prisoner microbiologists worked on a variety of new weapons and vaccines, including bubonic plague and tularemia (rabbit fever). By World War II the Soviets were prepared to retaliate vigorously to any use by the Germans of chemical and biological warfare agents.

After the war, Soviet research and development in chemical and biological weapons continued apace. However, much of the genetic work was hampered by Stalin's stern support of the autocratic control of agronomist Trofim D. Lysenko. Lysenko's crackpot theories on genetics, for example, held that genes did not even exist. After the death of Stalin, Lysenko's work was discredited, and the Soviets set forth immediately to "catch up" with the West in genetic applications such as recombinant DNA techniques.

Thus in the early 1960's the Soviets began sending Russian

scientists to the West to catch up with Western genetics research. One of these scientists was David Goldfarb, who later became a leading Soviet expert in the field of molecular genetics. He headed up the Laboratory of Molecular Genetics of Bacteria and Bacteriophages of the Soviet Academy of Sciences in Moscow. Although he did not work on secret Soviet projects, the Soviet authorities stopped him cold when he applied for a visa to leave in 1979. Goldfarb was a specialist in plasmids, antibiotic resistances, and recombinant DNA technology — all very, very useful to the Soviet effort in biowar.

One can readily understand the reluctance of the authorities to release scientists such as Goldfarb. After all, the Soviet "dirty work" with the deliberate AIDS contamination of the World Health Organization's smallpox vaccine had already been accomplished and a great Soviet biological warfare "strike" was already underway, thanks to the massive smallpox vaccination program of WHO.

In 1972, in the Biological and Toxin Weapons Convention, the Soviet Union and every major power agreed not to develop or use biological weapons. The agreement went into effect in 1975. Although it bans the development, production, and stockpiling of biological agents and toxins for hostile purposes, it has not slowed or altered the Soviet program.

In the early 1970's, Soviet leaders made a decision to use genetic engineering to produce new and improved BW weapons. Highly secret institutes for this purpose were set up in Moscow, Leningrad, and Novosibirsk. These laboratories specialize in seeking ways that genetic engineering techniques can be used to develop virulent strains and agents that their opponents cannot resist.

Every Soviet civilian institution dealing with bacteriology and epidemiology is responsible for certain military work as well. The Soviet Academy of Sciences in fact funds appreciable research of such nature at these institutions.

One of the major Soviet centers for recombinant DNA techniques in biological weapons research is in the village of Protvino, near Moscow. Research on chemical and biological weapons is very easy to conceal, and the Soviets are sure that they will not be caught. Satellites cannot detect what is going on in the labs. The payoff is big and the risk is minimal. The Soviets push this area vigorously.

A number of installations capable of producing disease agents and toxins on a large-scale basis and placing them in munitions and delivery systems have also been identified. One such facility is in the city of Sverdlovsk and has a long history of BW research and development and production, with emphasis on anthrax. During early April 1979, an accidental release of anthrax occurred in Sverdlovsk that caused many casualties and deaths in spite of heroic efforts by Soviet doctors and cleanup and decontamination crews.

Note that, according to DoD's 1987 edition of **Soviet Military Power,** page 110, "*Anthrax causes a high mortality rate when the infection results from ingestion (up to 70 percent fatal) or inhalation (almost 100 percent fatal) if treatment is not promptly begun.*"

In addition to military BW institutes, military officers and KGB agents are assigned to key posts in the Soviet Union's normal health and science ministries to monitor research and development that has possible military significance.

Also, the KGB has a continuing and highly active program to insert recruited Soviet Scientists in Western genetic research institutes and agencies. This is a high priority effort, and it has been very successful. Also, it obviously says something about the probability of Soviet agents penetrating U.S. and Western European cancer research institutes, particularly those using recombinant DNA techniques. To make it even worse, we simply invited them in with open arms!

Indeed, it was that KGB program plus the "open arms" in Western cancer virology research institutes that enabled the Soviets to set up and bring about a massive "first strike", using WHO and Western laboratories to do the actual dirty work unknowingly.

We Need An Immediate, Full Scale Investigation

Annually, President Reagan makes a report to the U.S. Congress on the subject of Soviet noncompliance with Arms Control agreements.

In April, 1984 Defense Secretary Caspar Weinberger put it this way:

"There is an apparent effort on the part of the Soviets to transfer selected aspects of genetic engineering research to their biological warfare centers... Soviet research efforts in the area of genetic engineering may also have a connection with the biological program...Normally harmless, non-disease-producing organisms could be modified to become highly toxic or produce diseases for which an opponent has no known treatment or cure. Other agents, now considered too unstable for storage or biological warfare applications, could be changed sufficiently to be an effective agent."

At the time that Secretary Weinberger made this statement, a devastating biological warfare strike using those exact techniques had already been unleashed on the Western world by the Soviet Union, cleverly disguised under the banner of the World Health Organization's smallpox vaccination program.

It is imperative that the Congress of the United States launch a full investigation of the entire background of the AIDS biological warfare strike, as a matter of the highest priority.

The investigation should include the role of the Soviet Union, fellow-travelers, and Western scientists openly sympathetic to the Soviet cause.

It requires little investigation to see that there is a well-marked trail for several decades, showing that such a biological warfare strike against humanity has long been considered — and even preferred — by those advocating the Communist cause and world domination.

For example, Bertrand Russell, philosophical spokesman for a group of Westerners, explicitly stated this diabolical BW capability for consideration, in his **Impact of Science on Society:**

"At present the population of the world is increasing at about 58,000 per diem. War, so far, has had no very great effect on this increase, which continued throughout each of the world wars... War has hitherto been disappointing in this respect... but perhaps bacteriological war may prove effective. If a Black Death could spread through the world once in every generation, survivors could procreate freely without making the world too full. The state of affairs might be

unpleasant, but what of it?"

The blood of every American — and every European, African, and Asian — should curdle at such words. We are now facing the very "Black Death" type of plague referred to by Russell in such glowing terms!

Highly influential followers of the Russell philosophy — and his callous approval of the periodic slaughter of much of the world's population — may have continued to view the great destructive power of new viral warfare agents as the best means to achieve their end: Selective thinning of the world's population.

At least a few such men may have continued to cooperate with the Soviet Union to work powerfully behind the scenes in international organizations, trying to arrange the proper opportunity to achieve their nefarious purpose.

The "East-West cooperative effort" in cancer research created and gave them the precise biological agent custom-made for the job.

WHO's massive, worldwide smallpox inoculation program gave them the precise means to rapidly get the deadly virus into enough human veins to assure a new "Black Death."

All that had to be done was surreptitiously contaminate the vaccine — the easiest thing of all.

This plague has been knowingly, with malice aforethought, unleashed upon mankind. The perpetrators should be hounded down like the wild beasts they are, uncovered in the full light of day, and suitably punished with the swift and sure justice they deserve.

At least one outstanding medical consultant had the courage to report to WHO that their vaccine was generating the AIDS epidemic. When WHO suppressed the evidence, the **London Times** had the courage to print the story.

I strongly urge every U.S. Senator and Congressman to introduce and/or support immediate legislation that would launch a full-scale, massive investigation, with no stone left unturned. I urge every concerned activist to demand and support such an investigation at the highest level.

By preoccupying ourselves with lesser things — "IranGate," Nicaragua, the Middle East, etc. — we are simply fiddling while Rome burns.

CHAPTER 2

THE SOVIETS KNEW THE U.S. WOULDN'T REACT

Administering the Coup-de-Grace

As we've seen, the present AIDS viruses were deliberately created in Western cancer research laboratories strongly penetrated by Communist scientists and Soviet agents.

In laboratory experiments that were a legitimate and vital part of the war against cancer, animal retroviruses were repeatedly injected into human cell cultures until they recombined to produce strains hostile to human life — strains that would thus live in human cell cultures.

Even though their work was accomplished for a totally different purpose, cancer laboratories produced the ultimate, made-to-order biological warfare agents.

The World Health Organization (WHO) is also strongly penetrated — and even controlled at some levels — by communist agents, as are many other such international agencies.

And WHO's massive smallpox vaccination program in Third World countries provided the Soviets a made-to-order opportunity to have (ostensibly) "someone else" deliver the actual BW strike.

In other words, the Soviet deception plan was complete.

It was very simple for Soviet agents to contaminate the cultures in which smallpox vaccine was being produced for WHO's inoculation campaign. This insured the production of vaccine contaminated with AIDS viruses, and the subsequent massive infection of the African peoples and other Third World nations.

It delivered what will be the knockout punch against the West, unless AIDS is countered.

Table 1. Interesting Soviet Statements

"WE HAVE A NEW WEAPON, JUST WITHIN THE PORTFOLIO OF OUR SCIENTISTS, SO TO SPEAK — SO POWERFUL THAT, IF UNRESTRAINEDLY USED, IT COULD WIPE OUT ALL LIFE ON EARTH."

NIKITA KHRUSHCHEV,
1960, SPEAKING TO THE PRESIDIUM

"WE WILL BURY YOU!"

NIKITA KHRUSHCHEV,
TO RICHARD NIXON, "KITCHEN" DEBATE

"IF A MEANS OF TOTAL NEUTRALIZATION OF FOREIGN MISSILES IS TO BE FOUND, IT CAN ONLY COME FROM *A GROUP OF NEW PRINCIPLES IN PHYSICS, CALLED ENERGETICS!"*

NOBELIAN PETER KAPITSA, TO NIKITA KHRUSHCHEV

"EACH SIDE SECRETLY DEVELOPS NEW MEANS OF WARFARE IN ORDER TO EMPLOY THEM UNEXPECTEDLY. HISTORY KNOWS MANY EXAMPLES HOW THE EMPLOYMENT OF A NEW WEAPON INITIALLY GAVE CONSIDERABLE SUCCESS BECAUSE THE ENEMY, CAUGHT UNAWARES AND NOT KNOWING THE COMBAT CAPABILITIES OF THIS WEAPON, WAS FOR SOME TIME INCAPABLE OF EFFECTIVE COUNTERACTION."

V.YO. SAVKIN, THE BASIC PRINCIPLES OF OPERATIONAL ART AND TACTICS, MOSCOW, 1972.

"OF PARTICULAR IMPORTANCE IS BASIC RESEARCH AIMED AT DISCOVERING STILL UNKNOWN ATTRIBUTES OF MATTER, PHENOMENA, AND THE LAWS OF NATURE, AND DEVELOPING NEW METHODS FOR THEIR STUDY AND USE TO REINFORCE THE STATE'S DEFENSE CAPABILITY."

PORTION OF A BOOK BY MARSHALL GRECHKO
DELETED FROM ENGLISH TRANSLATION, BY SPECIFIC REQUEST OF THE U.S.S.R.

"WILL SHORTLY SEE DEVELOPMENT OF NEW WEAPONS, MORE POWERFUL THAN NUCLEAR WEAPONS, AND THEY WILL BE NONVERIFIABLE."

LYSENKO (FIRST NAME UNKNOWN)
USSR REP/SOVIET EMBASSY WASHINGTON, D.C.
WORLD FURTURESCONFERENCE, WASH. D.C., 20 JUL. 82.

Murky "Behind-the-Scenes" Intentions

As was pointed out, the WHO inoculation program is well-correlated as the precursor or "initiator" of the AIDS epidemic.

Where WHO smallpox vaccination occurred, the mysterious symptoms of AIDS disease appeared in due time.

Even the eventual spread of the AIDS virus to the U.S. homosexual community is explainable.

For example, the economy of Haiti had earlier been made a shambles. The poor citizens of that impoverished island had been reduced to desperate straits.

In desperation many younger Haitian males had begun to prostitute themselves to visiting homosexual tourists. The Haitian males were not homosexual themselves; rather, they were desperate to gain money to provide for their starving families.

In response, U.S. homosexuals — particularly from San Francisco and New York — had made Haiti their vacation playground. They even ran ads to this effect in their gay newsletters and magazines.

WHO then vaccinated some 15,000 or so Haitians against smallpox, using the vaccine contaminated with the AIDS virus. This introduced AIDS into Haiti and into the Haitians.

The U.S. homosexuals quickly picked up the AIDS virus by direct contact, and brought it back to the U.S. with them. There the nature of the activities engaged in by homosexuals was responsible for enhanced spread of the virus among members of the homosexual community.

Engineering the AIDS epidemic appears to have been a collusion between Communists and the international control groups.

Apparently the control groups wished to "clean out the African continent and other Third World areas" — possibly to provide room for relieving population pressure in the developed countries. This may have been seen as the way to solve the problem of the ballooning human population — the so-called "biological time bomb."

The Soviets, however, realized that contamination of the smallpox vaccines would result in an epidemic of unparalleled proportions. They recognized the opportunity for safely initiating — and winning — World War III with a great first strike.

The Soviets themselves already possess an electromagnetic cure for diseases such as AIDS, but they have not unveiled it.

All such products of scalar electromagnetics (which the Soviets call energetics) are held tightly by the KGB.

That the Soviets have kept such a cure secret strongly implies that they regard it as a known antidote for biological warfare agents, and thus highly classified.

The importance of this can easily be seen: Presently the West has absolutely zero defense against a biological warfare strike using viruses as BW agents.

In such a strike, fast-acting viral strains can easily be used — say, agents which are highly infectious and kill within two or three days.

Development of a vaccine is impossible. There is simply no time to do that. Further, even if the virus was slow-acting, a vaccine could only be developed if the virus is stable. If it is unstable (constantly mutating), development of a vaccine is impossible.

The greatest vulnerability of the U.S. today is its total vulnerability to unknown BW viral agents. Absolutely nothing we have or are doing in our Department of Defense is of any consequence or protection against new BW viruses for which no vaccine is developed or possible.

The great ease with which such cheap new, highly lethal viral BW agents can be developed means that even a relatively small military power — such as Libya, Cuba, or Iran — can develop and use them against the U.S.

Such BW viral agents can also easily be clandestinely planted across the U.S., to devastate an unsuspecting, unprotected American populace.

In fact, even a single deranged madman can readily develop lethal BW viral agents sufficient to devastate even a great military power. Further, in an open society such as the U.S., that same madman can easily introduce such an agent he develops — and, if he's clever, not even get caught in the act.

Past isolated cases of "contamination" of on-the-shelf drugstore medicines is just a faint prelude of that which is to come.

Indeed, we may unwittingly do it to ourselves by accident, even without a BW strike by the Soviets, small enemy powers, or a madman.

Throughout the West, it is now most fashionable to experiment with the production of new bacteria and viruses. Gene-splicing, recombinant DNA genetics, etc. are being employed on a grand scale as the latest "scientific marvel."

Even some high school students have experimented with this sort of thing. Many other colleagues, universities, and private persons are proceeding full-tilt with casual experiments.

Most of this "casual experimentation" is uncontrolled. When finished, the residue gets dumped in the trash can or flushed down the drain. In any case, it goes into our biosphere. Some of this residue contains unstable, highly adaptable viruses.

It's only a matter of time until one of these unwitting agents gets loose and survives — one that's lethal, fast, and highly infectious.

Make no mistake: It's a *near certainty* that this will happen. The only question is *when*.

Also, with the recent Supreme Court decision allowing the patenting of a virus or bacteria, a number of laboratories and companies are now feverishly developing new agents to unleash in the biosphere upon persons, animals, and plants.

For the most part, these experiments are tightly controlled. However, it is impossible to test in the laboratory the result of the natural recombination and mutation of these agents once they are loose in the environment and in a free exchange with all the natural bacteria and viruses.

Once loosed in the biosphere, a new viral agent undergoes combinations and recombinations with the greater number of viruses already present. The situation is like an increase in a large factorial number: Only a few additional viruses will result in millions and millions of additional combinations — at least some of which inevitably will be lethal and quick-acting. This is *not* tested in those laboratories making, patenting, and releasing new viruses.

Humans have spent millions of years developing sufficient immunity to the natural BW agents to allow humanity to survive.

Very shortly we are going to have increasingly large numbers of new environmental BW agents emerging all around us. For some of them, it is a foregone conclusion that we have little or no natural immunity developed.

So we are going to enter an increasingly harsh environment, characterized by the rise of great epidemics and pandemics of many kinds.

Inevitably some of these coming scourges are going to rival the "Black Death" in ferocity and lethality.

Effective defense against one or more such BW viral attacks — either against our forces in the field or against our civilian population — can only be provided by a ready, fully developed technology of electromagnetic healing.

It does not really matter whether the BW strikes are performed by a hostile foe, a madman, natural mutations within our now drastically stimulated viral environment, or as a result of some particular "residue" discarded by an enthusiastic high school or college student.

The end result — the decimation of humankind — is going to be the same unless we develop and use electromagnetic healing technology.

However, with the present enormously self-hostile state of mankind, one or more enemies or madmen will almost certainly launch a strong, clandestine BW strike against the United States Armed Forces and the U.S. populace.

With EM healing technology, a specific "antidote" to any viral disease — known or unknown — can be developed in a matter of hours.

Mass electromagnetic treatment can then be started immediately, even for an entire army in the field or for our population in the heartland. Within hours of recognizing a BW strike, cure rates above 90% can be quickly achieved in exposed personnel.

Further, using electromagnetic healing technology, if necessary a more conventional vaccine can also be rapidly developed — say, in two weeks — for mass distribution and inoculation of the civilian populace.

The bottom line is this: Neither the U.S. Armed Forces nor the U.S. civilian populace can or will survive the coming lethal viral warfare strikes unless we quickly develop electromagnetic healing technology and have the necessary diagnostic and treatment devices already ready and waiting.

The clandestine AIDS strike by the Soviet Union is just the precursor of a great deal more to come.

The USSR Has Repeatedly Verified Our Nonreaction

The Soviet Union already knows that Western science and governments are too stereotyped and dogmatic to react to anything highly unorthodox.

For years, the Soviet have been proving this, over and over, in their development and testing of frightful scalar electromagnetic superweapons of unprecedented power. In the face of overwhelming evidence of this, the West has kept its head buried in the sand like an ostrich.

It wasn't invented in the West. Therefore it cannot be.

Years of substantial Communist indoctrination of students in our universities, by leftist/liberal professors, has placed a massive imprint into our society. An entourage of sympathetic groups has resulted — groups which believe that the Soviet leaders are just like us, that the Stalinist era is long since over, and that the Communist leopard has changed its spots and really isn't trying to take over the world anymore.

As a system, then, much of the West simply refuses to accept anything unorthodox, anything "not invented here", and anything that indicates Soviet aggression.

The Soviets know the U.S. is totally ignorant of advanced scalar EM weaponry. They have proven over and over that the U.S. will not even comprehend that it has been deliberately struck, if the strike is sufficiently unorthodox.

The Soviet scalar EM superweapons have already been documented in **Fer-de-Lance**, Tesla Book Company, 1986, and that documentation will not be repeated here.

Only a short summary of events will be presented, to put the Soviets' confidence into perspective. A longer chronology of selected events is included as Appendix IV.

The Soviets were quite confident in arranging for a great biological warfare strike, because of the total lack of the U.S. to comprehend incidents such as the following:

1. Beginning in the late 1950's, hidden Soviet transmitters across the street targeted "weak microwave radiation" against the U.S. Embassy in Moscow. Over the years the radiation continued, sometimes continuously, sometimes intermittently. The Soviets electronically induced diseases that resulted in extensive health problems of Embassy personnel, the death of two U.S. Ambassadors, and the sickness of a third. Several U.S. Presidents have protested the radiation. Both U.S. Intelligence and the U.S. scientific community have been totally baffled. They still do not know the true nature of the radiation, nor its purpose.

2. In the winter of 1957-58, an unexplained nuclear event happened near Kyshtym, within the Soviet Union. A huge explosion occurred in the stored nuclear wastes in the disposal section of the Soviet atomic weapons industry located in the southern Urals. Radioactive contamination covered 1,000 square miles. For years the story was opposed — or suppressed — by U.S. intelligence agencies, perhaps to allay public resistance to the U.S. nuclear industry. At the time, Soviet experimentation with large scalar electromagnetic transmitters was well underway. A large transmitter probably failed, discharging its built-up, giant electrogravitational potential (EGP) into the earth. Such a pulse would have propagated through the earth as a wave; the first nuclear material contacted would have been fissioned immediately. The stored nuclear wastes probably exploded due to receipt of an EGP from the inadvertent failure of one of the Soviet Union's new superweapons in development. Survivors reported that indeed the nearby nuclear wastes exploded.

3. In January 1960 Khrushchev announced to the Presidium that a new fantastic weapon was in development. He stated that the weapon was so powerful that, if unrestrainedly used, it could wipe out all life on earth.

Figure 4. The U.S. Embassy in Moscow. The Soviet Union has bombarded this facility with weak microwave radiation for decades.

Table 2. MICROWAVE RADIATION OF THE U.S. EMBASSY IN MOSCOW

- **SINCE 1959 OR 1960**
- **HIGH LEVEL TARGET (U.S. AMBASSADOR)**
- **GUARANTEES PERSONAL ATTENTION OF**
    - **PRESIDENT**
    - **NSA, CIA, DIA**
    - **TOP CONSULTING SCIENTISTS**
    - **STATE DEPARTMENT**
    - **LEADING SCIENTIFIC INSTITUTIONS**
    - **NATIONAL SECURITY COUNCIL**
    - **ETC.**
- **TWO AMBASSADORS DIED, ANOTHER SICKENED**
- **U.S. REACTION REVEALS ANY KNOWLEDGE OF TESLA ELECTROMAGNETICS**
- **FOUR U.S. PRESIDENTS REQUESTED SOVIETS TO CEASE**
    - **CUT FROM 18 WATTS/CM^2 TO 2**
    - **THEN AGAIN INCREASED**

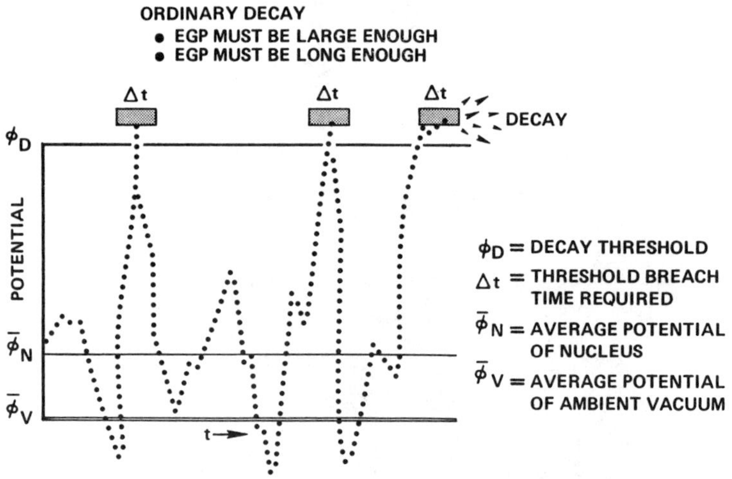

Figure 5. Decay of a radioactive nucleus. When it absorbs a scalar EM wave (electrogravitational pulse) that is long enough and large enough, the nucleus fissions.

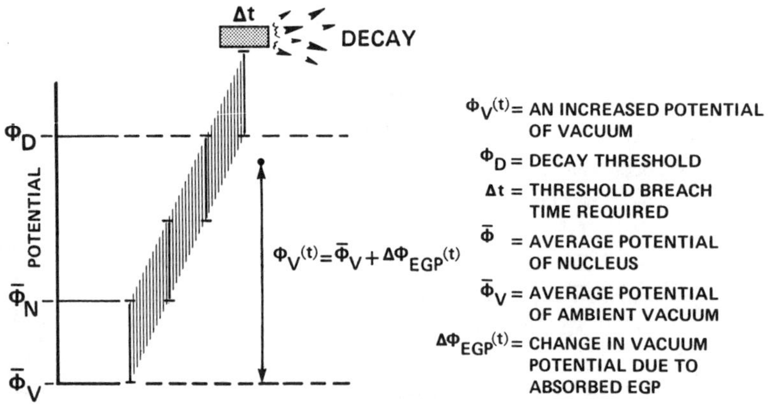

Figure 6. EGP fission of a radioactive nucleus. If an initial EGP is large enough and long enough, it will fission any and all radioactive nuclei it strikes.

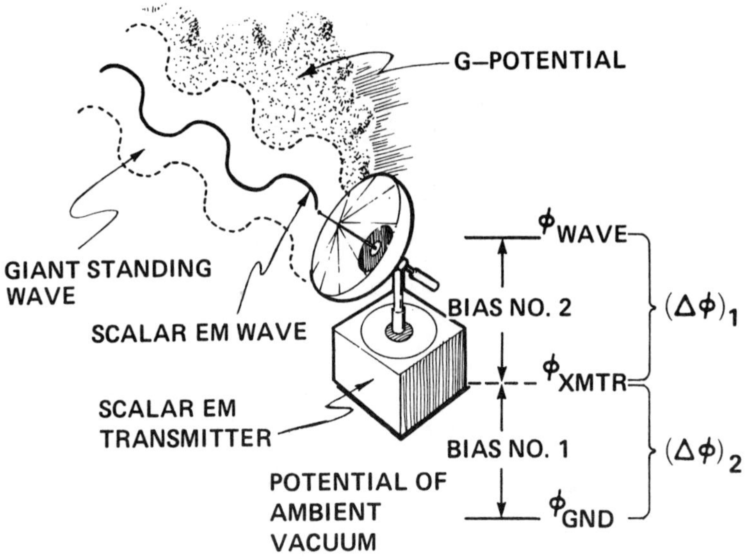

Figure 7. Bottled up energy in a standing scalar EM wave is a potential.

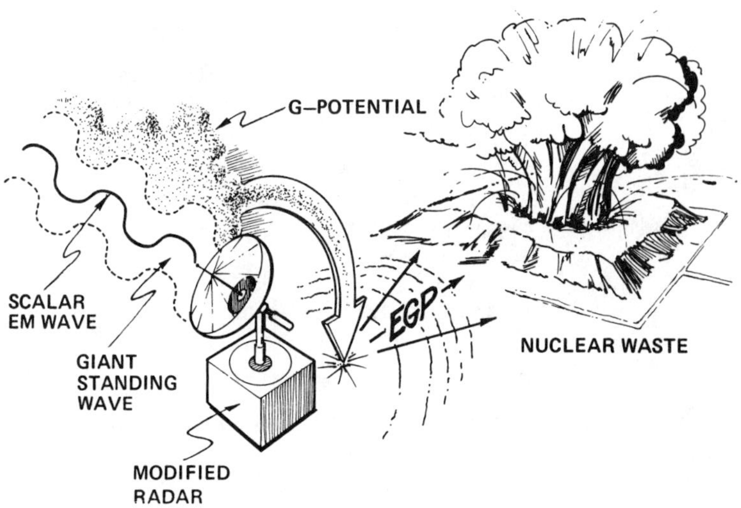

Figure 8. EGP short-out. Transmitter failure and consequent discharge of a giant standing scalar EM wave potential caused the explosion of stored nuclear wastes at Kyshtym, USSR, in the winter of 1957-58.

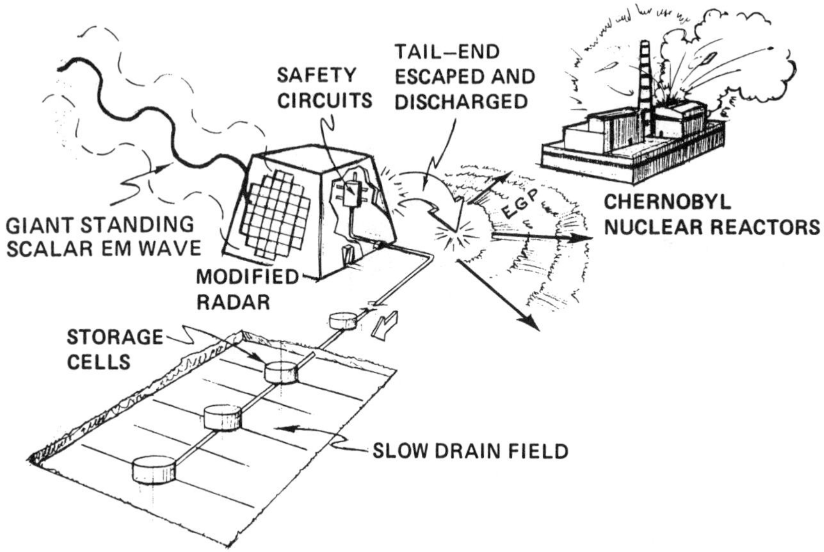

Figure 9. EGP initiation of the Chernobyl event. Failure of another giant transmitter near Chernobyl in 1986 eventually caused the eruption of one of the Chernobyl reactors by EGP-pulsing its nuclear fuel rods. When the transmitter failed, the alarmed Soviets shut down the four Chernobyl reactors while waiting for drain-off of the EGP potential by the safety circuits of the disabled transmitter. These circuits finally gave way, producing a mild EGP pulse into the earth. Had they failed immediately, all four reactors at Chernobyl would have violently exploded.

Table 3. KHRUSHCHEV'S 1960 STATEMENT

(Speaking to the Presidium)

WE HAVE A NEW WEAPON,
JUST WITHIN THE PORTFOLIO OF
OUR SCIENTISTS. . .
SO POWERFUL THAT,
IF UNRESTRAINEDLY USED,
IT COULD WIPE OUT
ALL LIFE ON EARTH!

4. In May 1960 Gary Powers' high-flying U-2 spy plane was mysteriously disabled over the Soviet Union, resulting in its subsequent crash and the Soviet capture of Powers himself. A flash appeared behind Powers' aircraft, as if from an explosion — except that *the flash persisted,* showing that it was not a normal HE explosion at all. A tracking radar, employed in a scalar EM mode, probably was used to cause the electromagnetic "flash ball" and disable Powers' aircraft. Harmless SA-2 missiles fired far below him may have been employed to deceive Western intelligence analysts.

Figure 10. The U-2 high altitude reconnaissance aircraft. On May 2, 1960 Francis Gary Powers' high flying U-2 spyplane was disabled over the Soviet Union. Some difficulties with the autopilot were first experienced. Then a single dull thump was felt, and a tremendous orange flash lit the cockpit and sky — *and persisted.* (See Francis Gary Powers with Curt Gentry, **Operation Overflight**, Holt, Rhinehart and Winston, 1970, p. 82.)

5. In April 1963 the Soviet Union utilized a newly deployed scalar EM weapon to destroy the submerged U.S.S. Thresher nuclear submarine, off the coast of the U.S. itself. In spite of intense and totally anomalous electronic jamming experienced by the U.S.S. Skylark, surface companion to the Thresher, the U.S. failed to recognize this major indication of a scalar EM attack. *One day later, a Soviet scalar EM weapon placed a giant*

underwater burst in the ocean, 100 miles north of Puerto Rico. With these two tests Khrushchev, still smarting from his Cuban Missile Crisis facedown by John Kennedy, avenged himself and convinced the Presidium to allow him to remain in power for yet awhile.

Figure 11. The U.S.S. Thresher disintegrates. © Hal Crawford 1979

Table 4. DEATH OF THE U.S.S. THRESHER

APRIL 10, 1963

- **DURING TRIALS OFF EAST COAST OF U.S. IN ATLANTIC**
- **SURFACE COMPANION: U.S.S. SKYLARK**
- **UNDERWATER PHONE BETWEEN THE TWO**
- **THRESHER DIVED AND WAS LOST**
  - **GARBLED MESSAGE**
  - **DID NOT RESPOND TO CONTROLS**
  - **SANK TO CRUSH DEPTH**
  - **IMPLODED**
- **SKYLARK ENCOUNTERED SEVERE ELECTRONIC INTERFERENCE**

Table 5. SEVERE EM INTERFERENCE EXPERIENCED BY U.S.S. SKYLARK

APRIL 10, 1963

- **SKYLARK JAMMED (1.5 HR TO TRANSMIT MESSAGE)**
- **MULTIPLE SYSTEMS**
- **SIGNATURE:**
  - **SCALAR INFEROMETRY**
  - **SKYLARK IN "SPLATTER" ZONE**
  - **THRESHER PROBABLE TARGET**
- **OTHER SYMPTOMS**
  - **ONE SYSTEM KNOCKED OUT**
  - **OTHERS THEN WENT OUT**
  - **LATER RESUMED WORKING**

6. In Afghanistan, in 1981 and at intervals since then, Soviet helicopters have sometimes attacked Afghan guerrillas or villages with a strange new weapon. A body struck by this weapon dies instantly and completely. It falls like a limp rag, and does not decay even in 30 days. Every cell, bacterium, virus, etc. in the body has been killed instantly. Nerve gas rockets and chemical rockets are also usually fired to provide a "deception cover" for the nature of the real weapon. This eery Soviet weapon has been mislabeled as some strong new gas, and is referred to as "Smirch", a combination of the two words "smert" (death) and "semerch" (sandstorm).

7. In April 1984 a monstrously huge scalar EM incident occurred off the coast of Japan, near the Kuriles. Subsequent interviews with the pilots sighting the incident have revealed that several combined tests of the various modes of a scalar EM howitzer occurred. A giant "cold explosion" occurred, raising a giant mushroom cloud to over 60,000 feet and greater than 150 miles diameter in two minutes. A glowing dome appeared, and expanded to monstrous size. According to Dr. Walker and colleagues, **the diameter of this great glowing, hem-**

ispherical shell expanded to several hundred kilometers. * He and his colleagues were able to rule out any possible known natural events or mechanisms that could have caused the incident.

8. Numerous incidents of hemispherical shells of light and giant balls of light within the Soviet Union have been seen from Iran and from Afghanistan. Such giant artificial phenomena have also repeatedly been seen over the oceans by mariners and airline pilots.

9. Several instances of anomalous disabling of jet engines of commercial airliners have occurred while the aircraft were in flight.

10. Direct and intensive weather engineering over the U.S. itself has been accomplished by the Soviet Union for a decade, using the interference grid resulting from the crossing of two or more giant beams from the woodpecker "over-the-horizon radar" transmitters. Specific cloud signatures (anomalous holes, giant radials, twin giant radials, and razor-sharp giant interference patterns) have continually occurred, but the orthodox system has blithely ignored them.

11. A giant test of over a hundred huge Soviet scalar EM weapons occurred in and around May 1, 1985 for the 40th anniversary of the end of WWII. The entire Western scientific and intelligence establishment remained sublimely unaware of the giant exercise. They had not a single scalar EM signal detector — even though the air, land, and ocean was filled with hundreds of Soviet scalar EM transmitters, chattering away to Soviet armed forces, submarines under the water, etc. Underneath our feet, the earth itself was in giant scalar EM resonance on 54 frequencies — 27 pairs, each of which tapped energy directly from the molten core of the earth and fed it to an ensemble of giant Soviet strategic scalar EM weapons.

*See **Science**, 227 (4584), Feb. 8, 1985, p. 607-611; **Science** 234 (4775), Oct. 24, 1986, p. 412-413.

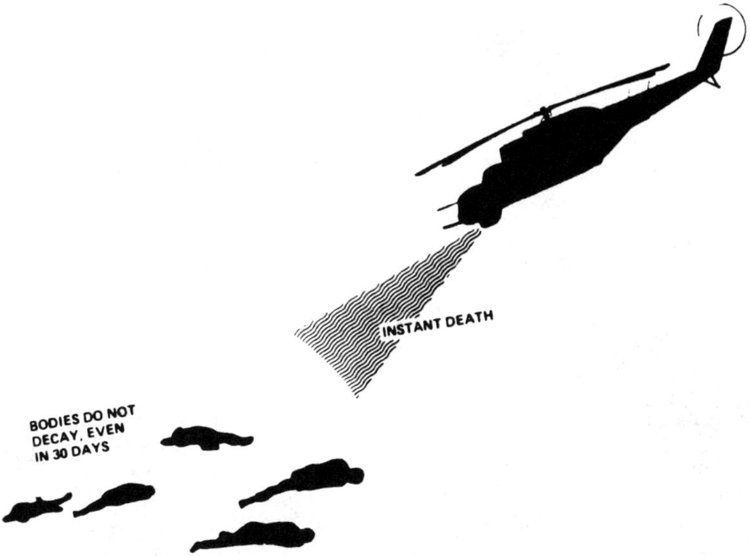

Figure 12. Soviet helicopters have used a "death ray" in Afghanistan.

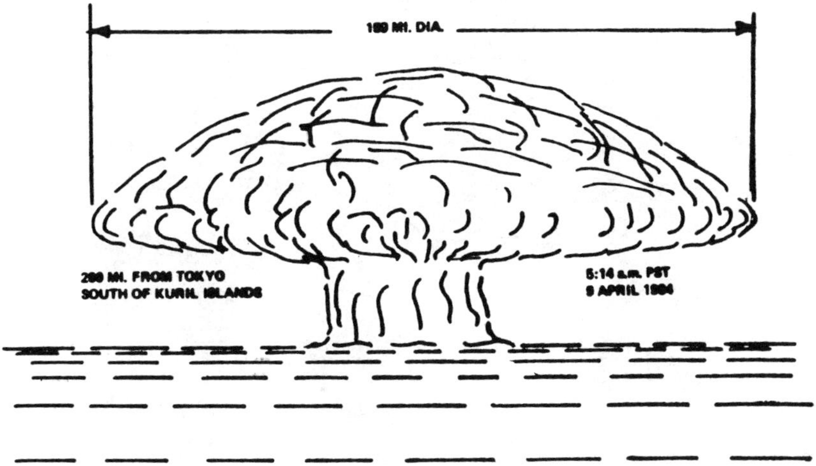

Figure 13. Mushroom cloud from the sea off Japan, near a Russian test area.

© Hal Crawford 1981

Figure 14. The Tesla shield, a giant hemispherical shell of energy. Seen repeatedly in Soviet tests in out-of-the-way places and remote regions of the ocean.

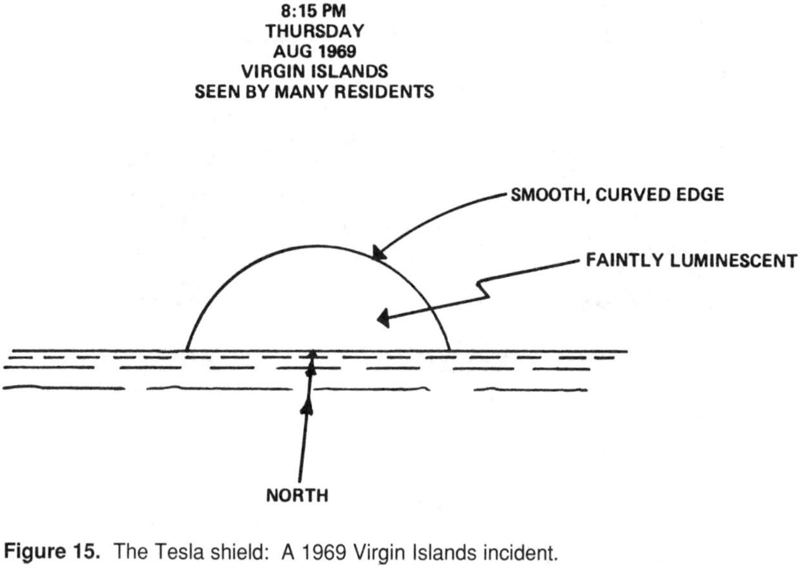

Figure 15. The Tesla shield: A 1969 Virgin Islands incident.

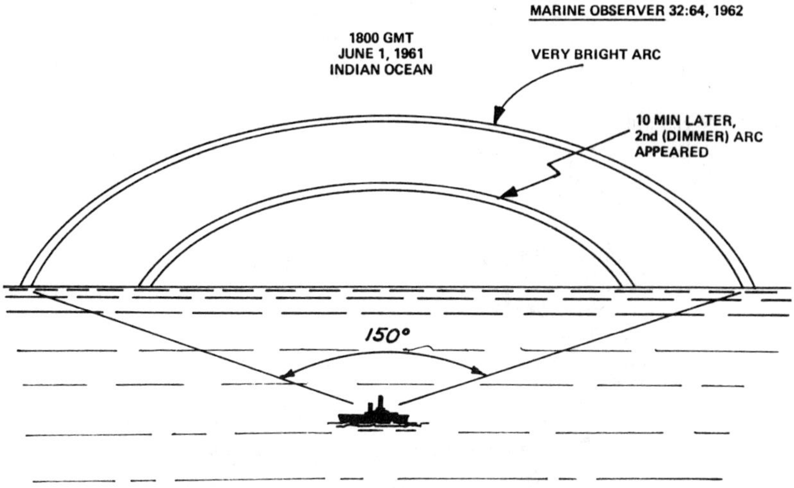

Figure 16. Tesla shields: Two nested arcs of light in the sky.

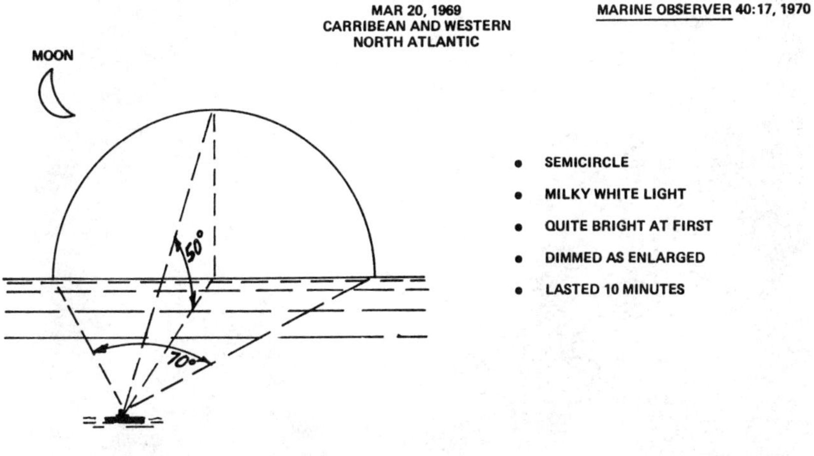

Figure 17. Tesla shield: An expanding hemispherical circle of light.

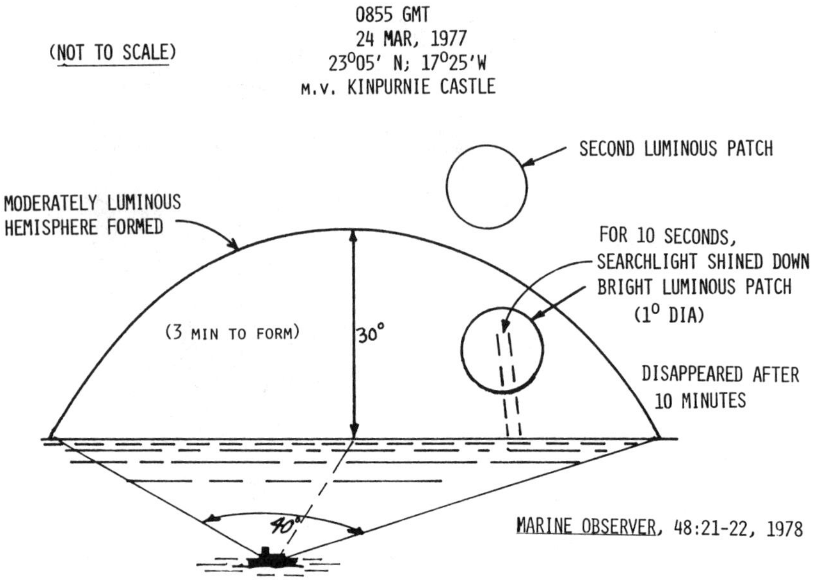

Figure 18. Tesla shield: Hemisphere and globes, 1977.

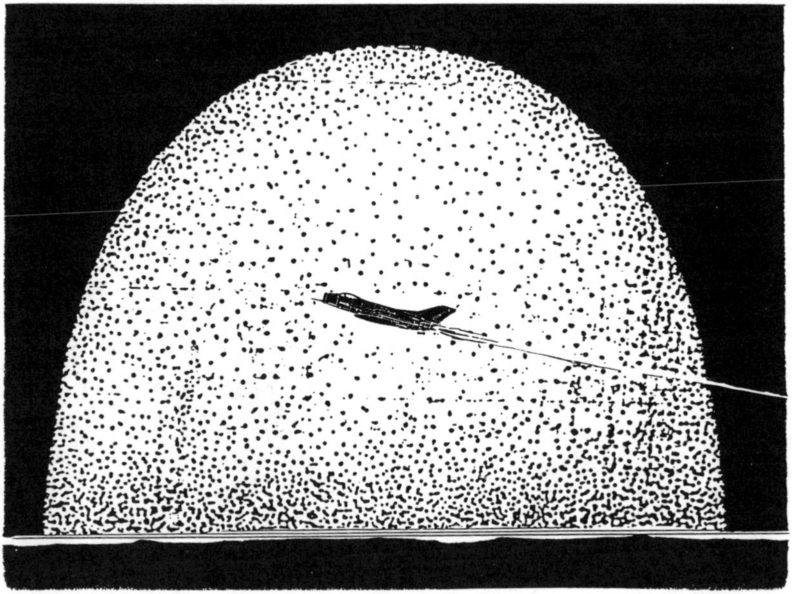

Figure 19. Large Tesla Shield observed by Red Chinese fighter pilots. Electrical difficulties in the aircraft were also experienced.

Figure 20. Large glowing "Tesla Globe," Red China. Observed by hundreds of persons.

© 1980 Hal Crawford

Figure 21. 1966 test of giant Tesla Globe, expanding deep within the Soviet Union. Seen from Teheran, Iran June 17, 1966 by two aircraft approaching Mehrabad Airport. Observed for several minutes.

Multiple events seen in Sept. 1979 from Afghanistan

Strange lurid glow that flared silently over the Hindu Kush; as described by Nick Downie.
The LONDON SUNDAY TIMES, 17 August 1980

Figure 22. A giant globe, deep within the Soviet Union in 1979. Seen several times from Afghanistan, looking toward Saryshagan.

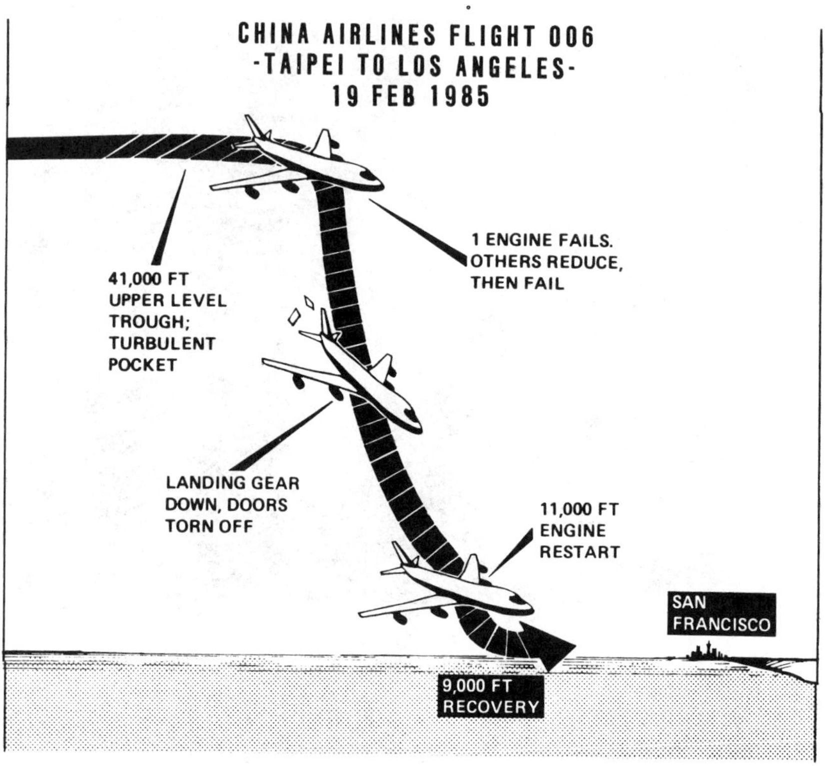

Figure 23. Engines disabled, a passenger jet drops six miles in two minutes.

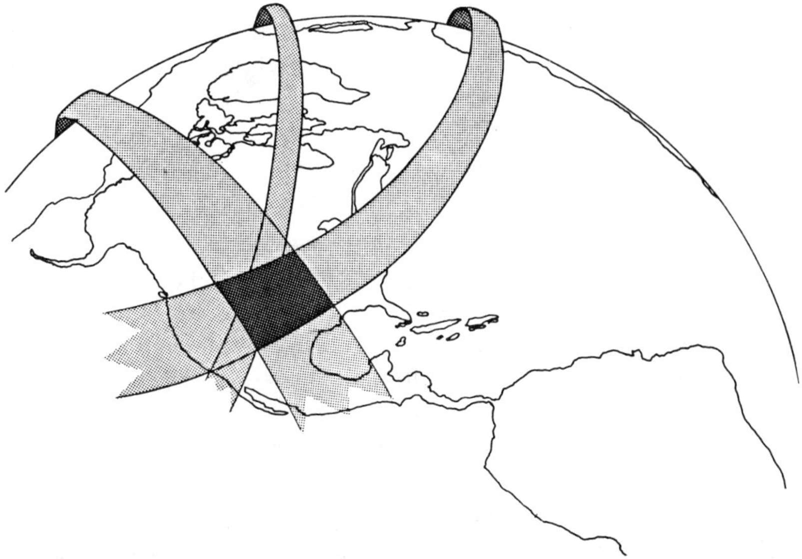

Figure 24. Giant "Woodpecker" beams intersecting over the U.S. Used for weather control, as a launch phase ABM and anti-bomber system, electromagnetic attack of distant populations, and disease conditioning. Using phase conjugate radar mirrors, any amount of energy desired can be delivered to any distant target from which a radar return has been received. Real-time distant holography, to produce powerful energy forms at a distance, can also be accomplished.

Table 6. MASSIVE 1985 STRATEGIC MAY DAY EXERCISE

APRIL/MAY 1985

- **BREZHNEV'S 1972 STATEMENT FULFILLED**
- **40th ANNIVERSARY OF WWII**
- **GORBACHEV NEWLY IN POWER**
- **EARTH IN GIANT SCALAR EM RESONANCE**
  - **54 FREQUENCIES**
  - **27 "POWER TAP" PAIRS**
  - **4 TO 6 WEAPONS EACH PAIR**

- **C^3I SCALAR EM LINKS**
  - **UNDERWATER SUBS**
  - **NAVAL FORCES**
  - **OTHER FORCES**

12. In late November, 1985 the Soviets tested their Launch Phase ABM system over Florida, using the launch of a U.S. space shuttle as a convenient test target. A marker beacon (ball of light) was placed in the sky, hovering near the launch area. It was seen by hundreds of persons, and photographed by George Suchary. During the final countdown to launch, a scalar EM "missile" (ball of intense energy) was fired, offset from the shuttle. This ball of energy was not in the visible spectrum, but may have been accidently photographed by Bob Gladwin. Twelve minutes offset after launch, a tremendous rumbling overhead boom echoed through the area — so huge it was heard for hundreds of miles up and down the East Coast. This was the third U.S. shuttle launch in which NASA had noted associated anomalous phenomena, but did nothing.

13. On December 12, 1985 the Soviets used the same weapon in the anti-bomber mode to destroy an Arrow DC-8 jet just after its takeoff from Gander Air Force Base, Newfoundland. **Over 250 U.S. soldiers and civilian crew members were killed.** Gander has long been a registration point for the Soviet scalar EM weapons. For example, in one 4-day period in 1982, 36 anomalous incidents occurred in and around Gander, involving moving lights, lights in the sky, etc.

14. On January 28, 1986 the Soviets destroyed the U.S. space shuttle Challenger, shortly after its launch. A dozen signatures are associated with this Soviet kill, too many to mention all of them. To give only a few: First, the Soviet ships monitoring the launch site suddenly departed at high speed, four hours before the launch. This was unparalleled. Second, according to General Daniel Graham, *the following evening KGB headquarters gave a party to celebrate the success of the KGB's perfect active measures against the Challenger!* Direct and unmistakable indications of extreme localization of the Soviet transmitters to the Challenger's launch site existed on the day of the launch. In addition, a metal-softening signal was confirmed on the Soviet Woodpecker beams as early as

January 1, 1986. Many other indicators also exist. The total is a very strong statement that the Soviets destroyed the Challenger with the same weapon they had tested against three previous shuttle launches, and which they had used to kill the Arrow DC-8 at Gander Air Force Base only six weeks earlier.

15. A whole series of anomalous missile failures occurred, involving Titan, Delta, and Ariane launches. The odds against all these launches failing in that pattern were millions to one. In one Titan failure, video taken of the event showed the anomalous "marker beacon" light in the vicinity, high overhead. Frame-by-frame analysis of the video showed that the light was indeed independent of the explosion, and it moved off separately after the rocket exploded.

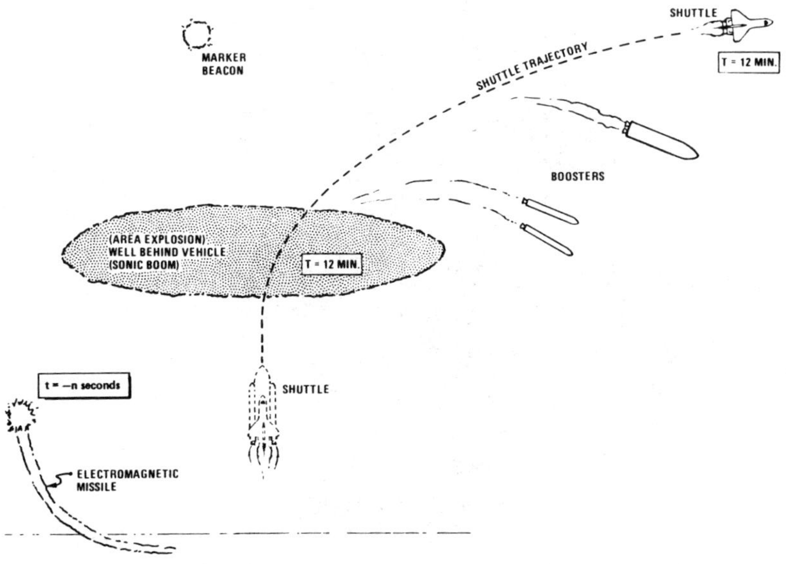

Figure 25. Third Soviet non-destructive testing against shuttle launches, Nov. 26, 1985.

Table 7. SHUTTLE LAUNCH ANOMALIES, NOV. 26, 1985

- **MARKER BEACON**
  - **PHOTOGRAPHED**
  - **SEEN BY HUNDREDS**
- **OFFSET SCALAR EM MISSILE**
  - **INVISIBLE TO HUMAN EYES**
  - **STRIKE PHOTOGRAPHED**
- **GIANT ATMOSPHERIC BOOM**
  - **T + 12 MINUTES**
  - **HEARD FOR HUNDREDS OF MILES**
- **THIRD LAUNCH WITH SUCH A BOOM**

Table 8. SOVIET ESCALATION AFTER 3RD TEST AGAINST SHUTTLE LAUNCH on Nov. 26,1985.

- **U.S. STILL UNAWARE OF SCALAR EM WEAPONS USE**
- **SOVIETS ESCALATED ACTION**
- **DESTROYED OR DISABLED:**
  - **ARROW DC-8 (DEC. 12, 1985)**
  - **CHALLENGER (JAN. 28, 1986)**
  - **TITAN 34-D (APRIL 18, 1986)**
  - **DELTA ROCKET (MAY 3, 1986)**
- **MAY HAVE DISABLED:**
  - **ARIANE II (MAY 31, 1986)**
  - **TWO U.S. NUCLEAR SUBS WHICH RAN AGROUND**
  - **STEALTH FIGHTER WHICH CRASHED**

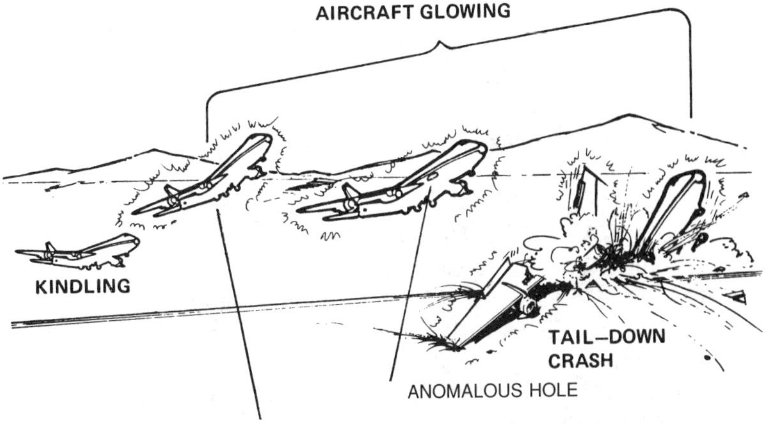

Figure 26. Death of the Arrow DC-8, Dec. 12, 1985. Three eye-witnesses saw the doomed airliner glowing. An anomalous hole was found in the fuselage, forward of the engines. Engine combustion was interfered with, by phase conjugate (negative) energy. Engines were rumbling laborously, not roaring with power, as the aircraft passed 100 ft directly over a witness.

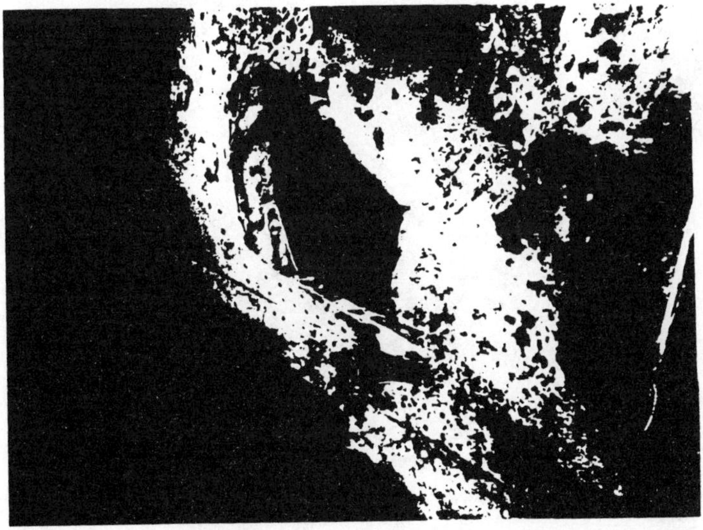

Figure 27. Anomalous hole in the right fuselage of the ARROW DC-8, ahead of the engines. With crossed over-the-horizon radar beams and multiple phase conjugate radar mirrors, real-time holography allows the production of a ball of EM energy at a great distance. The ball may be as small as desired, and contain as much energy as desired.

Table 9. ARROW DC-8 DISASTER, DEC. 12, 1985

GANDER AFB, NEWFOUNDLAND

- **AIRCRAFT LIFTED OFF**
- **AIRCRAFT WAS GLOWING YELLOW - ORANGE**
- **SANK TAIL-DOWN AND CRASHED**
- **SIGNATURE OF ENGINE/COMBUSTION INTERFERENCE**
  - **LAUNCH PHASE WEAPON**
  - **ANTI-BOMBER MODE**
  - **ANOMALOUS HOLE IN FUSELAGE, FORWARD OF ENGINES**
  - **STRUCK BY ELECTROMAGNETIC MISSILE?**
  - **EXTENSIVE "BALLS OF LIGHT" WEAPON TESTS IN AND AROUND GANDER**
- **CLOSELY FOLLOWED THIRD TEST AGAINST SHUTTLE NOV. 26, 1985, IN ABM MODE**

Figure 28. Part of the Soviet engineering of U.S. weather, just prior to the death of the Challenger. Three "giant radial" clouds sighted over the greater Los Angeles area by Margaret Wilson. Appeared one after the other, at 10 min. intervals.

DOD PHOTO

Figure 29. Soviet Trawler spyship. About four hours before the launch of the Challenger, all Soviet ships off coast, that normally monitor each launch, suddenly and mysteriously departed at high speed. Unprecedented event.

- **SOVIET WEATHER ENGINEERING**
- **SEVERE COLD STRESS**
- **METAL-SOFTENING**
- **BOOSTER SEAL PROBLEM**
- **SOVIET SHIPS ABSENT**
- **LOCALIZATION**
- **AIR TURBULENCE**
- **BIRDS NOT FLYING**

Figure 30. Launch of the doomed Challenger, Jan. 28, 1986.

Table 10. DEATH OF THE CHALLENGER, JAN 28, 1986

- **METAL-SOFTENING SIGNAL ON WOODPECKER GRID AS OF JANUARY 1, 1986**
- **SOVIETS ENGINEERED COLD WAVE INTO FLORIDA**
- **SEVERE COLD STRESS ON VEHICLE**
- **GRID LOCALIZATION SIGNATURES**
  - **BIRDS NOT FLYING IN LAUNCH AREA**
  - **BIRD FALLS IN BIRMINGHAM, AL (HINGE)**
- **SOVIET SHIPS/TRAWLERS DID NOT TRACK LAUNCH**
- **BOOSTER SEAL PROBLEM SEVERELY AGGRAVATED**
- **CAUSED SHUTTLE FAILURE**
- **SOVIET KGB HEADQUARTERS CELEBRATED "PERFECT SUCCESS OF ACTIVE MEASURES" AGAINST THE CHALLENGER!**

Table 11. KGB CELEBRATION

EVENING OF JAN. 28, 1986

- **AFTER DEATH OF CHALLENGER**
- **KGB HEADQUARTERS**
  - **JUBILANT PARTY**
  - **CELEBRATED SUCCESS**
  - **OF ACTIVE MEASURES AGAINST THE CHALLENGER**

SOURCE: GENERAL DANIEL GRAHAM, URGENTGRAM

- **NOTE: SOVIET SCALAR EM WEAPONS ARE CONTROLLED BY KGB**

- SHORTLY AFTER LAUNCH
- ANOMALOUS POWER SURGE
- "COMMANDED" ENGINE SHUTDOWN
- VEHICLE THEN UNSTABLE
- RANGE SAFETY OFFICER DESTROYED ROCKET
- EXTERNAL RANGE SENSORS DID NOT RECEIVE SURGE SIGNAL
- SIGNATURE OF TIME REVERSED WAVE
- WHICH LOCALIZED ON ROCKET

Figure 31. Loss of a Delta rocket, May 3, 1986.

16. In 1975, Brezhnev had surprisingly urged U.S. senators to have the U.S. cooperate in banning the development of new weapons of unparalleled horror. He used the phrase, "more frightful than the mind of man has ever imagined." Shortly after, at the United Nations, Gromyko had even introduced a draft agreement for all nations of the world to sign. Again, the West had not the foggiest notion as to what the Russians were talking about.

17. The orthodox U.S. news media has been, and is, almost totally "out of it." Ironically, at the time of our deadliest peril, and the most momentous period in history, incidents such as the indiscretions of a presidential candidate and of a television evangelist, and the "Iran Gate" actions of the National Security Council in trying to illegally get arms to the Contras, are the "burning issues of the hour" — and the week, and the month, and the year, and so on ad nauseam.

18. The Congress — great watchdog and the direct representative of the U.S. citizenry — is equally immersed in interminable hearings of little or no substance except news media coverage and publicity.

19. A belabored president, misled and now hemmed in on all sides and on the defensive, has had his power to act greatly constricted. In addition, the orthodox filtering networks surrounding him have effectively isolated him. He has been unaware of the extensive information that shows just how certain it is that the Soviets have fantastic superweapons and have been gingerly using them against us for decades. He and his immediate advisors are fed highly filtered, shaped and interpreted data. U.S. intelligence is very good at doing the things that it does. However, it is also very good at ignoring the things that it ignores! Further, the intelligence community is a past master at "slick-tonguing" the interpretation of anything new, and anything it really doesn't understand, in terms such as "We have no evidence that ..." For decades, the community has consistently underestimated the Soviet threat, and it has also usually projected any unpleasant present Soviet capability in the terms that "If the Soviets keep this sort of thing up, it may prove to be a real threat 30 years from now!" For years U.S. intelligence was unaware of a Toronto inventor's development and public demonstration in the late 1960's of an inertial field generator device, for example, because it simply did not place high value on simple overt intelligence such as reading the newspapers! The entire event was printed in detail in a Canadian newspaper. Only very recently, within the last few years, has the community again realized that the most important intelligence can only come from human (HUMINT) sources. And in relying on the scientific community — which itself knows nothing of scalar electromagnetics — the intelligence community has not received the technical advice necessary for it to properly task its collection agencies to collect information on the Soviet superweapons.

20. Western science has also shown itself to be highly dogmatic and ensconced in the comfortable "status quo." It has regally ignored the important Soviet developments in unified field theory. It has assumed an aristocratic stance, regarding the Soviet scientists as little more than peasants still trying to clean the mud off their boots. In fact, the Soviet scientists have been ahead of the rest of the world in *nonlinear* science — the truly hard stuff — since the beginning. They have always been the best nonlinear mathematicians in the world. Soviet scientific papers regularly appear which deal with local general relativity and the overcoming of the sacrosanct conservation laws as a matter of course. That subject is still a "no-no" in U.S. scientific publications, even though breaking symmetry and consequent violation of conservation laws has long been proven in particle physics. To my knowledge, with the exception of Hooper's obscurely published work, not a single U.S. scientific paper appears in the literature showing any detailed investigation of "bucking fields" as such and investigating the behavior of materials exposed to such "sum-zeroed" fields. Yet ironically a whole area of optical physics — phase conjugate optics (PCO) — has shown great activity since we discovered it in the open Soviet literature in the late 60's, and since two Soviet scientists visited Livermore* in 1972 and briefed us upon the subject (as another stimulus to see if we recognized the awesome weapon implications). In PCO, the scalar EM wave formed by two waves 180 degrees out of phase with each other, and locked (modulated) together by a nonlinear medium, is blithely called the *pump wave.* Using it on nonlinear materials produces extraordinary results — such as electromagnetic waves traveling backward in time. Further, the PC effect is known to be universal, and not just in the optics region at all; for example, it has also been done with sound waves. **The obvious experimental and theoretical proof of scalar EM has been in our literature for nearly two decades, and even in PCO our scientists do not yet realize that the "pump" wave is a scalar wave, a wave of**

*Lawrence Livermore National Laboratory

artificial potential, and a gravitational wave that pumps the nuclei of the atoms in the nonlinear medium. They also still do not understand that it is the nucleus of the atom that produces the phase conjugate replica wave in PCO.

Table 12. BREZHNEV'S 1975 PROPOSAL

AT THE SALT TALKS ON JUNE 13, 1975

- **THE SOVIETS URGED THE U.S. TO AGREE ON A BAN AGAINST RESEARCH AND DEVELOPMENT OF NEW KINDS OF MASS DESTRUCTION WEAPONS MORE TERRIBLE THAN ANYTHING THE WORLD HAS KNOWN!**
- **BREZHNEV PERSONALLY URGED VISITING U.S. SENATORS TO AGREE TO THE BAN.**
- **GROMYKO INTRODUCED A DRAFT AGREEMENT INTO THE UNITED NATIONS MEETING AND URGED THE NATIONS OF THE WORLD TO SIGN IT.**
- **THE WEST HAD NO IDEA WHAT THE SOVIETS WERE TALKING ABOUT!**
- **SOVIET HAWKS THEN GAINED DOMINANCE, AND THE USSR STARTED ITS MASSIVE BUILDUP FOR EVENTUAL WORLD TAKEOVER.**

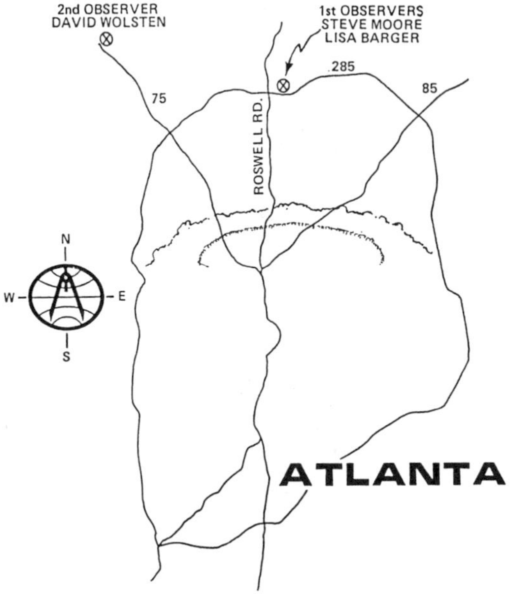

A. Location of the incident

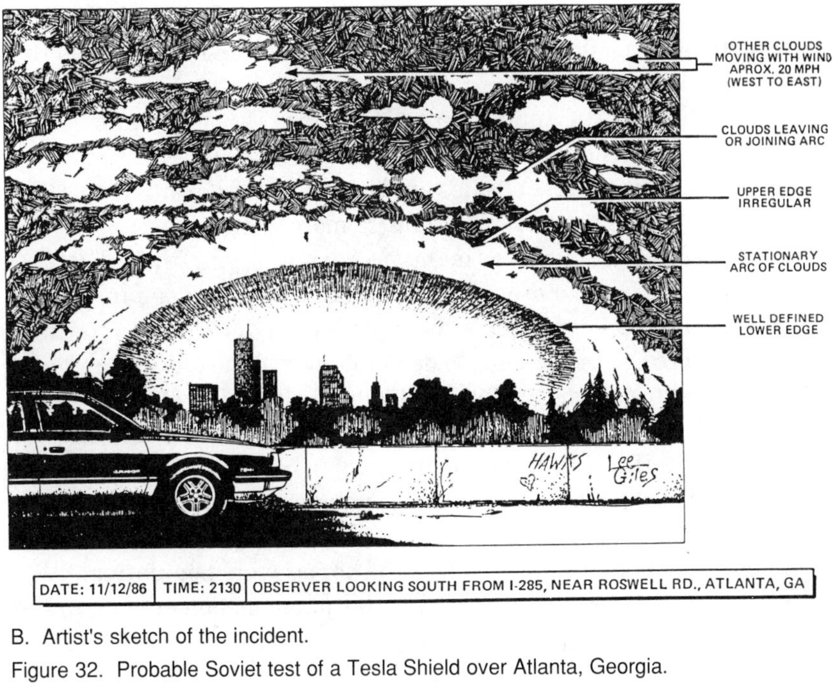

DATE: 11/12/86	TIME: 2130	OBSERVER LOOKING SOUTH FROM I-285, NEAR ROSWELL RD., ATLANTA, GA

B. Artist's sketch of the incident.

Figure 32. Probable Soviet test of a Tesla Shield over Atlanta, Georgia.

Continually assured that Western science and intelligence remained outrageously ignorant and would obstinately persist in wearing orthodox blinders, the Soviets felt quite safe in striking the U.S. and its Western allies a mortal death blow.

The Soviets knew there would be no retaliation, so long as the blow was sufficiently unorthodox.

After all, the Soviets have been waging a slowly increasing unorthodox war against us for decades, and totally getting away with it.

Consequently the Soviets manipulated the cancer research and the contamination of the World Health Organization's smallpox vaccine to produce the perfect biological warfare "first strike," administered unwittingly by the WHO itself in its mass immunization program to eradicate smallpox. The Soviets continue to manipulate the spreading AIDS viruses electromagnetically so that the West will be devastated, as well as Africa and the Third World.

At least one other spreading AIDS-strain has already appeared in Africa. Testing for exposure to the first strain in most cases did not detect exposure to this second strain.

Officially no one knows whether it will be as infectious as the first strain. However, a suspicious correlation has appeared between hepatitis vaccination in several large U.S. cities and consequent outbreak of AIDS among the persons inoculated.

Further, the latest studies are beginning to show that (1) AIDS may be just as spreadable, though more slowly spread, in the heterosexual community as in the gay community, (2) the AIDS tests themselves are far more unreliable than suspected; one may have the AIDS virus — and serve as an active carrier —for up to three years before the tests begin to detect it, and (3) no one has any real idea as to how many persons have already been infected.

As can be seen, even orthodox scientists are beginning to suspect a coming AIDS infection "asymptote" which may represent an explosion of the disease into a mass pandemic in the world population. In Africa, for example, AIDS is spreading freely among the hetersexual population as well as the homosexual population. * We may be on the verge of seeing a similar phenomenon emerge in the

*Although there is much speculation as to why African heterosexuals seem so vulnerable, at present no one knows why it is true.

Western world.

If so, we are looking full in the face of a forthcoming AIDS massacre that makes the 1918 influenza pandemic pale by comparison. Not only will AIDS decimate Africa and the Third World, but it will also decimate the West a little later.

In the Soviet plan, after the AIDS massacre has peaked, the remaining much smaller U.S. and European populations will be decimated and totally powerless. The demoralized and devastated Western nations will easily capitulate and pass under the Soviet hammer and sickle.

In their deception planning, the Soviets even are allowing some contamination of their own citizens by AIDS. Thus they can keep up a pretense that they are just as much victimized as we are, and just as much "in the dark" as we are about the whole thing.

Of course, once the AIDS infection does its lethal dirty work in the West, the Soviets can easily eradicate it in their own population at will, using the electromagnetic healing technology they already possess. The Soviet planners regard the loss of a few Soviet citizens along the way as one of the things necessary to insure the success of the Great Strike and the Final Revolution. Forward divisions in the standard Soviet attack are always regarded as such sacrificial pawns to guarantee the success of the follow-on echelons in the attack. In this BW strike, the sacrifice of some Soviet citizens is deemed necessary to the overall success of the attack.

Remember, these are the same type of Soviet communist planners who killed 20 million Kulaks — their own people — to forcibly collectivize Soviet agriculture. For their highest purposes, these planners are still quite capable of ruthlessly sacrificing millions of their own people to achieve their objectives.

The Asian Tiger Mosquito: A New and Efficient Vector

As almost everyone now realizes, in the past our government has greatly understated the AIDS problem. Past projections of the limitation of the spread of the disease have been far more optimistic than warranted.

For example, officially the government is still denying any possibility of insect vectors for the disease.

Don't believe it. In fact, highly efficient insect carriers of the disease are already on the way.

Insects in Africa have positively been verified to be harboring the AIDS retrovirus. Of course, such reports are always accompanied by the bland assurance that "We have no evidence... (that the insect bites will give AIDS to humans).

Let's see now: We're supposed to believe that a monkey bite will do enormously more than that. Even when the monkey didn't have the exact present form of the AIDS retrovirus. Even though monkey bites hadn't done the trick in thousands of years.

But we're supposed to turn right around and believe that an insect carrying the live AIDS retrovirus can bite you, inject into you some of his body fluid containing AIDS viruses, and you won't stand any chance of developing AIDS .

What are we supposed to believe? That the injected AIDS virus from an insect bite won't bother you, but the injected AIDS virus from other causes will?

Nonsense!

Anyone who believes that is a prime candidate for purchasing that bridge down the road...

Of course insect vectors will give you AIDS!

And we've got a real tiger — mosquito, that is, on the way to do just that.

The Asian Tiger mosquito has been introduced into the U.S. (it just "accidentally" appeared, of course!) and is now spreading through the Southeastern states. This vigorous and voracious mosquito prefers man as its target, and has an unusually wide range.

Recently U.S. scientists have reluctantly confirmed the presence of the AIDS virus in the Asian Tiger mosquito. However, as usual we are presented with the same tired refrain, "We have no evidence that... the mosquito's bite is capable of causing a human to develop AIDS."

Of course, you can be sure that eventually we *will* have evidence of precisely that!

The AIDS virus is now known to be able to live outside the body for up to at least 15 days, if not longer.

Also, the AIDS virus is an unstable virus — it's constantly mutating and changing its form. That means it's "highly adaptable" — that is, it's continually adapting to its environment, at a rate millions of times faster than normal stable viruses change and adapt.

That fact implies that some mutant strain of the virus will almost certainly be adapted to living in the Asian tiger mosquito and being introduced into its human host by the mosquito's bite.*

It's not a matter of "Can it do that?" or "We have (as yet) no evidence of that ."; instead, it's a matter of "How long will it be until that occurs and we confirm it?"

The Asian Tiger mosquito apparently is intended to serve as the major vector (carrier), or at least one of them, to eventually rapidly increase the AIDS infection rate and devastate the U.S. population.

As the vector spreads and the virus adapts to that mode of transmission, the rate of increase of the AIDS infection will itself accelerate. This means that all the projections for "doubling times" are seriously in error.

The latest data from Alabama, for example, shows that the disease is now doubling every six months instead of every year. Also, the doubling interval itself has been shortening, at least up to the present. Note also that, from the data of the new studies confirming a much longer lag time for the AIDS test to indicate the presence of the infection, even the present data on the number of persons infected and the doubling time are underestimated.

If these and other data are a true indication, it appears that we literally may have an "explosion" of the AIDS infection in no more than two to three years.

In addition, as we said the AIDS virus is an unstable virus. Mutations in the virus itself are occurring so rapidly that producing an effective vaccine essentially will be impossible. Without a totally new means applied to produce an AIDS cure, AIDS simply cannot be stopped.

*And one or more strains will eventually evolve that can be infectuously spread like the influenza virus is.

In fact, recenly it has been discovered that the AIDS virus is far more devious than previously susupected.* It attacks in more ways than suspected. It changes in the body, increasing its virulence as the disease progresses.

Macrophages, the immune system's scavenger cells, become infected and carry the virus to other body cells. It appears that macrophages may pass the virus to the T-cells, conditioning the destruction of the immune system. Infected macrophasges are found in rectal material of AIDS patients and in cervical fluid and semen. Thus through infected macrophages the AIDS virus is able to infect partners through exhange of semen, cerical fluid, and rectal material — even though there are no breaks or tears in the skin, and even though the number of free AIDS viruses in thefluids is too small to pass the infection.

Other immune system cells —such as Langerhans cells—are also suspected to be capable of serving as AIDS carriers when infected. The end result is that, as the AIDS patient sickens, the virulence of the AIDS virus increases, so that it attacks a greater variety of cells and can more easily infect them.

Present orthodox methods cannot cure AIDs in time, if ever.

Unless unorthodox technology is applied to solve the problem the West is already defeated.

*See Gina Kolata, "Fatal Strategy of AIDS Virus Grows Clearer," Science Times section, **New York Times,** Mar. 22, 1988; see also "Growth in AIDS Virus Virulence Found," **Los Angeles Times,** Apr. 1, 1988.

CHAPTER 3

WORLD WAR III IS RAGING AND WE'VE NEARLY LOST IT

More on AIDS Doubling Time

As we said, the AIDS problem is much, much worse than officially announced. As stated, in some areas at least, the number of new AIDS cases diagnosed has been doubling every six months instead of every year. New studies have shown that the tests to identify infection by the AIDS virus may themselves have a 3-year lag period in which they do not reliably indicate the presence of the infection.

These facts probably make all previous "officially announced" estimates and projections off by several orders of magnitude (at least three).

If the incubation period (nominal) is, say, 5 years, then there is a factor of up to 2 (exp 10) of AIDS cases already in incubation.

The lag in accuracy of the AIDS tests however, may mean that there are even more AIDS cases in incubation than this.

And we may have a new entry into the equation at any time, once the AIDS virus adapts to its transmission by the Asian tiger mosquito and possibly even other insect vectors.*

Remember, we've got the U.S. data for only a relatively few years since 1981. So it's statistically difficult to project ahead with any accuracy. However, the best interpretation of the data we can make shows a spiraling (speed-up) trend in the rate of acceleration of the disease, indicative of a forthcoming asymptote. If that interpretation of the data holds true, the asymptote represents literally an "explosion" of the disease.

That is, the six-months "doubling interval" is slowly becoming the six-months "tripling interval," the six-months "quadrupling interval," etc.

The best indication/projection I can tentatively arrive at is this: If the total cure is not accomplished within about two to three years, then — considering the incubation ongoing by then and the speedup

*Another HIV virus has now been identified.

ahead — somewhere between a third and two thirds of all humans on earth will perish.

In other words, nominally half the humans on earth will inevitably die, say within five years (the incubation) after that two to three year point.

Most of the people who die are going to be highly selected. Most of them are going to be Westerners, Africans, Asians, and Brown people.

And all of our tanks, ships, bombers, missiles, nuclear weapons, and armed forces put together can't save a single AIDS victim.

We've got more generals than ever before in our history, including World War II. And not a one of them has a single tactic or a single weapon to use against this mortal attack.

Understand, our generals have not failed us against the enemy they know and recognize. The bellies of our B-52 bombers and the aircraft aboard our distant aircraft carriers are filled with nuclear bombs sufficient to destroy the world many times over. Our powerful nuclear-tipped missiles sit in land-based silos and in sleek submarines cruising silently under the oceans, waiting to respond in an instant to hostile attack, again with the power to destroy the world many times over.

Yet the fine men and women who have built and maintained that awesome force, and who man it in constant vigilance to protect our nation, are absolutely vulnerable and defenseless against the smallest foe of all — just as were the Martians in H.G. Wells' **War of the Worlds.**

With all our awesome forces, we do not have the power to stop a single AIDS virus — or indeed, any other similar new BW virus.

We can be defeated with ridiculous ease by even the tiniest determined hostile nation — or even by a single terrorist, madman, or genetic accident by a high school youth.

And if there's one thing that we can learn from history with iron certainty, it is this: If we can be defeated with ridiculous ease, then most certainly we will be!

Since the strike has already occurred, then our defeat is just a matter of time if we continue our present courses of action.

All other threats — nuclear, chemical, scalar EM, the works — pale in comparison to this seemingly innocuous, doomsday BW viral weapon that has already been unleashed upon an unsuspecting world.

World War III is Already Raging

World War III has long been unleashed and a final, decisive first strike has now occurred. We've already lost the war unless unbelievably heroic measures are taken immediately.

This thing is deliberate. It's fiendishly clever. It's effective. And a smiling Gorbachev — master propagandist — is just part of the icing on the cake to deceive us until it's too late.

Ironically, Soviet announcements have cleverly started claiming that the U.S. has produced the AIDS virus and unleashed it.

That's a very clever propaganda trick to shift suspicion from themselves. Indeed, in the Third World the propaganda has been very effective. Most Third World peoples now give at least credence to the Soviet claim.

Unless we move immediately to effect a total cure, the armed forces and the populaces of all the Western nations will shortly be devastated — perhaps even worse than if they been attacked with nuclear weapons.

With our armed forces and populations devastated, we surrender. We lose.

The Soviets get the U.S. (and European) farmland. That's what they really need.

Of course they also will have rid themselves of about 200 million Americans or so along the way.

That solves the old "winner's problem" of what to do with, and how to effectively control and care for, a conquered, resentful populace. That problem will have already been taken care of, for most of the U.S. populace will essentially have been eliminated.

There won't be many U.S. military prisoners, for example, since most of the military personnel will also have been eliminated by the virus or viruses clandestinely released.

Communism Is Savage Enough to Do Diabolical Things

The Communist's doctrine is to wage total war. Win any way, with any weapon, at any cost.

Also, communism has always taught that it is necessary to

destroy capitalism. That equates with destroying the U.S., the major capitalist country. Communists have always taken the long view, willing to struggle for decades to eventually accomplish their aim.

If you think no modern nation could be so incredibly savage as to deliberately destroy untold millions of people, look at the actual record of the Communists.

When the Khmer Rouge took over Cambodia, they murdered a third of their own people.

The Soviets murdered some 20 million or so Kulaks when they collectivized the Soviet farms.

The Red Chinese also slaughtered Chinese peasants by the tens of millions — perhaps as many as twenty or thirty million — when they collectivized the farmers.

Lenin's followers have proved over and over that they are capable of murdering even their own people, on a scale of millions.

Dedicated communists are highly religious people — even fanatics. Deliberate murder to achieve communism's goals is part of the accepted dogma.

The communists are quite capable of killing a billion or more "foreigners" and "enemies," given the chance. Particularly when the goal is to win the "Final Revolution."

The opportunity to strike the decisive final blow without consequences, using as simple and unorthodox a weapon as the AIDS viruses, could simply not be ignored by men who have spent their lives trying to control the world.

The unparalleled strike opportunity was particularly irresistible since someone else (the Western cancer research institutes) would develop the weapon itself, someone else (the World Health Organization) would unwittingly deliver the strike, and the blow could easily be clandestinely arranged (simply by secretly contaminating the WHO smallpox vaccine) and accomplished without repercussions to the Soviet Union.

Western Medicine is Inadequate

But what of Western medicine? Doesn't it always come through to save us?

Present Western medical science is totally inadequate to do the task required.

For example, present medicine is largely based on "slowing or killing the invader of the body." Whether that invader is a germ, bacterium, virus, or whatever.

If there's a mechanical difficulty, then present treatment is to try to mechanically remedy it — remove a bad appendix, set a broken leg, etc.

However, then it's strictly up to the body's own natural healing system — its immune system and its repair system — to actually do the healing and repair/reconstruction.

The problem with AIDS is that it directly affects and suppresses the body's systems for healing and repair.

Once this protection and repair system is in disarray, any disease organism can attack the body and infect it. If the immune system can't handle the problem, eventually the invading disease organism kills its host.

Even if a way is found to destroy the AIDS virus itself, present medicine has not the foggiest notion of how to restore the healing and repair system from the damage and destruction it will have already sustained by massive AIDS infection.

Compare the situation to division combat: Hostile invaders are met at the front of the division by the division's combat forces. A battle ensues, with penetration and damage to the rear area support and sustenance facilities. After the enemy is beaten back or destroyed, the rear support and the combat forces must be renewed and restored. If that cannot be done, the seriously weakened division can still literally be bolled over by almost anything that comes along and hits it.*

*For this reason, standard Soviet doctrine is to attack in echelon, say, by three divisions — one behind the other. Thus, even if the first division is annihilated in the attack, the second and third divisions meet a seriously weakened enemy division and blast right over it. Similar tactics in the BWcrisis — multiple viral strikes, one after the other — can almost inevitably be expected, now that the "first division" — AIDS — has engaged us.
The Soviet "repetitive attack" method *works*, in case anyone has doubts. For example, see George C. Wilson, "Army training exercises raise troubling questions," **The Washington Post**, as printed in the **Huntsville (AL) Times**, Feb. 28, 1988, p. 21A. Repeated U.S. Army tests in the Mojave Desert have shown that, in nonnuclear combat, when attacked by multiple Soviet echelons with 3:1 strength, U.S. forces lose every time! In particular, U.S. troops have poor anti-tank defenses.

Modern medical dogma has concentrated almost entirely on the combat forces' problem of destroying and/or repelling the invader.

Western medicine has almost no tools or means of restoring the support and rear maintenance functions.

Even in a paroxysmal effort, dogmatic Western medical science would take decades to totally reorient its medical thinking to where it could even attack the real problem of AIDS and catastrophic sickness due to other viral BW warfare agents.

The same inability to cope with the problem also applies to our government bureaucracy, government agencies, the private companies, the universities, and to Western science in general.

If we have to depend on any or all of our present "system," the war is already over and we are all already doomed. Half of humanity will die within possibly five years after the upcoming two- to three-year "point of no return."

Medical insurance, treatment centers, and even private physicians are quickly going to be bankrupted as the AIDS plague increases. With the collapse of Western medicine, panic and pandemonium will reign in the streets. Martial law will be a necessity, and rioting on a scale unparalleled in American history will occur. We are likely to see our own U.S. dictatorship, in the form of a military junta making a coup and seizing power "to restore order and keep the lid on."

Study carefully the performance of governments and military regimes in such countries as Korea and South Vietnam, when those countries were hard pressed by enemy forces and in great disarray.

You may be looking at your own future.

The Soviets Will Not be Decimated

With the devastation of our armed forces, our governmental and civil agencies, and our population at large, a simple show of strength by the Soviets will collapse any further resistance. The hammer and sickle will wave supreme over the residue.

That's because the Russians *do* have the necessary developed scalar EM medical technology, not only to control and destroy the AIDS viruses, but also to directly restore the immune and repair systems.

The Kaznacheyev experiments alone show they have extensively studied electromagnetic induction of cellular disease and death.* We will have much more to say on that later.

If the Soviets extensively studied cellular death transmission by electromagnetics, you can bet they also studied the reverse: electromagnetic healing, or time-reversing the electromagnetic "death" signals themselves to produce specific "healing" signals for any type of cellular disease.

This is particularly certain since the Soviets also discovered and possessed the necessary "time reversal" electromagnetics: phase conjugation. This had been widely used by the Soviets in developing their enormous scalar EM weaponry, beginning about 1950 or so.

The curative signal technology was kept secret, of course, since the Soviets realized that it provided the only viable defense against viral biological warfare weapons.

The Soviets most certainly have the necessary AIDS cure. They can readily make the correct electromagnetic healing signal, by phase conjugating the AIDS death signal from dying human cells that contain AIDS retroviruses.

They also know we most certainly do *not* have the necessary EM cure. Years of weak microwave radiation of personnel in the U.S. Embassy in Moscow, and inducing illnesses in those personnel and even U.S. ambassadors, have shown that our own intelligence and scientific communities don't know what's really going on there.

Specifically, we've demonstrated (after checking with the DIA, CIA, NSA, and the orthodox scientists) that we do not recognize *electromagnetic biological warfare* — the deliberate introduction of cellular disease and death by electromagnetic means. Not only do we not recognize it, we can't do anything about it when it hits us.

And make no mistake, time-reversed electromagnetic medicine is shockingly cheap and effective, once developed. Specific healing signals for specific diseases — viral or whatever — can be quickly developed (within hours) and immediately used for mass treatment of entire populations.

For example, given the developed healing or "antidote" signal, it can even be recorded and played over ordinary transmitters, using

*There is now reliable information more closely associating Kaznacheyev with military institutes near Moscow, engaged in microwave weapon (directed energy) research.

their normal transmissions as carrier waves. A populace continually bombarded by such "healing" television, radio, and powerline signals simply doesn't get the disease. And those already infected recover when continually exposed to such healing signals.

So the Russians can stop the AIDS epidemic cold, anytime they choose to do so.

Electromagnetically they can also gently guide and stimulate the progress of a disease such as AIDS, once the disease is introduced into a targeted population.*

Or, the Soviets can pull out all the stops and induce the disease in a distant population directly, placing the "death signals" on common carriers. Such as on our power lines, radio stations, televisions, and directly by induction from the Woodpecker over-the-horizon radar signals which continually bombard us.

The West cannot do any of these things. Neither can the West counter them, or defend against them effectively.

Unless a totally different tack is taken in the Western effort to counter this viral BW threat, Gorbachev's entrancing smile has already lured us to our doom. We are faced with a direct realization of Lenin's words:

> **"In the final revolution it does not matter if three-quarters of the earth is destroyed, so long as the remaining quarter emerges communist."**

And Khrushchev's ghost will have the last laugh after all. We will have fulfilled the prediction he made to Nixon in their famous "Kitchen debate":

> **"We will bury you!"**

Quite simply, for some decades the Soviets have had a new science — one they call *energetics,* and one which I have called *scalar electromagnetics.* The keystone or "heart" of this new science is time-reversed (phase conjugation) electromagnetics and electrogravitation.

*A candidate for an eery test of just this capability may be the highly anomalous deaths of numerous dolphins off the East coast of the U.S. in 1987. Nearly 500 died in the summer and late fall, apparently as a result of the weakening of their immune system to the common bacterium Vibrio. See Julia Lawlor, "Key: Failure of Mammals' defenses," USA Today, Jan. 19, 1988, p. 1A-2A.

Chapters 4 and 5
deal with complex scientific material
and are suggested for those who are
technically proficient.

CHAPTER 4

EXTRAORDINARY PHYSICS

Maxwell's Lost Unified Field Theory

About the time of the U.S. Civil War, James Clerk Maxwell succeeded in unifying magnetism and electricity. Actually he did far more than that, in his theory as originally written.

In fact, he had produced a theory which also captured the free interchange between electromagnetic energy and gravitational energy, but no one — including Maxwell himself — realized it at the time.

Maxwell wrote his original theory in quaternion and quaternion-like mathematics. The modern form of vector mathematics had not yet been finalized by Gibbs and Heaviside. It is most instructional to examine some of the fundamental differences between a vector and a quaternion.

In a conventional 3-dimensional vector, one may have three vector components, such as

$$\mathbf{v} = a\mathbf{i} + b\mathbf{j} + c\mathbf{k} \qquad (4\text{-}1)$$

where **i**, **j**, **k** are unit vectors in the directions of the x, y, and z axes respectively and a, b, and c are constants.

Obviously if the vector components of vector v are zero, then

$$\mathbf{v} = \mathbf{0} \qquad (4\text{-}2)$$

We shall be interested in the "vector product" of two identical vectors v, where

$$\mathbf{v} \times \mathbf{v} = AA \sin\emptyset = \mathbf{O} \qquad (4\text{-}3)$$

and A is the length (magnitude) of vector **v**, Ø is the angle between the two vectors (in this case zero), and **O** is the zero vector.

Now let us look for a moment at the quaternion situation.

First, in addition to the three vector components, a quaternion also has a separate scalar component, w. So the quaternion q for this situation is

$$q = w + a\mathbf{i} + b\mathbf{j} + c\mathbf{k} \qquad (4\text{-}4)$$

Now when this quaternion is multiplied times itself, the vector part zeros, just as it did for the vector expression. However, the scalar part does not go to zero. Instead, we have

$$q \, X \, q = A^2 = a^2 + b^2 + c^2 \qquad (4\text{-}5)$$

There is a very good physical interpretation of this result. It is a square of the amplitude, hence for the vector part of a wave, it is directly proportional to the energy density of the vacuum, as a function of time, at the particular position. However, we now need to make a short explanation of variation of stress energy density of spacetime.

First, we note that, according to general relativity, the "gravitational potential" is just a conglomerate of potentials of all kinds. Basically, a potential represents a G-potential, and consequently a curvature of spacetime. The potential also represents "trapped energy."

Second, we note that Kaluza combined electromagnetics and gravitation as a unified theory in 1921. Kaluza added a fifth (spatial) dimension to Minkowski's 4-space, and applied Einstein's relativity theory to 5 dimensions.

To Kaluza's delight, a common 5-d potential is responsible for both electromagnetic field and gravitational field. The "bleed-off" of this 5-potential in the 5th dimension (which is wrapped **around** each point in our 3-space) is what we know as the **electromagnetic force field.** The bleed-off of this 5-potential *in and through* our 3-space is what we know as the **gravitational force field.**

Since the EM field is very much stronger (by a factor of 10^{42} for electrons) than the gravitational field, it is obvious that most of the bleed-off of the 5-potential is in the 5th dimension, as EM force field. Only a tiny bit is left to bleed-off in 3-space, producing a very weak gravitational field.[1]

We state this fact: as a mass moves in space, it generates increased "activity" with the virtual particle flux of vacuum itself. The increased virtual particle flux activity exchange between vacuum and mass is analogous to a strange kind of "virtual resistance." Since the resistance is virtual, it does not observably slow down an observable object moving in an (unobservable, virtual-particle flux) vacuum.

The increased flux activity represents an increased "virtual energy density" of space time, and an increased "trapped potential" (mass; resistance to an accelerating force) of the moving object. It represents a rotation of the spacetime frame, vis a vis the laboratory observer).

In the virtual vacuum (which contains both positive and negative time), one sees two antiparallel virtual forces: one in positive time, along the velocity vector of the object, and one in negative time (time reversed, or phase conjugated). The reason one sees virtual forces is that each virtual (subquantal) change in the virtual flux activity represents an individual (unintegrated), separate change, hence a virtual acceleration. The observer (where things are integrated), sees the integral of all these accelerations, hence observable velocity.

The vector sum of these two virtual forces in the vacuum is a zero vector; however, the two taken together represent a stress in the local energy density of vacuum.

Since we may regard an EM wave as a stream of virtual electrons/positrons, each engaging in tremendous virtual particle flux exchange with the vacuum, then the same basic picture applies.

Now for our physical interpretation of (4-5): If we refer to an EM wave moving in the vacuum, the rotation of the frame is maximum (90 degrees). But this same rotation is just the same as additional vacuum stress, so the vacuum stress is maximum.

[1]Electromagnetics is 5-gravity sliding around our 3-space. 3-gravity is 5-gravity oozing through our 3-space.

This leads to these conclusions: An electrical force field vector represents a local maximum linear stress in spacetime, along the line of the vector. (Note we specifically deny that the electrical force field vector, of an EM wave in vacuum, is transverse. Instead, it is longitudinal. That has been addressed elsewhere by the author and will not be covered further here.)

Another electrical (stress) vector interacting with the first one adds more "urging" stress to the first. However, this action is occurring in the rotated frame of the moving wave, and so is rotated 90 degrees from the electrical velocity vector. Therefore it is lateral (but in a hyperdimension, not in 3-space) at right angles to the electrical velocity vector.

The combined "urging" action of the two vectors thus sweeps out an area with respect to the laboratory observer.

This means that the total "urging" or "stressing" action of the two vectors is analogous to a vector area.

It also means that this "area" function may be taken as the "swirl" of the electrical vector, but in a hyperdimension, not in 3-space. That is, we have described the magnetic force field.

Thus any two electrical vectors that interact will have an "area" or "resistance" component generated. *Any two that interact.* Whether they add vectorially, cross-product multiply, or dot-product multiply.

What is actually happening is that the wave exists in the 5-potential. The **E** and **B** fields just represent the oscillations in that 5-potential. They represent oscillations in the bleed-offs of that potential as **E**-field (longitudinal) and **B**-field (swirl).

The drag-area represents the accumulation of extra potential — hence the local rotation of spacetime. Since this accumulation is moving (along with the EM wave), as it passes a point it represents a change in the local virtual particle flux density of vacuum at that point, **hence a local curvature of spacetime.**

Hence, the EM wave makes a 5-dimension G-potential wave as it travels. The 3-dimensional gravity wave associated with this is normally very, very much smaller in magnitude — say, by a factor of 10^{-42} or so.

However, if the two vectors interact so as to produce a vector zero resultant, then all the electromagnetic energy of the two vectors is captured. That is, all the "EM vector zero" resultant means is that the EM bleedoff of the 5-space gravitational potential wave has been stopped. The 5-potential is still oscillating, and now all its trapped 5-energy must bleed off as 3-gravity force field.

Mass acts as an accumulator for this "trapped-EM energy turned into local curvature of 5-space." If we continually irradiate a mass with such a wave, the atomic nuclei of the mass slowly charge up with the new energy. Note that this potential delta may be positive or negative, if one adjusts accordingly.

In this fashion one may change the mass of a static object in the laboratory. One may either increase the mass or decrease it, or cause it to float, or even cause it to accelerate upwards.

But to return to our vector interaction and our interpretation of the scalar remainder of the quaternion.

The rule is, when the two EM vectors interact so as to form a zero EM resultant, then the EM energy represented in each of the two vectors has been converted into a special form of 5-space gravitational potential, one that is not bleeding-off in the fifth dimension (electromagnetically), but one which will gradually produce a 3-gravity potential in a mass's atomic nuclei as a function of time, the individual element, permeability and absorption factors of those nuclei, etc.

Therefore in our mathematical theory we ought to have a scalar component remaining when two EM vectors interact to form an EM vector zero resultant. That scalar component represents what is happening in the 5-potential, that will only bleed into 3-gravity.

With exploration of this phenomenology in the laboratory, one can work out the functions, constants, coefficients, and parameters which specify how the "5-G to 3-G and vice versa" component works in conjunction with mass, motion, and other fields.

That's the magic secret of electrogravitation.

It was captured inherently by the quaternion theory of Maxwell published during the American Civil War!

After Maxwell's death, when the scalar portion of the quaternion was discarded (by Oliver Heaviside) to form "modern" EM theory, that also discarded the unified field interaction between electromagnetics and gravitation.

Electromagnetic field and gravitational field were then modeled and regarded as mutually exclusive. EM field, therefore, was thought to produce no specific gravitational effects in the vacuum itself.

Hence when Albert Einstein was formulating general relativity some decades later, he knew only one way to "curve" spacetime: that was gravitationally, by "attraction of mass" forces.

But gravitational force was so weak that only a huge collection of mass would exert enough of it to measurably curve spacetime. That would require a sun or star. Since the observer and his instruments would never be on the surface of the sun or a star, **Einstein assumed that the local spacetime of the observer would not be curved.**

Hence he severely crippled his general relativity theory. In the West, it remains an assumption to this day. It is not a universal assumption in the Soviet Union, however, since the Soviets have long since written — and developed in the laboratory — unrestricted general relativity with *local* spacetime curvature, and hence *local violation of conservation laws.*

So the scalar part of the quaternion interaction, that remains when the vector part of the resultant is zero, is magic indeed.

That is the magic unified field portion that everyone has been seeking for decades and decades!

It was there at the beginning. Then we inexplicably threw it away!

But to return to our vector/quaternion examples.

Note also that the two vectors

$$\mathbf{v}_1 = a\mathbf{i} + b\mathbf{j} + c\mathbf{k},$$
$$\mathbf{v}_2 = -a\mathbf{i} - b\mathbf{j} - c\mathbf{k} \qquad (4\text{-}6)$$

sum to zero vectorially when added, such that

$$\mathbf{v}_1 + \mathbf{v}_2 = \mathbf{0} \qquad (4\text{-}7)$$

However, quaternions may behave quite differently, even under addition. For example, the two quaternions

$$\begin{aligned} q_1 &= w + a\,\mathbf{i} + b\,\mathbf{j} + c\,\mathbf{k}, \\ q_2 &= w - a\,\mathbf{i} - b\,\mathbf{j} - c\,\mathbf{k} \end{aligned} \qquad (4\text{-}8)$$

sum their vector parts to a vector zero resultant, but do not sum to a scalar zero as well. Instead, they sum to

$$q_1 + q_2 = 2w \qquad (4\text{-}9)$$

As can be seen, quaternions which have the same vector parts as vectors, do not necessarily yield a complete zero when the vector parts sum to zero. And when two vectors multiply to provide a zero vector resultant, corresponding quaternions may yield a scalar term that is equal to the product of the magnitudes of the two vectors.

In this way, the quaternion approach can capture the *stress of the medium,* induced by opposing or multiplying vectors. In the vector approach, the stress of the medium is entirely lost when the two vectors sum or multiply to a zero resultant.

Let us see just how important this "vacuum stress" can be.

First, the "stress in the medium" represents curvature of spacetime when that medium is the vacuum/spacetime.

In other words, the quaternion approach captures the ability to utilize electromagnetics and produce local curvature of spacetime, in an engineering fashion. Heaviside wrote a subset of Maxwell's theory where this capability is excluded.*

*Dr Henry Monteith has independently discovered that Maxwell's original quaternion theory was a unified field theory. See his important "Dynamic Gravity and Electromagnetic Processes," in publication.

Note that, by Maxwell's original quaternion theory, however, Einstein's assumption need not be true at all. For example, look at equations (4-5) and (4-9): Here we may utilize electromagnetic force quaternions to produce zeroed EM forces, and an increased stress in local spacetime. In other words, we have curved local spacetime electromagnetically. Since (with electrons) electromagnetic forces are about 10^{42} times as strong as the gravitation force, this local curvature of spacetime is not negligible.

That is, we have produced a scalar effect from zeroing vector operation between electromagnetic forces. I have called this **scalar electromagnetics,** and pointed out that it is truly *electrogravitation.*

We stress again that this violates one of the severely limiting assumptions that Einstein placed upon his theory of general relativity. He assumed that curving spacetime could only be done by the weak gravitational force due to mass. Since gravitational force is so weak, only a stupendous collection of mass — such as the sun or a star — could curve spacetime enough to notice experimentally.

Since obviously the observer and his laboratory instruments would never be located on the surface of the sun or a star, *Einstein assumed that the local spacetime would never be curved!* In other words, the local frame would always be a Lorentz frame. This meant that, locally, the familiar conservation laws of physics would always apply. Curvature of spacetime would only occur at great distances, and at huge collections of mass such as a star or dwarf star.

Einstein did not write a complete, unlimited general relativity. He wrote a sort of "special relativity with distant perturbations."

If Einstein had had electromagnetic theory in quaternions, the scalar "vacuum pressure" parts would have been there for him to ponder. It is highly probable that he would have captured the "electromagnetics-to-gravity conversion remainder" in the quaternion interactions.

If so, he would have written the full theory of general relativity, involving local violation of conservation of energy, a unified field theory, and the direct engineering of

gravitational and antigravity effects on the laboratory bench by electromagnetic means.

In that case, we should long since have navigated all around the solar system, colonized the planets, produced practical free energy devices and power systems, and avoided two great world wars and a host of little ones.

But let us now see if we can make a gravitational wave, electromagnetically.

Again, regard equations (4-5) and (4-9). Suppose these are instantaneous operations of EM force quaternions whose vector parts are varying in magnitude, but in such a manner that the vector parts always form a zero vector resultant. Now one can see that the scalar part remaining — which represents the stress of local spacetime — is varying as the product of the magnitudes of the vectors in the interaction vary.

This means that one has now produced a scalar wave that represents the local variation of spacetime curvature in an oscillating manner.

Rigorously this is a gravitational wave. It has been produced locally. It has been produced by Maxwell's original unified theory.

Again, I have called this area *scalar electromagnetics.* The Soviets call it *energetics.*

Where local spacetime curvature is varied, conservation laws (energy, conversation, etc.) need not hold. Curved one way, the local spacetime acts as a source (of energy, charge, etc.) Curved the other way, the local spacetime acts as a sink (of energy, charge, etc.)

The Soviets often do not utilize the same restricted kind of general relativity that Western scientists adhere to.

Soviet papers in general relativity regularly point out the complete and unrestricted theory, where local spacetime curvature is allowed. They also point out that all conservation laws may be violated by such local curvature. Thus the Soviets have no unduly dogmatic respect for conservation laws.

Further, by assuming the possibility of local spacetime curvature, Soviet scientists have assumed the possibility of direct experimentation with general relativity on the laboratory bench.

In the West, we have assumed that such cannot possibly be done, because of Einstein's limiting assumption of no local spacetime curvature. Thus Western physicists are strongly conditioned away from electrogravitation.

This is particularly ironic since the basis for just such an experimental theory was produced by none other than Maxwell himself in his original theory of electromagnetism.

Indeed, shortly after the U.S. Civil War, we should have been developing antigravity spaceships. We should have developed electromagnetics a la Maxwell and been on our way to the planets of our solar system. For Maxwell had — admittedly somewhat unwittingly — given us the basis for the necessary engineering theory of unified electrogravitation.

Heaviside's Mutilation of Maxwell's Theory

Well after Maxwell's death,Oliver Heaviside helped to finalize what is today vector analysis.

Then he undertook to "translate" Maxwell's theory from quaternion form to the new vector mathematics form.

Now quaternions were devilishly difficult to calculate in. So much so, that a majority of the electrical scientists (there were not very many of them in those days!) were in despair.

Not to worry! Heaviside took a broadax, figuratively speaking, and simply chopped off the scalar term, leaving only the vector components.

With that artifice, he greatly simplified the calculations to be performed.

Of course, he also threw away the EM stress of spacetime! That is, he threw away the "gravitation" part of Maxwell's theory!

Let me stress this fact most strongly. **After Maxwell's death a single man — Oliver Heaviside — directly altered Maxwell's equations, eliminating localized electrogravitation and producing the form of the theory taught throughout the West today as "Maxwell's theory."**

Maxwell's theory has never been taught in Western universities! Only Heaviside's crippled subset of the theory has been taught!

Then, shortly before the turn of the century, a short, sharp "debate" erupted in a few journals — mostly in the journal **Nature.** Only about 30 scientists took part in the "debate."

It wasn't really much of a debate! The vectorists simply steamrolled right over the remaining quaternionists, sweeping all opposition before them.

They simply threw out the remaining vestiges of Maxwell's quaternion theory, and completely adopted Heaviside's interpretation.

Thus, a little over a decade later when Einstein wrote his general relativity theory, he did not know that the original work of Maxwell already indicated the unification of gravitation and electromagnetics, and indicated the ease with which local spacetime could be electrogravitationally curved locally and *engineered.*

Accordingly, he placed the scientists of the West on a road which rigorously assumed that a unified field theory was yet to be discovered. It also strongly discouraged any experimentation aimed at curving local spacetime, for it assumed that such could not be done.

After Potsdam and World War II, a frustrated Stalin was to drive his scientists to review the entire scientific literature of the Western world, actively seeking a great new technical breakthrough area such as the Allies had demonstrated with the development and use of the atomic bomb.

Great Soviet institutes — one staffed, for example, with over 2,000 PhD's — were set up to thoroughly review all the Western scientific literature from its very beginning. Anything interesting, anomalous, or unknown was put aside for further examination.

It is a good bet that the meticulous Soviet scientists discovered the difference between Maxwell's original electromagnetic theory and Heaviside's mutilation of it. Great mathematicians that they are, Soviet scientists would have realized the implications of the difference. With their knowledge of unlimited general relativity, they would have made the connection to electrogravitation.

By 1950 they had indeed done so, and were deeply into the development of what they called "energetics", and I have called *scalar electromagnetics.*

They had also reached another milestone about the same time — 1950 or so.

After WWII, both the Soviets and the U.S. were keen on securing the best of the German scientists. The U.S. particularly wanted missile scientists and rocket engineers. The Soviets wanted them too; but they also wanted the German radar specialists and infrared specialists.

The West didn't care about the German radar scientists and engineers, and the IR fellows. The Soviets did, and they got them. That was to prove a most spectacular benefit indeed.

During the war, the Germans had placed extreme emphasis upon radar and radar absorbing materials (RAM). The German scientists had fantastically developed and extended the science of radar cross section — which is the heart of the matter and very, very complex. **They were much further ahead in radar cross section theory at the end of WWII than where the U.S. is today, in the opinion of some U.S. radar experts.**

So the Soviets started with a great jump on us in radar knowledge, and they have steadily increased the lead over the years.

In addition, the Germans had developed highly successful radar absorbing materials, and much of the theory to accompany them.

Such materials turn out to be the key to how to build and develop a radar phase conjugation mirror, to produce a time-reversed radar wave.

Thus, because of the German scientists, by 1950 or so the Soviets had already discovered phase conjugation. And they had discovered it in radar first, not in optics!

They would have been primed for the discovery by their great review of Western literature and the foundations of science, since they would probably have noticed that the time-reversed wave is a solution to the wave equation. If so, they would certainly have realized its generality throughout all physics, all frequency bands, and all types of waves.

Superb mathematicians that they are, the Soviets would certainly have made the Kaluza-Klein theory connection, and also realized that phase conjugate waves carry negative energy as well as negative time. They would quickly have seen the gravity and antigravity implications.

So about 1950 or so, the Soviet Union would have started phenomenology experimentation in earnest, with phase conjugate radar mirrors and phase conjugate radars. This is what was referred to as *energetics*. The Soviets began a massive program in energetics about the time of the beginning of the Korean War.

By 1957-8 the Soviets had progressed to the point of a giant scalar EM accident in the Urals which exploded nearby atomic wastes, devastating the area. They had also progressed to development of great new superweapons using their new energetics — weapons to which Khrushchev referred in 1960 when he informed the Soviet Presidium of a new, fantastic weapon in development, a weapon "so powerful that it could wipe out all life on earth if unrestrainedly employed."

About the same time (mid-to-late 50's), the Soviets had also started the eery low-level microwave radiation of the U.S. Embassy in Moscow, to see if the U.S. knew of scalar electromagnetics (energetics) and was developing its own electrogravitational weapons and defenses.

Building Upon Whittaker's Fundamental Work

In 1904, a most fundamental paper in the foundations of electromagnetics was delivered by the British mathematician E. T. Whittaker. (E. T. Whittaker, "On an expression of the electromagnetic field due to electrons by means of two scalar potential functions," **Proc. Lond. Math. Soc.**, Series 2, Vol. 1, 1904, p. 367-372.).

In this important paper, Whittaker showed that the electromagnetic force field equations can be replaced with the derivates of two scalar potential functions.

He also derived the most general form of electromagnetic disturbances in the ether.

This means that the coupling of two dynamic scalar functions can replace vector electromagnetics in the vacuum.

Note that Whittaker's work pointing out the overriding importance of scalar fields also accents the erroneously discarded scalar part of Maxwell's quaternion electromagnetic theory even more strongly.

Let me explain now how I got from Whittaker's paper to scalar electromagnetics, Soviet Tesla weapons, free energy, antigravity, and electromagnetic healing.

When I discovered Whittaker's paper, I had already strongly objected that "charges" and electromagnetic vector force fields — as presently included in the Heaviside version of Maxwell's equations — included observable mass. Of course there was no observable mass in the vacuum, hence the prescribed kind of EM force fields could not exist as such in the vacuum.

Obviously the foundations of our ordinary electromagnetics theory were seriously flawed. Although my objections fell on deaf ears, I determined to examine the foundations of EM theory, discover the flaws, and at least point out the necessary corrections to be made.

Though this was an arduous task to undertake and it required many years, slowly the flaws showed themselves, and the necessary corrections slowly became clearer.

Most exciting of all, in working with several unorthodox researchers, I was able to see many of these new ideas tried, adjusted, and demonstrated. In addition, the proprietary discoveries of these colleagues continued to reveal new and unique principles and concepts. The only disadvantage was that I could not reveal the propriety apparatuses and demonstrations of my inventor associates, but only the principles and concepts that developed. In turn, I also developed principles and concepts to explain what they were doing and the results they were obtaining.

So over the years I have slowly been releasing the principles and concepts. Some of them are my own discoveries, many of them are the discoveries of my associates. Some of them are simply a mixture of both.

Early on, it became obvious that the Soviet Union was far ahead on this path, and was already utilizing the new unified field theory to build eery, powerful new superweapons.

Since no one else in the U.S. seemed to be "watching this particular store" (I was rather universally regarded as some peculiar sort of fool!), I also began to compile information and data on the Soviet weaponization of this unrecognized technology. This information I have released in a series of papers, briefings, and books, the most recent being a 1-hour videotape, "Soviet Weather Engineering Over North America," 1985, and a detailed book, **Fer-de-Lance: A Briefing on Soviet Scalar Electromagnetic Weapons,** Tesla Book Co., Greenville, Texas, 1986.

Building upon Whittaker's important work, I formulated a conceptual revision to electromagnetics, which I dubbed *scalar electromagnetics* to accent that the observable EM vector force fields did not exist as such in vacuum, but dynamic scalar fields did. I also wished to call strong attention to the fact that observable force does not exist until an observable particle of mass is coupled to the interference of the two scalar fields (much like in the Aharonov-Bohm effect). The Soviets, of course, call this area *energetics,* Energetics technology has been used in gigantic weapons programs of the Soviet Union for decades, and it appears to be developed under the most highly classified program that the Soviet possess. All development and deployment of energetics weapons is under the KGB and controlled directly by that organization, not by the Soviet Armed Forces.

Peter Kapitsa, the great Soviet physicist, was once pressed by Nikita Khrushchev for a total defense against missiles and air- and space-borne vehicles. Kapitsa replied that it could only come from the new energetics. In 1960, of course, Khrushchev gleefully announced to the Presidium that a new, fantastic Soviet weapon was in development, "so powerful that, if unrestrainedly used, it could wipe out all life on earth."

Ironically, Khrushchev "jumped the gun" before his new superweapons were deployed. In the fall of 1962 he began inserting long range missiles into Cuba, bracketing the U.S. with nuclear firepower in an attempt to immediately change the balance of power. Kennedy, of course, backed him down "eyeball to eyeball," so to speak, in a blunt confrontation, but promised not to invade Cuba.

Khrushchev, with his days numbered, was desperate to deploy his new superweapons and provide a dramatic demonstration to recover face.

By destroying the U.S.S. Thresher on April 10, 1963 and, on the next day, producing a gigantic underwater explosion 100 miles north of Puerto Rico, the Soviets demonstrated that the new superweapons had been deployed. Khrushchev managed to retain his position a while longer.

In the 1960's and early 1970's, I was also deeply involved in the study of paranormal phenomena.

In 1969, I entered the Georgia Institute of Technology to pursue a Master's Degree program in nuclear engineering, graduating in 1971.

In 1973, I published a rather simple paper, "Quiton/Perceptron Physics: A Theory of Existence, Perception, and Physical Phenomena," in which I pointed out the nature of quantum change, gave a new definition of mass and acceleration, and pointed out the fundamental nature of inversion of time. The paper also contained a simplified derivation of Newton's laws of motion, relativistic form. The elements of this paper had been worked out in 1971 while I was finishing my Master's program in nuclear engineering. Finishing the work had been interrupted by a slight sidetrack — a tour in Vietnam from summer of 1971 until summer 1972.

At about the same time, I formulated a fundamental correction to Aristotle's logic, adding a fourth law of logic to Aristotle's three, and a proof of it. The new logic was of great use in discovering and uncovering new concepts in unified field theory.

Incorporating Kaluza-Klein 5-dimensional concepts, scalar EM became a field theory that unifies electromagnetics and gravitation.

Incorporating dynamic sum-zeroed EM vector systems (which are discarded in normal EM theory) allowed the direct engineering of the unified field theory, including structuring the vacuum, curving local spacetime, and producing effects at a distance and in higher dimensions. Actually it allowed the recovery of much of the scalar part of Maxwell's original theory.

I then realized that, inside a vector zero EM force field summation/multiplication, the virtual particle flux of vacuum/spacetime was ordered and controlled locally and macroscopically. This of course violated one of the major assumptions (a postulate) of quantum mechanics; the assumption that the structure of vacuum was randomized, and could not be deliberately ordered, engineered, and curved locally.

Adding phase conjugation (time reversal) aspects and extended quantum mechanical concepts allowed local antigravity and local curvature of spacetime to be included — again, on an engineering basis. It also allowed one to produce a mechanism responsible for Newton's third law, and to engineer the reaction force at will. Further, it revealed that the law of entropy was simply the *positive time* statement; it showed that there was another half of the law, the *negative time* part or the law of **negentropy.**

In addition, a startling new concept of mind, thought, life, biofields, disease, and healing emerged from all this — again, on an engineering basis. As we stated in the beginning of this book, it is now an urgent necessity to release my work on the basis for electromagnetic disease and electromagnetic healing. **We must produce a very quick, positive treatment and cure of AIDS and other coming lethal viruses before the world is decimated.**

Accordingly, this work is being released in this book.

In this chapter we will next present some perhaps surprising material on phase conjugation, from the scalar EM viewpoint, after first briefly explaining symmetry and parity.

In following subsections, we will cover briefly the remaining major concepts in scalar electromagnetics. This will then set the stage for the following chapter, **Extraordinary Biology,** in which we will deal with the basis for unparalleled electromagnetic healing.

Symmetry and Parity

The basic idea of symmetry is the arrangement of the parts of a body or system about an axis so that two or more parts appear the same with respect to some operation.

The most obvious example is to look in a mirror, where we notice that our image has been reversed, left to right. Yet otherwise there is no difference; and so we may say that the reflection has "mirror symmetry." It's the same except that left and right are reversed.

If you know the details of a system at one point, and at another point you know that the system will possess mirror symmetry, then you can predict exactly what state the system will be in at the latter point. It will be "left to right reversed." You don't have to calculate the laws of reflection and the laws of motion of the system.

All the laws of nature that possess "mirror symmetry" have a special property: If the words "right" and "left" are interchanged in the statement of the law, then the behavior of a system that obeys the law is unchanged.

Thus symmetry became a powerful idea in physics. For a system with a great number of possible interactions, etc., one can usually eliminate a very great number of them due to symmetry considerations. In other words, if one can assume that symmetry of the system will not be violated, then all the possible interactions that would yield "broken symmetry" can be eliminated.

On the other hand, if symmetry is broken in a physical interaction, at least one of the conservation laws is broken in that interaction. Broken symmetry — and hence violation of individual conservation laws — is a well-established fact in particle physics today.

Another concept intimately associated with mirror symmetry is parity. Each particle is assigned a number (+1 or –1), depending upon what kind of particle it is. One adds up these numbers for an assembly of particles, to obtain an overall "parity" number for the system. If parity is conserved in an interaction, then this total number does not change in the interaction.

Table 13. SYMMETRY

- **SOMETHING IS SYMMETRIC IF IT REMAINS UNCHANGED UNDER A CERTAIN OPERATION**
- **A SPHERE IS SYMMETRIC WITH RESPECT TO ROTATION ABOUT ITS CENTER**
- **A CATHEDRAL ARCH IS LEFT AND RIGHT SYMMETRIC ABOUT A VERTICAL LINE THROUGH THE CENTER**
- **LAWS OF ELECTRICITY ARE SYMMETRIC WITH RESPECT TO REVERSAL OF POSITIVE AND NEGATIVE CHARGE**

Table 14. A FORCE FIELD IS A SPECIAL LOCAL SYMMETRY

"... THE FORCE OF GRAVITY IS SIMPLY A MANIFESTATION OF AN ABSTRACT SYMMETRY — A LOCAL GAUGE SYMMETRY — THAT UNDERLIES THE PHYSICS OF THE WORLD."

"ALL FOUR FORCES OF NATURE CAN BE GENERATED IN THIS WAY."

PAUL DAVIES, SUPERFORCE,
1984, p. 115

Table 15. GRAVITY AND LOCAL SYMMETRY

- **THE LAWS OF PHYSICS CAN BE MADE SYMMETRIC EVEN UNDER LOCAL GAUGE TRANSFORMATIONS**
- **A GRAVITATIONAL FIELD IS INTRODUCED TO COMPENSATE FOR PLACE-TO-PLACE VARIATIONS**
- **THE GRAVITATIONAL FIELD IS NATURE'S WAY OF MAINTAINING A LOCAL GAUGE SYMMETRY**
- **IN THE ABSENCE OF GRAVITY, THERE IS ONLY GLOBAL SYMMETRY**

Table 16. HINDSIGHT IS BETTER THAN FORESIGHT

- **FROM THE TWIN REQUIREMENTS OF**
  - **SIMPLEST LOCAL GAUGE SYMMETRY**
  - **LORENTZ-POINCARE SYMMETRY OF SPECIAL RELATIVITY**

- **ONE CAN CONSTRUCT OR INFER**
  - **MAXWELL'S EQUATIONS**
  - **ALL THE LAWS OF ELECTROMAGNETICS**
  - **THE EXISTENCE OF RADIO WAVES**
  - **THE POSSIBILITY OF MOTORS AND GENERATORS**
  - **ETC.**

- **IN REALITY THESE WERE FIRST DISCOVERED EXPERIMENTALLY**

Table 17. WHEN SYMMETRY IS VIOLATED [BROKEN]:

- **A "NON-OBSERVABLE" TURNS OUT TO BE AN OBSERVABLE**
- **AN INVARIANCE IS BROKEN**
- **A CONSERVATION LAW OR SELECTION RULE IS BROKEN**

  COMMENTS:
  - **A VIRTUAL OBJECT BECOMES AN OBSERVABLE OBJECT**
  - **LOCAL SPACETIME BECOMES CURVED, AT LEAST TO SOME POTENTIAL INVOLVING THAT OBJECT**

Table 18. SOME PROVEN ASYMMETRIES

- **POSITIVE AND NEGATIVE SIGNS OF ELECTRIC CHARGE**
- **TIME REVERSAL**
- **RIGHT/LEFT HANDEDNESS**

Table 19. SPONTANEOUS SYMMETRY BREAKING

PRESENT VIEW

1. **IF 4-MOMENTUM $K\mu = 0$,**

   $$Ø_{(X)} = Ø_{VAC}$$

   WHERE $Ø_{(X)}$ IS AS COMPLEX AS ANY SPIN-0 FIELD
2. **FOR VOLUME Ω >> RELEVANT MICRODIMENSION.**
   - **$K\mu \neq 0$ BUT $K_M \sim 0$**
   - **$\langle Ø_{(X)} \rangle \neq Ø_{VAC}$ [INSIDE Ω]**
   - **$\langle Ø_{(X)} \rangle \neq Ø_{VAC}$ [OUTSIDE Ω]**
3. **INSIDE Ω, SYMMETRY PROPERTIES DIFFER FROM THOSE OUTSIDE Ω**
4. **T. P AND CP MAY BE SLIGHTLY ASYMMETRIC**
5. **CPT REMAINS INTACT**

SCALAR EM VIEW

1. **IF ARTIFICIAL POTENTIAL $Ø_{ART}$>> 0, VOLUME Ω MAY BE SMALL**
2. **$Ø_{ART}$ MAY BE ENGINEERED IN**
   - **SPATIAL SIZE**
   - **LOCATION**
   - **MAGNITUDE**
   - **SUBSTRUCTURE**
3. **SYMMETRY PROPERTIES INSIDE Ω MAY**
   - **DRASTICALLY DIFFER**
   - **BE DELIBERATELY ENGINEERED**
   - **BE PATTERNED**
4. **T, P, AND CP MAY BE APPRECIABLY ASYMMETRIC**
5. **CPT MAY BE ASYMMETRIC**

Table 20. WHY SUCH DRASTIC DIFFERENCE?

IN PRESENT THEORY

- **$Ø_{(X)}$ IS USED ONLY AS A PHENOMENOLOGICAL DESCRIPTION**
- **MICROSCOPIC STRUCTURE OF $Ø_{(X)}$ OF NO CONCERN**
- **ONLY LONG-WAVELENGTH LIMIT OF FIELD IS OF INTEREST**
- **VACUUM ENGINEERING IS ONLY A REMOTE POSSIBLITY**
- **ACTION AT A DISTANCE IS NOT POSSIBLE**
- **LOCAL SPACETIME NOT CURVED**

IN SCALAR EM

- **$Ø_{ART}$ REPRESENTS A LOCAL CURVATURE OF SPACETIME [LOCAL GENERAL RELATIVITY]**
- **MICROSCOPIC STRUCTURE OF $Ø_{(X)}$ IS DETERMINISTIC AND COHERED INTO MACROSCOPIC STRUCTURE**
- **ALL WAVELENGTHS OF THE FIELD ARE OF INTEREST**
- **$Ø_{ART}$ WAVES ARE REAL, ENGINEERABLE AND ELECTROGRAVITATIONAL**
- **VACUUM ENGINEERING IS A REALITY**
- **ACTION AT A DISTANCE IS POSSIBLE**

Table 21. ASPECTS OF STRONG LOCAL ASYMMETRY

- **PROPERTIES OF AN OBJECT MAY DIFFER APPRECIABLY FOR**
  - **DIFFERENT OBSERVERS**
  - **DIFFERENT DETECTING MEANS**
  - **ONE TIME TO ANOTHER**
  - **ONE POSITION TO ANOTHER**
- **CONVERSATION LAWS MAY BE APPRECIABLY VIOLATED**
  - **ENERGY**
  - **CHARGE**
  - **SPIN**
  - **MOMENTUM**
  - **ANGULAR MOMENTUM**
- **LOCAL SPACETIME IS CURVED**
- **LORENTZ INVARIANCE OF VACUUM IS VIOLATED**
- **MAY BE A LOCAL "SINK" OR "SOURCE"**
- **GRAVITATIONAL/INERTIAL EFFECTS FROM EM**
- **TRANSLATION BETWEEN VIRTUAL AND OBSERVABLE**
- **ELECTROGRAVITATIONAL SOLITONS**
- **ACTION AT A DISTANCE**
- **TRANSMUTATION EFFECTS MAY EXIST**
- **SCALAR/PSEUDOSCALAR FIELD TRANSLATION**

For years the idea of conservation of parity convinced physicists that it would never be possible to tell right from left in the universe. Then in 1956, Yang and Lee pointed out a class of reactions where parity need not be conserved. This effect — broken parity — was confirmed experimentally, and so certain parts and interactions of the universe do possess asymmetry.

The result of all this was that particle physicists established that

(1) symmetry can be, and is, sometimes broken, (2) individual conservation laws can be, and sometimes are, broken.

Particle physics, however, concerns itself primarily with microscopic interactions. Most of the delightful new things discovered in the microworld have not yet been applied — by *physicists,* that is — in the macroworld.

If you can successfully apply broken symmetry in a major system, for example, you should be able to violate the conservation of energy law and thus produce a "free energy" engine. Several inventors with whom I work have done precisely that. The techniques and technology are still primitive and they need much further development, but the principle has been clearly established and replicated.

Physics is correct in certifying broken symmetry, and you can do it in large systems as well as in microscopic particle interactions. Of course you also *curve local spacetime* as well, something which Einstein and his followers have assumed cannot be done.

Charge-Parity-Time and Negative Energy

The upshot of all this is that the physicists came up with the idea that what is really conserved is a consolidated thing called Charge-Parity-Time. You don't have to conserve any one or two of these three, but only the combined product.

Here they overlooked one key factor that is very important to our thesis: In the photon interaction, if you reverse charge and time, you reverse the sign of the energy.

That is, a photon that is emitted from a positive charge carries negative time and negative energy. It is different from a photon that is emitted from a negative charge, for that one carries what we have conventionally established as positive energy.

Thus physics has not considered the exclusive use of negative-energy /negative-time photons, even when some of its interactions produced them. Instead, it has just lumped together photons and antiphotons, and considered them both to have positive energy.

Antimatter systems don't have positive energy, for example; they have negative energy. *Here we don't use the positive and negative signs to indicate the direction the energy is traveling, but the fundamental kind of energy that it is--time forward or time reversed.*

For example, consider the local conservation of energy. As conditioned, one almost always unconsciously thinks of the conservation of *positive* energy, without so stating. Yet one is perfectly free to build a system into which he inputs 100 joules of positive energy, and from which he outputs 300 joules of positive energy and 200 joules of negative energy!

For the real conservation law, that's the equivalent of putting in 100 joules of positive energy and outputting 100 joules of positive energy.

Now negative energy will run motors, light lamps, etc. —often much better than positive energy. It can be transmitted, transformed, stepped up or down in "voltage," rectified, received, etc. It can be translated into positive energy or vice versa.

Circuits run "cool" when using negative energy. If you short out a circuit of negative energy so that a violent discharge occurs, it produces cooling instead of heating , greatly lessening the danger of fire and destruction. If you mix negative energy onto a line that is carrying the same amount of positive energy, however, the two negate each other and there is suddenly "no power" on the system.

Think of what you were taught in simple arithmetic. You can take a zero — the absence of any single specific number — and replace it with any set of multiple numbers whose algebraic sum is zero. The presence of this special set of numbers you choose does not violate the condition that the zero means that you could not use just a *single* number.

Although zero is the absence of just a *single* thing, it can be the presence of *multiple* things.

The same thing works with energy. In the microworld, everything is fantastically energetic, and wildly fluctuating. For example, in a copper wire carrying a current of one ampere, wild momentary fluctuations at extremely high frequencies are occurring.

According to classical electrodynamics, the instantaneous current in a single one of these micro-micro fluctuations may reach thousands of amperes, and the instantaneous voltage may reach 10^{40} volts or more. As can be seen, the instantaneous energy and power are enormous. Yet outside the wire, we see a very placid and peaceful situation.

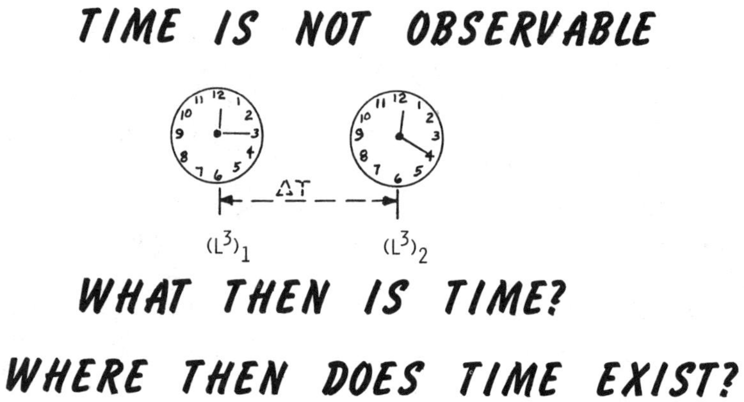

Figure 33. The riddle of time. Unsolved by both physicists and philosophers.

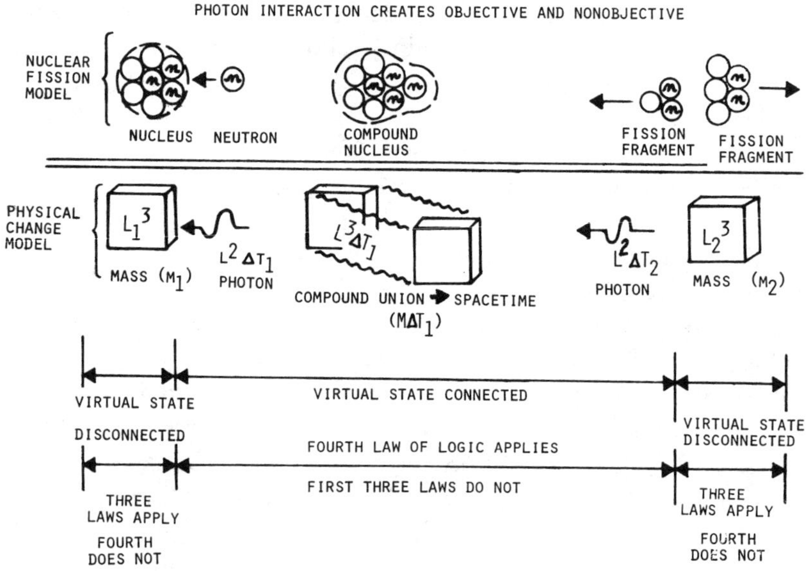

Figure 34. Raindrop model of physical change.

Table 22. FLOW OF TIME

- **PHOTON INTERACTION CONSTITUTES TIME CHANGE**
- $\sim\!\rightarrow$ ⟨ NEGATIVECHARGE⟩ $\rightarrow$ + ΔT
- $\sim\!\rightarrow$ ⟨ POSITIVECHARGE⟩ $\rightarrow$ − ΔT
- **CHARGE-PARITY-TIME [CPT]**
- $\sim\!\rightarrow$ ⟨ e⟩ $\rightarrow$ + ΔT (note: ~ = photon)
  - **UBIQUITOUS**
  - **PREDOMINANT**
- **ANTIPHOTON IS A PHASE CONJUGATE REPLICA**

Table 23. PHYSICAL CHANGE

- **COMPOSED OF ACTION**
- **h = BASIC QUANTUM**
- **TWO CANONICAL VARIABLES**
  - **ENERGY/TIME (ΔEΔt)**
  - **MOMENTUM/LENGTH (p L)**

  ETC.
- **ENERGY/TIME**
  - **h = (+ E) (+ t)**
  - **h = (- E) (- t)**

Free Energy and Antigravity

Let's say the current flowing in the wire is alternating current at a frequency of one megahertz. Let's say we have one watt of power in the wire (there's one volt on it, and one ampere of flowing current). As a working rule-of thumb for engineering use, the available absolute micropower in an alternating current in a wire can be taken as:

$$P_a = 40 \times f \times P_c \qquad (4\text{-}10)$$

where P_a is the absolute power available, in watts; f is the frequency in Hertz; P_c is the conventional power available, in watts; and 40 is a constant of proportionality.

In our example, the absolute power actually available in the current is 40 million watts! We've got about 20 megawatts of positive power, and about 20 megawatts of negative power, in there — *in the microstructure of the electrical current itself--but disintegrated*

By applying unconventional scalar EM engineering techniques, we ought to be able to take such an "input" (a straight wire with one watt of power at a frequency of a megahertz) and get an "output" of up to 40 megawatts. It is relatively straightforward to get out 1 megawatt; such ratios have actually been achieved on the laboratory bench by my associates.

Of course we will have curved the local spacetime to do such a thing. But it is absolutely permitted to do that, by the laws of nature as best we know them from particle physics.

It is also possible to do that by Maxwell's original theory. And it has been proven in the laboratory.

Table 24. NEGATIVE ENERGY

- **CAN BE**
  - **GENERATED**
  - **TRANSMITTED**
  - **TRANSFORMED**
  - **RECTIFIED**
  - **RADIATED**
  - **TRANSLATED**
- **EASILY POWERS**
  - **AC MOTORS**
  - **DC MOTORS**
  - **LAMPS**
  - **TRANSFORMERS**
  - **RECTIFIERS**
- **CIRCUITS STAY COOL**

In scalar electromagnetics, we deliberately seek to produce such effects and systems by nonclassical application and extension of the modern conservation law CPT. And we include negative energy/ negative time production in those systems and effects.

Here's the extended magic rule: First we write down the expression **CPTEGS**.

In this expression, C stands for charge, P stands for (space) parity, T stands for time, E stands for energy, G stands for gravity, and S stands for entropy.

We are referring here to the algebraic sign of each term, and to a complete photon interaction (absorption and re-radiation) with a charged particle inside an atom of matter. Specifically, we are referring to the result, after the reaction has occurred.

Normally the photon interacts with one of the electrons in the atom's outer shell. This interaction with the negative electron charge *produces* the "normal" physical world/physical reality we see around us. In the interaction, normal parity is produced, and normal gravitation (attraction of mass) is produced. Also, in a series of such interactions, the normal entropy (movement from order to disorder) is experienced and produced.

So in the expression CPTEGS normally the charge term is negative, and every other term is positive, for the complete photon interaction in an atom.

Now here is the magic engineering rule: **In the complete photon interaction with a charged particle in an atom, if one of these terms is reversed in algebraic sign, all the others will be reversed also.**

For example, if the photon interacts with the positively charged nucleus, then parity is reversed, the bit of time-advance is reversed, a negative/time-reversed photon is emitted, a tiny bit of antigravity is produced in the nucleus, and negentropy is produced. By negentropy, we mean that the emitted photon exhibits the strange characteristics of time reversal, and hence it will return from disorder to order.

This rule is actually a statement of phase conjugation and time reversed waves, as we shall see later.

For example, using the rule, the production of antigravity is straightforward. Simply produce a great excess of negative energy and negative time in an object or generator by scalar photon interaction with the nucleus, at a sufficient rate.

In negative time, gravitational force is reversed. Thus in negative time gravity is a repulsion, not an attraction. Production of excess negative time in the atomic nuclei of a system produces antigravity in that system. Period.*

*At 100 Hz about 500 negative watts/lb is required for flotation. At 1 GHz, the effect is so weak it cannot be measured, and no amount of power will float the mirror.

Let me amplify that statement. There are two kinds of energy, negative and positive. Normally, everyone thinks only of positive energy.

Take Einstein's formula for the amount of energy that's "bottled up" and stored in mass:

$$E = mc^2 \qquad (4\text{-}11)$$

That's positive energy and positive mass. It automatically implies that we are looking at things where time is forward-going.

Now suppose we "charge up" that mass with negative energy: Then the mass is negative, like this:

$$-E = (-m)c^2 \qquad (4\text{-}12)$$

And negative mass is repelled by positive mass. (Like mass G-charges attract, unlike mass G-charges repel.)

That's all there is to it! Simply charge up the protons/neutrons of the atomic nuclei of a mass with excess phase conjugate (negative) energy/time, and it exhibits antigravity compared to the earth. Nothing could be simpler.

Again, it's been done in the laboratory by an associate.

So, with respect to a negative energy/negative time generator, you just add more load and draw more negative power from the machine, forcing it to produce more. It produces more negative time, and hence more antigravity and more "repulsion." When the repulsion balances the earth's attraction, the system "floats in air." Draw still more power by adding still more load, and it accelerates upward. Draw less power by decreasing the load, and it sinks downward again. That's all there is to it.

We should have been working upon this, shortly after the U.S. Civil War.

Again, there exist two completely different kinds of electromagnetic energy: positive and negative. These have been totally and hopelessly confused by modern physics, even though physicists sometimes use these terms.

But in dealing with CPTEGS in the photon interaction in an

atom, we must clearly keep in mind what kind of energy we are dealing with.

The basic engineering rules are these: (1) If any one of the factors — C, P, T, E, G, or S — is reversed, all the others are reversed. (2) If positive charge is involved in the photon interaction, then time (carried by the emitted photon) is negative and so is the energy carried by it. (3) The simplest scalar EM wave may be considered as two EM waves locked together (modulating each other), where one component wave carries positive energy and time and the other component wave carries negative energy and time. (4) Separation of the two components by interaction with charged particles creates both positive and negative time and energy. (5) If the interacting particle is negatively charged, the positive energy/positive time component will interact with it. (6) If the interacting particle is positively charged, the negative energy/negative time component will interact with it. (7) The interacting particle phase conjugates (time reverses) the component with which it interacts. (8) The primary interaction with negative electron shells of atoms yields positive energy and positive time: constituting ordinary physical reality as we observe it. (9) The secondary interaction with the positive atomic nucleus produces phase conjugated (time-reversed) physical reality. (10) Secondary interaction (nuclear phase conjugation) normally produces Newton's third law of motion. (11) In Newton's third law, the reaction force need not be equal, and need not be antiparallel. Note, however, in such case local spacetime is curved. (12) The present law of entropy is only the positive-time half; the other (negative time) half is the negentropy law.

Phase Conjugation (Time Reversal)

It is a most remarkable fact that Soviet radar engineers and radar scientists are also trained in optics. While this seems little short of astonishing by Western standards, the Soviets have an exceedingly good reason: **As a matter of course, most Soviet radar systems are also operable in, or associated with another system that is operable in, a time-reversed (phase conjugate) mode.**

In this mode the radar and/or its associated system is also an extremely powerful directed energy weapon, having capabilities undreamed of in the West.

A phase-conjugate (time-reversed) wave actually is a wave that travels backward through time.* That is, it is capable of precisely retracing the path through space, taken by another wave that traveled that path to a nonlinear mirror, stimulating the reflection of the time-reversed wave.

Further, in retracing its invisible path through space, the phase conjugate replica wave does not diverge as do normal waves. Instead, it continually converges upon its invisible trace.

Consequently all its energy arrives back at the distant source that emitted the stimulus wave originally. This was Tesla's original secret of his "wireless transmission of energy at a distance with no losses."**

It can easily be shown, however, that the phase conjugate wave is a legitimate solution to the wave equation. Hence it is a general property of all types of waves: sound, magnetohydrodynamic, etc. It is not confined just to the optical band.

Obviously such a startlingly different wave has phenomenal uses. Literally it ushers in a new physics.

Let us turn now to look at this strange wave that has emerged on our scientific horizon.

In the late 1960's, Soviet researchers cautiously pointed out the possibility of a time-reversed wave. Papers appeared in the open Soviet scientific literature, and shortly thereafter U.S. physicists began to read about it.

In 1972, Soviet scientists visited Lawrence Livermore Laboratory and specifically briefed U.S. scientists on the optical phase conjugation (OPC) phenomenon. Thereafter the effect became of increased interest to American scientists.

(Note, however, that phase conjugation (PC) is a major phenomenon of all physics. It is not confined merely to the optical spectrum, nor just to electromagnetic waves. Phase conjugation is a general phenomenon true of all waves, regardless of type. We will primarily discuss OPC, since most Western experimentation has

*The external positive-time observer sees this time reversal as length (space) reversal.

**The great electrician had actually discovered what today is known as phase conjugation or time reversal of EM waves.

been in the optics domain, and the literature is rich in that respect. However, we also point out that Western scientists have absolutely no inkling of the mechanism causing OPC. They have simply written a model for a time-reversed wave by taking the equation of a normal wave and writing the conjugation (adding an asterisk exponent) to the appropriate term, and pointed out that this new equation also satisfies Maxwell's wave equation. They also do not clearly recognize that an EM wave carries time and energy, and that a time-reversed EM wave carries negative energy and negative time. Further, they do not at all comprehend the startling implications for generating gravitational fields, including antigravity and inertial effects, directly on the laboratory bench.)

In optical phase conjugation, when an input EM wave (ordinary) enters a nonlinear medium, the medium "reflects" or produces a strange, time-reversed EM wave in response.

Figure (35a) shows the effect. In the figure, E1 is the normal input wave, entering a distorting, nonlinear medium (the "blob") as shown. Wave E_1 moves on through the blob, emerging on the other side and continuing, though now in distorted form.

The medium produces a second wave, E_2, which precisely retraces the steps of E_1. That is, everywhere E_1 is, E_2 now appears. The phases of the E_2 wave are precisely reversed from those of E_1. The only difference in the two waves is that wave E_1 carries positive time and positive energy, while wave E_2 carries negative time and negative energy.

(U.S. physicists are well aware of everything in the above statement except for the negative energy portion.) The historical background of the phase conjugate wave is given in Table 25.

(We strongly stress that the West did not discover the time-reversed wave; the Soviets did. At the time (late 1960's) this appeared in the open Soviet literature, the Soviets had already been using it for about two decades in their giant energetics (scalar electromagnetics) weapons development program.)

However, to return.

The time-reversed wave is called the **phase conjugate replica** of wave E_1. The overall characteristics of the phase conjugate replica E_2 are summarized in Table 26.

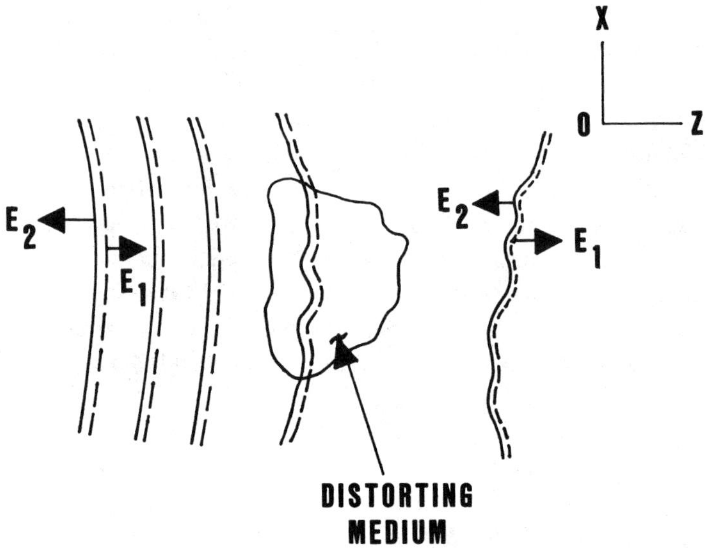

a. Phase conjugation by a nonlinear, distorting medium.

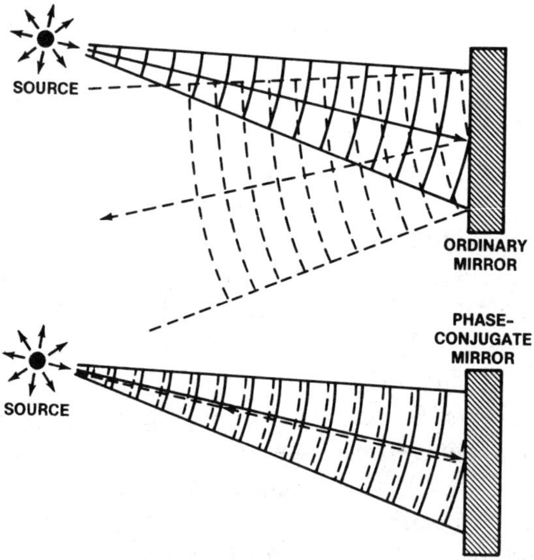

b. Ordinary mirror reflection versus phase conjugate mirror reflection.

Figure 35. Phase conjugate reflection of a time-reversed wave.

Table 25. PHASE CONJUGATE WAVES

- **NONLINEAR OPTICS TRANSIENTS**
- **DISCOVERED BY SOVIETS**
- **LATE 60's - EARLY 70's**
- **PRESENTLY "HOT ITEM"**
- **INITIALLY THOUGHT RARE**
- **NOW KNOWN WIDESPREAD**
- **THIRD POWER OF E-FIELD**
- **STILL MUCH UNEXPLORED**

Table 26. PHASE CONJUGATE REPLICA

- **TIME-REVERSED**
- **CARRIES NEGATIVE TIME**
- **CARRIES NEGATIVE ENERGY**
- **"HEALING" PROPERTY**
- **DISTORTION CORRECTION**
- **FROM DISORDER TO ORDER**
- **MAY DWARF INPUT WAVE**

Table 27. DISTORTION CORRECTION THEOREM

"If a scalar wave E_1 (r) propagates from left to right through an arbitrary but lossless dielectric medium, and if we generate in some region of space [say near z=0] its phase conjugate replica E_2[r], then E_2 will propagate backward from right to left through the dielectric medium, remaining everywhere the phase conjugate of E_1."

We point out here that the basic nonlinearity (nonlinear medium) in spacetime is a single particle of mass. In a photon interaction with that particle of mass, the interacting (input) photon (positive energy, positive time) causes the generation and emission of a phase-conjugated (time-reversed) photon. This time-reversed photon provides the precise mechanism for generating Newton's third law: **For every action there is an opposite and equal reaction.** This will be covered later.

But back to our nonlinear medium, and the two waves E_1 and E_2.

E_1 and E_2 are "locked together" as a scalar EM wave unless something else is specially done to separate them. That is because the nonlinear medium is a *modulator,* and the two waves modulate each other (lock together as a single wave).

(We interrupt again to strongly point out this fact: This directly shows that all EM waves in vacuum exist as scalar EM waves, not as the so-called Maxwell-Hertz transverse waves of conventional theory. Nikola Tesla, the greatest electrical scientist the world ever produced, always adamantly insisted that EM waves were "sound" type waves, not "transverse" waves. For one thing, the vacuum-medium would have to be a solid to produce transverse waves! Tesla even visited Hertz in Europe and tried to convince him of the error of his so-called "proof of transverse EM waves." Tesla found Hertz adamant on the subject, however, and returned without changing Hertz's mind. Ironically, Tesla was right and all the textbooks in the Western world have been consistently in error as to the nature of the EM wave in vacuum.)

We simply state here that, for a single-frequency EM sine wave in vacuum, a "full photon" of that wave in vacuum is actually a *single sine-wave oscillation.* The positive (positive energy, positive time) half of that sine wave is the same thing as a virtual electron (negative charge). The negative (negative energy, negative time) half of that sine wave is the same thing as a virtual positron — a virtual electron travelling backwards in time, or "time-reversed", which we detect as length-reversed and charge-reversed.

Further the vacuum — including the vacuum inside each relatively empty "mass structure" such as an atom or molecule — is a seething inferno of activity of virtual particle fluxes. It is upon that medium that all physical reality and physical changes are impressed. Thus there is nothing static in the world; what actually exists is *switching of virtual particle fluxes.* What we call a "static thing" is only an equilibrium in this switching activity. And, once switched on, any stream continues until switched off or switched to change it.

For that reason, the full photon has always contained twice as much absolute energy as is provided by the presently used equation

$$E = hf \qquad (4\text{-}13)$$

Where E is energy, h is Planck's constant, and f is frequency.

One half the photon carries negative energy and negative time, while the other half carries positive energy and positive time. In the full photon interaction, one half of the photon interacts and "switches off" the stream. Thus the photon interaction makes a single change of action, energy x time, both switching on the beginning of the quantum change and switching off the ending of it.

The full photon in vacuum is, and has always been, a scalar EM photon. It rigorously is the presently accepted photon plus its directly "hooked on" and accompanying phase conjugated replica photon.

That is, in terms of the present physical view, the scalar electromagnetics view of a full photon in vacuum is that it consists of a photon and its antiphoton, directly combined in serial fashion. Further, this antiphoton part is not identical to the photon, since it is time- and energy-reversed.

The present physics makes no distinction between the two types of photons, hence makes no distinction between positive and negative photon energy. It also still considers "static" things to independently exist. It does not pursue the fact that all things appearing "static" are equilibrium states in nearly unbelievably intense virtual particle streams. Since it does not pursue that fact, it does not build a "switching" model for quantum change, not does it arrive at a method of directly engineering these "switching" operations.

For that reason, present physics has totally missed local general relativity and the engineering of spacetime curvature by electrogravitational methods, as was contained in

Maxwell's original theory.

For the same reason, present Western physics has not worked out the basic mechanism that produces phase conjugation, and it has not realized that all conservation laws can be locally violated with the new methods — methods actually hailing back to Maxwell's original theory!

Now returning again to our nonlinear medium and waves E_1 and E_2:

It is possible to separate (demodulate) wave E_2 from wave E_1. In that case, E_1 is an ordinary EM wave, carrying positive energy and positive time. E_2 is a phase conjugate replica, carrying negative energy and negative time.

Irradiation of an atom in a new sample of material with a normal EM wave such as E_1 just provides the normal photon interaction with the electron shells. That is, the electron part of the full photon adds to the orbital electron's energy state in positive time, raising the orbital electron to an "excited state." (Remember, this has switched on a continuous process of "keep raising the energy level of the electron" in positive time.) The "state-increasing" orbital electron then interacts with the second, positron-part of the full photon, which switches off the increasing, leaving the electron in its "static excited state." Simply put, one half of the full photon turns on an uplifting spray, and the second half of the full photon turns off the uplifting spray, leaving the electron in equilibrium state at a new level.*

Thus in orthodox physics we have taken the view that an electron in a shell absorbs a "photon" from the incident wave, taking extra energy and being raised into an excited energy state.

In the orthodox view, the excited-state electron then decays to release another ordinary photon (since it comes from a negative charge).

What actually happened was that, when the "full photon" of the incident wave is absorbed by the orbital electron, increase of the electron energy is switched on, then switched off, leaving the elec-

*We state here a magnificient principle without proof. When one furnishes (inputs) electrical power to a system, all the "input work" is expended purely upon switching fields by fighting against them in brute-force fashion. E.g., electrical power furnished to an electric motor does **not** run the motor, but only continually wrestles the internal fields to switch them. Obviously, to build an over-unity device, one must get it to switch its own fields, at least a significant fraction of the time.

tron in equilibrium at a new energy level.

What happened in the middle was phase conjugation. In absorbing the first half of the incident full photon, the electron acted as a phase conjugate mirror (we will explain that term shortly). It emitted a forward-travelling phase conjugate replica (PCR) of that first photon half, and this conjugate replica entered the nucleus, where it is absorbed to cause the Newtonian reaction force. Note that this PCR emission by the electron does not generate recoil in the electron-PCM, as is well known in OPC theory and experiment.

The same type of phase conjugation happened when the state-increasing electron absorbed the second half of the incident full photon. It phase conjugated again, sending this half to the nucleus to accompany the former PCR half. In the nucleus, this second half switches off the increase in excited state of the nucleus that was engendered by absorption of the first half.

The photon interaction is a process for switching on and off a continuous rate of action increase or decrease.

At the conclusion of the full photon absorption, both the orbital electron and the nucleus are in excited states. The nucleus has increased its gravitational mass.

Then the situation precisely reverses. Both nucleus and electron decay, again emitting full photons and again phase conjugating.

The PCR photon emitted by the nucleus reduces the positive mass of the nucleus. The PCR photon emitted by the electron is reversed from the electron's absorption record, reducing the negative charge's energy state, and the electron is said to "decay" from its excited state. The PCR photon emitted by the electron now (to the observer) will appear to carry positive time and positive energy.

(In passing, we point out that, actually, the situation is far more complicated. Both the electron and the positively charged nucleus are enmeshed in continuous streams of virtual particle flux, including intense streams of virtual photons. One must go to n-wave mixing, where n is greater than 4, to fully understand the total reaction. The main points are, the Newtonian reaction forces within the atom are generated by phase conjugation, the photon emitted by the decay of an excited state electron will normally carry what we call positive energy and positive time, and the photon emitted by the decay of an excited state positive charge will normally carry what we call negative energy and negative time. Full coverage of these interactions is beyond the scope of this book, and must wait for another effort in the future.).

Now once again we return to our simplified model of phase conjugation, and waves E_1 and E_2 in our nonlinear, modulating medium!

As we stated, we can engineer the situation so that the phase conjugate replica E_2 can be separated from E_1. A separated E_2, however, is a quite different breed of cat. It is a phase conjugate wave, carrying negative energy and negative time.

E_2 is a magic wave indeed!

Irradiation of the nucleus of an atom in a new sample of material with a phase conjugate replica such as E_2 causes the nucleus of the atom to interact in reverse of its normal interaction.* That is, one of the positive charges in the nucleus interacts with a photon resulting from wave E_2, and goes into an excited "negative energy" state. That state, in decaying, emits an ordinary virtual photon which promptly interacts with a virtual positive charge in the nucleus, which decays to emit the virtual photon, which interacts with another positive charge in the nucleus, etc.

In other words, the negative energy of the absorbed antiphoton is captured by the nucleus, and the nucleus overall does not *immediately* decay to discharge the negative energy.

Instead, the nucleus acts as an accumulator or capacitance, charging up and then discharging far more slowly than the normal photon/electron interaction.

(For the purist, the nucleus does phase conjugate the input negative energy/negative time wave, and phase conjugates it again — upon an electron in the electron shells, through spin coupling. This second phase conjugate replica is now just a normal EM wave, and the electron exhibits a normal EM interaction. Thus our instruments (Which are electron wiggle detectors) detect a normal

*Irradiation of the nucleus with a PCR wave is easily accomplished by using ordinary magnetic resonance, and modulating the PCR wave upon the magnetic carrier, as Antoine Priore did.

EM wave detection and do not discriminate between photon and antiphoton halves of a full photon. For that reason, scientists have not clearly noticed the difference between positive and negative energy, and between photons and antiphotons. They have also not resolved the basic conflict between the particle and wave theories of electromagnetics. *Note that the full photon concept, where the full photon is a normal photon and phase conjugate replica of that photon hooked together into a single sine wave, resolves the long-standing wave-particle controversy.)*

In most of their instruments, present scientists are detecting a secondary normal EM wave for the phase conjugate replica interaction, since the phase conjugate interactions in the instrument are not sorted out, and since the instruments measure only one kind of PCR, that emitted by a negatively charged electron. Hence scientists think the antiphoton has positive energy, and interpret it in positive time. Consequently they tend to accent that the wave is "phase-reversed," and not accent the negative time/negative energy implications since they have not clearly sorted them out.

Let us return to our consideration of the irradiation of the nucleus of an atom (with an incident E_2 phase conjugate replica wave carrying negative energy and negative time, with respect to our electron-wiggle-detecting observer).

As irradiation continues, the actual "structured charge pattern" existing on the incident E_2 wave slowly charges up the nucleus of the atom with that exact charge structure, in the negative energy/negative time state.

We shall find that most interesting fact of great utility when we later discuss the mind, thought, cellular control systems, and generating a specific electromagnetic phase conjugation pattern to reverse cellular disease.

We shall also find that it is of great interest in accomplishing antigravity when we use extremely low frequency PCR irradiation.

The Phase Conjugate Mirror

Any system which phase conjugates the input wave and returns a phase conjugate "reflection" is called a **phase conjugate mirror,** or PCM for short.

But the phase conjugate mirror has some very unique properties, as can be seen in figure 35b.

For example, if you look in a *normal* mirror, you see your own reflection. You see your shoes and legs, for example. Light from your shoe scatters across the mirror, and it hits one spot on the mirror which reflects it at the proper angle to strike your eye.

But that simply doesn't happen with a *phase conjugate* mirror! If you were looking into a phase conjugate mirror (PCM), the light that left your shoe and scattered across the mirror would be reflected right back to the shoe, since it would retrace the path taken by the previous light striking all across the PC mirror from the shoe. So all you would be able to see would be two black dots: the retinas of your eyes. Light reflecting off them and striking the PCM would be reflected back to the source — the retinas — so you could see that light and that light only.

This path reversal is most important to keep in mind. With a phase conjugate signal, you are not functioning with an ordinary signal. Further, it has a "precursor" path taken by the incident wave that stimulated its emission from the PCM. Unless interfered with, the PCR will trace back down the invisible vacuum trace of that incident wave, or back down its wave path, like electricity goes down a wire.

This, by the way, is the secret of Tesla's wireless transmission of energy at a distance with no losses.

When broadcast into space, a normal EM wave (positive time, positive energy) diverges or scatters from its path.

Precisely the opposite happens with a PCR wave. When broadcast (reflected) into space, the PCR wave continually converges back upon the invisible trace taken by its incident stimulus precursor. Thus all the PCR energy is continually converging upon an invisible beam or "wire" through the vacuum, back to the source of the original incident wave.*

If the PCR wave is highly amplified (and means to do this are now well-known), then large amounts of EM energy can be precisely

*One can effectively move the entire imprinted vacuum path, however, by adding an additional input vector wave computed so that the **resultant** input would have come from the desired shifted distant point. In this way the PCR can be steered in space to lead and intercept a distant moving target.

returned to distant points from which a stimulus wave of any kind is received.

If a micro-microwatt is received from a point thousands of miles distant, then a gigawatt can readily be returned precisely to that distant point.

This was Tesla's magic secret. The great electrician had discovered phase conjugation, though he did not use that term. He did, however, point out that he could create an invisible wire through space to a distant point, and could send any amount of energy to that distant point without any scattering losses along the way.

He also accomplished the same thing with sound waves and mechanical waves. He pointed out that he could produce an undiminished physical (mechanical) effect at any distant point, and could eventually split the earth if he added power long enough.

Tesla had given the principles of radar in World War I! He later even spoke of his "big eye that can see at a distance." Here he was probably referring to stimulating the emission of a PCR return from that target. The PCR would automatically correct for the distortion in the intervening medium, and fairly sharp pictures of the distant scene — without showing the size dispersion of distance — could probably be obtained. Note that a non-scattering signal to a distant observer does not make him suffer any loss in field or apparent size and detail of the scanned object, which can be recovered to any resolution, limited only by the state of the art of the physical realization technology.

The implications for far greater resolution microscopy — far beyond the present limitation to about 4,500 — should be immediately obvious. The implications of such a microscope — that can see directly inside atomic nuclei; photograph nuclei and fundamental particles directly; see living viruses, molecules, and atoms directly; and theoretically see even into the virtual state itself — should be immediately obvious.

In discovering phase conjugation, the Soviet Union was attempting to break Tesla's secret of wireless transmission of energy without losses, and the Soviet scientists did so by about 1950. They highly weaponized the effects of phase conjugation, phase conjugate mirrors, and amplified phase conjugate mirrors, both in radar waves, mechanical waves, and sound waves, for nearly two decades. Then the Soviets cautiously stimulated the open literature with a limited paper on optical phase conjugation, to ascertain whether or not we realized the severe weapon implications of time-reversed waves, their production and use, and their amplification.

So phase conjugate mirrors can do very useful things. For example, look again at figure 35a. Suppose we are trying to photograph something on the other side of the distorting medium, say through a distorting gas, such as a turbulent atmosphere. In that case E_1 on the left is, say, light coming from an object on the left and passing through that distorting medium. If we just used ordinary waves in a camera on the right, we would see a very distorted wavefront, as represented by the distorted E_1.

However, if we illuminate the object by sending a wave through the distorting medium, and detect the *phase conjugate* signal that returns, it will have reversed the distortion when it gets to us, and we will get a clear picture. A very nice photo of just this process is contained in David M. Pepper, "Applications of Optical Phase Conjugation," **Scientific American,** 254 (1), Jan. 1986, p. 75.

Phase conjugation has many more uses than we have covered in this brief paper, of course, but this is an important use: the removal of distortion effects from optical systems.

It would, however, be nice to be able to amplify the effect. And so we can.

Amplifying the Phase Conjugate Effect

Let's look now at figure 36, where we will develop how to amplify the phase conjugate replica.

Be careful to notice that we are changing subscripts on you. By convention, optical scientists use A_1 and A_2 as two additional waves, called the *pump waves,* that are used to stress the nonlinear medium, and input signal wave A_4. Wave A_3 then is the stimulated PCM output, or the phase conjugate replica (PCR) wave.

In this figure we show a scheme for amplifying the phase conjugate signal that is generated and returned by the phase conjugate mirror (PCM).

We do this by adding two opposing waves of the same frequency (in this simplified case). These are the two "pump waves", and impressing them upon the PCM is called "pumping" the PCM.

Actually, in producing the pump wave, we are adding two input waves of the same frequency, 180 degrees out of phase with each other. Since the nonlinear medium is a *modulating* medium, the waves are forced to modulate each other and "lock together" as a single *scalar* EM wave of most interesting characteristics. Indeed, its E fields sum to a zero resultant vectorially, and its B-fields sum to a zero resultant vectorially. However, the scalar parts remain and are multiplied together, as in the original Maxwell quaternion theory. Since the magnitudes of the vector components in the scalar summation (quaternion multiplication, since we are addressing modulation) are varying, then the magnitude of the remaining scalar part is varying. We have therefore produced a standing scalar wave in the nonlinear material medium, having zero vector EM gradient components. **We have produced a purely scalar EM wave of pure potential — and this is an electrogravitational wave, rigorously, since it represents a time oscillation of the local energy density (local virtual particle flux density) of vacuum.** This scalar EM wave passes through the electron shells and enters the nuclei, where it is phase decoupled by the extreme nonlinearity of the violent virtual particle currents of the nucleus. Its energy is then absorbed by the nucleus, raising it to an excited pseudopotential. This potential decays, returning the scalar EM stress wave into the local vacuum and area. We are now pumping the atomic nuclei of the nonlinear PCM material with our two pump waves, and we have created an oscillating local gravitational field around the PCM.

This increased nuclear G-potential, looked at in Kaluza-Klein theory, is a 5-space potential. It is ready to burst out in the 5th dimension (as electromagnetic bleedoff) at the slightest provocation. That provocation is the entrance and absorption of the input signal wave, E_4. Note that E_4 acts as an "initiator" (or a pinprick into a highly inflated balloon, if you will) on the built-up, excited 5-dimensional gravitational pseudopotential of the nuclei. The moment so initiated, the entire 5-space G-pseudopotential collapses, emitting a time-reversed phase conjugate replica (PCR) of E_4. This emitted, highly amplified PCR is labelled E_3. It now "backtracks" down the invisible trace through space taken by the incident stimulus wave E_4, returning to the distant source that originally emitted E_4.

Voila! Tesla's wireless transmission of energy to a distant point without losses. *Voila!* The Soviet Launch Phase ABM system and the Soviet Launch Phase Anti-Bomber System, when used in conjunction with an over-the-horizon radar (such as the giant Wood-

Table 28. FOUR-WAVE MIXING

- **NONLINEAR MEDIUM**
- **OPPOSING PUMP WAVES**
    - **- CROSS MODULATION**
    - **- SCALAR WAVE**
    - **- INTO NUCLEI**
- **TRANSMISSION WAVE**
- **REFLECTION WAVE**
- **REFLECTION GAIN**

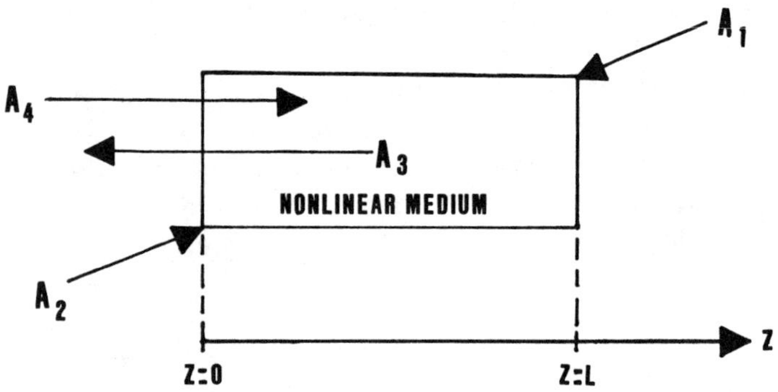

Figure 36. Phase conjugation by four-wave mixing.

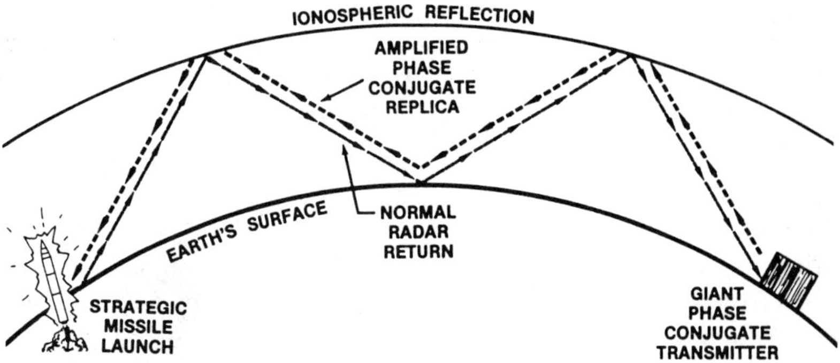

a. Soviet Launch-phase and midcourse ABM system.

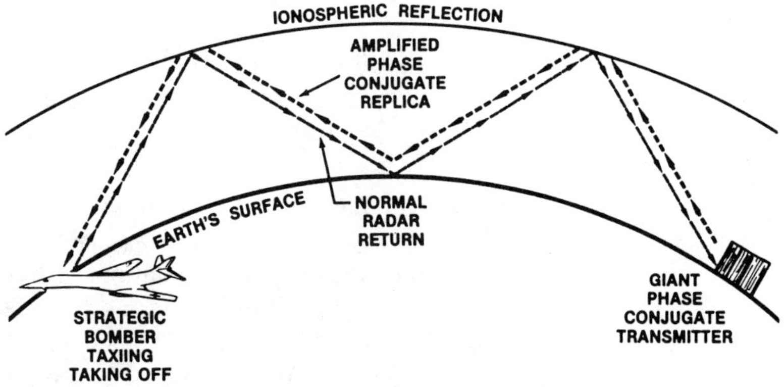

b. Soviet launch-phase and midcourse anti-bomber system.

Figure 37. Soviet launch-phase and midcourse strategic defense system.

peckers) to provide a reflection signal from a distant target. *Voila!* The true use of Soviet Stand-Off-Jammers to knock out enemy antiaircraft, air control, and anti-tactical missile radars wholesale. *Voila!* The Intermediate Phase ABM system, where a long range strategic radar is used to provide reflections from incoming targets. "Fire and fire again!" is the rule, and 100% defense is directly achievable. *Voila!* How the Soviets knocked down Gary Powers' high-flying U-2 reconnaissance aircraft. *Voila!* How SA-2 missile system radars were temporarily modified in North Vietnam to knock down several hot new F-111 aircraft. *Voila!* How the Arrow DC-8 aircraft, Titan missiles, Delta rocket, and Ariane rockets were "electromagnetically surged" from inside to destroy them. *Voila!* Why the Soviets almost never throw away old radars, since they can now add PCMs and make them formidable destroyers of incoming targets. *Voila!* How one solves the ABM problems of discrimination and weapon kill; simply pulse-fire everything — nuclear material explodes in a full nuclear explosion when struck with potential pulses of sufficient magnitude and duration.

Summarizing figure 36 and amplification of the phase conjugate replica:

When we consider the addition of the input wave and the resulting phase conjugate wave that will be produced, we shall have a total of four waves. Thus this particular process is called *four-wave mixing.**

On the diagram in Figure 39, A_1 and A_2 by convention are taken to be the two opposing EM pump waves. Notice that these two pump waves stress the medium. Since the medium is nonlinear, it is a modulator. Hence the two pump waves modulate each other. The two waves thus lock together into a scalar EM wave. This scalar EM wave is an oscillating artificial scalar EM stress wave, and it goes directly into the atomic nuclei of the medium and pumps the nuclei themselves.

The atomic nuclei are now rhythmically stressed with the oscillating scalar wave.

*Probably the best single introduction to optical phase conjugation in the English language is David M. Pepper, "Nonlinear optical phase conjugation," **Optical Engineering,** 21(2), Mar./Apr. 1982, p. 156-183. Especially read Pepper's footnote on p. 156.

We now input a weak signal (wave A_4) into the "pumped nuclei" medium.

By our CPTEGS rule, the positively- charged nuclei generate a negative energy/negative time wave — in short, a phase conjugate replica wave. Further, it is a highly amplified PCR, and may contain as much raw energy as was fed into the pumped mirror by our pump waves. This "seeker wave" or "electromagnetic missile" wave then sets out on its invisible path through space, seeking a distant "A_4 source point" and delivering all its energy intact to that point.

The Phase Conjugate Mirror as a Vacuum Triode

The pumped phase conjugate mirror (four wave mixing) can best be understood as a special kind of **vacuum triode.**

The pumped artificial potential on the atomic nucleus provides a powerful cathode in positive time, and a powerful plate as well in negative or reversed time. The electron shields, in their spin coupling to the nucleus, act as a grid in positive time. The input signal A_4 itself acts as a relatively weak signal onto the grid of the triode.

The positive charge difference in potential between the powerful pump potential of the nucleus (cathode, in forward time) acts as the plate voltage. The decrease of this potential when discharging (increase of the negative time, negative aspect) acts as the production of a plate signal to the negative time operation (production of the amplified, time-reversed PCR wave).

The excited nucleus immediately decays upon stimulus by the "grid signal" A_4, emitting a "time- and energy-reversed" strong signal — in short, amplified phase conjugate replica wave E_3.

The amplified phase conjugate signal moves from the cathode (nucleus) out to the electron shells and beyond, precisely because it is time-reversed. To a time-reversed signal, the grid (normal input) acts as the final plate (external output) — that is, in negative time, the elements of the triode are reversed. This makes it possible for the material to emit the powerful PCR.

I have called this effect/analogy a **vacuum triode,** to accent the direct engineering possibilities. My associates have already engineered this effect to obtain enormous amplification of energy ("free energy") and practical antigravity, from solid-state devices, directly

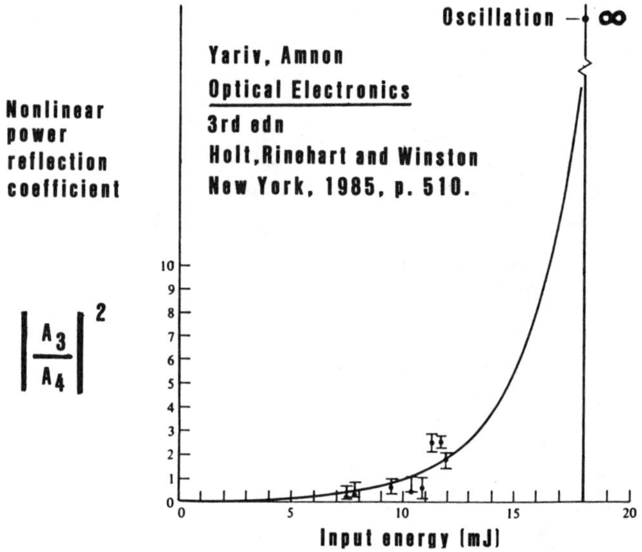

a. Typical nonlinear power reflection coefficients.

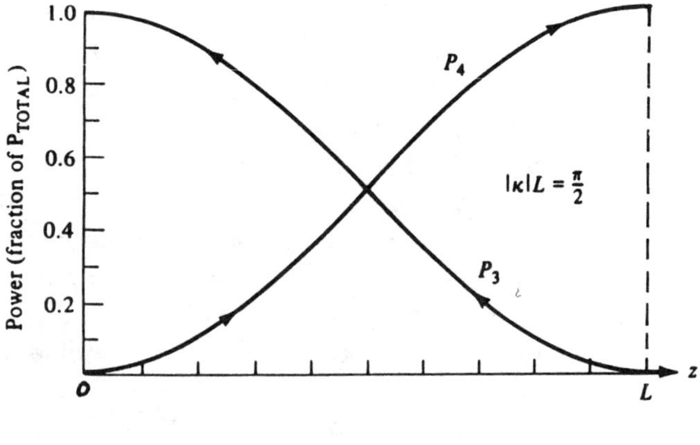

b. Intensities for the oscillation condition.

Figure 38. Power reflection coefficients and oscillation.

on the laboratory bench.

The actual "amplitude gain" of the vacuum triode is the ratio of the amplitude of A_3 to the amplitude of A_4. The square of the amplitude gain is proportional to the power gain; this entity is called the nonlinear power reflection coefficient.

Figure (38a) shows the typical nonlinear power reflection coefficient for a pumped phase conjugate mirror, as a function of the input energy and the depth of the material. As the input signal increases, the gain increases. The ultimate condition would be that the "free oscillation" condition is approached. This occurs when the angle between the input wave A_4 and the pump waves A_1 and A_2 is 90 degrees.

Figure (38b.) shows the oscillation condition and the fraction of the total pump power that is in the input wave A_4 and its output phase conjugate replica A_3.

At the oscillation condition, an "infinite" gain exists at the correct depth in the medium. This means that essentially all the energy being fed into the pump waves A_1 and A_2 will now be emitted in the output wave A_3. At that point, "saturation cutoff" of the triode output occurs, and it cannot output higher energy, since it has no more.

Notice that, at the oscillation condition, for the slightest output, the full power of the pump waves is fed into the phase conjugate replica. This powerful wave then retraces the path taken by the original input signal, unless something else is done to divert it.*

The interesting question then arises: Since we can have infinite gain, can we get a special oscillation condition so that the pump wave furnishes its own energy? In other words, can the pump wave "resonate" with the vacuum flux in such a fashion that it is self-pumping and self-perpetuating?

In at least three materials, the answer is yes. Such effects have been experimentally accomplished in special forms of barium titanate. See, for example, J. O. White et al, "Coherent oscillation by self-induced gratings in the photorefractive crystal $BaTiO_3$," **Appl. Phys. Lett.**, vol. 40, 1982. p. 450.

*Recall that the PCR can be steered by introducing a minute wave A_5 to vectorially sum with input A_4. In that case, the effective input is the vector resultant of $(A_4 + A_5)$. The apparent distant source point and invisible vacuum path are shifted correspondingly.

Phase conjugation is a universal phenomenon. Theoretically it applies to any sort of wave: electromagnetic, scalar, sound, mechanical, etc. By using it, incredible new effects and an entirely new physics can be accomplished. It is a new and exciting field, little-known outside specialist circles, and still not well-understood. Most discoveries in the field are yet to be made.*

Newton's Third Law and the Full Law of Entropy

For example, the present author noticed that Newton's third law— for every action there is an opposite and equal reaction — is actually a result of phase conjugation. To explain that, we diverge a bit.

First, phase conjugation is also involved in the fact that a charged particle of mass is a little "dynamo" or engine.

Actually, a particle of mass is itself a "nonlinearity" in vacuum spacetime. When a photon (virtual or observable) strikes a particle of mass and is absorbed by it, it's the same as "interacting with a nonlinear medium."

In terms of virtual photons, the charged particle is continually bombarded with them, from the vacuum flux. The charged particle, being a "nonlinear medium", phase conjugates each input virtual photon, emitting a phase conjugate replica.

If it absorbs a normal virtual photon, it emits a "negative energy, negative time" phase conjugate replica.

If it absorbs a normal virtual photon, it emits a "negative energy, positive time" phase conjugate replica — just a normal virtual photon. Note that the particle of mass thus does not exist in time. Or, it exists equally in positive and negative time. Since we only observe particles, it follows that time is not normally an observable, as quantum mechanics has assumed.

The emission of a phase conjugate replica does not affect the momentum of the emitting PCM, as is well-known.

For an observable photon, the particle (nonlinear medium) absorbs the normal photon, which does not affect the energy and momentum of the PCM particle of mass.

If there is no other mass to accept the PCR, it just moves off.

*TheU.S. may finally be waking up. SDI is now starting to study EM missiles "in the timedomain" as opposed to frequency. See **Av. Wk. & Space Tech.**, Feb. 29, 1988, p. 55.

If there is another mass to accept the PCR, the PCR is absorbed and phase conjugated by it.

A charged particle in vacuum is continually bombarded by a flux of essentially "randomized" fluctuations. However, on the average these all "average out" to zero. Any particle is automatically in a very high vacuum potential, and is in a state of great agitation at all times, even if it's "at rest" with respect to ordinary observers. It's really "smeared all over the place," so to speak.

When we expose a charged particle to a *normal* potential, the interior virtual particle flux of that potential is disorganized. Hence the particle just "wiggles a bit more frantically," so to speak, randomly in every direction.

However, when we expose a charged particle to an *artificial* potential made by zero summed/multiplied EM force fields or waves, the particle wiggles more frantically in *organized directions.**

This is just as true for virtual particles as it is for observable particles.

Thus the use of such artificial potentials in scalar electromagnetics enables us to overcome the disorder of the internal structure of normal electromagnetics. By this means, we can structure the vacuum, organize electricity and electromagnetic waves, accomplish negentropy, curve local spacetime in complex, deterministic fashions, produce free energy and antigravity, reorganize and transmute nuclei (transmute elements) with miniscule input energy, etc.

Rigorously, this means that the present law of entropy is only half of the full law of entropy. Specifically, it is the "positive time, positive energy" half of the law, and it states that in closed real physical systems, continuing operations of ordered "positive time, positive energy" effects tend to inevitable "disordered" effects produced in the apparatus or system.

In other words, the present law of entropy really states that no ordered system is totally closed. The system will inevitably have energy and actions that escape the system's order, and hence (to the system) this escape represents "loss of order" — or in short, disorder.

The present law of entropy specifically excludes (by implication)

*I.e., the electronic noise is partially organized. This is a major key toward building scalar EM detectors. It is also a primary cause of many solid-state circuit malfunctions. The exact principle is: ⟨Random changes⟩ + ⟨artificial potential⟩ equals ⟨chaos⟩.

© 1978 Hal Crawford

Figure 39. Photons have virtual substructures. These may be statistical or deterministic.

negative time aspects, where external (disordered) energy time-reverses to again enter the ordered system, in perfect order. By implication, it also excludes negative energy production and operations.

However, **experimentally we can produce both negative energy and negative time, in deliberately time-reversed operations such as phase conjugation and with devices that serve as phase conjugate mirrors. Further, we can amplify the phase conjugation and disorder-to-order operations.**

Hence the present law of entropy is incomplete, and states only half the true possibilities. The other half of the law is the **law of negentropy.** In this law, disordered operations outside the ordered system undergo time-reversed (and possibly amplified) effects. These reordered energy effects — which may be highly amplified in comparison to the disordered escaped energy — reenter the "ordered system", restoring order. Since this process moves in negative time, it goes from disorder to order. Hence it is negentropic.

Therefore we have solved the old thermodynamic problem of the "eventual decay of the universe into disorder." Not to worry; the other half of the full law of entropy prescribes negentropic operations in negative time/negative energy, and these restore the order of the universe. That takes care of the problem.

It also means that, in highly disordered systems of many degrees of freedom and far from thermodynamic equilibrium (that is, when the disorder law is saturated), then one can expect to see further stress "create" negative time and hence create order emerging and stabilizing from disorder.

And of course that is exactly what is seen. Ilya Prigogine was awarded the Nobel Prize in 1977 for writing a new thermodynamics predicting precisely such effects, and experiments have proved his case.

But to return to Newton's third law:

Newton abstracted his third law from the classical interaction between two colliding balls.

If one ball is at rest and another approaches it at some velocity, the approaching ball carries momentum and kinetic energy. As it "collides" with the resting mass, quantum mechanics tells us what actually happens: Particles of mass in the moving ball are producing virtual photons continually, and these virtual photons strike the particles of mass of the resting ball and are absorbed by it.

The resting mass now acquires extra energy and momentum from the absorbed photons. At the same time, it acts as a nonlinear medium. It produces phase conjugate replica virtual photons, and these time-reversed virtual photons are emitted. These photons produce no change in momentum or energy upon the emitting mass. However, being phase conjugates, they precisely follow back along the paths taken by the first or "stimulus" virtual photons, striking the moving ball. They are absorbed by that ball, producing (to the external observer) negative momentum and negative energy in it.

These subtract from the kinetic momentum and kinetic energy of the moving ball, reducing them.

The virtual photons emitted by the approaching ball perform positive work upon the target ball.

The virtual, phase conjugated photons, emitted in return by the mass of the struck ball as a PCM, reverse to strike the approaching ball to do negative work upon it.

Notice that twice as much absolute work is always done on the system of two balls as we "input" with the approaching ball.

Also notice that, if we directly "engineer" the phase conjugation of the struck system, we can directly tamper with, and drastically change, the production of the negative energy and negative momentum in the moving ball. Hence we can drastically alter Newton's third law. We can now make a Maxwell's Demon.

This alone clearly establishes that it is perfectly possible to build a so-called free energy device. Though subtle mechanisms must be used, it's nothing more spectacular than putting a paddle wheel in a river, and extracting shaft power from the wheel, furnished by the river's current. Phase conjugation yields other exciting possibilities

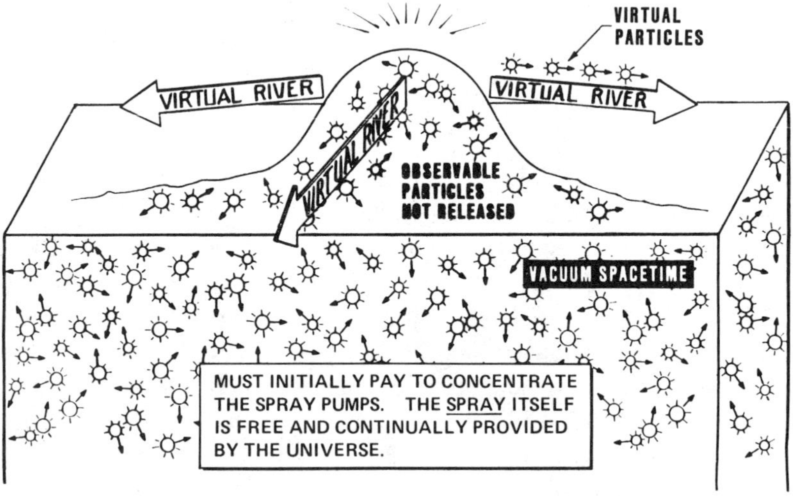

Figure 40. Once established, a virtual river is for free.

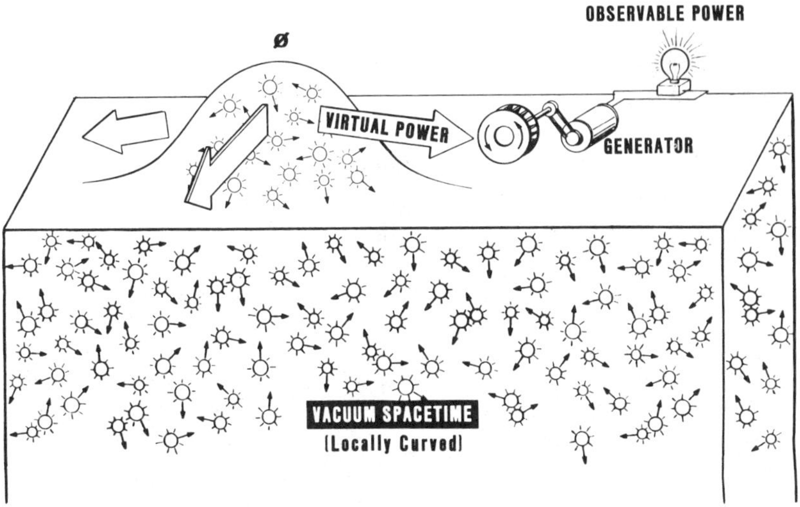

Figure 41. Local energy conservation can be violated.

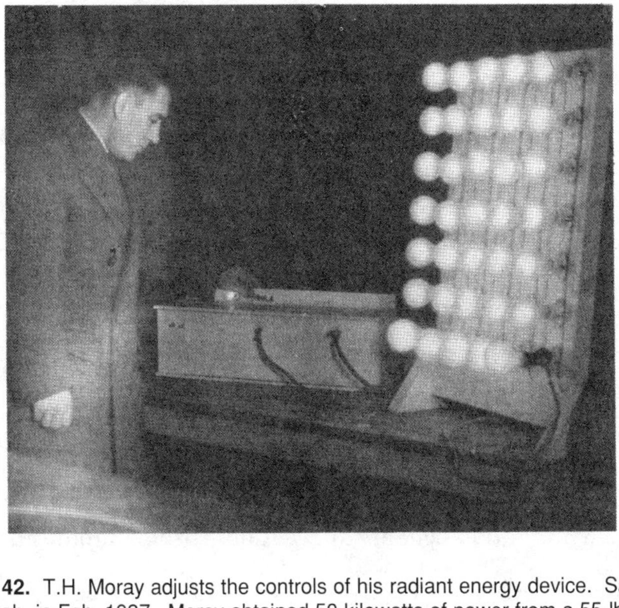

Figure 42. T.H. Moray adjusts the controls of his radiant energy device. Salt Lake City, Utah, in Feb. 1937. Moray obtained 50 kilowatts of power from a 55-lb. device, straight from the ether. Its characteristics (cool circuits, brilliantly lit lamps) reveal that it was negative energy.

too numerous to explore here. For just one example, by phase conjugation, real-time holography can be accomplished without having to separately make and illuminate the holograms.

Now with holography and multiple projectors — and particularly with two intersecting "normal" beams to backtrack upon with ever-converging PCR signals — you can assemble a "form of energy" at an appreciable distance from the projectors in three dimensional space. With phase conjugation, you can do it in real time. And you can do it at a great distance back along the path of any signal you use as an input.

By using PCM holography, degradation with distance is not appreciably experienced. After all, the PCR waves utilized are ever-converging. The energy does not diverge and spread. Therefore, if you can make a 6" diameter ball of intense EM energy at a short distance in the laboratory, you can make that same 6" diameter ball of intense energy at several thousand kilometers distance, using PCR real-time interference holography.

With highly amplified PCM's, you can put far more energy into the distant interference form than you can with normal holography. Conceivably it is possible to assemble so much energy in the holography "object" that it condenses into a real material object! In other words, it materializes or semi-materializes.

Both the "intense light form" usage and semi-materialization of forms (such as light forms, flying geometrical forms, etc.) have been created worldwide by the Soviets for decades, to stimulate UFO reports and provide a deception plan for their development and testing of large, strategic energetics weapons using highly amplified PCMs and PCR holography.*

Other bizarre considerations also arise. For example, in **radionics** one utilizes a "witness" — such as a photograph — of the object one is attempting to send "energy" to. (For example, this might be a sickly plant one is attempting to spruce up). Now when the plant was photographed, the light from it struck the photoemulsion of the film, producing a photochemical reaction. It also produced phase

*For an example of highly reliable detection and observation of "Soviet hololography UFOs," see Leif Havik, "Project Hessdalen," MUFON UFO Journal, Jan. 1988, p. 4-7. The present author certainly does not imply that all UFO phenomena are due to Soviet PCR holography, only that **some** UFO phenomena are.

conjugation in the atomic nuclei of the film emulsion, since the emulsion acts in some respects as a nonlinear medium.

There exists a continuous, invisible "stimulus photon and its connections" trace in time and space, between the plant when the photo was taken and that photo now, even if one or both of them have moved. That trace is highly persistent (as Australian experimenters Reid and Barsamian have shown). A phase conjugate (time-reversed) signal can be made to retrace that track and travel all the way back to the plant, in the present. The effect of using the photo (or sample of the object) as such a "witness" of the real plant and directing weak PCR energy back along the invisible trace into the object is called **radionics.** In most cases, the two cerebral hemispheres of the operator's brain are depended on to form the necessary scalar "pump wave" to pump the "witness" and produce phase conjugated signal energy, time-reversed to travel back into the distant object.*

The problem with present radionics is that it is far too weak, and it is "operator dependent", changing with the mood, temperament, and skill of the operator. It does objectively work, however, though often erratically. In countries such as England, France, and Germany, use of radionics to treat human disease is legal and permitted, though operators (for example, in England) must undergo extensive training and certification. Its results are roughly comparable to the results of normal medical doctors. Radionics does not replace orthodox medicine. It can successfully treat certain things that orthodox doctors have little or no success with (such as lupus), and orthodox medicine can successfully treat many things that radionics has little success with (a broken leg or ruptured appendix, for example). The two treatments are best used in conjunction with each other.

However, we must point out that a new, amplified PCM radionics is likely to emerge in the near future. Such a new approach will offer highly effective, powerful treatment of diseases, even at a distance, by amplified PCR electromagnetics. Again, the radiation in and from a photo or witness of a diseased patient can be used as a "grid signal" into a powerful, pumped phase conjugate mirror. The

*Again recall that we observe time-reversal of waves as **spatial path** reversal, not as time travel.

PCM will produce a specific, powerful, amplified signal that will travel directly to the patient, be absorbed in his entire system, including the atomic nuclei comprising his cells, and directly reverse the chemistry, toxins, and cellular damage in the patient from that disease. It will also kill or destroy the harmful viruses, bacteria, etc. causing the disease, and it can even reverse the actual genetic changes in the cell caused by disease-inducing viruses.

Of course, any powerful tool is two-edged. It can be used for harm as well as good. I think the reader can appreciate the damage that can be done to systems and persons at a distance by means of such powerful new amplified PCM radionics devices.

You can also see the security problems posed to large computing facilities in banks, federal facilities, state and municipal facilities, the IRS, U.S. military weapon systems, ships, aircraft, etc.

Obviously such devices are going to have to be highly regulated and controlled. Else criminal operators will be killing people and destroying things wholesale, secretly and at a distance, and they will have perfect legal alibis to allow them to escape prosecution.

To summarize: if a photograph or witness pattern of an object or person can be correctly stimulated by phase conjugate electromagnetics so that the emulsion acts again as a PCM, can one not argue that — theoretically — phase conjugate energy from the photograph and the instrument can be sent back along all paths, all the way back to the original object? After all, this has been rigorously demonstrated by University of Sydney researchers. Is there not an actual physical mechanism for radionics? For highly amplified, powerful radionics where the operator himself is removed from the circuit? Just because it changes our present notion of physical reality, must we dogmatically reject the results being shown on the laboratory benches, some of which are in the hard-core scientific literature?

Phase conjugation and time-reversed engineering have a diversity of applications unparalleled in the history of science. They literally present us with a new physics. New rules apply.

Most of the major discoveries in phase conjugation have yet to be made.

Scalar Electromagnetics

The scalar electromagnetic approach modifies classical electromagnetics (EM) to include gravitational waves and effects.

To do this, scalar EM utilizes summed-zero vector forces and force fields to construct polarized vacuum potentials.

Although externally it has zero E and B vector gradients, an "artificial" potential possesses an internal, dynamic E and B vector field structure. This "infolded" (Bohm's term) structure has finite size and is deterministic. The infolded structure of the artificial potential in turn deterministically structures and polarizes the vacuum and curves spacetime locally, contrary to presently assumed limitations of general relativity.

Since in free vacuum a potential normally extends to infinity in a decaying exponential fashion, then this infolded E and B vector structure of an artificial potential extends to infinity in a decaying exponential fashion.

The artificial potential itself may be rhythmically varied either in structure, magnitude, frequency, or all of the above. This produces waves of potential, and waves of the structure of vacuum/ spacetime — again, in the free vacuum case, reaching to infinity in a "decaying exponential" fashion. These "scalar EM waves" are gravitational waves.

Each photon (one major wave length of the "carrier", complete with modulations) of the scalar EM wave also has structure (its included modulations).

Modulated waves have compound or "giant" photons — photons containing infolded photons.

Each compound photon of such a scalar EM wave is a vacuum engine. It deliberately structures and patterns — dynamically — the energy density and charge of vacuum.

(1) By canonically varying two or more components of the electromagnetic vector structure of the zero-summed EM force vector system, the local structure of vacuum spacetime is macroscopically varied in its internal composition. This is the compound variation of "curvature within curvature" — and hence hyperdimensional.

Table 29. A ZERO VECTOR SYSTEM:

- **IS AN ACCUMULATOR**
- **DOES "INTERNAL" WORK ON MEDIUM**
- **HAS NO "ENERGY" EXCEPT STRESS OF VACUUM, YET**
- **CAN YIELD THE ENERGY OF ITS COMPONENTS WHEN DISSIPATED**
- **IS A SPECIAL SORT OF "PUMP"**
- **CAN YIELD CONTINUOUS ANENERGY FLOW IF NOT DISSIPATED**

(2) By prohibiting internal canonical variance while coherently varying the amplitudes of all the EM components, the total stress of vacuum/spacetime — and hence its overall curvature — is locally varied, without modifying its structural form. This is simple variation of overall curvature of local spacetime, involving primarily relativistic effects.

Rigorously, each of these two methods produces a localized gravitational wave, where the local stress of vacuum is deliberately patterned as well as oscillated in amplitude.

Both methods may be applied simultaneously (and multiple infolded times) to produce an even more sophisticated gravitational wave, and more sophisticated structuring of the local stress energy density of vacuum.

The resulting unified electromagnetics/gravitation is called **scalar electromagnetics,** since the electrogravitational effects are obtained by deliberately opposing EM vector force fields so that they vectorially sum or multiply to a zero vector EM resultant, while the infolded (Bohm's term) EM vector components structure and vary the stress energy density of vacuum.*

*Gravitational potential is just "in-folded and locked in" dynamic electromagnetic forces. The infolded EM energy is locked-in, representing a change in the local energy density of vacuum and hence a curvature in spacetime. Electromagnetic force fields are just the out-folding of the G-potential's inner EM contents into the 5th dimension. Ordinary gravitational force field is just the "trickle leakage" of the G-potential's infolded contents, out into and through 3-space.

Note immediately that scalar EM also deals with internally structured and patterned electricity and electromagnetism.

"Normal" electromagnetics has no deterministic internal structure.

The new electrogravitational (EG) wave is called a scalar EM wave, and is believed to have been originally discovered by Nikola Tesla.

James Clerk Maxwell was aware of the potential for electromagnetics to stress and structure the vacuum ether.

His original electromagnetic theory — written in quaternions, not vectors (which had not yet been completed by Oliver Heaviside) — can allow for these effects to be expressed.

Unfortunately Heaviside's interpretation of Maxwell's work

Table 30. STRESS IS FUNDAMENTAL

- **THE MOST FUNDAMENTAL REALITY <u>IS STRESS</u>**
- **THE COMPONENTS COMPRISING STRESS ARE THE GREAT CAUSATIVE AGENTS**
- **MOST OF THESE ACTIVE AGENTS ARE HIDDEN INSIDE <u>ZERO-VECTOR SYSTEMS</u>**
- **THE COMPONENTS OF STRESS MAY BE STATISTICAL OR DETERMINISTIC**

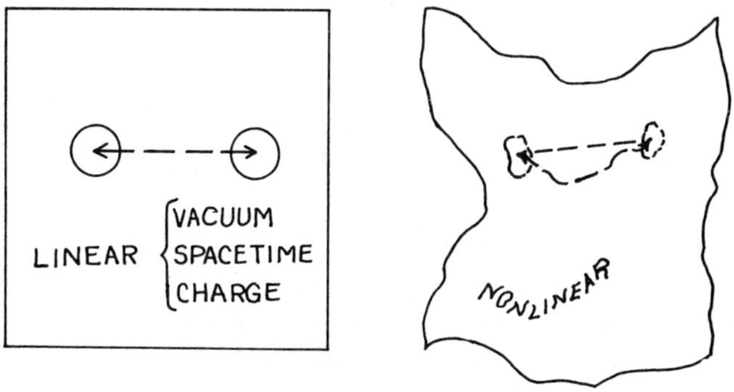

Figure 43. Charge affects anything existing in spacetime.

eliminated these effects, and they have remained eliminated from the Western EM theory to the present day.

The use of the scalar EM wave directly engineers the virtual state and the vacuum itself.

Hooper's work represented important work in this respect, as does other related experimental work by Bedini, Watson, Golden, Dea, Faretto, Beck, and other inventor colleagues who do not wish their names mentioned.

Scalar EM theory also bears a strong relationship to the Kaluza-Klein unified theory of gravitation and electromagnetics. At least five dimensions — four spatial and one time — are required as a minimum.

Nested levels of virtual state may be modeled as identical to successive hyperspaces.

Internested levels of zero-summed vector EM force fields allow the direct engineering of those hyperspaces.

Negative energy and negative time flow are especially important when building free energy devices and antigravity. The mechanism producing negative energy and negative time flow is the forced amplified production and absorption of phase conjugated waves.

In addition, phase conjugation is a basic phenomenon of nature: for example, as previously pointed out, it is the direct mechanism that generates Newton's third law of motion. It also adds a negentropy law (for negative energy/negative time).

Accordingly, if we engineer phase conjugation, we can change Newton's third law to our will. And we can invoke the negentropy half of the total law of entropy, so that we can go from disorder back to order. Again, we can make a Maxwell's Demon at will!

In Newton's third law, when manipulated locally, the reaction force need not necessarily be equal in magnitude to the action force. It also need not necessarily be parallel to it. It can even be phase conjugated itself to yield an addition force, assisting the propelling of a particular engine or device.

Phase conjugation may also be manipulated so as to cause like magnetic poles to attract, and unlike poles to repel.

Magnetic "force field lines" of a bar magnet normally exist in conjugate co-existing pairs. One of the pair is in observer positive time, and (by convention) runs from the north pole to the south pole. The second line of the pair is a phase conjugate of the first, and exists in negative observer time. Thus, to the "positive time only" observer, it will appear to run from the south pole to the north pole, perfectly retracing the path of its twin.

Howard Johnson uses a "two particle" theory of magnetic field, for example, where one particle (photon) is the phase conjugate of the other. This is identically the same as the scalar electromagnetics concept of phase conjugate pairs of field lines. By very complex, specialized, compound permanent magnets, Johnson is able to partially separate the two lines, and spatially concentrate or diminish the phase conjugation (negative time) component in a given area of operation.

If the negative time component lines are concentrated to outweigh the positive component lines in a local region, then the laws of magnetics are reversed in that region. There like poles attract and unlike poles repel.

In his rotary permanent magnet motor design, he concentrates the negative time component in that part of the rotation where a north rotor pole is approaching a north stator pole. Normally, in this part of the cycle, one has to overcome the repulsion of like poles to "force energy" into the device for later extraction.

However, *now* in that region *like poles attract*. There the north pole of the rotor is attracted toward the north pole of the stator, adding impetus to the rotor.

As the rotating north pole passes the stator north pole, it leaves the region of negative time concentration and returns to a normal "positive time" region again. Now the north poles repel again, and impetus is again added to the rotor.

In that manner Johnson is able to violate local conservation energy, and make a "free energy" permanent magnet motor. The motor will rotate itself and deliver constant shaft power to a mechanical load. By attaching a standard electrical generator, normal electrical power is continually and freely produced by the complete motor-generator power system.

Johnson's complex nonlinear magnets severely curve local spacetime, allowing *local* violation of energy conservation.

Scalar EM View of the Vacuum

In the modern quantum mechanical view, the vacuum is not an emptiness, but instead is a plenum.

Today the vacuum is considered to be filled with incredible virtual particle activity. From nowhere, virtual particles continually arise — even with fierce energy — then disappear again into nowhere, so rapidly that they cannot be individually observed.

However, these virtual particles are quite real, for they cause all the forces of nature when they interact in the aggregate with observable particles.

To the observer, the fleeting particles also appear and disappear in both positive time and negative time. That is, the flux consists of both particles and antiparticles.

Thus the vacuum is a seething inferno of virtual particle fluxes.

The concept of an **ether** is again accepted. It refers to this "virtual flux" vacuum.

Note, however, that this is an ether far different from the old material ether that was theorized prior to relativity.

In the new vacuum ether, every imaginable type of particle continually and spontaneously arises (creation) and disappears (annihilation) at every point in the vacuum, according to modern quantum mechanics.

The rate of this seething virtual particle creation and annihilation is essentially unlimited. Hence the "flux density" of vacuum is essentially unlimited.

Further, any virtual particle created has a flux of even finer virtual particles associated, and so on without limit.

The vacuum's virtual particle flux is thus comprised of nested levels of ever finer virtual particle fluxes, in the modern view. We state without proof that **each deeper virtual level may be modeled as a higher dimension (hyperdimension). This yields an infinite-dimensional vacuum spacetime (hyperspace) that is identically the infinite nested levels of virtual state.**

At the same time, every nucleus in the universe is continually absorbing and emitting scalar EM (electrogravitational) waves. The emitted scalar EM waves of pure potential are waves in the stress and structuring of the vacuum itself.

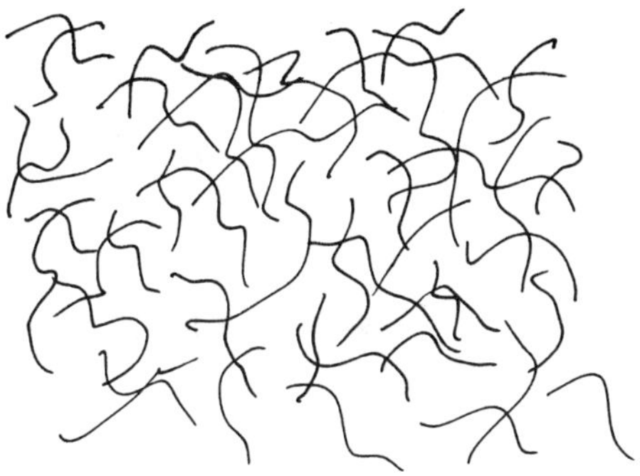

VACUUM IS IDENTICAL TO:

- VIRTUAL PARTICLE FLUX
- SPACETIME
- ANENERGY
- $Ø_O$
- MASSLESS CHARGE

VACUUM IS:

- MADE OF UNQUANTIZED ACTION
- WITHOUT DEFINITE LENGTH INTERVALS
- WITHOUT DEFINITE TIME INTERVALS
- N-DIMENSIONAL (UNFIXED)

Figure 44. Vacuum/spacetime is pure virtual particle flux.

Table 31. VACUUM IS:

- SPACETIME ($L^n T$, WHERE $n \geq 3$)
- CHARGE (MASSLESS)
- ELECTROSTATIC SCALAR POTENTIAL ($Ø_O \neq 0$) (ERROR IN PRESENT THEORY)
- BROKEN BITS OF ENERGY (SUBQUANTAL)
- PURE VIRTUAL PARTICLE FLUX
- Ø - WAVE FLUX
- MULTILEVEL, STRUCTURED, PATTERNED
- A VIRTUAL PLENUM
- AN OBSERVABLE EMPTINESS

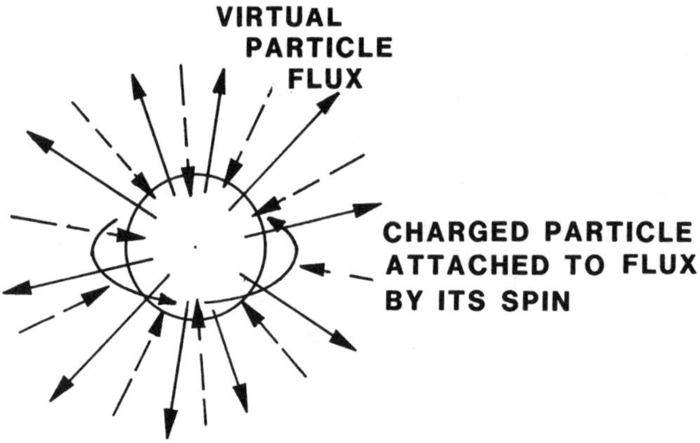

Figure 45. A simplified charged particle.

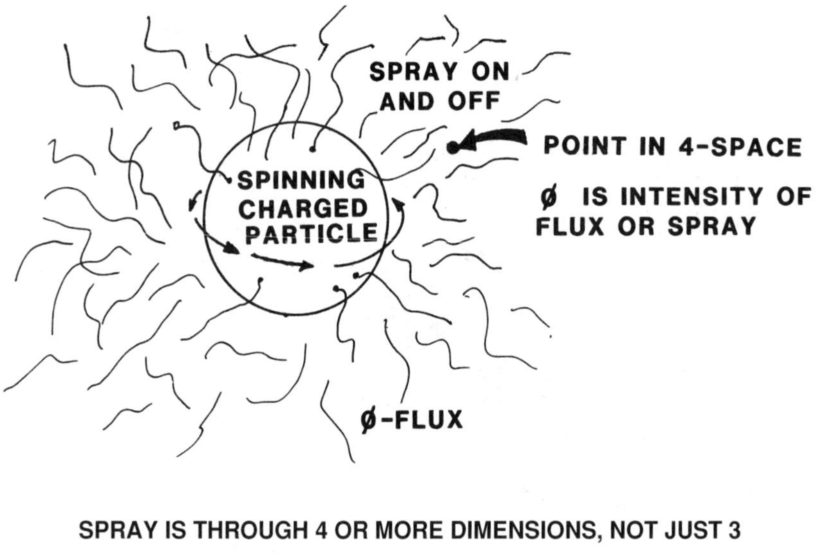

Figure 46. A charged particle is a special kind of "spray nozzle."

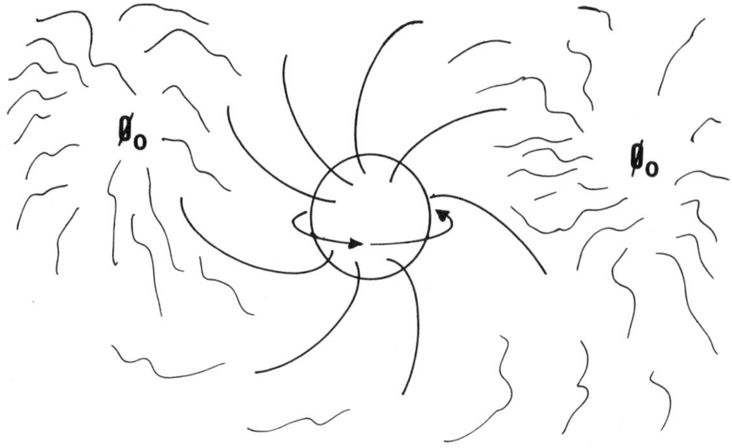

Figure 47. An observable charged particle is directly connected to virtual particle vacuum flux.

Table 32. SPIN COUPLES VACUUM TO PARTICLE

- **SPHERICAL ROTATION IS THE KEY**
- **A PARTICLE CAN BE MODELLED AS A SPHERICALLY ROTATING VORTEX OF SPACETIME**
- **ITS MASS IS DUE TO ITS SPIN**
- **THE SPINNING OBJECT IS CONTINUALLY CONNECTED TO ITS ENVIRONMENT**
- **VERY HIGH VALUES OF ELECTROSTATIC POTENTIAL CAN INDUCE RELATIVISTIC CONDITIONS**
    - **CHANGE RATE OF FLOW OF TIME**
    - **EVEN THOUGH VELOCITY IS NONRELATIVISTIC**

E.P. BATTEY-PRATT AND T.J. RACEY,
"GEOMETRIC MODEL FOR FUNDAMENTAL PARTICLES,"
INTL. J. OF PHYS. 19, NO. 6, 437-475, 1980

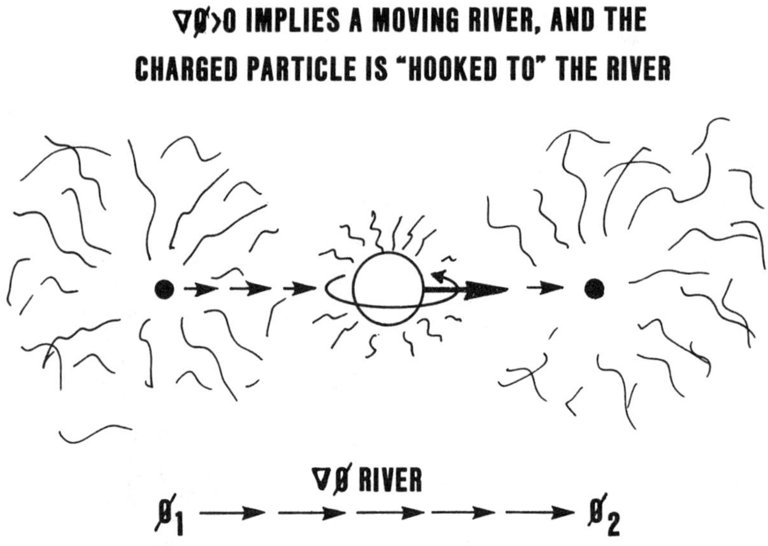

Figure 48. In a flux gradient (virtual particle river), a charged particle moves itself.

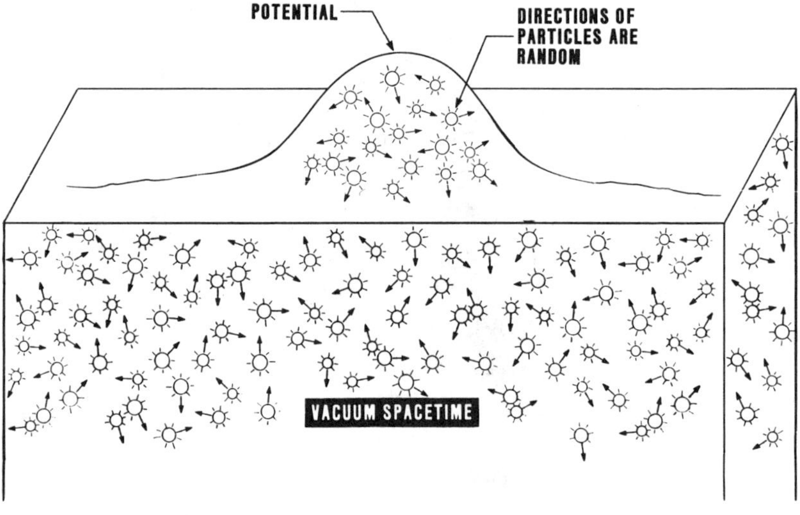

Figure 49. A natural potential is a disorganized change in the stress of vacuum. It has a random virtual substructure.

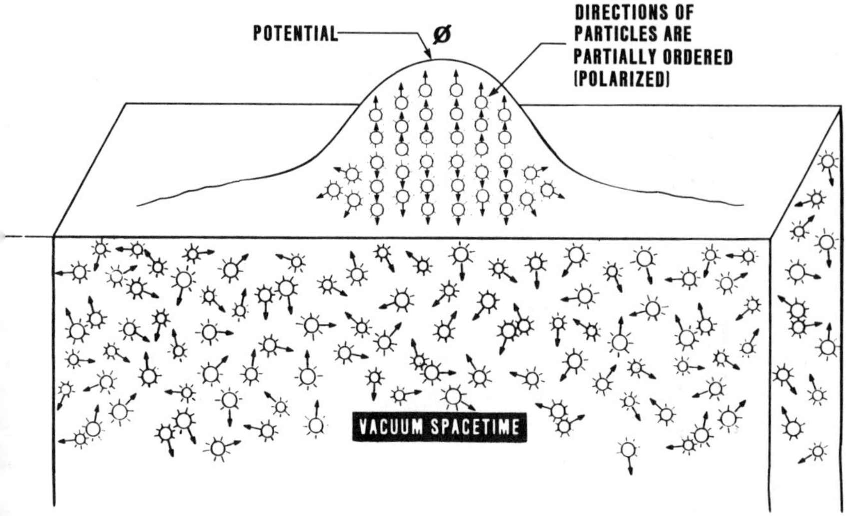

Figure 50. An artificial potential is an organized change in the stress of vacuum. It has a deterministic virtual substructure.

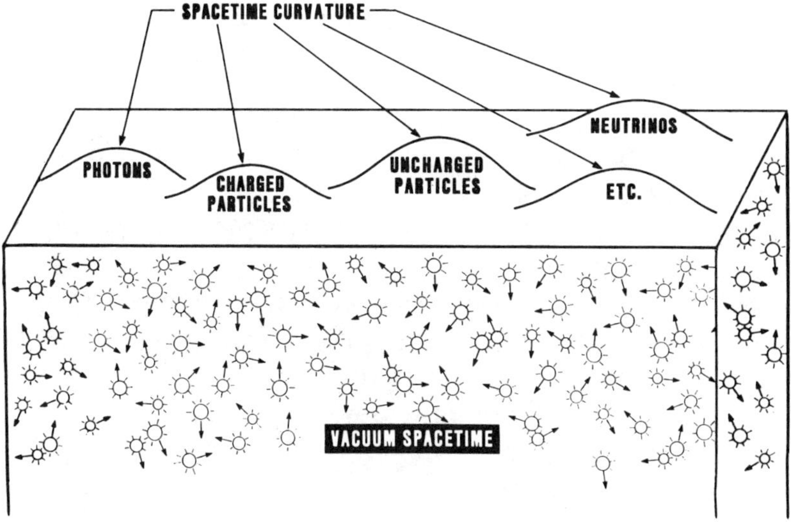

Figure 51. Gravitational potential is a conglomerate of stresses, organized or disorganized.

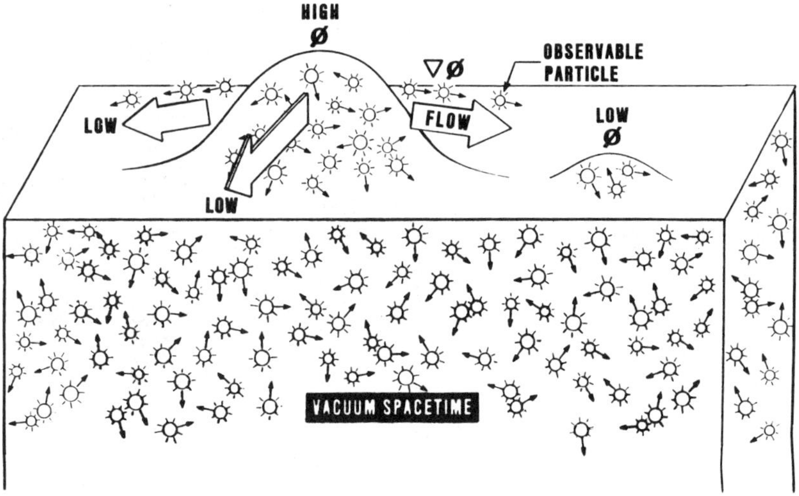

Figure 52. EM force fields are releases of gravitational potential via observable charged mass flows.

Table 33. RESIDUE UNIVERSE, RESIDUE SCIENCE

- **VECTORIALLY, STRESS IS SUM-ZEROED**
- **THE VECTOR FORCE FIELDS REPRESENT NON-ZERO GRADIENTS IN MORE FUNDAMENTAL STRESS**
- **FORCE FIELDS ARE THE RESIDUE LEFT OVER FROM THE SUM-ZEROED STRESSES**
- **PHOTON INTERACTIONS ARE FORCE-FIELD INTERACTIONS**
- **PHOTON-DETECTED REALITY IS ONLY "FIRST ORDER." IT SHOWS ONLY "RESIDUE-LEVEL" REALITY**
- **WE HAVE BUILT A "RESIDUE SCIENCE" AND A "RESIDUE PHILOSOPHY" BASED ON FORCE FIELDS AND PHOTON DETECTION**

Hence at every point in the vacuum, an intense flux of these scalar EM waves, with concomitant interferences, exists — in both positive and negative observer time.

This scalar EM flux causally drives (constitutes) all the enormous quivering of the vacuum spacetime medium itself. In other words, it drives subquantum (virtual) change, which in turn drives quantum change.

This is a drastic reorientation of quantum mechanics. In scalar EM, we view that the virtual flux of vacuum is *causally driven or created* by interacting scalar EM waves. This replaces the present view that the virtual flux is entirely chance. It opens up the direct engineering and structuring of the vacuum — and hence the atomic nucleus — by scalar EM means.

However, it does not replace the normal *statistical nature* of the basic changes of the background vacuum medium. We normally have little or no knowledge of the myriad of drivers that cause the basic background waves of that medium. We may, however, deliberately create special vacuum potential waves which are deterministic, and which we have knowledge of.

To the observer, from a purely statistical viewpoint, in this violent vacuum flux *any* and *every* finite pattern of virtual particles is also continually being momentarily created and destroyed — and at every level and in every hyperdimension.

Thus, in the vacuum there continually exists — at any and every point, and in any and every region — the ghostly image of anything and everything, whether in the past, present, or future; and whether potential, probabilistic, or actual. Even everything that could have been in the past but wasn't, or might be in the present but isn't, or could be in the future but won't be, is continually present in thin, ghostly form.

Rigorously, the universal vacuum may be taken to be a sort of giant hologram, for the whole is in each part, albeit in ghost-like manner. Everything that is, or was, or shall be; and everything that could be but isn't, wasn't, or shan't be; already exists *at once*, anywhere and everywhere, in this ghostly, holographic, virtual state.

We point out in passing that, conceivably, one can engineer any part of this "potential for reality." That is, one can directly engineer physical reality itself, in the scalar EM view.

All that must be done is to amplify (continuously and coherently

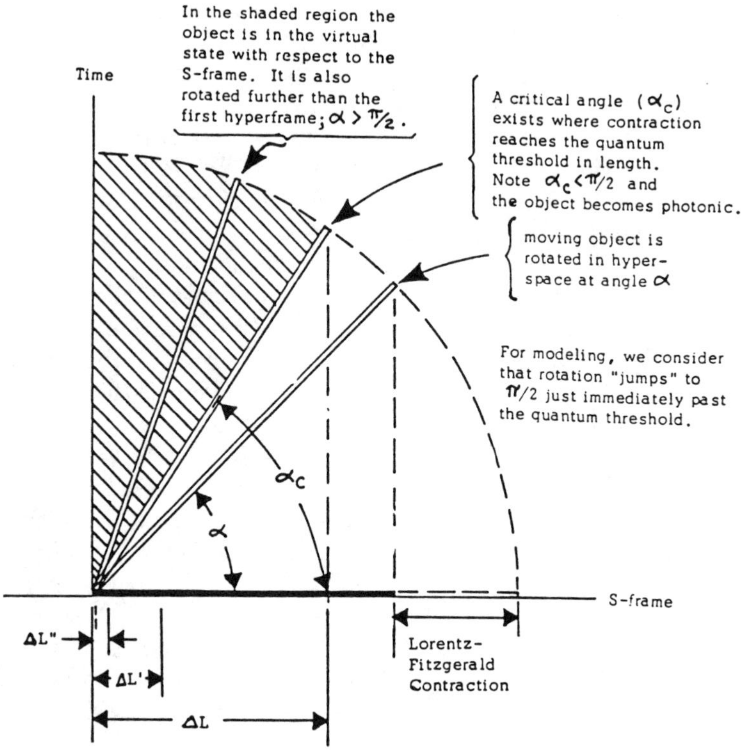

Figure 53. As beyond (without), so within. Hyperspaces are internested virtual states, and rotated orthogonal frames. They are also substructures within and of vacuum state potentials.

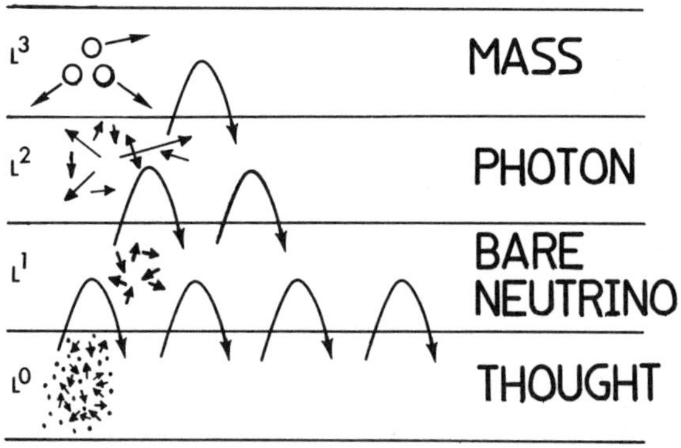

Figure 54. Internested levels of virtual state vacuum interact with neutrino, photon, and mass. "Thought" or "mental state" refers to the third and more levels down in virtual state.

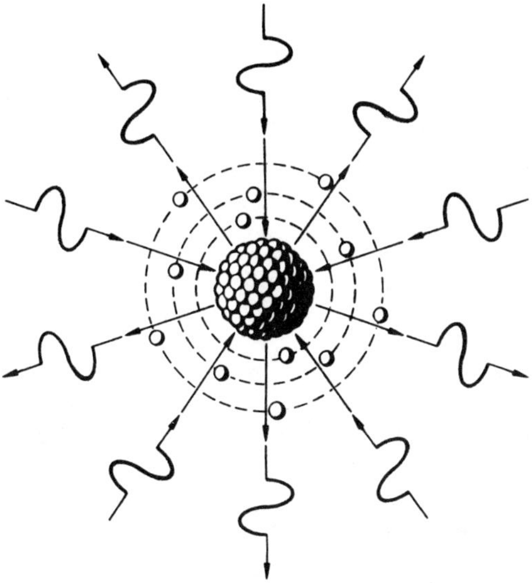

Figure 55. Virtual state patterns are absorbed and emitted by the atomic nucleus. The built-up nuclear "charge" in that particular pattern is a partial potential — for that pattern only.

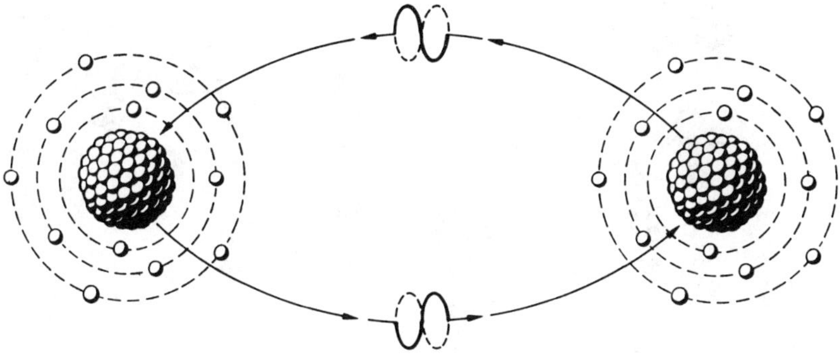

Figure 56. Nuclei of the universe continually exchange scalar EM waves and virtual particle fluxes.

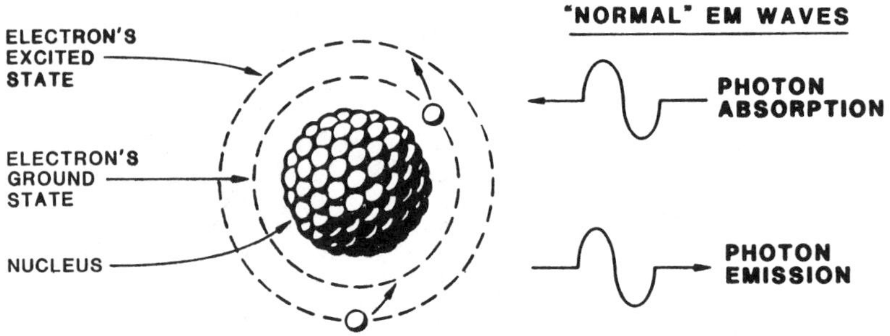

- **HEAVY NUCLEUS RELATIVELY UNAFFECTED**
- **MACROSCOPICALLY, MASS APPEARS STABLE AND "BRICK-LIKE"**
- **SPECIAL RELATIVITY APPLIES**

Figure 57. First order reality. Rough-hewn by observable photon interaction with electron shells of the atoms of physical mass. This process is "physical observation."

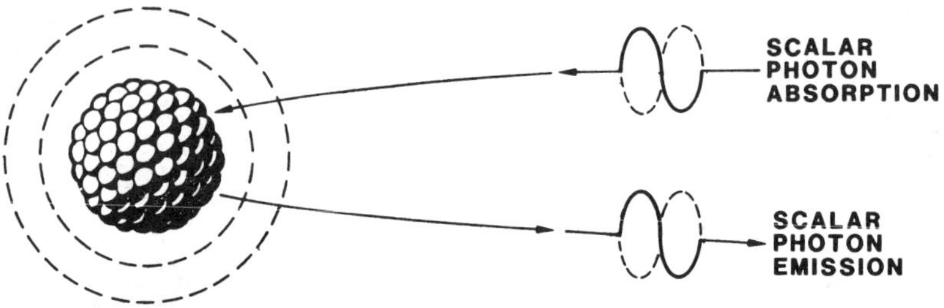

- **HEAVY NUCLEUS AFFECTED**
- **MACROSCOPICALLY, MASS APPEARS FLUID AND CHANGEABLE**
- **GENERAL RELATIVITY AND KALUZA-KLEIN GEOMETRY APPLY**

Figure 58. Higher order (hyperspatial) reality. It exists as stored in the potentials of the atomic nuclei of physical mass.

add energy to) one of these "ghost images" virtual state forms. In that case, the form becomes "denser and denser," until eventually it starts to breach the quantum threshold. At that time, the form will be seen emerging as a sort of "coalescing form of light," where the light seems to be forming in little "chunks" or pieces. As the coalescing operation continues, the light-form will eventually become fully formed. If it continues, it will start to coalesce further into *thin, ghostly material* form, appearing much like a faint fog-form. With continued coalescing, it will become a very solid, material form which exerts pressure on tree limbs, breaks them, leaves traces, etc.

Long ago I dubbed this process *kindling*. It is rather widely met in paranormal phenomena of many types.

But back to the basic idea of ghostly images in the virtual states of vacuum.

In this view, Everett's many-worlds interpretion (MWI) of quantum mechanics is literal and real, albeit the additional worlds are to be taken as virtual and hyperdimensional to the laboratory observer.

(It is rather simple to show that ever deeper, nested levels of the virtual state are exactly the same thing as ever higher dimensions. By "rotating" an object in many-dimensional space, one can show that, after three rotations, a physical object has lost all physical intersections with our normal 3-space, to us now only occupying *time*. Since this is the precise characteristic of a *thought form*, I used this phenomenon and spatiotemporal model to make a multidimensional space model directly including thought, mind and matter. That is, one is thus able to form a unified field theory of mind, thought, life, and matter — a model that is testable, makes predictions, and actually unites physics and metaphysics. That work and its implications, however, are largely beyond the scope of this book.)

It is stressed that the basic scalar EM image (interpretation) of reality is directly implied by quantum mechanics. It is not idle metaphysics. Other than the scalar EM wave causality for the observer's statistical microscopic dynamics (and the extended model unifying mind, thought, life, and matter), it is not the construct of this author. Instead, it follows from interpretation of the equations and axioms of quantum mechanics (QM) itself, as changed and extended by the "zero vector system" dynamics.

Charge, Potential, and Curvature of the Vacuum/Spacetime

The flux of one type of virtual particle through a point in the vacuum may be examined.

A single type of virtual particle flux (VPF) at a point constitutes one particular type of charge at that point. For example, the flux of virtual photons constitutes the electrical charge.

Further, the magnitude of the selected flux (usually expressed as a flux density) through the point may be taken as the magnitude of the vacuum's charge there in that type of particle. In other words, at a point the magnitude of the vacuum's charge (VPF) is one type of *potential* at that point.

Various kinds of fluxes constitute various kinds of charge, and comprise various kinds of potentials. Immediately we see that one type of charge may always be decomposed into other kinds of charge, as can potentials. This point is beyond the scope of this book and will not be further amplified.

Continuing our example, the magnitude of the electrostatic scalar potential at a point in vacuum represents the magnitude of the flux of virtual photons through the point, and hence the electrical charge at the point.

Table 34. REALITY IS A HOLOGRAM

TO ESTABLISH THIS:

1. **ALL DETECTION IS INTERNAL**
   PHYSICAL REALITY CONSISTS OF THE INTERNAL DETECTIONS OF THE PERCEIVER/OBSERVER.

2. **THE OBSERVER MAY BE AT ANY POINT IN THE UNIVERSE**
   THE UNIVERSE CAN BE DETECTED FROM ANY POINT INSIDE ITSELF.

3. **THE PHYSICAL UNIVERSE IS TOTALLY INSIDE EACH POINT IN ITSELF**
   THIS DEFINES A HOLOGRAM: THE WHOLE IS IN EACH PART.

Twin Flows of Time

In quantum mechanics, each virtual photon is continually turning into an electron/position pair, and vice versa.

By Dirac theory, *a positron is an electron traveling backwards in time.*

Further, pair production produces time-smeared particles — an electron and a positron.

Pair production, then, actually produces two *electrons*, one coupled to (smeared in) a positive piece of time and one coupled to (smeared in) a negative piece of time.

Thus in the vacuum two discretized streams of time, one positive and one negative, are continually created in conjunction with pair production, and destroyed by pair annihilation.

Further, integration of tiny virtual pieces of time (from virtual photons) to form "passage of time" *macro*scopically is directly associated with the charge (the absorption and emission of virtual particles) of an observable particle.

This is what is meant by an object "existing" (persisting). Its continual virtual photon interactions are integrated by its mass (timeless part) to continually create its energy states and its march through time.

The absorption and emission of an observable photon, however, moves the mass (timeless part) in (comparatively) larger jumps through time. The absorption of the photon connects a positive piece of time to the mass of the particle, converting it to **masstime.** The subsequent emission of an observable photon "tears off the little time-tail," so-to-speak, and leaves behind a totally spatial mass entity, having no large connection to "the flow of time."

This is what is really meant by "observation."

Because the "observation" disconnects time from the previously "excited mass" (masstime), then it follows that time is not an observable.

It also follows that the twin streams of time are not continuous. Each is broken into incredibly tiny bits.

The bits of time are continually interlaced between negative and positive, and neither of the two streams of time bits is integrated in the vacuum. The vacuum is disintegrated!

A photon — the basic quantum — is composed of discretized energy and time, bound together (integrated) as action (angular momentum). That is, a photon is a little piece of energy, welded to a little piece of time, with no seam in the middle.

Two kinds of photons exist: the normal photon exists as (+ΔE) (+Δt). The phase conjugate photon exists as (–ΔE) (–Δt).

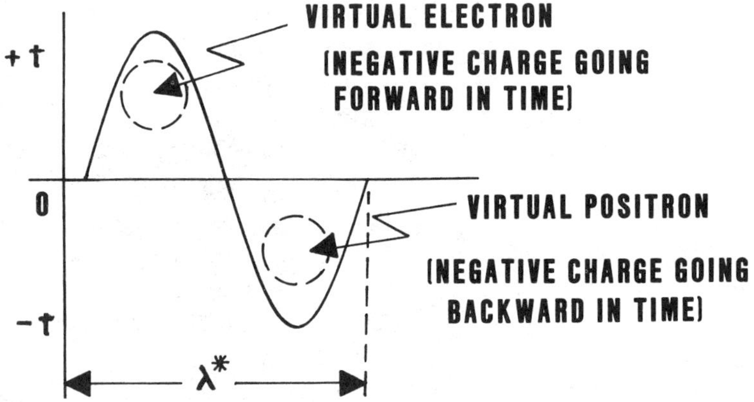

Figure 59. A photon is a single oscillation of a carrier wave. It is also two virtual electrons, one going forward in time, and one going backward in time. With internested modulations (subphotons), the structure of the photon becomes extremely complex.

Table 35. PHYSICAL CHANGE

- COMPOSED OF ACTION
- h = BASIC QUANTUM
- TWO CANONICAL VARIABLES
  - ENERGY/TIME (Δ E Δ t)
  - MOMENTUM/LENGTH (Δ p Δ L)

  ETC.
- ENERGY/TIME
  - h = (+ Δ E) (+ Δ t)
  - h = (- Δ E) (- Δ t)

If the photon is of a certain magnitude, given by Planck's constant, then it is an **observable photon.**

If the photon is less than h in magnitude, then it is a **virtual photon.**

A simple photon in vacuum can also be considered to be one cycle of a sine wave. One half of the sine waves exists in positive time, hence is/contains a virtual electron.

The other half of the sine wave exists in negative time, hence it is/contains a virtual positron — an electron traveling backward in time. This second half of the full photon (a single sine wave oscillation) is the phase conjugate (time reversal) of the first half.

As we stated previously, the full photon in vacuum actually exists as a presently visualized "positive time" photon and a phase conjugate "negative time" photon , a "serially linked pair," where each photon is only one-half the sine wave. This resolves the conflict inherent in wave/particle duality.

It also has a great deal to say about engineering the vacuum and about detectors and the detection process.

In the spontaneous decay of a virtual photon, it can be seen that one part (the virtual electron) is associated with positive energy and positive time; the other part (the virtual positron) is associated with negative energy and negative time.

The continual "switching" between positive and negative time in an observable particle's absorption and emission of virtual photons (and the associated electron/position +t/-t pairs) means that the positive flow of time, to the macroscopic observer, is continually being "started" and "stopped" (created and destroyed).

This continual attachment and detachment of positive time to and from the "observer particle" creates the "past" and the "future" to which the observer seems somehow to be connected, and yet not connected.

Engineering Local General Relativity

In a flat spacetime (linear vacuum), the two time flows are balanced, as are pair creation and pair annihilation. In this case, conservation of charge and energy hold.

Table 36. ORDINARY GENERAL RELATIVITY (OGR) IS A SPECIAL CASE

- **OGR HAS ASSUMED AWAY MOST LOCAL GR SYSTEMS, OF THE TYPE WHERE MAXWELL'S EQUATIONS AND THE CONSERVATION LAWS CHANGE LOCALLY.**

- **PHYSICISTS ARE THUS STRONGLY DISCOURAGED FROM CONSIDERING THAT GR CAN EASILY BE ENGINEERED IN A LOCAL EM SYSTEM.**

In a curved spacetime (nonlinear vacuum), one of the two triplets (positive electron/energy/time or negative electron/energy/time) predominates. Hence in a curved spacetime the rate of flow (production) of the two time streams is unequal, as is the production of the two kinds of energy and the two kinds of electrical charge.

A locally curved spacetime thus produces a predominance of either positive or negative electrons, and either positive or negative energy, and a predominance of the addition of either positive or negative time production.

The curved spacetime acts as a local source or sink accordingly, and both conservation of energy and conservation of charge can be locally violated in such a curved spacetime region.

As we stated, the locally curved spacetime produces either positive time or negative time more predominantly, acting as a source or sink for normal (positive) observer time. The local rate of flow of the observer's time can thus be speeded up or slowed down, depending upon the type of local spacetime curvature utilized.

It follows, then, that standing local gravitational waves can result in localized, stable gradients in the vacuum virtual particle flux, between the "high potential" part of the standing wave and the "low potential" part.

This allows the violation of conservation laws such as charge and energy in the local gravitational gradient, utilizing the localized curvature of vacuum to provide a special source.

For proof that conservation laws need not apply to a curved

spacetime, see A.A.Vlasov and V.I. Denisov, "Einstein's formula for gravitational radiation is not a consequence of the general theory of relativity, **Theoretical and Mathematical Physics,** 53(3), June 1983 **(English translation);** Russian, Dec. 1982, p. 406-418. Quoting:

"This result is a particular consequence of the general assertion to the effect that in general relativity there are no energy-momentum conservation laws for a system consisting of matter and the gravitational field."

See also V.I. Denisov and A.A. Logunov, "New theory of spacetime and gravitation," **Theoretical and Mathematical Physics,** 50(1), July 1982, p. 3-76. This paper (p. 3) points out that:

". . . **the gravitational field in general relativity is completely different from other physical fields and is not a field in the spirit of Faraday and Maxwell."**

A 1984 Soviet paper by senior Russian physicist C. Yu. Bosgoslovsky, "Generalization of Einstein's relativity theory for the anisotropic spacetime," is also very relevant.*

In composing his theory of general relativity, Einstein assumed that the local spacetime of the observer could never be curved, and instead would always be represented by a Lorentz frame (flat spacetime).

This severe assumption had the effect of "saving" the sacrosanct conservation laws, and maintaining the exclusion of electrogravitation.

Since then, Western physicists have raised Einstein's assumption — and the conservation laws — to a dogmatic belief system — in some cases, to near fanaticism.

To see a clear statement of these limiting assumptions imposed on general relativity to provide the severely restricted version taught in almost all Western universities, see Charles W. Misner, Kip S. Thorne and John Archibald Wheeler, **Gravitation,** W.H. Freeman and Co., San Francisco, California, 1973, p. 19-21, 71-72, 367-369.

In other words, Western physicists still use a sort of "special

*See also V.I. Denisov and A.A. Logunov. "The inertial mass defined in general relativity has no physical meaning," preprint p. 0214, Institute of Nuclear Research, USSR Academy of Science, Moscow, 1981.

relativity with distant curved spacetime pertubations," and call it *general* relativity!

The Soviets do not limit themselves to the same restricted general relativity theory as does the West.

Santilli (Ruggero Maria Santilli, **Ethical probe on Einstein's followers in the U.S.A.: An insider's view,** Alpha Publishing, Newtonville, Massachusetts) has documented what essentially amounts to a conspiracy in Western physics to shut out any generalization of Einstein's severely limited relativity.

It is precisely this near-total Western scientific prejudice — along with Heaviside's mutilation of Maxwell's original theory — that has excluded electrogravitation from being developed in the West.

Note also that, by embracing a "locally flat spacetime" assumed to be decreed by the "laws of the universe," in their rigid mindset Western physicists have excluded any possibility of performing simple laboratory experiments in locally curved spacetime.

They do not believe it can be done, so they have never tried.

But let us further address the importance of the negative triplet (electrical charge/energy/time) and its concomitants parity, gravity, and entropy:

Engineering Antigravity

In negative time flow, gravity is a repulsion, not an attraction.

Producing antigravity in an object is simply the production of excess negative time flow in that object.

That is readily achieved by curving local spacetime in the appropriate direction, and forcing the object to produce excess negative energy.

Mass, for example, is just a special form of trapped energy — and trapped energy (potential) is just trapped charge of one kind or another, whether observable or virtual.*

As such, mass represents a "localized potential" in the ambient vacuum, of a certain kind of "trapped energy/time charge."

*Actually, since it is in equilibrium in a dynamic and continual flux, a mass particle is actually a special trapped **rate** of action flow. A defining equation for mass in terms of the rate of action flow was given by the author in **Quiton/Perceptron Physics,** NTIS, 1973. Report AD-763210.

The mass/potential is continually being charged by the vacuum flux, and discharging and emitting charge flux into the vacuum flux. The mass is "in equilibrium" at its fixed potential.

Normal ("positive") mass is simply charged up with positive energy and positive time. And its external electron shells result in it presenting a "negative charge" face to the world.

If we charge up the mass, however, with negative energy and negative time, so that some of its charge potential now is of this second type, the trapped energy will now consist partially of negative energy. In addition, the mass will partially exist in negative time (be charged up partially with negative time).

When excess negative time flow is produced in a mass, the mass begins to be repelled by the earth as well as still being attracted to it in its positive time stream. The net result of the object's fixed attraction and increasing repulsion is that the object begins to lose weight in the earth's gravitational field and gets lighter.

When a sufficient rate of excess negative time flow (sufficient local spacetime curvature) is produced, the mass floats freely.

With additional negative time production rate, it accelerates ("falls") upward.

The rate of excess negative time produced may be controlled very simply by using a "negative time/negative energy" generator and varying the amount of the load applied to the device.

The negative time/negative energy generator can be rigidly affixed to a flying apparatus, serving as a sort of gravitational rocket or gravitational propulsion system.

Of course, the negative energy produced in the propulsion process can be used to light lamps and power electrical loads, as well as host of other things. (Yes, Virginia, it can also be used to generate force fields, power weapon systems, etc.)

Thus one can "eat his cake and have it too"; by using negative energy flow for power, a very practical antigravity spaceship can be developed.

An additional side benefit to the passengers probably exists: they should age at a slower rate when traveling in the vehicle.

As can be seen, since many kinds of VPFs exist in vacuum, the vacuum is filled with (and consists of) many types of "potentials." Overall, this matches very closely the view of general relativity, if we regard the vacuum itself as indefinite "spacetime", where no ordered universal frame with a fixed metric has yet been associated or prescribed.

Curved Spacetime and the Disintegrated Vacuum

From general relativity, additional characteristics of the modern vacuum/spacetime may be inferred or interpreted.

First, we may take a "flat spacetime" to consist of a charged vacuum, such that both the magnitude and structure of the VPF are essentially unchanged from point to point, and the flux of virtual particles and virtual antiparticles are balanced. Equal positive and negative time flows/charges exist.

Note, however, that we can have what casually may appear to be a "flat spacetime" but instead is "warped." This case exists when the magnitude of the overall VPF comprising the vacuum does not change from point to point, but the component structure of the VPF does vary from point to point.

In other words, the overall vacuum potential remains the same from point to point, but two or more individual potentials may canonically vary. Let us further clarify this point by analogy.

Suppose we view the vacuum/ether/spacetime as a special sort of gas, where the "gas" is actually a mixture of many, many gases.

It is a rather peculiar sort of gas; it exists in five or more dimensions and is composed of very strange, fleeting particles which spontaneously are created and destroyed, each arising out of nowhere and returning to nowhere almost immediately.

There is only minuscule (negligible) time overlap (integration) of the existence of these virtual particles in the main.

That is, mostly each virtual particle — along with its associated energy, movement, momentum, charge, and increment of time — exists almost entirely as an individual.

The energies, movements, momenta, charges, and time increments of the individual virtual particles do not integrate or sum to any appreciable degree in vacuum.

Thus, although casually this ether/gas may seem to contain enormous "energy density", momentum density, charge density and time increment density, these are not *integrated* energy density, momentum density, and time density in the normal sense.

Instead, they are the densities of *disintegrated* energy, *disintegrated* momentum, and *disintegrated* time flow.

In scalar electromagnetics, we have called the disintegrated energy of vacuum **anenergy.** This clearly distinguishes that it exists in a fashion altogether different from normal, *integrated* energy with which we are accustomed.

By integrating anenergy, of course, one obtains ordinary energy — but it first requires an integrating agent. The most usual integrating agent/operation is the spin of an observable particle of mass.

Similar considerations apply to momentum and time.

With this more precise interpretation, the vacuum contains enormous anenergy, but essentially no energy. It contains enormous virtual energy, but no observable energy.

Unfortunately, however, orthodox physics does not yet clearly differentiate between the two states of energy, virtual and observable (disintegrated and integrated).

Instead, it continues to loosely utilize the term "energy" for both states, whether integrated or not. Thus it exclusively uses the term "energy density of vacuum." Rigorously, the term should be "anenergy density of vacuum."

Indeed, most physicists are not clearly aware of the distinct difference between the two different states of energy, insofar as the implication of integration or nonintegration.

Regrettably, then, we will continue to utilize the orthodox term, "energy density of vacuum." but the reader should be clearly aware that the vacuum "energy" and vacuum "stress energy density" as such are totally disintegrated.

Separation of Vacuum and Observable States

Because the energy density of vacuum is unintegrated, an integrated physical body — including one's personal body — can exist "in" the vacuum medium of incredible "energy" density, yet observably exist in a medium of zero energy density.

The unintegrated vacuum ether has enormous spatial density of *virtual* energy, but essentially has zero spatial density of *observable* energy.

Note, however, that in our hyperdimensional interpretation of the levels of virtual state, the vacuum spatially does not exist in the normal 3-space of observable matter.*

The vacuum occupies the 4th dimension (time) and all spatial dimensions (hyperdimensions) greater than the third — it occupies all levels of virtual state, but not observable state. It occupies all levels of disintegration, but not the levels of observable integration.

Exchanges occur between normal 3-space and the hyperspatial vacuum, through the common connecting dimension, time.

These exchanges (of virtual particles) are integrated by the spinning observable mass particle into the first quantally excited state — a delta (change) representing a single entrapped quantum — of the 5-space potential represented by the particle and its accumulating VPF. At that time a sharp electromagnetic (fifth dimensional) discharge of the quantum occurs, converting the accumulated 5-G quantum to the ordinary EM quantum of the 4th (time) and 5th (infolded space) dimensions.

This accounts for the so-called "collapse of the wave function", the production of unitary quantum change, and the discretizing of observable change.

We note in passing that time is the only "dimension" where everything can be considered to occupy the same "point" or "interval", but it is discretized and chopped into pieces (disintegrated), quite different in nature from the familiar three spatial dimensions of the observable (integrated) universe.

The dimensional separation (spatially) of the seething vacuum "energy" (anenergy) and the 3-space of normal matter allows a physical body to enormously interact with the vacuum at or near equilibrium at the microscopic level, but maintain its macroscopic form and stability as if no interaction were going on.

Partial Potentials, Curvature, and Warping

At any rate, we view the magnitude of the overall "potential" of this vacuum gas mixture, as the magnitude of the entire "stress

*Here we sharply differ from conventional physics, which hopefully confuses the concepts of vacuum, spacetime (indeterminate), spacetime (determinate), and frame.

ENERGETICS OF A POTENTIAL
Running in Place and Getting Nowhere
"NOWHERE"

Figure 60. A potential is trapped energy. A potential in vacuum is trapped virtual-state "energy" or flux. A natural potential is trapped random energy. An artificial potential is trapped organized energy.

energy" or "pressure" of the mixture — IF AND ONLY IF this stress energy or pressure were somehow integrated.*

As can be seen, we can now look at each of the component gases in the mix as contributing a partial pressure or partial stress energy (an individual component potential) of the vacuum conglomerate.

We may have the overall pressure remain the same, yet canoni-

*Thus it's really the **potential** stress energy density. The vacuum is nothing but potential!

cally change the partial stress energies (individual potentials).

In that case one has an internally twisted or "warped" spacetime.

A warped spacetime may prove quite useful, for example, for direct translation of one type of "energy" into another. In that fashion, one may conceivably obtain radiation energy at the expense of mass, or mass at the expense of radiation energy.

Or one may convert between potentials where one or more of the converted potentials are as yet unknown to orthodox physics.

Kaluza theory, for example, contains many potentials that are as yet unknown and undiscovered in nature. When undue simplifications are made to arbitrarily exclude the unknown potentials, the adapted theory leads to error in its predictions.

This was originally regarded as a great imperfection, and Kaluza theory fell into disfavor for decades. Then as modern particle physicists began to produce fundamental particles of an astounding variety, a Kaluza-Klein theory of 11 or more dimensions was found to very reasonably describe the emerging situation. Once again, then, Kaluza-Klein theory became a moving force among modern theorists.

One may also convert electromagnetic field energy into gravitational field energy, for example, and obtain enormous amplification of gravitational effects.

This is precisely what scalar electromagnetics seeks to do.

Since the electrical field between two electrons is about 10^{42} times as strong as the gravitational force between them, conversion of the EM charge flux into gravitational charge can conceivably yield up to 10^{42} times as much gravitational force as normal, depending upon the efficiency of the conversion process. Even with a process or device that uses electron currents and has an efficiency of only 10^{-22}, gravitational/ inertial gains of 10^{20} are possible.

Note, however, that the levels of vacuum may also be compared to horizontal planes beneath the ocean.

For example, we may take a particular level of vacuum potential, and that level constitutes a sort of included "flat spacetime" of its own. By biasing the potential of a scalar transmitter and receiver to a given level, one may transmit (in either direction) at that level only. Receivers at higher or lower levels will detect nothing.

The immediate application to engineering the nucleus for such things as nonradioactive transmutation of elements, controlled nuclear fusion, electromagnetic healing, and processing nuclear wastes to render them harmless should be apparent.

To recapitulate our analogy, a true "flat spacetime" is a vacuum whose VPF does not essentially vary overall or in each constituent part, between two comparative points.

A "curved spacetime" is a vacuum whose overall VPF varies in overall magnitude, between two comparative points.

A "warped spacetime" is a vacuum whose VPF may or may not vary in overall magnitude between two comparative points, but whose partial VPFs vary their ratios, between the same two points. Note that a vacuum/spacetime can be both warped and curved.

It is stressed that we have not limited the number of dimensions that can be placed on the vacuum to Minkowski's four. We hold the number of dimensions necessary to represent both vacuum and observable matter to be arbitrary, but greater than four.

To unify electromagnetism and gravitation (which is what scalar electromagnetics is about), we must take five dimensions — four spatial and one time — to be the minimum necessary in modeling the unified theory, similar to Kaluza.

We state now a major characteristic: **Vacuum/spacetime consists entirely of potentials, nothing else, and these are hyperspatial a priori.**

The vacuum does not contain observable force fields nor any other *non-potential* entity.

We also state without proof that in scalar EM theory it seems very possible to model the mind and its unification with physical reality, in a fashion subject to experimental verification.

Force and Mass Are Inextricably Intertwined

In foundations of physics, it is well-known that, paradoxically, force and mass can only be defined one in terms of the other.

We may use that paradox for a new interpretation of force and force fields: a force may be interpreted **to consist of** the time rate of changing the "mv" momentum of a mass system or object, instead of **being the cause of** its dp/dt.

That is, we may take the view that

$$\mathbf{F} \equiv \mathbf{dp}/\mathrm{dt} \qquad (4\text{-}14)$$

not just that

$$\mathbf{F} = \mathbf{dp}/\mathrm{dt} \qquad (4\text{-}15)$$

We have previously pointed this out and called it the "strong definition of force."

This immediately suggests the question: If force is an effect and not a cause, what, then, causes force?

Quantum mechanics already provides the answer: A differentiating operator must be applied to (coupled to) potential in order to produce a force field. The most usual "differentiating operator" is an observable spinning charged particle.

A charged particle exposed to the variation of electrostatic scalar potential between two points is exposed to a gradient (flow) in the virtual photon VPF, and hence to a directional "stream" of virtual photons. The observable charged particle couples to that stream. Its spin integrates the unobservable, disintegrated anenergy of the gradient flux into integrated, observable energy of the particle.

With greater integrated "pressure" on one side of the particle than on the other, the observable particle accelerates and translates. This produces or "detects" (and comprises) an electric force between the two points.

Force is the mass particle(s) accelerating, either in time or in mass. Observable force is observable particle(s) accelerating. Virtual force is virtual particle(s) accelerating.

In **Quiton/Perceptron Physics,** I gave a new definition of mass that is consistent with this viewpoint:

$$1 \text{ kg. mass} = 17.053 \times 10^{50} \text{ switches/sec} \qquad (4\text{-}16)$$

where a switch is h/4π), having the units of action/time, or energy. This directly defines mass in terms of energy accumulation, where the energy accumulated is in equilibrium in a differentiated action flow.

Note that "energy" is the time rate of flow of action. Energy can only be accumulated (as a mass or a potential) by possessing two rates of flow of action simultaneously, one in positive time and one in negative time. This is a very deep statement that affects all of physics, but unfortunately it is beyond the scope of this present book.

To return:

The observable electric force field does not exist as such in vacuum. The vacuum and all its constituents are totally virtual. Only the potential ("potential for the electric force field, given a coupled charged observable particle") exists in vacuum, as pointed out by Richard P. Feynman et al, **The Feynman Lectures on Physics,** Addison-Wesley, Reading, Mass., 1964 vol. 2, p. 2.

The Concepts of Zipped and Unzipped Forces

As noted previously, the potential exists as an unintegrated virtual particle flux (VPF). Further, each little moving virtual particle is smeared in length and time, is coupled to finer VPF, and thus may be said to constitute a minute "force vector" while it exists.

Thus, the electrostatic scalar potential is composed of a myriad of little individual "virtual particle force field" vectors.

Since these little virtual vectors are essentially separate and unintegrated, one may say that the electric field is *unzipped* in vacuum. By "unzipped" we mean that the individual virtual particle E-field vectors are unintegrated.

A potential, for example, is composed of unzipped vector fields since it is comprised of unintegrated, virtual vectors.

To be static, the potential must be comprised of a pair (at least one pair) of unzipped vector fields, one in positive time and one in negative time. These unzipped vector fields must in turn be locked together. In this case, the positive time observer sees nothing (vacuum only), until he "observes" or detects. Normal detectors detect (and in so doing, they zip together) only the positive time unzipped component. The negative time (phase conjugate) vector field retraces the positive time field, in Newton's third law. Or, if generating a wave or pulse, it would be seen as a phase conjugate replica which affected the disturbing source.

Let us be very plain. **A "scalar EM potential" is actually two vector fields zipped together: one is in positive time, and the other is in negative time.** Each half is composed of microvectors. A dynamic gradient in this scalar EM potential (i.e., a scalar wave, for example) actually consists of two waves: one is the normal" positive energy/positive time" EM wave, while the other is the phase conjugate replica. When we detect the normal half (with electron detectors), we actually detect the second half with the atomic nuclei. Since it is a phase conjugate, it produces a negative momentum change on the nucleus {since one has p/(-t)} instead of LeSage's positive momentum change. In other words, it produces a drawing (attracting) force on the absorbing nucleus, instead of LeSage's assumed repelling force on it.

That is the entire secret of gravitation. And of electrogravitation. Knowing that, you can easily work out how to apply the necessary engineering to get antigravity.

But to return.

The potential can also be comprised of many unzipped vector fields at once. These may be deterministic (artificial potential) or randomized (natural potential).

The "force field" is disintegrated (unzipped) in vacuum, and integrated (zipped) on, of, and by an observable charged particle. In vacuum, it is always accompanied by its phase conjugate twin. When detection by an observable particle occurs, the spin of the particle acts as the "zipper," producing an observable force (which is actually of the particle accelerating, not "acting independently upon it.")

Vacuum is unzipped; observable mass is zipped.

Any zipped entity exists observably in 3-space; any unzipped entity exists in hyperspace outside 3-space, and is unobservable and virtual to the 3-space observer.

This interpretation is still consistent with the extended quantum mechanical view, where ultimately all observable forces are considered to be generated by absorption and emission of virtual particles by/from an observable particle (mass), at least insofar as what we may observably measure or detect.

Force, Force Field, and EM Waves in Vacuum

In the new interpretation, consistent with the quantum mechanical view, observable force becomes an effect, not a cause.

One may interpret quantum mechanics as stating that **any observable is an effect, since it is assumed to have a virtual state cause.** In the axioms of quantum mechanics, an operator is required for every observable.

The primary causative agents are potentials, not force fields, as is now firmly established in quantum mechanics.

The Aharonov-Bohm (AB) effect is a striking illustration of the primary reality of the potential rather than of the force field.

In the AB effect, potentials may still exist when the force fields are zero, and their interference can still cause real effects. The AB effect has finally become generally accepted by physicists after nearly three decades of controversy.

The immediate result is that, contrary to the outdated view imbedded in classical EM, observable E and B force fields do not exist *as such* in vacuum. This allows a totally new interpretation of the nature of the EM wave in vacuum: It is longitudinal. And actually, it exists in longitudinal pairs: the second is the phase conjugate of the first.

But of course we detect transverse waves with our detectors! However, this has a simple explanation.

Examine, for example, a straight-wire antenna. The spinning conduction electrons are longitudinally constrained, as is well known. The electrons are relatively unrestrained transversely in the wire, but can only "drift" longitudinally down the wire with a speed usually on the order of centimeters per second. The signal potential, however, moves longitudinally down the wire at almost the speed of light.

Obviously it is not the longitudinal movement of conduction electrons that constitutes the "signal", even though classical electromagnetics represents it that way.*

We note that a spinning electron whose movement is longitudi-

*Actually, we do not really know how current/electrons travel down a wire, or even if it does/ they do. See three articles by Chappell Brown in Electronic Engineering Times: "Railgun Research Shoots Holes in Lorentz's Theory," April 6, 1987,p. 49-50; "Anomalies in Electromagnetic Law Spur Debate," Sept. 14, 1987, p. 58; "Electrons and Conduction: Not So Simple After All," Dec. 28, 1987, p. 21-22.

nally restrained, but is unrestrained transversely, may be characterized as a gyroscope. Further, the axis of this gyroscope may be taken as lying in a plane perpendicular to the straight wire conduction path, since the electron is relatively unrestrained transversely.

If now disturbed by a vacuum potential gradient, the gyroscopic electron is free to precess at right angles to the length of the wire. In other words, given a disturbing force, the electron will move transversely, or radially in the cross sectional plane of the wire, because of gyroscopic precession.

Thus, assuming a gyroscopic electron and its longitudinal constraint, we will detect transverse oscillations in the electron gas in the wire, IF AND ONLY IF the incoming disturbance in the vacuum is longitudinal, and IF AND ONLY IF the unzipped vacuum disturbance "couples" to (is zipped by) the gyroscopic conduction electrons.

Two things are certain in our electron-detector model: First, by the nature of a gyroscope, the conduction electrons move (precess) at right angles to the "disturbing force." Second, we only detect the movement of the electrons themselves.

Since we do detect transverse oscillations of the precessing electrons in the straight wire antenna, then it follows that normal electromagnetic waves in vacuum — that is, the component half that interacts with the atom's electron shells and not with its nucleus — are (1) longitudinal, and (2) of such form that they couple to electrons.

Note that Tesla always insisted that electromagnetic waves in vacuum were longitudinal. For example, he called them "electromagnetic sound waves" in the ether. In "Tesla Maps Our Electrical Future," H. Winfield Secor presents Tesla's view of transverse waves in this fashion:

"Tesla upholds the startling theory formulated by him long ago, that the radio transmitters as now used, do not emit Hertz waves, as commonly believed, but waves of sound... He says that a Hertz wave would only be possible in a solid ether, but he has demonstrated already in 1897 that the ether is a gas, which can only transmit waves of sound; that is such as are propagated by alternate compressions and rarefactions of the medium in which transverse waves are absolutely impossible."

In his "The True Wireless," **Electrical Experimenter,** May 1919, Tesla himself further stated:

"The Hertz wave theory of wireless transmission may be kept up for a while, but I do not hesitate to say that in a short time it will be recognized as one of the most remarkable and inexplicable aberrations of the scientific mind which has ever been recorded in history."

It should also be pointed out that our analogy permits the option of making a longitudinal wave in the vacuum in such a fashion that it will not couple to electrons.

In that case a normal"electron gas" conduction detector will not detect the new wave. Such a noncoupling EM longitudinal wave is referred to as a **scalar electromagnetic wave,** where by use of the term "scalar" we call attention to the fact that the vacuum potential is varying, but electron coupling to form vector force fields in an electron gas does not occur.

Since according to general relativity the variation of a potential in vacuum rigorously is a gravitational wave, then the scalar EM wave is a gravitational wave.*

We often say it is an *electrogravitational* wave to call attention to its electromagnetic origin, and to the absence of EM force field "bleeding away" of the 5-space Kaluza-Klein gravitational potential. We will discuss the 5-space G-potential shortly.

The conventional equation

$$\mathbf{E} = -\nabla \varnothing \qquad (4\text{–}17)$$

thus applies in the detecting electron gas, but not in the vacuum. Instead, in the nonmaterial vacuum, rigorously

$$\nabla \varnothing \neq -\mathbf{E} \qquad (4\text{-}18)$$

and this states that a gradient in a vacuum electrostatic scalar

*It is also a very powerful gravitational wave, since for electrons it is some 10^{42} times as strong as "mass attraction" gravity waves.

potential produces an antiphased electric force on and of a particle, on condition that a particle is present. The intent of equation (4-17) should be stated as

$$\nabla \varnothing = -\mathbf{E} \Big|_{\mathbf{cp}} \qquad (4\text{-}19)$$

where the vertical line means "on condition that", and cp means "charged particle" (i.e., "that a charged particle is there.).

Equation (4-19) clearly shows that, in the vacuum, only the organized potential for an **E** field exists due to the quantity $\nabla \varnothing$ essentially as pointed out less strongly by Feynman et al in **The Feynman Lectures on Physics.**

Certainly, in the quantum mechanical interpretation, it is the potential that is real. The force field can only be made from the potential by a differentiating operation.

Since there is nothing in vacuum to perform this differentiating operation observably, one may interpret quantum mechanics as already prohibiting the existence of observable electromagnetic force fields in vacuum, at least in the form prescribed in classical electromagnetics.

Figure 61. A force-field vector is a movement of mass in one direction.

One may regard quantum mechanics — and physics in general — to be incomplete until electromagnetic theory is changed to incorporate the implications of quantum mechanics.

In scalar electromagnetics a new interpretation is taken, and the "overhaul" of electromagnetic theory is in progress.

We accent that scalar electromagnetics is still embryonic. It is at a stage similar to that where electromagnetism was when experimenters were still rubbing glass rods with cat fur and experimenting with little charged pith balls.

Early experiments are enlightening and encouraging; nonetheless, the phenomenology and the myriad of variables are not at all well-understood, even by the experimenters themselves, and certainly not by this author.

Zero-Summed Vector Systems: Shortcoming in Vector Analysis

It has long been pointed out by this author that a fundamental shortcoming exists in classical vector analysis itself when applied to physical systems. Let us briefly look at the construction of the vector mathematics theory, to clarify this shortcoming.

First, an abstract entity called a "vector" is conceptualized. This vector has both direction and magnitude, as contrasted to a "scalar" quantity, which only has magnitude.

Next, an abstract "vector space" is defined; this is a sort of "container" for mathematical objects called vectors, with certain inherent properties of the system specified. In other words, a vector space is an abstract "system" or "space" which can contain objects called "vectors."

Next certain other properties, operations, and entities are defined, one of which is the "zero vector."

Essentially the zero vector is defined by a set of operations; however, one simplified interpretation is "the absence of any vector of finite magnitude." By implication, in the abstract vector theory, all zero-vectors are defined to be identical.*

*Because, by their nature assumed in the concept, they have no internal structures. That is, effectively the zero vector has been too restrictively defined as "the absence of any and all finite vectors." It should be redefined as "the absence of any single vector being present alone." In that case the definition would admit "the presence of multiple translation vectors, where their combined translation action is zero."

In the vector addition operation, a group of finite vectors adds to a single vector called the "resultant."

It is standard practice in abstract vector analysis to replace a system of summation vectors by their resultant, since all appropriate properties of the summation system are retained by the vector resultant, in the abstract mathematical model.

This, however, is only possible because the abstract vector space has no such thing as stress, and a zero-vector has no substructure by definition. In the abstract space, only translation and rotation are possible, *by assumption*

It is also possible for two or more finite vectors to add to a zero resultant, in which case the system is replaced with a zero vector. Note that all further action by the summing vector components is eliminated by this assumption.

Again the appropriate properties of the summation system are retained by the zero resultant, in the abstract mathematical model, only because the *medium* (the abstract vector space) is not subject to stress, translation, rotation, and structuring.

Note however, that in physical systems, one cannot simply

Figure 62. The zero-summed vector system is an engine and an artificial potential.

replace a zero summation system of force vectors with a zero vector and retain all characteristic physical effects caused by the replaced system. The physical medium - including the virtual flux of the vacuum, *is* subject to stress, translation, rotation and structuring.

Physically, the presence of the summing vector component forces creates a stress and a dynamic macroscopic structure in the physical medium in and on which the forces are acting. Therefore the stress of the medium and its structure must be preserved and accounted for, even though a zero vector resultant force exists.

This is particularly true in the vacuum, where internal (in-folded) stresses cause charge and energy conversion between one kind of charge/potential and another.

Maxwell's Theory Was Altered and Curtailed

In fact, Maxwell seems to have been well aware of the electromagnetic stress of the ether and its importance. After all, he believed the ether to be material and mechanical, and developed his theory accordingly.

For example, in his **Treatise on Electricity and Magnetism,** he wrote:

"There are physical quantities of another kind which are related to directions in space, but which are not vectors. Stresses and strains in solid bodies are examples of these, and so are some of the properties of bodies considered in the theory of elasticity and in the theory of double refraction. Quantities of this class require for their definition nine numerical specifications. They are expressed in the language of quaternions by linear and vector functions of a vector."

Maxwell worked out his theory in quaternions since, at the time, the modern form of vector analysis had not been originated by Heaviside and Gibbs.

To recapitulate what we stated earlier: A quaternion consists of a vector part and a scalar part and can readily take into account the stress and strain of the medium. A vector consists only of the vector part, and does not take into account the stress of the medium.

It seems certain that Maxwell knew that the scalar part of the quaternion could be present and vary, even though the vector part was sum-zeroed. Quaternions, however, are devilishly difficult, and even in the time of their founder, Hamilton, few mathematicians and scientists ever mastered them.

Maxwell's theory was transposed (shortly after his death) to its modern vector form by Oliver Heaviside. Many of the characteristics of the scalar part of the quaternion were effectively discarded.

In the remodeling, the "unified" basis was omitted, and electro-

Table 37. MAXWELL'S EQUATIONS

- **INVARIANT**
  - **UNDER CONFORMAL GROUP OF TRANSFORMATIONS**
  - **IN 4-D MINKOWSKI SPACE**
- **GROUP INCLUDES**
  - **TRANSLATIONS**
  - **ROTATIONS**
  - **REFLECTIONS**
  - **INVERSIONS WRT HYPERSPHERES OF M-SPACE**
- **HENCE MAXWELL'S EQUATIONS INCLUDE TRANSFORMATIONS THAT**

  CHANGE INERTIAL FRAMES INTO FRAMES THAT ARE NOT INERTIAL.

  PROVED IN 1910 BY
  H. BATEMAN AND E. CUNNINGHAM

gravitation was accordingly discarded. Heaviside wrote a severely limited subset of Maxwell's theory; he did not by any means capture all of it.*

The new Heaviside vector reinterpretation of EM was far easier to calculate in than Maxwell's quaternions. Many physicists (there were really very few scientists in those days!) immediately loved it.

FitzGerald wrote glowingly of Heaviside's translation (and mutilation!) of Maxwell's theory:

"Since Oliver Heaviside has written, the whole subject of electromagnetism has been remodelled by his work. No future introduction to the subject will be at all final that does not attack the problem from at least a somewhat similar standpoint to the one he puts forward."

Thus it was that Heaviside discarded the basis for scalar electromagnetics and electrogravitation from Maxwell's original work, and the so-called "classical Maxwell Equations" appeared for the first time in their modern vector form in Heaviside's work.

Then in the early 1890's a short but vigorous debate on vectors and vectorial methods occurred, involving eight journals, twelve leading publications, and over 30 scientists. Over half the publications were in the leading British scientific weekly journal **Nature.**

This debate, which Lord Rayleigh characterized by the statement "Behold how these vectorists love one another," together with the far greater difficulty of quaternion methods as compared to Gibbs' and Heaviside's vector analysis, spelled the death knell to the position of quaternions.

After some years, the Gibbs-Heaviside vector theory was firmly entrenched. The quaternion theory of Maxwell was forever modified and limited to the form we know today as "Maxwell's equations."

What really happened was that electrical physicists, faced with the formidable difficulties of quaternions, simply stampeded down the far easier road blazed by Heaviside, bowling over all protests against Heaviside/Maxwell/Hertz theory.

*Specifically, Heaviside wrote the subset of Maxwell's theory where gravity and electromagnetism do not interact and are mutually exclusive.

In Western universities today, no one actually teaches Maxwell's true theory! Instead, Heaviside's curtailed reinterpretation — a severely restricted subset of Maxwell's theory — is taught.

And so that is the EM theory that is learned and applied.

One may rightly argue, therefore, that **Maxwell's theory has only been partially applied in its modern translated form, and the modern form of the Maxwell/Hertz electromagnetic theory is very much incomplete.**

To recover the stress factor in Maxwell's original theory, electromagnetics must take into account the *artificial* potential, which has a deliberately ordered, dynamic, deterministic structure. Scalar electromagnetics takes the patterned stress into account and deliberately uses it. Normal electromagnetics only considers the *natural* potential with randomized VPF structure implicitly assumed.

Scalar Waves and Polarization of the Vacuum

Let us use a simple analogy. This will lead us into the profound implications of the deliberate vacuum polarization and curving of local spacetime that is provided by the vector zero summation (artificial EM potential) method of scalar electromagnetics.*

Visualize two sets of opposing and balanced forces pressing on the sides of a plate.

The forces sum to zero, so the resultant force acting on the plate for translation is zero. Hence the plate does not translate (move away or accelerate).

However, the plate is under internal stress (compression), and is in a quite different condition than when it has no external forces at all acting on it.

Now visualize the forces being applied with rigid rods welded to the sides of the plate, so that the forces may alternately "pull" as well as "push." Let the forces rhythmically vary, alternately "pulling" and "pushing", but always remaining balanced so that their summation for a translation resultant is constantly a zero vector.

The plate never accelerates or moves in translation, but it now contains an internal stress wave which rhythmically varies between compression and tensile stress. Rigorously the plate internally

*Vector **multiplications** that yield a zero vector product are also highly significant.

possesses a scalar stress wave, or a wave of "internal stress in the medium."

Now visualize a similar "plate-like" region of vacuum, with its virtual particle flux, instead of the material plate. Visualize two opposing sets of (unzipped) EM force fields, acting in and on the plate-like region, so that they rhythmically increase and decrease, changing direction also, but always with a zero vector summation.

In this case, there is an unzipped zero resultant EM force field (it is zero, by our assumed conditions), but there is a rhythmic oscillation of the intensity of the vacuum flux (intensity of the vacuum potential) and the vacuum structuring in the region. That is, there is a rhythmic and steady oscillation of the stress energy and structuring of vacuum, and hence of the curvature of spacetime, in the plate-like region.

Rigorously, this oscillation — which we call a **scalar electromagnetic wave** — is a gravitational wave, since the local curvature of spacetime is being oscillated.

Further, it differs from a "natural" gravitational wave in several respects:

1. It has a deterministic pattern or substructure,

2. It patterns or "polarizes" the vacuum,

3. It constitutes local curvature of spacetime, and hence localized general relativity - something which ordinary general relativity assumes cannot be accomplished,

4. It deterministically engineers the virtual state and local spacetime,

5. Since it is achieved by converting EM field energy into artificial G-field energy, one can expect tremendous gains of gravitational and inertial effects in and around electrical circuits utilizing such fields precisely,

6. It affects the Schroedinger wave and the probabilities of the

states being propagated forward by the Schroedinger wave. **With the scalar EM wave, one can thus deterministically engineer the emergence of quantum change, and violate one of the fundamental assumptions of quantum mechanics, that of the totally statistical nature of quantum change,**

7. The scalar wave can accomplish direct and localized change of the rate of flow of time (even to its reversal) and variation of mass and inertia, without concomitant translation of matter,

8. By locally curving and patterning vacuum spacetime, a stabilized standing scalar EM wave can provide macroscopic violation of the conservation laws, which rigorously depend upon a locally flat spacetime (Lorentz frame),

9. Since the components in the zero summation may be EM waves, and may be "locked together" and broadcast to a great distance and interfered there, effects at great macroscopic distances may be achieved, in violation of present assumptions of physics, and

10. Since excess negative time flow may be locally produced, antigravity, negative energy, and negentropy may be locally produced.

These are the startling implications inherent in correcting classical electromagnetics' improper treatment of zero-summed EM force vector systems in vacuum.*

By classically replacing the force vectors in a zero EM force field summation with a zero vector and discarding the components, one is totally discarding the fact that such a patterned system of oppositive forces forms a deterministically patterned stress in the vacuum medium.

By this innocuous error, classical EM discards electrogravitation, and avoids unification of gravitation and electromagnetics. It

*And its zero - multiplied force vector systems as well.

also avoids direct engineering of gravitation, vacuum/spacetime, inertia, rate of time flow, free energy, and quantum change.

Generations of Western physicists and electrical engineers have acquired a mindset in only one aspect of the vastly expanded electromagnetics actually available.

Vector Zero Systems and the Kaluza-Klein Approach

Prior to 1921, Theodor Kaluza applied Einstein's new general relativity to five dimensions.

He produced a unified theory of electromagnetism and gravitation.

In Kaluza's theory, the ordinary 4-dimensional gravitational field and the electromagnetic field are but two different aspects of a single more fundamental field: the 5-dimensional gravitational field.

Kaluza's theory was published in 1921, on the personal recommendation of Albert Einstein, who had had Kaluza's paper for two years.

In Kaluza's model, electromagnetics is the 5th dimensional aspect of the 5-d G-field, while the ordinary 4-d G-field is the intersection of the 5-d G-field with our ordinary world.

Five years after Kaluza's epochal paper, Oskar Klein explained where the extra space dimension — the fifth dimension — was. He modified it as "wrapped around" each point in our ordinary 3-space.

In the Kaluza-Klein model, then, an electromagnetic wave— which moves spatially only in the fifth dimension — does not move through our 3-space at all. Instead, on its trajectory it "flows around" each point in our 3-space along its path.

Using Kaluza's model, we may regard the EM field as the normal "bleed-off" or escape of the 5-dimensional gravitational potential in the 5th dimension.

Any gradient in a potential represents a bleed-off of the potential from the high point to the low point. The way to prevent effective bleed-off of a potential at a point is to add an equal amount of bleed-in! The bleed-out and the bleed-in at the point then become balanced, so that an equilibrium state exists in the potential.

By this mean, the magnitude of the potential can be fixed by the two opposing bleed processes in equilibrium.

Table 38. KALUZA GEOMETRY

- **THEORDOR KALUZA, POLISH PHYSICIST**
- **UNIFIED THEORY OF ELECTROMAGNETICS AND GRAVITY [1921]**
  - **5 - DIMENSIONAL SPACETIME**
  - **5 - DIMENSIONAL GRAVITY FIELD**
  - **ELECTROMAGNETISM IS THAT PART THAT OPERATES IN THE FIFTH DIMENSION**

Table 39. 5-D G-FIELD BLEED-OFF [KALUZA 5-D THEORY]

- **FAR EASIER TO BLEED-OFF AS ORDINARY EM FIELD**
- **VERY DIFFICULT TO BLEED-OFF AS ORDINARY 4-D G-FIELD**
- **E.G., BETWEEN TWO ELECTRONS:**

$$\frac{\mathrm{EM}}{\mathrm{G(4)}} \approx \text{[illegible]}$$

- **BETWEEN TWO PROTONS:**

$$\frac{\mathrm{EM}}{\mathrm{G(4)}} \approx \text{[illegible]}$$

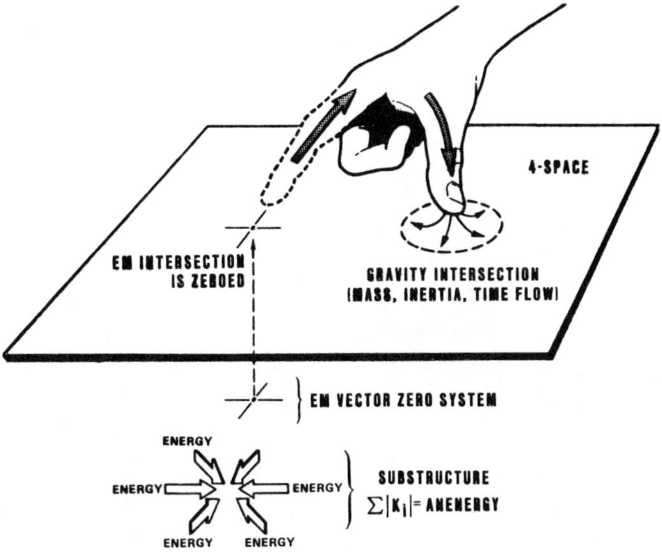

Figure 63. An analogy for how scalar electromagnetics can engineer Kaluza-Klein unified field theory.

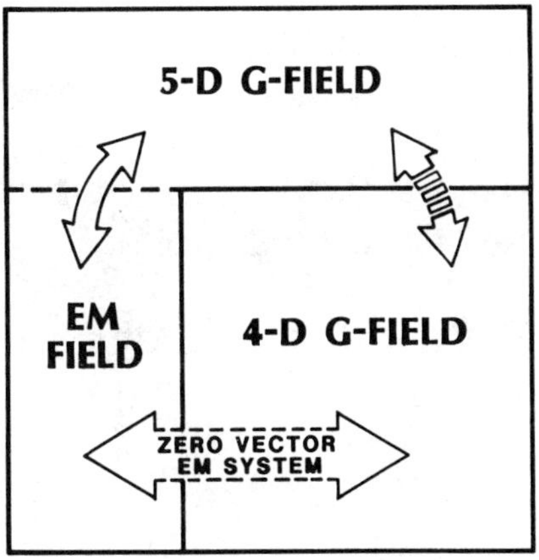

Figure 64. The zero-vector system can engineer Kaluza-Klein theory.

WHERE DID THE EXTRA DIMENSION GO?

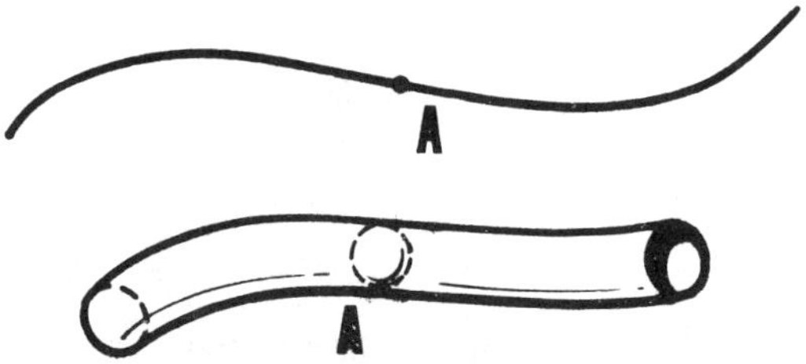

- **FROM A DISTANCE, A HOSE-PIPE LOOKS LIKE A WIGGLY LINE**

- **WHAT WE REGARD AS A POINT IN 3-SPACE IS REALLY A TINY CIRCLE AROUND ANOTHER DIMENSION OF SPACE**

Figure 65. The basic idea of Klein's explanation of where the extra dimension is.

Table 40. PHYSICAL REALITY IS ELEVEN DIMENSIONAL

- **IN THE KALUZA-KLEIN THEORY THE GAUGE FIELD SYMMETRIES BECOME CONCRETE**

- **THEY ARE THE GEOMETRICAL SYMMETRIES ASSOCIATED WITH THE EXTRA SPACE DIMENSIONS**

- **AN 11-SPACE IS REQUIRED BY THE GRAND UNIFIED FORCE THEORY**

PAUL DAVIES, SUPERFORCE,
1984, P. 160-161

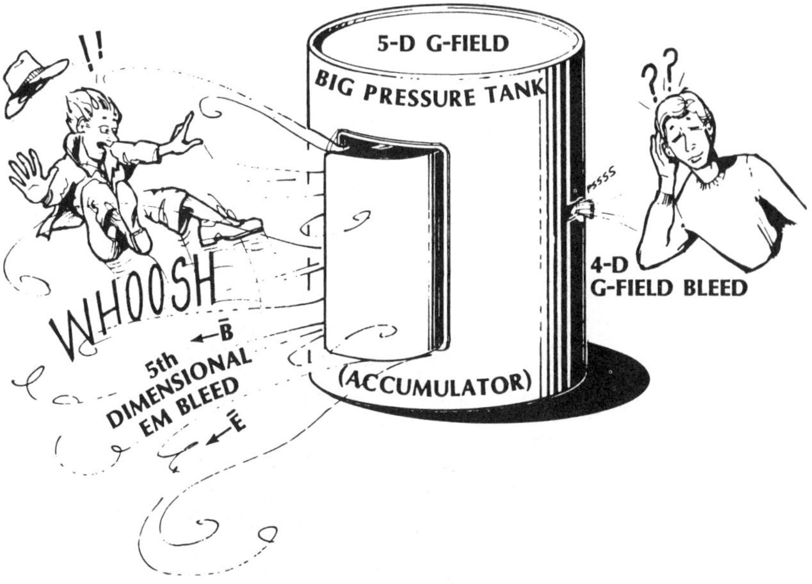

Figure 66. Normal EM bleeds off G-field.

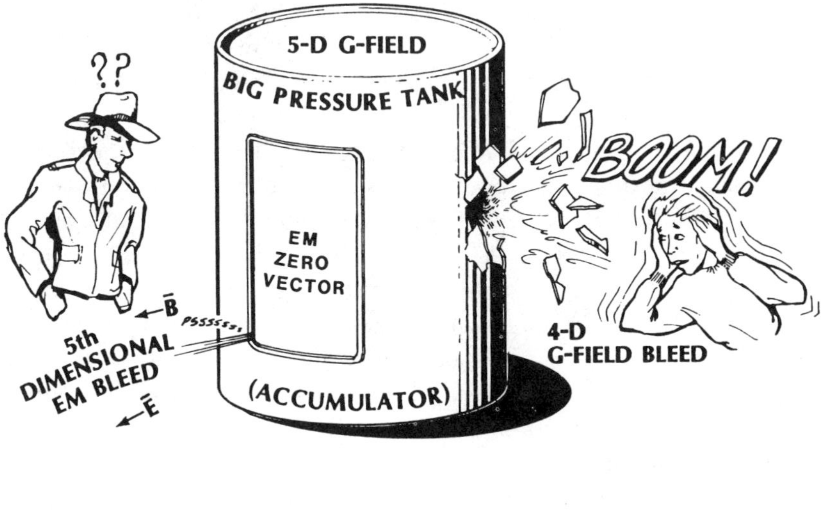

Figure 67. Scalar EM forces 4-dimensional gravitational field.

Note that this positively establishes that two or more zero-summed EM force field gradients produce and stabilize an artificial potential.

Usually, very little bleed-off of the 5-potential occurs in our normal 3-space. When the 5-space G-field is bled off on electrons, e.g., the resulting 5th dimensional **E**-field bleed-off is on the order of 10^{42} times as much as the 3-space **G**-field bleed-off.

This accounts for the enormous magnitude of the ratio of the electrical force between two electrons to the gravitational force between them.

Even when the 5-space G-potential is bled-off on and against the greater inertia of much more massive protons, its 5th dimensional **E**-field bleed-off is still on the order of 10^{36} or so times as much as the 3-space bleed-off.

Note that if we can stop the acceleration of the charged particles, bleed-off of the 5-space G-potential as EM force field cannot occur, and instead all of it must bleed-off as 3-space G-force field. This 3-G bleed-off normally occurs only minimally in electromagnetics, even for so-called "static" charges. This can be seen as follows:

When one charges a conductor such as a large metal sphere, for example, the electrons are unconstrained on the surface of the sphere. They are in constant agitation and motion on the surface, thus constantly bleeding-off the 5-space potential as myriads of squirming little **E**-fields. Only a very little is bled off as 3-dimensional G-field.

On the other hand, when one charges a dielectric, the electrons cannot be in as much agitation movement as they are on a conducting surface. Hence slightly more of the 5-dimensional G-potential is bled off as 3-dimensional **G**-field.

Therefore, charged conductors and charged dielectrics should exhibit slightly different gravitational and inertial properties when exposed to a gravity field potential difference. Highly charged capacitors, for example, should exhibit a small but detectable unidirectional thrust in vacuum. Apparently they do, as exhibited by the Biefield-Brown effect.

In addition, different materials should exhibit slightly different fall rates gravitationally. Again there is some evidence that they do, as exhibited by the Eotvos experiments in a modern reinterpretation by Fischbach et al.*

Electrogravitation Amplification Factor

If the movement of two free electrons could be entirely stopped, all EM bleed-off of the 5-d G-potential between them would be effectively zeroed or blocked. Then the 5-d G-potential would be forced to totally bleed-off into ordinary 3-d **G**-field.

For two electrons, this could increase the gravitational force between them by a factor of 10^{42}, if the EM bleed were perfectly blocked.

Such perfect blockage of the 5th dimensional EM bleedoff cannot be accomplished in practice. Normally, with the increase in potential caused by zero-summing, agitating electrons in a statically charged object agitate more intensely, moving and squirming in local, erratic constraints.

However, conversion efficiencies on the order of 10^{10} or even 10^{20} appear to be achievable in ordinary circuitry. In that case, gravito-inertial amplification gains of up to 10^{22} or even 10^{32} appear to be achievable. Gains of 10^{10} or more appear to be fairly readily achievable.

Time delay in producing the gravito-inertial effects may be experienced, however, because mass (nuclei) acts as a capacitance to incident scalar waves, exhibiting capacitive charging and discharging "time constants" when charging scalarly for a particular effect or to a particular pattern.

In these achievable amplification ranges, a single milliwatt of electrical power can control enormously powerful local gravitational and inertial effects, once the scalar EM charge is built up in the nuclei of the target material.

Excessive and frustrating "fiddling time" with the circuits is usually required, however, due to the charging "time constant" effect, the general lack of adequate measuring instruments, and the great uncertainty as to the phenomenology and major variables involved.**

*Ephraim Fischback et al, "Reanalysis of the Eotvos experiment," Phy. Rev. Lett., 56(1), Jan, 1986, p. 3-6.

**A series of scalar EM instruments, however, is being developed by Bedini, Schnur, Golden, and perhaps even Hewlett-Packard.

However, with persistence, in rather ordinary EM circuits and devices, the use of "summation to zero-vector" techniques and "multiplication to yield a zero-vector" techniques can lower the EM bleed-off of the 5-potential sufficiently to allow substantial local gravitational/inertial effects. By beaming and wave interference, effects at a distance can be achieved.

When gravito-inertial amplification of many orders of magnitude are involved, the assumption in ordinary general relativity of a local Lorentz frame (local special relativity, with local conservation laws applying) is readily violated.

Now one may have local general relativity, with concomitant violation of conservation laws, and local broken symmetry on a macroscopic scale.

Soviet papers already strongly point out that such unrestricted general relativity allows the violation of all conservation laws.

In the Soviet Union, scalar electromagnetics is called *energetics.*

Comparison of EM Concepts

Table 41 shows a comparison between three concepts of electromagnetics: classical, quantum mechanical, and scalar electromagnetic views.

As can be seen, scalar EM re-introduces Maxwell's original potential for electrogravitational variation and structuring of the stress energy density of vacuum spacetime. It applies Kaluza-Klein 5-dimensional unified theory in an engineering fashion.

It deliberately utilizes phase conjugation as a tool to achieve startling negative time/negative energy capabilities and results, including "free" energy and antigravity.

With scalar EM, it should be possible to overcome or circumvent most of the severely limiting assumptions of present physics and engineering.

The great conservation laws yield to direct manipulation and violation. The previously inviolate statistical structure of quantum change becomes deterministic and engineerable.

General relativity becomes an experimental scientific discipline in the laboratory, instead of a complex description of effects only observable in distant, massively curved regions such as on the surface of a star or near a black hole.

God does not play dice with the universe after all, just as Einstein suspected.

The Aharonov-Bohm Effect

In 1959, Y. Aharonov and David Bohm published a fundamental paper in **Physical Review** which pointed out the quantum mechanical implications of potentials.

The seminal paper is Y. Aharonov and D. Bohm, "Significance of Electromagnetic Potentials in the Quantum Theory," **Physical Review,** Second Series, 115 (3), Aug. 1, 1959, p. 458-491.

In classical electromagnetics, the potentials had largely been regarded as mathematical conveniences, having no real effects.

Table 41. Comparison of EM Concepts

CHARACTERISTIC	THEORY		
	CLASSICAL EM	QM VIEW	SCALAR EM (ARTIFICIAL ϕ)
VACUUM SPACETIME	LINEAR, NO CHARGE	LINEAR, CHARGED (VIRTUAL) STATISTICALLY	NONLINEAR, CHARGED (VIRTUAL) W/DETERMINISTIC COMPONENTS
VIRTUAL SUBSTRUCTURE	NONE (FLUID EQUATIONS)	YES, STATISTICAL	YES, STATISTICAL, DETERMINISTICALLY WEIGHTED.
FORCE, IN VACUUM?	CAUSE, YES	EFFECT, YES	EFFECT, NO
ZERO FORCE FIELDS	NO EFFECT	BOHM–AHARONOV EFFECTS	SUBSTRUCTURE EFFECTS, ENGINEERABLE
POTENTIALS	FICTICIOUS	REAL, PRIMARY, STATISTICAL SUBSTRUCTURES.	REAL, PRIMARY, DETERMINISTIC SUBSTRUCTURES.
CAUSATIVE AGENT	FORCE FIELDS	POTENTIALS	POTENTIALS AND INFOLDED FIELDS OF SUBSTRUCTURES
CHARGE	WITH MASS	WITH MASS	MASSLESS
RELATIVISTIC EFFECTS DUE TO	VELOCITY	VELOCITY, INTERFERING POTENTIALS	INTERFERING POTENTIALS
HIDDEN VARIABLES	NO	STATISTICAL, NEGLIGIBLE	DETERMINISTIC, MAJOR ROLE.
VECTOR THEORY APPLIED TO EM	OKAY	OKAY	REQUIRES REVISION
VACUUM EM WAVE	TRANSVERSE	TRANSVERSE	LONGITUDINAL W/SWIRLS
ENERGY/MASS CONSERVATION	YES	YES	NOT NECESSARILY. ANENERGY CONSERVED
CHARGE CONSERVATION	YES	YES	NOT NECESSARILY.
ACTION AT A DISTANCE	NO	NO, EXCEPT BOHM–AHARONOV EFFECTS	YES, SCALAR INTERFEROMETRY
SCALAR (ZERO-VECTOR) RESONANCE	NO	NO	YES
INERTIA IS ELECTRICAL	NO	NO	YES
GRAVITY IS ELECTRICAL	NO	NO	YES
MASS IS ELECTRICAL	NO	NO	YES
ELECTRO-GRAVITATIONAL WAVES?	NO	NO	YES
PRIMARILY INTERACT W/ (IN ATOM)	ELECTRONS	ELECTRONS	NUCLEONS
SPACETIME DIMENSIONS	4	4	≥ 5
GEOMETRY	MINKOWSKI	PRIMARILY MINKOWSKI	KALUZA–KLEIN
ZERO-SUMMED VECTORS REPLACED BY	ZERO VECTOR	ZERO VECTOR	ARTIFICIAL POTENTIAL
RELATIVITY ASPECTS: LOCAL, DISTANT	SPECIAL, SPECIAL	SPECIAL, MAY BE GENERAL	GENERAL, GENERAL
CAN AFFECT SCHROEDINGER EQUATION	NO	NO	YES. CAN ENGINEER IT.

Table 42. THE AHARONOV - BOHM EFFECT

- **IN FIELD-FREE REGIONS**
    - **E - FIELD IS ZERO**
    - **B - FIELD IS ZERO**
- **POTENTIALS STILL EXIST**
    - **CAUSE REAL EFFECTS**
    - **INTERFERENCE IS KEY**
    - **CONTAIN SUM-ZEROED SUBSTRUCTURE**
- **DOES NOT FOLLOW FROM**
    - **MECHANICS**
    - **CLASSICAL ELECTROMAGNETICS**

However, according to quantum mechanics, the potentials are the real entities, while the electromagnetic force fields are just effects derived from the potentials by imposed operations on them.

Aharonov and Bohm showed that, even in the absence of the EM force fields, the potentials may still exist and interfere to produce real effects in physical systems. They suggested experiments to prove these predictions.

Interference of the potentials is the key mechanism producing real effects in charged particle systems, even in the presence of zero E-field and zero B-field.

Unfortunately, Aharonov and Bohm did not address this issue of zero-summed systems of EM force fields as one way of producing artificial potentials having unique interference characteristics.

That is, by implication they did not consider the deterministically substructured "artificial" potential, but only the randomly structured "natural" potential.

At any rate the "AB effect," as it came to be called, was rather hotly debated and fiercely resisted over the years. Steadily, more and more experiments were added, validating the AB effect. Finally, in 1986 it came to be generally accepted as proven to any but the most die-hard skeptic.

The AB principle represents a violation of both classical mechanics and classical electromagnetics. It is absolutely required, however, by quantum mechanics. And experiments have now established it as proven beyond question.

The potential, then, can be a free and independent field. Further, it can directly act on charged particle systems, even when classical electromagnetics does not recognize the interaction.

Curl-Free Magnetic Vector Potential (A-Field)

As an example, in classical EM the vector magnetic potential (the **A**-field) had been defined as a mathematical convenience by the equation

$$\nabla \times \mathbf{A} = \mathbf{B} \qquad (4\text{-}20)$$

But if the potentials are real, then conceivably the A field can be loosed from its enchainment to the ∇x operator. In that case, it

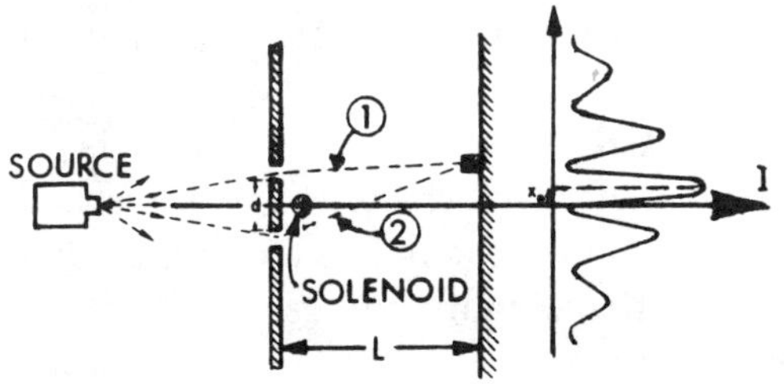

A – FIELD CAN INFLUENCE THE MOTION OF ELECTRONS'.

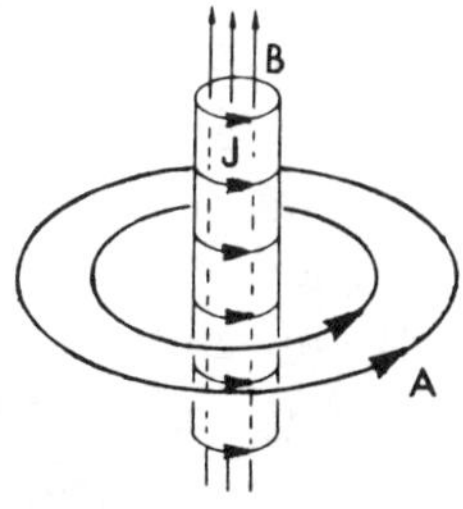

MAGNETIC FIELD AND VECTOR POTENTIAL OF A LONG SOLENOID.

THE FEYNMAN LECTURES ON PHYSICS, VOLUME II

Figure 68. The curl-free A-field. The magnetic vector potential (A-field) may be freed from its attachment to the magnetic field (B-field) and electric field (E-field). It can interfere at a distance to cause real effects. From it, either E-field or B-field, or both, can be made at a distance.

becomes a free, new, and independent field of nature with potentially unique characteristics.

For instance, its defining equation shows that magnetic force field can be made from it, and the rightmost term of the equation

$$\mathbf{E} = -\nabla Ø - d\mathbf{A}/dt \qquad (4\text{-}21)$$

shows that its time rate of change makes an electrical field.

Let us explain this in simpler terms, and somewhat more precisely than conventional theory. We will use the Kaluza unified G-EM interpretation and electron flow in our explanation.

In the **A**-field, we have a certain kind of 5-dimensional G-potential which can bleed-off as EM force fields in two ways: (1) in a swirl fashion, where the vortex producing the swirl moves parallel to electron movement, and the swirling is a torque or spin, and (2) in a linear fashion, where the time rate of change of the **A**-potential produces a linear **E**-field on the electrons.

The first bleed-off as given by equation (4-20) constitutes the magnetic **B**-field, and the second bleed-off as given by the rightmost term of equation (4-21) creates a component of the overall electrical **E**-field. Bleed off of the electrostatic scalar potential produces the other component of the **E**-field.

Now in general relativity (GR) theory, "the" G-potential is just a conglomerate of many things, each of which has the characteristic of curving spacetime. "The" gravitational field is not a single thing at all, but is composed of a collection of many things.

Thus if we realize that both the electrostatic scalar potential (Ø-field) and the magnetic vector potential (**A**-field) are components of the 5-d G-potential, then we see immediately that bleed-off of these two components of the 5-d G-potential creates all normal EM fields.

It follows that, if we produce a zero-vector summation of the two or more EM bleed-offs, we are actually "putting as much back in" to the 5-d G-potential through its **A** and Ø components as we are taking out electromagnetically.

In that case, the 5-potential is in a state of equilibrium with respect to EM bleed-off in the fifth dimension. It is now forced to bleed-off in the only other way it can: as ordinary 3-dimensional gravitational field. Thus by vector-zeroing EM force fields, we turn EM field energy into G-field energy and vice versa, via the intermediary of the 5-potential.

At any rate, soon after publication of the Aharonov-Bohm paper, experiments showed that, if the magnetic field is trapped inside a long solenoid, a phase shift still is induced in the two-slit electron experiment, even though — classically — no contact of the enclosed magnetic field and the moving electrons occurs. This phase shift is explained by the fact that the freed **A**-field exists outside the trapping solenoid, even though the **B**-field does not. Consequently, interaction of this curl-free **A**-field with the electrons produces a phase shift of the QM interference detection pattern.

This proves that curl-free **A**-field is real and causes physical effects.

It also proves that a form of "action at a distance" is real, just as required by quantum mechanics.

Years ago, Frank Golden and this author — together with Dr. William Tiller — experimented with "free **A**-field" devices. Golden went on to develop prototype transmitters and receivers and a prototype underwater communication system.

Since that time, Gelinas has patented several curl-free magnetic vector potential (free **A**-field) devices. See U. S. patents numbers 4, 447,779, May 8, 1984; 4, 429, 288, Jan. 31, 1984; 4, 429, 280, Jan. 31, 1984; and 4, 432, 098, Feb. 14, 1984. These patents are assigned to Honeywell.

Fractional Charges, Magnetic Monopoles, and Magnetic Currents

Fifteen years ago, a most distinguished gathering of physicists occurred in Trieste, Italy to review the physicist's conception of nature and how it developed. Seven Nobel Laureates were in the prestigious audience. The keynote address, appropriately, was given by P.A.M. Dirac, and — appropriately — was entitled "Development of the Physicist's Conception of Nature."

Dirac called attention to the possibility of fractional charges, and unexpectedly presented some of the data from experiments done long before by Felix Ehrenhaft.

Years earlier Felix Ehrenhaft, former director of the Physical

Institute at the University of Vienna, had reported a number of experiments where — purportedly — he easily obtained fractional electrical charges.

Whereas Millikan had used liquid oil drops in his experiments to determine the charge of the electron, Ehrenhaft used little solid, red selenium oxide spheres. Not only could Ehrenhaft get a fractional charge, but he could actually vary the size of the fraction by varying the size of the spheres.

(Knowing what has been discovered in the last two decades on the complex bond structuring of water and liquid hydrocarbons, one might very well suspect that a solid — which has one less degree of freedom than a liquid — could possibly yield a very different experimental condition from a liquid, from first principles. However, no one seems to have noted that, or taken it into account.)

(Also, Ehrenhaft's results were replicated by other researchers who used his experimental methods. They published scientific papers, but that made not a whit to the scientific community, which simply rejected the experimental evidence.).

Dirac pointed out that Millikan himself, in his oil drop experiments that established the charge of the electron, reported one anomalous experiment which yielded a fractional charge. He discarded the results of that experiment.

Ending his speech, Dirac stated that it all made him wonder if perhaps Millikan did have a fractional charge in that one experiment after all. And well he might wonder. Ehrenhaft — almost unknown now to the present generation of physicists — may have found not only fractional electrical charges, but the magic magnetic monopoles as well.

Over and over, Ehrenhaft reported the results of experiments which disagreed with the notions of magnetic theory at the time.

Again, some of these experiments were replicated, and reported by those researchers replicating them.

It didn't make any difference at all.

Now, finding a magnetic monopole — and the accompanying magnetic charge current — would be most satisfying to many theorists. That would make the equations of magnetics quite "balanced" with respect to electricity.

However, no one —at least whose results have been accepted - —

has yet found a magnetic monopole or magnetic current.

Stanford researchers have perhaps come closest, and even reported the results of one exciting experiment that found the magnetic monopole. However, the team has consistently failed to be able to replicate those results. And in science, "no replication, no acceptance" is necessarily the dictum.

In a moment we will address a possible cause for this failure to find the magnetic monopole and magnetic charge current.

Some Ehrenhaft Experiments

Let's look at some simple, rather informal experiments that Ehrenhaft showed. We call attention to Alden P. Armagnac's excellent article , "Magic with magnetism," in **Popular Science Magazine,** June 1944, p. 130-133, 222, 226. In the first experiment, Ehrenhaft seems to have dissociated water with a permanent magnet.

First, Ehrenhaft seals two rods of pure iron, in holes through opposite sides of the U in a U-shaped glass tube filled with water. Then he uses the two rods — which protrude through the tube into the water — as the pole pieces of a horseshoe magnet — either an electromagnet or a permanent magnet. Dilute sulfuric acid — one percent by volume — is in the water, to give it a very slight acidity.

Bubbles of gas rise up through the twin vertical columns of water, and are collected and analyzed. Most of the gas is hydrogen, as is to be expected from common chemical interaction of the iron rods with the very dilute sulfuric acid. However, some of the gas — ranging from two to twelve percent — is oxygen, and most of the oxygen is produced at the north pole of the magnet.

The pole pieces may be short-circuited with wire, to insure they are at the same electrical potential and prevent any electrical dissociation of the water.

Without the magnet, all the gas liberated is hydrogen, as is to be expected. No oxygen at all is produced.

And another very interesting phenomenon occurs. A strong permanent magnet of the Alnico type gradually loses a marked fraction of its strength — say, 10% in 24 hours. It appears that the energy dissociates water — very similar to electrical energy from a battery draining away when electric current is used to dissociate water.

The real question is: Is this experiment a demonstration of magnetic current?

If it is, then the textbooks are wrong, and there's another constituency in magnetism that has not been taken into account. Further, if it proves magnetic current exists, it has also proven magnetic charge — the magnetic monopole — exists.

If it is not a demonstration of magnetic current, then what is it? Why don't you get any oxygen liberated when the magnetism is removed? What causes the magnet to discharge its magnetic strength?

These serious questions do not appear to have ever been resolved.

In all fairness, however, we must warn the reader that other factors in the water can very seriously affect the outcome of this

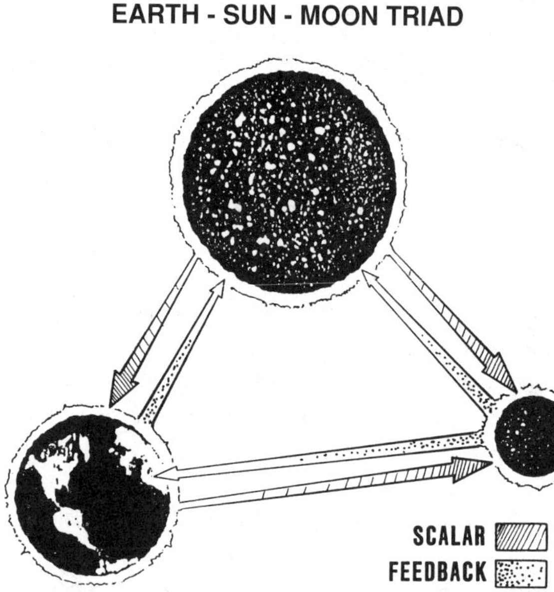

Figure 69. Earth, sun, and moon are locked into a triad system. They exchange both normal energy and phase-conjugate energy. The phase-conjugate energy (negative energy, negative time) streams affect all "subtle-energy" earth experiments.

experiment. As we now know, the bonding structure of water is incredibly adaptive. Every bit of water you examine, for example, is absolutely unique in many respects. And in other respects, it's a sort of "single giant molecule."

Be forewarned also that subtle experiments with water are affected by just about everything under the sun. Including the sun!

Ehrenhaft himself was quite embarrassed when this "decomposition of water" failed to be 100% repeatable. It can be done — but you may have to work at it a bit. The best water for this experiment is the most natural, pure ground water you can obtain.

At any rate, it may be that these experiments of Ehrenhaft's are related to the old notion of "watergas" — the changing of water in some fashion so that, as it enters an internal combustion chamber, it decomposes into hydrogen and oxygen, and is ignited by the spark and burns as a fuel. In the typical watergas case, the experimenter has a "green powder" which, when added to water, will allow it to be burned as a fuel when it is used in an ordinary engine. Such a capability, for example, seems to have been exhibited at least once, to the U.S. Navy, by an unorthodox experimenter named Anderson.

Of course, if fractional charges exist and can be controlled (and Ehrenhaft's experiments certainly seem to confirm this), then it is conceivable that a material could be found that would do the "green powder" function. That is, if the bonding electron that bonds hydrogen and oxygen in water were replaced by a fractional charge, the "fractionated water molecule" could just barely be holding together as a liquid. A strong hydroshock — such as going through the jet nozzles in a carburetor — could then cause many of these molecules to break apart, effectively dissociating the water.

A possibly related phenomenon was reported by Le Bon in his **Evolution of Matter.** The experiment was to hold a piece of ordinary aluminum under the surface of mercury in a container for a period of time. Then the piece of aluminum is taken out and thrown into a container of water, where it violently dissociates the water. At least one colleague was able to replicate this experiment by holding the aluminum beneath the mercury for 36 hours.

These Ehrenhaft experiments may also be related to the extensive use in the Soviet Union (and to some extent, in the U.S.) of magnetic treatment of water pipes so that boilers do not develop so much hard precipitate. Magnetic treatment of water, for example, can rigorously be shown to alter some of a liquid's properties.

Ament, for example, in numerous well-controlled repetitions has clearly shown an increase in auto gas mileage by using a strong magnetic apparatus on the fuel line. Best results are obtained by a magnet which only has one polarity facing the fuel line, and using three stages where the middle polarity is reversed. The effect of this apparatus is definitely scalar EM (gravitational) and expressed in the atomic nuclei in the molecules of the fuel flowing through the line.

Again, the Ehrenhaft experiments may be related to the strange results of Viktor Schauberger, who obtained motive results with water and natural energy that have not been duplicated before or since, so far as anyone can tell.

Schauberger utilized "implosive" energy rather than "explosive" energy — strongly suggesting he was using the negative time aspects of energy, hence negentropy. Schauberger also conceptualized this energy in a spiral form — and that is precisely the type of motion Ehrenhaft observed in many of his bubble experiments. That such negative time/negative energy is "natural" energy will be apparent from our next chapter, where we point out that all living things must use negative time/negative energy processes if they are to defeat the inexorable law of entropy — the increasing disorder of a system as its positive flow of time progresses.

Note, for example, that a system that is 20% efficient in positive time would be 500% efficient in negative time.

Let's look at another of Ehrenhaft's magnetic experiments.

Taking the air gap between two very flat, very parallel pole pieces of sufficient width, one obtains a very accurately-parallel, uniform magnetic field in between them. Now suppose you place some very small particles of material — both magnetic and nonmagnetic — in the air gap.

Common sense assures us that, if closer to the south pole, for example, one of the little magnetic particles will be attracted by the preponderance of south polarity. That is, a little magnetic north pole will be induced on the side of the particle nearest the south polepiece, and a little south pole will be induced on the particle on the side away from the south polepiece. The little particle will then be attracted to the south polepiece.

Again, common sense assures us that, if closer to the north pole, the situation is reversed and the little particle is attracted to the north polepiece.

Well, that isn't quite what happens. Some move to the south polepiece, and some move to the north polepiece. And it seems to vary by the type of material the little particle is comprised of.

Now try another experiment. Let's make a permanent magnet motor. Understand, this one is not quite "for free," for we'll consume "fuel" — the strength of the magnet and the acidified water solution.

In this one, we use a glass cylindrical cell, with one vertical iron rod at the top and another at the bottom, and the rods serving as the pole pieces of a giant horseshoe magnet. (Or, for ease you can use an electromagnet). The cell is filled with the same acidified solution as before.

Without the magnet, hydrogen bubbles can be seen rising as before.

Now put on the magnet (or turn on the switch). Voila! the situation with the bubbles changes drastically. A spectacular miniature merry-go-round — a "whirligig" — of bubbles forms between the faces of the poles and parallel to them.

Add some copper particles to the solution. The particles will rotate in the same plane, but in opposite directions from the bubbles. The stronger the magnetic field, the faster the particles and bubbles will contrarotate.

If the magnetic field is reversed, the rotation of both the bubbles and the copper particles is reversed.

Only a few months after this was reported in **Popular Science Magazine,** Brother Gabriel Kane of Manhattan College and Charles B. Reynolds of the Federal Communication Commission confirmed Dr. Ehrenhaft's discovery of magnetic currents.

They made a drop of copper sulfate solution spin between the polepieces of a permanent magnet. They also made an interposed microscope cover glass spin from the rotation of the copper sulfate.

It was hinted they were heading toward power machinery. If so, nothing else was heard — possibly because they never solved the problem of consuming the magnet's strength and the acidified solution.

Bill Mueller, the present inventor of a free-energy device, has also demonstrated the spinning of a piece of plastic in a magnetic field.

After WWII, Dr. Ehrenhaft returned to his post in Vienna, published later work in French and other scientific journals, and died not long after.

What is a magnetic monopole?

First, let's reiterate what we mean by "magnetic field." It'll take a little bit to get there, so please bear with me.

By electric charge, we mean the virtual photon flux connected with a particle of mass or an object (of mass). One type of charge (by convention, positive) is modeled to constitute a "source" of this flux. The second type of charge (negative) is modeled to constitute a "sink" of this flux.

Everything in electromagnetics is fluid flow, you see. The old guys who formed the theory believed that electricity was a thin material fluid. So they modeled it that way.

They modeled the positive charge as an everlasting "sprayer" and the negative charge as a "sink" or everlasting accumulator.

They reasoned that of course this "stream" of electric fluid could "swirl" or rotate, just as normal fluids can.

This "swirl" in the stream of virtual photons is magnetostatic scalar potential — or magnetic pole for short.*

Obviously there can be two directions of swirl — one right-handed, and one left-handed, with respect to the direction of the virtual photon stream. So there are two kinds of "magnetic pole" — north (right-hand swirl) and south (left-hand swirl).

The strength of one of these "swirls" can vary, of course, and that's a variation in the strength of the corresponding pole.

You can also think of the "pressure" of the swirl, so to speak, at least for modeling purposes. In that model, north swirl is "higher

*Rigorously, a permanent magnet does not produce an observable B-field in vacuum! Instead, it produces the dynamic, swirling "potential" for that field — i.e., an **unzipped** field. A particle of observable mass placed in this field integrates and "zips" — producing the observed B-field **on** and **of** the spinning observable particle.

than ambient" pressure, and south swirl is "lower than ambient" pressure, where "ambient" means "with respect to right-hand swirl." The swirl pressure is then considered to "bleed off/flow" from north pole to south pole. This is modeled by Faraday's "flux lines of force." This bleed off (gradient) from north pole to south pole is called the magnetic force field, or just "magnetic field" for short, even though in vacuum it's really an *unzipped* magnetic field.

Note that the original modelers didn't consider negative time and negative energy at all. And they didn't know anything about phase conjugation — in fact, the electron had not even been discovered when all this model was originally put together.

But back to the model. Considering the swirling fluid as "conserved", if you produced a concentration of one kind of swirl at one place, you had to decrease the concentration elsewhere, which is the same as producing and adding opposite swirl there. Thus, conceptually, in the simplest case (only two swirls allowed), a north pole and a south pole always occur together in a pair — though of course there's no limit to the distance between the pair.

Notice that if you have a conservative field such as we assumed, you are keeping your overall frame of observation Lorentzian — in other words, conservative. You do not have a "curved spacetime" to speak of, by assumption.

Now of course, you can have compound and very complicated magnets and magnetic fields — you don't always have to have everything so neat and simple. In that case, conceptually you could have — for example — one north pole and two south poles.

In fact, it's easily possible to demonstrate that: a bar of magnetic material is simply magnetized so that a north pole is in the middle, and a south pole is at each end. Now bend it around a bit, and you get the point.

However, now let us suppose that we curve spacetime itself, locally — something they avoid in present physics by pure assumption.

Specifically, we curve our local spacetime in such a fashion that there's more right-hand swirl in the local region than there is left-hand swirl there.

In that case, we have a north-pole region there , all by itself. We have a magnetic north monopole. If that "curved spacetime" region of trapped swirl is moving, that constitutes magnetic current, and it may be either positive (north polar) or negative (south polar) flow.

It's as simple as that! Only when you curve local spacetime can you get a magnetic "charge" or monopole. Everyone who's trying to demonstrate a magnetic monopole in uncurved spacetime is doomed to failure a priori. It takes but little reflection to see that, conceptually, a magnetic monopole is a curvature of local spacetime. Indeed, each of the two poles of a bar magnet is precisely that anyway.

Now a monopole can indeed be "made", by bending local spacetime correctly. It can be made in two ways: in the virtual state vacuum itself, or in and on physical materials. It's easiest to make it in the virtual state: just curving the local spacetime will do that. When this "excess swirl flux without corresponding antiswirl flux" is impressed into and onto matter, however, the atomic nuclei are affected, producing excited "magnetic states." In addition, a great deal of physical stress is created in the material, due to monopolar repulsion between the various "nuclear monopoles deposited in it."

If a sufficiently strong monopole intensity (magnetic charge) is produced in the material, the material will violently fragment from internal stress. When a metal, for example, undergoes such a "monopolar fragmentation", it is common to see "tiled edges" of the metal rupture, much as twisted little "planks" or tiles of metal unfurled and "split." Such a break may be a positive signature of the involvement of virtual magnetic monopoles (i.e., by the metal having acquired virtual magnetic monopolar charge, causing the disruption).

This precise type of metal fracture has been very well demonstrated in experiments by Canadian experimenter John Hutchinson. Anomalous, powerful breaks in metal have been obtained by Hutchinson where the two ends that break apart both have a north pole or a south pole.

The anomalous hole in the fuselage of the Arrow DC-8 destroyed at Gander Air Force Base, Newfoundland on Dec. 12, 1985, strongly suggests that an electromagnetic missile struck the aircraft, inducing monopolar effects. That would also match the three eyewitnesses' description of an anomalous glow on part of the aircraft as it faltered and then fell.

Supercharges and Fractional Charges

Now without further ado, let me just state flatly that the only way to get a fractional charge is to have an appreciable curvature of local spacetime.

To get that local curvature, it's going to be very difficult to use liquid. For weak effects, it will almost always change its bond structure and not localize the curvature in the nuclei. So "fractional charges" in liquid are much harder to come by.

However, with solids it's a different thing, particularly if you make the solid material very, very small and nonlinear — precisely like Ehrenhaft's little red selenium oxide spheres. There you can get the curvature to localize without so much bleedoff through the bonding lattice.

The greatest electrical wizard of all, Nikola Tesla, reported producing electrons with 50 times the normal electrical charge of an electron. That's readily understandable if you look at what's happening to the charge of a particle: To have 50 times as much charge, the electron must be exchanging virtual photon flux with its surrounding vacuum at 50 times the rate of the normal vacuum.

In other words, *it's the vacuum (spacetime) which must be*

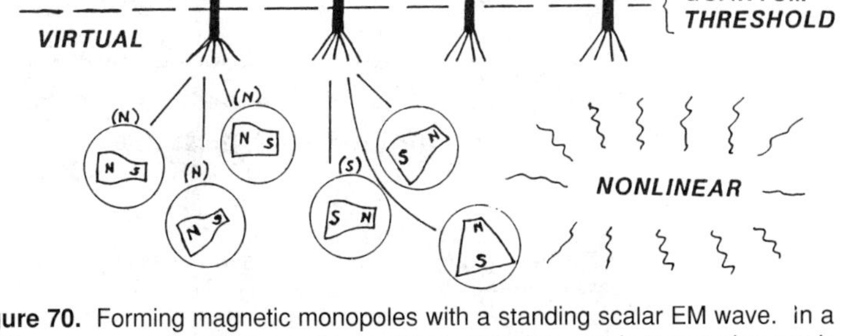

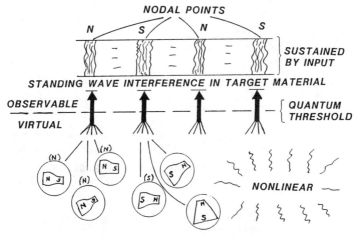

Figure 70. Forming magnetic monopoles with a standing scalar EM wave. In a nonlinear vacuum (locally curved spacetime), virtual magnetic monopoles can be formed and deposited in materials.

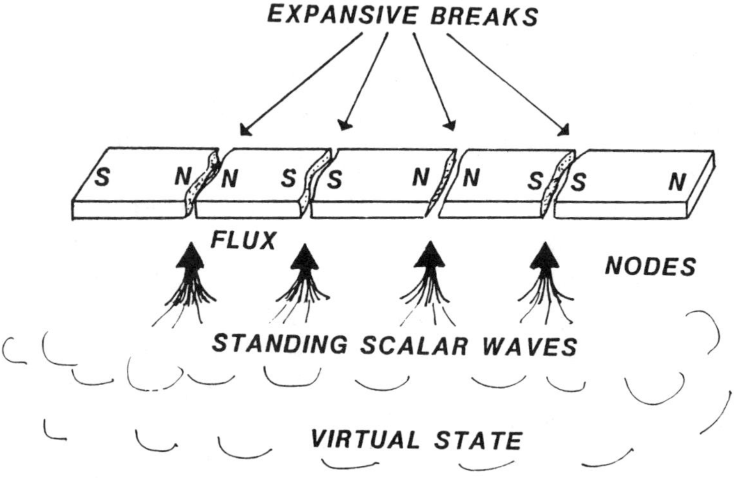

Figure 71. Metal fracture by depositing magnetic monopoles. Demonstrated by Canadian researcher John Hutchinson.

changed, not the electron! Actually, that happens anyway whenever the electron is in an electrical potential field. There are many unrecognized assumptions in the postulate that the electron charge is fixed.

If you curve local spacetime in one direction, you get the charge of an electron increased. If you curve it in the other direction, you get the charge decreased. In that case it's called a *quark*.

At any rate, our own scientists have been looking in the wrong way and in the wrong place for magnetic monopoles and fractional charges.

Work such as that of Ehrenhaft and others should be re-evaluated. And, most certainly, the basis of the present electromagnetic theory should be both re-examined and reformulated.

*Such as the implication that the free electron is always free to move, and that potential surrounding the electron always possesses a translating gradient when it changes. It does not consider the case where the virtual flux exchange between electron and vacuum increases isotropically, centered on the electron. That, of course, represents an *excited charge* of the free electron.

CHAPTER 5

EXTRAORDINARY BIOLOGY

Kervran's Proof of Biological Transmutation

In orthodox chemistry, one of the strongest dogmas is the stubborn insistence that it is impossible to create another element by chemical reaction. Most chemists also insist that all reactions occurring in living systems are chemical in nature. They believe fervently that chemistry can and must explain life itself.

In the early 1960's, a French researcher named Louis Kervran published work which flew directly in the face of the accepted chemistry dogma. Kervran reported the astounding results of his research showing that living plants were able to accomplish limited transmutation of elements. Kervran was then the Conferences Director at the University of Paris, and his first paper was published in **La Revue Generale Des Sciences**, July 1960.

What was so revolutionary was that, according to the prevailing wisdom of science, you can't transmute elements (permanently change the nucleus) except with enormous energy — certainly not with the microvolts and millivolts (and microwatts and milliwatts) that living systems can muster electromagnetically. *

Rutherford, the British physicist who discovered the nucleus of the atom, had shown in 1919 that you can bombard elements with alpha particles and transmute them. The accepted wisdom of today is exactly the same, except that the physicists have used heavier and heavier "bullets" in their artillery approach. No one has tried a controlled approach, for the catchecism is that you have to use the *wham it harder!* approach.

In other words, to most scientists the whole thing had to be preposterous, and Kervran had to be deluded.

Kervran published further details of his work in a book, **Transmutations Biologiques**, Maloine, Paris 1962. But the initial reac-

*Note, however,that since gravity is infolded EM, one can have extremely powerful infolded EM, yet only have miniscule electrical (outfolded) residues. Thus the actual "available power" in artificial biopotentials may not be quite so small after all.

tion of most scientists was disbelief and skepticism. Few scientists would stoop to repeating Kervran's experiments, which of course they knew could not work anyway.

Actually the effect is widespread amongst living systems. As Kervran pointed out, the ground in Brittany contained no calcium; however, every day a hen would lay a perfectly normal egg, with a perfectly normal shell containing calcium. The hens do eagerly peck mica from the soil, and mica contains potassium — a single step below calcium in the standard table of elements. It appears that the hens may transmute some of the potassium to calcium.

Further, if one tests this assumption, it is quickly shown to be true. Hens denied calcium but not potassium, stay perfectly healthy and lay perfectly normal eggs. Hens denied both potassium and calcium will be sickly and lay only soft-shelled eggs. If these sick chickens are allowed to peck only mica — which they will frantically do — everything returns to normal again.

Most orthodox scientists nevertheless remained skeptical or downright hostile.

However, a few other scientists began to repeat Kervran's

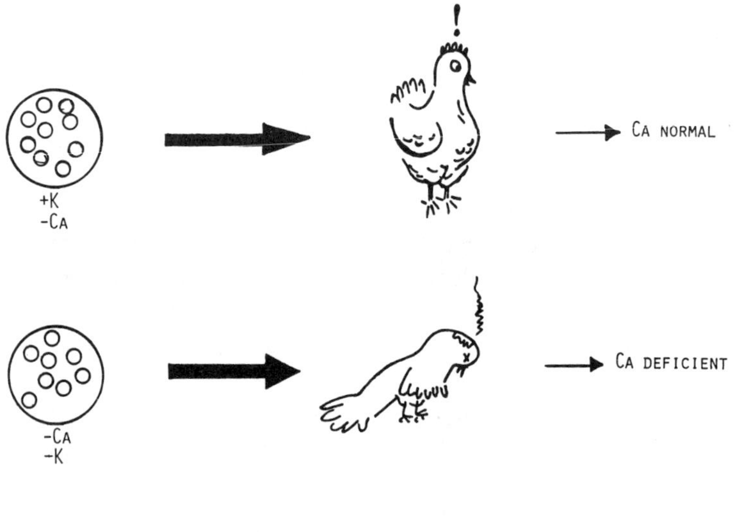

Figure 72. The Kervran effect. A biosystem can accomplish limited transmutation of elements.

experiments and replicate his results. Several of these corroborating scientists were (1) Professor Hisatoki Komaki, Chief of the Laboratory of Applied Microbiology at a leading Japanese university, (2)Professor Pierre Baranger, Head of the Laboratory of Chemical Biology of the Ecole Polytechnique in Paris, and (3) J.E. Zundel, then head of a paper company with a chemical analysis laboratory, and later a chemical engineer of the Polytechicum School of Zurich, Switzerland.

Later work by Zundel was particularly decisive: he utilized the mass spectrometer at the Microanalysis Laboratory of the French National Scientific Research Center, and neutron activation mass analysis at the Swiss Institute for Nuclear Research in Villigen to positively confirm an increase in calcium of 61% to an accuracy of 2%. Such results and instrumentation, of course, removed any doubt that the effect could be due to statistical variation. In the same experiments, the plants increased their phosphorus 29% and their sulphur 36%.

Komaki became head of a research laboratory at Matsushita Electric Company. There he conducted research conclusively proving that microorganisms (including some bacteria and two kinds each of molds and yeast) could transmute sodium into potassium. In fact, he placed a brewer's yeast product on the market that, when applied to composts, increases their potassium content.

Extensive work in the area has been done in the Soviet Union, where results similar to Kervran's have been substantiated.

Thus all doubt (to an open-minded scientist) was removed: living systems are able to change one element into another by some unknown means, using very feeble energy.

A noted French physicist, O Costa De Beauregard, suggested a mechanism for the transmutations, using weak force interactions and advanced waves.

No one — even Kervran himself — thought of negative energy/negative time interactions. The jury is still out on the actual mechanism, but it is absolutely clear that the transmutation does indeed occur.

The Japanese researchers, having replicated Kervran's astounding results to their complete satisfaction, recommended him to the Nobel Committee for a Nobel Prize for such epochal work. Thus Kervran became a Nobel nominee, though he was not granted the prize.

Kervran has since passed away, leaving behind his books and papers that point to a revolution in chemistry and physics — transmutation of elements at very weak energy.

Biological Transmutation Has a History

Actually biological transmutation — and transmutation of elements (alchemy) in general — has a history, of both results and suppression.

Louis Nicolas Vauquelin, a celebrated French chemist, discovered that chickens could produce more calcium in their eggshells than entered their bodies. Hence they had to be able to "create" the calcium, else their own bodies would have been completely depleted.

One of his contemporaries, however — Antoine Laurent Lavoisier — became the "father of chemistry." Lavoisier laid down the dictum that nothing was created. So chemistry fixed upon the notion that the combinations of elements could be shifted, but the element itself could not be transformed.

Not until the discovery of radioactivity did any crack in this solid wall appear. But still, the basic ideas of chemistry said the element couldn't be transformed chemically. It could only be transformed if one blasted the daylights out of it with an atomic or particle bullet.

Today most chemists still hold that exact same opinion, unshaken.

To resume: Over a century ago, a chemist named Albrecht von Herzeele proved that germinating seeds somehow transmuted elements in the process. In 1873 von Herzeele published a book, **The Origin of Inorganic Substances,** where he showed research proving that plants continuously create material elements.

Even earlier, in 1822 an Englishman named William Prout had studied chicken eggs in incubation. He found that hatched chicks had more lime (calcium) in their bodies than was originally present in the egg!

Another French scientist named Henri Spindler discovered that a kind of algae called Laminaria could create iodine.

A German researcher named Vogel had planted cress seeds in a bell jar. They were fed nothing but distilled water; still, when grown they contained more sulphur than had been in the seeds originally.

Lawes and Gilbert, two British researchers, also found that plants could "extract" more elements from the soil than the soil actually contained in the first place.

Baranger performed thousands of meticulous experiments in plant transmutation of elements. He proved that the transmutations do occur. He also discovered that many things affected the germinating seed transmutation process: the time the seeds germinate, the type of light they are exposed to, the phase of the moon, etc.

None of these experimenters understood the transmutation process used by the living organism. But they proved beyond question that the process existed, and universally occurred.

Surplus-of-Energy Mechanisms Proposed by the U.S. Army

There has also been other very positive support for the thesis that if living systems transmute elements, they can produce a net source of energy in the process.

In 1978 an officially-funded effort of the U.S. Army Mobility Equipment Research and Development Command, Fort Belvoir, Virginia positively confirmed that mechanisms for elemental transmutations could occur in biological systems, from an energy consideration.

The work was performed under the direction of Emil J. York, Chief of the Material Technology Laboratory. Solomon Goldfein was the principal investigator for the effort. Robert C. McMillan, Chief of the Radiation Research Group of the laboratory, provided guidance on matters of physics and nuclear physics.

The abstract of the final report (S. Goldfein, Report 2247, **Energy Development from Elemental Transmutations in Biological Systems**, U.S. Army Mobility Equipment Research and Development Command, May 1978. DDC No. AD A056906.) reads as follows:

"The purpose of the study was to determine whether recent disclosures of elemental transmutations occurring in biological entities have revealed new possible sources of energy. The works of Kervran, Komaki, and others were surveyed, and it was concluded

that, granted the existence of such transmutations (Na to Mg, K to Ca, and Mn to Fe), then a net surplus of energy was also produced. A proposed mechanism was described in which Mg adenosine triphosphate, located in the mitochondrion of the cell, played a double role as an energy producer. In addition to the widely accepted biochemical role of MgATP in which it produces energy as it disintegrates part by part, MgATP can also be considered to be a cyclotron on a molecular scale. The MgATP when placed in layers one atop the other has all the attributes of a cyclotron in accordance with the requirements set forth by E.O. Lawrence, inventor of the cyclotron."

"It was concluded that elemental transmutations were indeed occurring in life organisms and were probably accompanied by a net energy gain."

The researchers also concluded that elemental transmutations occurring in life organisms are accompanied by losses in mass representing conversion to thermal energy, and that such energy probably is a net gain when compared to the amount required to effect the transmutation.

All in all, they concluded that the little cell with its feeble energy does quite well! It's in control of cyclotrons, and cyclotron forces, and direct conversion of mass to energy. Pretty good for a little bitty beastie, wouldn't you say?

Actually, one should point out that, according to nuclear physics, an atom gets a little heavier when it absorbs (usually by means of an orbital electron) a normal "positive energy" photon. That is, the addition of positive energy results in the addition of a little bit of "positive mass."

Negative energy, of course, does a similar thing to the nucleus — except that it adds "negative mass." Thus the nucleus of the atom, when it absorbs negative energy, gets lighter. This is seen in the external world as "loss of mass."

With our present nuclear physics, only positive energy is assumed except in extremely rare cases.

Thus the Army study — which was conducted and controlled by some excellent scientists — worked out a "loss of mass" the way they're trained to.

By adding some positive energy, the nucleus would gain some positive mass. By adding some negative energy, the nucleus would lose some corresponding positive mass. The conventional physics then would equate this "loss of mass" as the direct conversion of mass to energy. And so it is, only it's conversion to negative energy!

However, by pointing out the cyclotron mechanism in the cell MgATP , the Army researchers have made a most important contribution.

Note also that the whirling motion may be very much related to Viktor Schauberger's work and to Wilhelm Reich's work. Both of them worked with what they viewed as an unusual kind of living, spiraling energy.

All the orbital electrons of an atom also are whirling around in orbit, in the simplest model. Further, these orbits themselves move and rotate or precess.

Similar orbits and shells occur in the nucleus, at least in some models (several rather independent models are used there for specific things.)

It may be that a whirling, spiraling (cyclotron) energy motion is necessary to connect positive energy to orbital electron (negative charge) shells, and to connect negative energy to positive charge shells in the atomic nucleus. *

Alchemy and Unusual Critters

In ancient times, the old alchemists pursued the dream of making gold. Obviously, if one could do that economically, one could become quite wealthy.

Just as obviously, the kings and rulers of the world took rather a dim view of such proceedings. After all, much of their own power rested on their ability to get and control gold. And if some "loose cannon" could make all the gold anyone wanted, then the national treasury of the king wouldn't be worth a plugged nickel. And that would finish the king, for he would be powerless.

*The spinning/whirling motion may be viewed as integrating the unzipped vacuum flux virtual vectors into zipped observable force vectors — just as great grandma's spinning wheel integrated fibers into continuous threads.

There are some unorthodox researchers today who take the view that the alchemists were stamped out — *not because they failed, but because they succeeded.*

I subscribe to the same view.

T.H. Moray had a process to "recover finely divided gold from quartzite sands." My personal, strong belief is that he possessed a practical transmutation process. His knowledge and techniques, of course, are still possessed by his sons, and reside through them in Cosray Research Institute, Salt Lake City, Utah.

The possession of such a technical secret may be one of the major reasons why the Morays have met with such intrigue, harassment, and suppression over the years.

To speak further on "making gold, " we first have to present some details on some special "critters" that live, but that can't be observed through a normal microscope — even an electron microscope.

In that vein, toward the end of this chapter, we will present some of Royal R. Rife's fundamental discoveries. Pay particular attention to his discovery of "finer" living forms — which today we could only refer to as "living energy, virtual-state forms."

Let's call them **critters** for short.

At one time, when the earth was young and the radiation from the sun was different, conditions on earth were much hotter. Great volcanic activity and fiery eruptions were commonplace and nearly continuous. Huge storms, of size and magnitude undreamed of today, swept the primitive atmosphere. The oceans were frenzied.

Under those conditions, many types of "critters" were highly active. Most of the critters, for example, lived in and worked on the atomic nuclei of matter .

After all, the critters are living, virtual-state organisms. There's a continual exchange between the virtual state (the vacuum, or spacetime) and mass (the observable state). An atomic nucleus is like an island in the "virtual state ocean", and the flux interchange is like waves breaking onto the island and then washing back to sea. The critters live in that ocean, and wash upon, so-to-speak, the mass-islands and interact with them.

In those primal days, many of the present great mineral deposits of the earth were created due to the transmutation activities of the critters.

One kind, for example, lived in copper. In an "energetics" sense, this critter "ate" copper and "excreted" gold, so-to-speak. Much of the gold that occurs in great copper deposits today was formed this way in the old days under primal conditions.

When conditions on earth changed, these little "copper critters" ceased their incessant activity and became dormant, just as viruses can do. But the critters are still there in the copper ore, waiting to be activated.

And activate them you can! You can even get the critters into a solution, and then crystallize them out as crystals.

These crystals are what the alchemists of old called the **philosopher's stone**, with the power to transmute base elements into gold. There are several kinds of philosopher's stones; this kind is for copper.

At any rate, you can then place these special crystals on some copper (and add another thing or two), and restore them to a similar primal environment as of old. That is, heat them in an electric furnace. Blast them with terrible electrical bolts. Bathe them in intense ultraviolet light. That's just a nice, refreshing spring day for the critters!*

That stimulates them and revives them. They wake up after a long sleep — and they're immediately "hungry." So they go right to work on the copper. Boom! In a little bit there isn't any more copper, just mostly gold, with a little other miscellaneous residue thrown in, such as black ruby and silver (in the experiments of one of my close colleagues).

The gold is radioactive when first made. Fortunately, all isotopes of gold are very short-lived: just minutes suffice for the radioactivity to die away. So you wait half an hour and everything's okay.

That's all there is to it.

And if you do that and try to capitalize upon it, your life expectancy is about 24 hours.

I don't know whether or not biological systems, in their Kervran-

*Note the probable similar effects involved in the Miller-Fox-Urey experiments in biogenesis.

transmutations at weak energy, deliberately manipulate similar "critters." I suspect, however, that they do, at least to some extent.

The Cell Also Lives and Functions in the Virtual State

Obviously, to transmute elements the living system has to be able to directly affect and influence the atomic nucleus.

It has been shown that this is a cellular capability, for single-celled organisms can do it.

As we shall see, Rife's work showed that the living cell is connected to at least 16 internested deeper levels of reality than a relative "point" under an ordinary microscope. Further, all levels are structured and organized.

Think of it! Each one of those levels is to the preceding level as microscopy today is to the normal world. Sixteen levels!

I think it's reasonable to state that the life of the cell is patterned and dynamically structured and functioning all the way into the virtual state; indeed, to very deep internested levels of the virtual state. That is, it also functions *hyperspatially*.

We shall also see that the mind and thought involve these more subtle physical (though virtual) levels.

Thus the living virtual-state levels are a reality, for Rife proved it.

The living organized structures at each level are a reality, for Rife proved it.

The living ordering and control of dynamic functions on all those levels is a reality, for Rife proved it.

Those living virtual-level parts of the living organism — plant or animal — thus affect, function in, and reside in the atomic nuclei of the material that composes its bodily structures.

Beasties like bacteria and viruses also have living, organized energy structures in multiple levels of virtual state. Apparently, for these more primitive life forms, the virtual-state "energy part" can be separated and pass through a filter, then re-engender the physical form and/or itself cause the disease in a host! At least that is what Rife and other scientists showed.

"Bigger fleas have smaller fleas to bite 'em, And so on, ad infinitum."

Of course the living system can "work on" the nucleus and

change it a little bit! If it couldn't do so, it couldn't stay alive and function in there in the first place!

The Kaznacheyev Experiments

Dr. Vlail Kaznacheyev is Director of the Institute for Clinical and Experimental Medicine in Novosibirsk.

For 20 years he has been directing highly unusual experiments with twin cell cultures. These experiments are vital to understanding disease and healing on a more fundamental basis than is presently utilized by orthodox medical science.

The Kaznacheyev experiments (several thousand) in the Soviet Union proved conclusively that any cellular disease or death pattern can be transmitted electromagnetically, and induced in target cells absorbing the radiation.

In the experiments, two sealed containers were placed side by side, with a thin optical window separating them. The two containers were completely environmentally shielded except for the optical coupling.

A tissue was separated into two identical samples, and one sample placed in each of the two halves of the apparatus.

The cells in one sample (on one side of the glass) were then subjected to a deleterious agent — a selected virus, bacterial infection, chemical poison, nuclear radiation, deadly ultraviolet radiation, etc. This led to disease and death of the exposed/infected cell culture sample.

If the thin optical window was made of ordinary window glass, the uninfected cells on the other side of the window were undamaged and remained healthy. This of course was as expected in the orthodox medical view.

However, if the thin optical window was made of quartz, a most unexpected thing happened. Some time (usually about 12 hours) after the disease appeared in the infected sample, the same features of disease appeared in the uninfected sample.

This startling "infection by optical coupling" occurred in a substantial percentage of the tests (70 to 80 percent). From an orthodox medical view, these results were unexpected and unheard of.

Further, if the originally uninfected cells were in optical contact

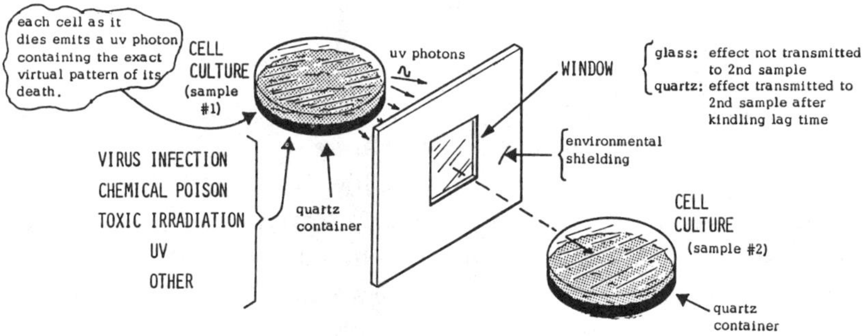

Figure 73. The Kaznacheyev effect. Thousands of experiments proved that (1) cellular disease is electromagnetic, and (2) it can be induced electromagnetically at a distance. Also called the cytopathogenic effect.

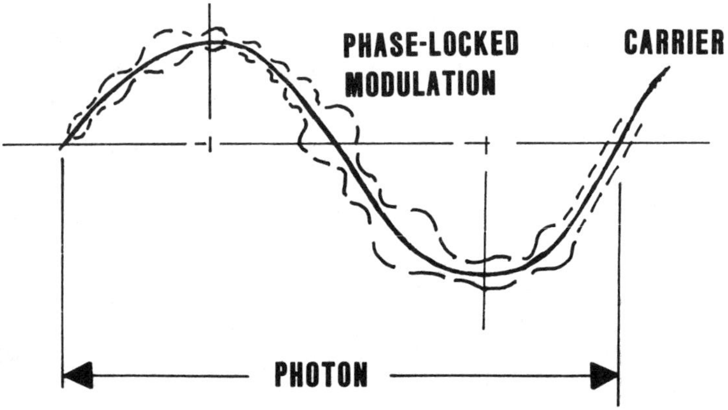

Figure 74. A photon is one oscillation of an electromagnetic carrier. It may have substructures that are modulations. Such a structure is called a "giant photon," or a "compound photon."

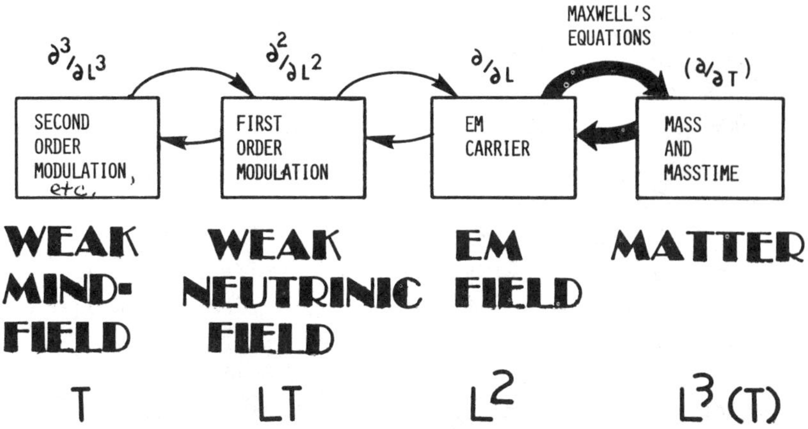

Figure 75. Nested modulations are the key to hyperspatial engineering.

with the infected cells for 18-20 hours or so, and then were correspondingly exposed (optically coupled) to another uninfected cell sample, symptoms of the infection appeared in this third sample an appreciable portion of the time (20 to 30 percent).

Guided by A.G. Gurvitsch's work that showed that cells give off mitogenetic radiation (photons) that can affect other cells, the Kaznacheyev team sought an answer by looking for photons given off by the infected culture sample as its cells died.

They found that the cells in the infected culture gave off photons in the near ultraviolet when they died. The normal window glass was opaque to these near-UV photons and absorbed them. In that case, the uninfected culture on the other side of the glass was not exposed to radiation by the UV "death" photons from the dying cells, and they remained serenely healthy.

However, the quartz window was transparent to the UV "death photons". When the quartz window was installed, the UV "death photons" passed through it and were absorbed in the uninfected culture on the other side of the window. Most of the time, the uninfected culture which absorbed "death photons" sickened and died with the same disease symptoms.

The Kaznacheyev experiments proved conclusively that cellular death and disease patterns can be transmitted and induced electromagnetically.*

Structuring and Charging a Biopotential

Kaznacheyev thus demonstrated that a photon information/regulatory system exists in biological systems due to a continual influx of EM energy from outside the system. That is, the cells of the biosystem are charged with an electromagnetic potential, and additions and changes to the potential are continually received. The cell is thus in minute disequilibrium.

Usually the myriad of continual inputs from the external environment into the cell's potential charge pattern (in its atomic nuclei) may be taken to be potential changes whose substructures are *disordered*. In that case, no specific environmental effect is observed except slight fluctuations without order — a miniscule form of "heating."

However, if a continual *ordered* substructure exists in the input from the external environment into the cell's potential, the cell's potential will gradually "charge up" with that pattern.

An analogy will prove helpful. Imagine an accumulator, a large pot, that holds a volume of water. Several pipes are connected to the pot, some are inputs for water coming in, and some are outputs for water flowing in.

Imagine the inputs all containing "blue" water, just in slightly varying shades. The water in the pot is blue, and may slightly rise and fall in level as the input flow rates vary. The water in the pot may also vary slightly in its blueness as the inputs vary. However, it will still be blue.

Now suppose that yellow water starts flowing through one of the input pipes, and at a goodly rate. Slowly the water in the pot will start to turn greenish as a greater percentage of yellow builds up. In other words, the pot slowly charges up with some of the "yellow" charge, in the process acquiring a "green" charge.

*We point out that this effect has been investigated in both the infrared and ultraviolet. IR to UV may be taken as a single harmonic interval — an **octave**, musically speaking. The same effect can be reproduced in any other "octave" (single harmonic interval) of the electromagnetic frequency spectrum. The **reversal** of the effect can also be achieved in any harmonic interval. The mechanism for these effects involves the cellular biopotential, Popp's master cellular control system, and the deterministically-tailored substructure of photons.

The biopotential in the cell experiments works the same way.

A cell has a biopotential built up, which represents the "nominal equilibrium" of the scalar charge on the cell. This biopotential, being mostly a "sum-zero" of virtual state vectors, is centered in and on the atomic nuclei of the cell, constituting charge patterns in these atomic nuclei. The biopotential extends out of the atomic nuclei, through the electron shells, into and through the molecules, through the internal cell structures and membrane, and outside the cell.

From the atomic nucleus on out through the cell, every layered structure or organization of the cell will layer, structure, and organize the biopotential accordingly.

This organized, structured cellular biopotential is continually receiving "charge patterns" contained in incoming photons absorbed by the cell. The biopotential is also continually exhausting some of its biopotential charge pattern in the photons (heat, light, etc.) that the cell emits.

The Cell's Electromagnetic Breathing

Via structured photon exchange, the biopotential of the living cell thus "breathes in" the virtual state charge structure of its environment, and "breathes out" its own internal virtual state charge structure.

So, in the experiment, the uninfected cells are continually absorbing photons from their surrounding environment, and emitting photons back to it as well. According to our scalar EM view, each photon it absorbs has a substructure that depends upon the part of the environment from whence it came.

These "substructures" are actually patterns of the sum-zeroed virtual vectors comprising the potential of the absorbed photon carriers.

Normally, since a large number of very different substructures are continually being "input" into the cell's potential from the absorbed photons, the substructure of the cell's potential receives an essentially disorganized continual input from the environment. This equates to the fact that the environment does not normally specifically influence or change the cell's potential with ordered information (organization).*

When a cell dies, it ceases to maintain the bio-dynamics that sustained its artificial potential (that part due to bio-ordering by its organized life processes, above the background level of its "inert matter" potential). The dead cell's built-up artificial potential then "discharges" by emitting a structured photon.**

Since this photon (energy) comes from an *organized potential drop, the virtual substructure of the emitted photon is organized.* The photon, then — among other things — carries the exact organized virtual charge pattern of the dying cell's disease.

We strongly insist on the quantum mechanical view here: All physical changes — chemical, material, mechanical, whatever — at root level are constituted and caused by virtual state interactions, in direct patterns of virtual particle exchanges.

In the full QM view, what's really going on in primary physical reality is just a complex set of patterns and changes in potentials anyway.

The Summed Virtual Structures of Kaznacheyev's "Death Photons" Physically Kindle the Disease

At any rate, the Kaznacheyev experiments showed that the dying cells from the infected culture emitted photons in the near UV that contained artificial (structured) potentials. The virtual-state, patterned-substructures in this photon flux directly represented the cellular disease pattern caused by the original cell's specific infection.

In other words, as the infected cells died, they emitted "death photons" which contained the **template** pattern of their death condition.

When these "death photons" are absorbed into uninfected cells, their deterministic substructures gradually diffuse into the cell's bio-potentials. Gradually the biopotentials of the new cells are

*There may be sufficient ordered input from the environment, however, to have something to do with territoriality in living things, salmon returning to a fixed place to spawn, turtles returning to the same beach to lay eggs, the migration of birds, etc.

Note that this photon is emitted from an atomic nucleus. Hence it is a phase conjugate (time-reversed) photon. It will interact with the biopotential of targeted cells, and thus reach their own atomic nuclei. This is the mechanism for Kaznacheyev's cytopathogenic effect. See particularly C.W. Rietdijk, **Found. Phy., 7(5-6), Jun. 77, p. 351.

Table 43. THE LIVING AURA: THE CELL'S ELECTROMAGNETIC BREATH.

- **VIRTUAL EM FIELD**
- **STORES VIRTUAL PHOTONS**
- **ENVIRONMENTAL INPUTS**

* **OUTPUTS BIOPHOTONS**

- **COHERES ORGANISM**
- **TENDS TO STABILIZE**
- **EXPERIMENT ESTABLISHES**

Popp, "Photon Storage in Biological Systems," Electromagnetic Bio-Information, 1979

"charged up" with the integrated pattern of the disease.

The master cellular control system of the biosystem is itself a dynamically changing, ordered pattern in the biopotential of the cells, which is centered in the atomic nuclei comprising the cell materials. As the bio-potentials of the cells gradually acquire the "death photon's" substructure pattern, this pattern is also diffused throughout (modulates) the master cellular control system. All the cells in the sample (or in a biosystem) are now slowly charging up with the "death photon" pattern.

As Popp discovered, photons continually "leak out" of the virtual photon master control system of the biosystem. Some of these *leakage photons* are observable photons, **but most are virtual photons**.

Further, they are *structured* photons.

In other words, as leakage photons spill out of the master control system, observable change is now being slowly initiated in the physical structures, biochemistry, etc. of the biosystem's cells — and these changes are in consonance with the integrated "cellular death pattern" of the originally infected cells.

Note particularly that it is already well-known in quantum mechanics/electrodynamics that, when a photon is emitted from the surface of a dielectric body, the entire dielectric body participates in that emission. If a photon is absorbed on the surface of the dielectric body, the entire

dielectric body participates in that absorption.

Thus as irradiation by the "death photons" continues, the "death structure" in the irradiated cells increases. It is spread throughout the cell culture by the master communication system, gradually charging the virtual state structure of that system with the death pattern.

Spillage photons from the cellular control system occur throughout the culture. These photons are structured with the death pattern, and gradually affect the cell and its biochemistry physically. The previously uninfected cells thus physically start to acquire and exhibit the symptoms and characteristics of the disease pattern that killed the infected cells.

Electromagnetic Infection Results in Physical Disease

The new cells are now electromagnetically infected and physically diseased.

After all, that is all a cellular disease is in the first place — physical, electrical, and biochemical changes in the normal functioning of the cell.

For a given pattern of changes in the cells, a specific "disease" exists in them.

It absolutely does not matter what causes this exact pattern. If the specific physical pattern is there, the specific disease is there.

Note that **any ghost pattern in the virtual state flux can charge up physical matter — that is, the atomic nuclei of a mass. All that is necessary is that a continual flux of this virtual pattern continually bathe (irradiate) the mass's atomic nuclei.**

The eventual emergence of this "ghost template pattern" into observable physical reality is called **kindling**. Kindling is charging up one or more atomic nuclei with an integrated virtual charge pattern until the integrated pattern breaches the quantum threshold, resulting in emergence of that pattern into observable physical change.

A Possible Cure for AIDS

One of the things going for the "good guys" and EM defense

against AIDS is that cells are a lot tougher than viruses. Thus even non-structured EM signals can be used to effect cures in many disease cases.

In fact, ordinary ultraviolet (UV) irradiation of the blood has already been utilized to cure or control severe infections, including severe viral infections. I am indebted to Dr. William C. Douglass for pointing this out to me, and for permission to reproduce the following information from his important newsletter, **The Cutting Edge**, Nov. 1987, p. 3. The following material is quoted verbatim, with no editing.

"It's amazing what you can find by nosing around in the dusty archives of a good medical library. I came across another remarkable therapy that the AMA and drug industry (or whoever is in charge of supressing non-toxic treatments that work) have shoved down the memory hole."

"Back in 1933, Doctors Hancock and Knott treated a patient dying of septicemia (blood poisoning) with ultraviolet irradiation of the blood.[1] The patient was moribund with a blood stream infection and obviously near death. (Remember that this was before antibiotics and there was nothing to lose.) The patient made a complete and uneventful recovery."

"Searching further, I found that in 1928 a similar terminal infection was treated by ultraviolet light to the blood. This patient also made a complete recovery.[2]"

"So in 1928, practically in the middle ages, an incurable disease, blood stream infection, was cured with ultraviolet light. With such a breakthrough why wasn't it tried again for *5 years?* According to the record, *another 6 years* passed before it was tried for a third time.[3]"

"Back in those days infection was the number one cause of death. You can't help but wonder how many lives could have been saved if doctors weren't so resistant to new ideas. Just imagine a cure for AIDS being set aside for 11 years. Yet bacterial infections of the blood were uniformly fatal in 1935, just like AIDS is today."

[1] Northwest Medicine, 33:200, 1934.
[2] Knott, AM. J. Surg., Aug. 1948, pp. 165-171.
[3] Am. J. Med. Sci., 197:873, 1939.

"Finally, in 1940, 110 cases treated with ultraviolet spectral energy were reported. The results were uniformly good. Between 1940 and 1948 many other conditions were successfully treated, including vein inflammation (phlebitis), polio and asthma. Up to the late 40's *over 40 thousand* treatments were given with ultraviolet blood irradiation."

"And now for the most interesting part. In 1947, Dr. G.P. Miley reported on 79 cases of virus infection.[4] Miley stated that ultraviolet blood irradiation therapy could be relied upon consistently to control an infection of a virus in a safe and efficient manner.[5]"

"AIDS is a virus. AIDS-II is a virus (the HTLV-IV leukemia and lymphoma now sweeping the world). Remember that these killer viruses are within the cell and any chemical agent that enters the cell to kill the virus will often kill the cell as well. But ultraviolet irradiation *kills the virus without harming the cell.*"

"A fine piece of crystal can be shattered by exposing it to just the right frequency. You can be standing in the room and the energy from that frequency won't harm you in the least. Viruses have the same characteristics, and so, in my opinion, frequency irradiation of the blood in the ultraviolet range is our greatest hope for curing AIDS."

"But the treatment is simple, safe, inexpensive and unpatentable. That doesn't bode well for its future, at least until a few *senators* get AIDS."

The Mirror Cytopathogenic Effect and Factors Influencing It

The cellular disease induction effect was called the **mirror cytopathogenic effect** (CPE for short) by the Kaznacheyev group. Mirror CPE appeared only when the quartz or mica window was no thicker than 0.8 mm. A. F. Kirkin also duplicated the experiments using a thin plexiglas window.

There are conditions which enhance the effect, and others which inhibit or degrade it. Irradiation of the detector-culture with a low dose of UV prior to its optical contact enhances the effect, increasing

[4] Rev. Gastroenterol. 15 271-277, 1948.
[5] Am. J. Surgery, Aug. 1948, pp. 170.

it to certainty (99-100%). Increasing the temperature to 38.5 degrees centigrade also enhances the effect (from 37% to 90% for example).*

A necessary condition for the success of the experiment is the rotation of the holder with its two optically-coupled samples at a rate of about 24-25 revolutions per hour. Optical contact between the inductor and detector cells for a minimum of 4-6 hours is necessary, after which the cell cultures can be separated. A longer contact time is necessary for complete development of the irreversible effect.

Both cultures must be maintained in complete darkness throughout the experiment. Use of the detector as a new inductor in a successive state reduces the effect by 20-30%. Three or four such stages is sufficient to eliminate the effect.

There is a seasonal variation in the results. In more than 15,000 experiments, monthly variations and daily variations were noted. (The present author's interpretation of this is that it is due to the monthly variations in the virtual photon substructure input from the moon to the substructure of the cell's bio-potential. The daily variation is due to the daily variations in the virtual photon substructure input from the sun to the substructure of the cell's bio-potential.)

Negative results appear more often in winter. (The present author's interpretation of this is that it is due to the fact that the scalar potentials of the earth and the biopotentials of each living cell on earth are lowered in winter by the weaker flux from the sun.)

Effects are correlated with the polarity of the interplanetary magnetic field. Negative polarity of the field usually precedes the appearance of mirror CPE. (This is because of the positive nuclei — which prefer one direction of the magnetic field over another). Disturbance of the geomagnetic field several days before a culture planting also results in enhancing the mirror CPE effect. (Disturbing the geomagnetic field provides a "dithering magnetic disturbance" in the atomic nuclei which "livens" them. Consequently their readiness to charge-up and emit structured virtual state charges is increased).

Kaznacheyev further discovered that the Sun's activity and the

*This is very important. Preconditioning the cells by "dithering" them in the frequency band of interest, or in a subharmonic band, "livens" the cells for developing the irradiated pattern. This is similar to a dither voltage placed on a missile fin, making it much easier and quicker for the fin to move when an actual order is placed on it.

Earth's magnetic field greatly affected the results of his experiments. Large flashes on the sun seem to inhibit the effect. (Such flashes cause substantially increased irradiation of the atomic nuclei by sun-emitted substructures, charging them mostly with this disordered substructure pattern and literally "burying" the disease structure several decibels below it.) In a season of active sunspots, the mirror CPE effect becomes highly unstable. (The sun emissions are sporadically jamming the effect.) Under active sun conditions, the effect varies from 90-100% on some days to complete absence on others.

Some Biological Warfare Implications

The Soviets reported detecting near-ultraviolet photons — bioluminescence — as carriers of the death/disease pattern.

However, scientists at the University of Marburg in West Germany also duplicated the effect in the infrared. This shows that bioluminescent photons in the near UV and in the IR can definitely carry "disease and death" information between cells. Further, integrating a continuing input of such photons coherently integrates the disease or death pattern from the virtual state into the observable state.

Note also that portions of the infrared spectrum are a subharmonic of the near ultraviolet. Harmonics are well-known in nonlinear oscillator theory, and biological systems are filled with nonlinear oscillators. It may be that harmonics and subharmonics are directly involved in the death pattern.

If so, the induction of such "death patterns" upon normal electromagnetic carriers is directly indicated. For example, modulations covering several octaves in the region of 10 gigahertz and above might be constructed that are the analogues of some particular cellular disease. This modulation pattern could then be added to a common microwave carrier — say in the communication band, from 3 to 30 megahertz. Say, that is, to something like the giant Soviet Woodpecker "over-the-horizon radar" signals as carriers.

In that case, a large population could be bombarded, even on the other side of the earth, with "death photons" whose virtual state substructures carry the particular disease pattern. With sufficient time, many of the targeted persons would develop the disease.

Note that, even if the power and/or irradiation time is reduced so that the absorbed "death photons" are insufficient to actually kindle the disease in the targeted population, a heightened change in the substructure of the biopotentials of the cells of the targeted persons is still accomplished.

In that case, a precursor pattern — a predisposition for that disease — exists in the targeted persons.

If the actual disease agent is now loosed on that population, the agent will be far more infectious and lethal than it otherwise would.

In this way, even diseases which normally do not kill or seriously debilitate the infected person can suddenly become very lethal agents indeed.

Influenza, the common cold, etc. can become devastating killers if the exposed population has been electromagnetically "pre-conditioned" for enhanced susceptibility.

What Kaznacheyev Hid: The Role of Phase Conjugation

If cellular disease can be electromagnetically induced, can it not be electromagnetically corrected or healed?

If one could time-reverse the exact signal structure (the information) that kindled the effect, and bombard the diseased cells with that reversed pattern, would not the cell deviate back to "normal" and be healed?

The burning question as to whether cellular disease conditions can be corrected by time-reversed disease signals must certainly have occurred to the Soviet experimenters.

It is highly significant that they did not openly publish those results.*

As we have explained in the sections on phase conjugation and scalar electromagnetics, there are really two major kinds of photons:

*Recent information indicates the strong connection of Kaznacheyev with the Institute of Physiology and Biophysics and the Frank Institute in Pushkino, just outside Moscow. Since these institutes are deeply involved in microwave and coherent microwave "directed energy" weapons, it is highly probable that the Soviets are applying Kaznacheyev's "death photons" to microwave weapons -- such as the Woodpecker transmitters. If so, obviously they would develop phase conjugate countermeasure signals as well.

(1) the "normal" photon carries positive energy and positive time. (2) the "time reversed" or phase conjugate photon carries negative energy and negative time.

Further, the Soviets certainly knew all about phase conjugate signals. After all, they discovered and developed the effect. We discovered it only from the open Soviet scientific literature!

Let us assume that the "death photons" in the mitogenetic radiation emitted by the dying cells are ordinary photons. Their virtual state structures (in positive observer time) are exact "templates" for the disease pattern.

Now suppose we detect the "death photons" with a phase conjugator, which by definition will produce a time-reversed counterpart to the input signal detected. In other words, the death photons are allowed to strike a phase conjugate mirror (PCM). Time-reversed counterpart photons — carrying the exact time-reversed template of the death pattern — will be created and emitted by the PCM.

These newly emitted photons now carry the exact "healing pattern" for that specific "death/disease pattern that was received and detected."

Further, if we "pump" the phase conjugate mirror, we can greatly amplify the output pattern, and hence greatly increase the healing pattern!

If one records the pattern of the "death photons" for a specific disease, one could of course modulate that pattern upon ordinary photons/signals — such as the Woodpecker signals — and accomplish disease induction or precursor conditioning.

By phase conjugating the pattern of the "death photons," one can produce an exact antidote. One can modulate this specific healing pattern upon ordinary photons/signals — such as the Woodpecker signals — and accomplish healing induction for that specific disease.

In other words, one can create the healing pattern — the antidote, if you will, for any biological warfare agent. Cancer, leukemia, AIDS, viral diseases, bacterial diseases, whatever. One can create the antidote within minutes after the first symptoms of the disease or death pattern appear.

One can then simply add the negating (healing) signal to power line signals, television and radio signals, special transmitters, etc. —

and immediately start to "administer the antidote" to the irradiated population one wishes to protect. *Now one can see why the Soviets are so ready to expose the entire world to something like AIDS. It doesn't represent a real problem to them, the instant they decide to negate it.*

So they can devastate the rest of the world, with the assurance that their population is safe.

They can allow some of their own people to develop AIDS — and even some to die of it — as a deception plan to delude the West while Western populations are succumbing en masse.

Then they can snatch their own population right back to health, from "the brink of the grave," so to speak.

Our government must immediately develop the same capability. It is straightforward. As weapons and counterweapons go, it is enormously cheap. It can be immediately and widely implemented. And it can protect our population against AIDS or any other biological warfare strike by the Soviet Union.

We can save our people from the AIDS knockout already unleashed upon us by the Soviet Union.

First let us do that. *Then* let us negotiate.

Remember this: **You can negotiate with the Russians only from a position of strength. If you are weak, they will bury you.**

If we do not immediately develop this biological warfare countermeasure, we are already as good as dead.

Popp's Master Cellular Communication System

Dr. Fritz Albert Popp has already discovered and pointed out the "virtual state" master communication system that controls all cells in the body, and all their functions.

Based on a thesis derived to best fit experimental results by Ruth and others, Popp postulates that biological systems generally have the capacity to store coherent photons that come from the external world.

In other words, the biosystem is open to environmental communication and exchange.

He has shown that the cell population is in a quasistationary state that is far away from thermodynamic equilibrium, as pointed out by Ilya Prigogine.

Popp also concludes from his analysis that ultraweak photon emission within biological systems can influence chemical reactivity. In fact, his analysis strongly implies that "ultraweak" photon intensity can regulate the whole cell metabolism and related phenomena.

The cell takes up photons from external radiation. This includes both "observable" photons and "virtual" photons. Since it stores virtual photons, it stores charge, or biopotential changes. Since its stored virtual photons may be coherent virtual photons, it effectively "polarizes" or structures its stored photon charge, hence its biopotential.

The cell emits "spillage" photons — both coherent and incoherent — from its stored potential.

Although Popp only uses conventional "unstructured" photons in his analysis, he shows that, at the molecular level, there is a stationary equilibrium, as far as photon storage and emission are concerned, between the molecular photon traps, the cell population, and the external world.

It follows that *coherent* photon/charge inception from the external world can directly and precisely influence the cell's biopotential, hence its functioning and control, by information input.

Incoherent photon inception, on the other hand, can only grossly affect the cell, such as by heating or sporadic effects.

In his "Photon Storage in Biological Systems," Popp points out the master cellular communication and control system as follows:

"The photons which we have measured can be seen as a sort of "waste" from a virtual electromagnetic field with a high coherence. This field has a tendency to become stationary over the whole organism."

After additional analysis, he adds:

"....Consequently, biological systems must exhibit 'holographic' properties to an extremely high degree. The successful trials in

finding 'pictures' of various organs in each other organ, such as the ear, the hands, the eyes (acupuncture, iris diagnosis) support these conclusions. Our assumption that the entire genetic information of the DNA is stationarily delocalized over the body in form of genons may be seen as a further striking example."

"From this we can easily deduce that pattern recognition, as, for example, repair mechanisms and immunity, depends finally on the coherence of the photon field within the body."

Finally, Popp states a most important conclusion:

"...In medicine new aspects have developed, and not only for cancer problems. Diseases in general can possibly be understood in terms of electromagnetic interactions within the organism."

Scalar EM Comment on Popp's Communication System

Popp and his colleagues have produced most important work and results indeed. They only need to add the impact of the zero-summed/multiplied electromagnetics (electrogravitation).

As we cover in this book, the biopotential of the cell is rooted in the nuclei of the atoms of the cell's constituent materials. To be sure, every internal physical structure of the cell correspondingly "levels" and structures the biopotential. The overall cellular communication system is actually the exchange of "leakage" photons — both observable and virtual — throughout the overall biopotential of the organism.

Further, going beyond Popp's work, both the biopotential and the leakage photons have extensive, complex internal substructures. Leakage and intercommunication occurs laterally at all levels of the biopotential, and vertically among cells and substructures.

The master cellular control system's primary electrical conductivity path is not through the electron shells of the atoms, but is through the nuclei-to-nuclei scalar EM "biopotential levels" pathway.

With scalar EM methods, organized signals (signals with specific internal nonzero vector EM waves, but which externally sum to zero vector resultant E and H fields) can be constructed for essentially any specific purpose. This includes "killing" a cancer or leukemia cell, destroying a virus, changing the DNA, etc.

This approach can directly reach and manipulate all immune and repair system functions.

The entire biochemistry and functioning of the cell — including its genetics — **is totally engineerable**. The Soviets have long known this, and have long since done it.

Further, a specific "charge pattern" of desired specific immunity (antibodies, etc.) can be designed and used to "charge up" the nuclei of the biosystem. This charge is then maintained by the system to provide permanent immunity. Thus one can develop, for example, an "electromagnetic innoculation" for AIDS, one for cancers and leukemias, etc.

Since the cellular control system is holographic, the "charge pattern" of immunity resides in every cell, including the blood cells.

Injecting a drop of blood from a scalarly immunized animal into another non-immune animal carries the scalar EM immunity pattern into the new animal. That charge diffuses throughout the overall biopotential of the organism, and the charge pattern activates the animal's immune system, including causing it to produce antibodies — according to the EM-transferred antibody template.

Antoine Priore demonstrated this effect numerous times. This was one of the great mysteries that confounded the orthodox members of the French Academy of Sciences.

The French Academy did not know of scalar electromagnetics, the cellular biopotential rooted in atomic nuclei of the cellular material, the cytopathogenic effect of mitogenetic radiation from diseased and dying cells, phase conjugation, and phase conjugated electromagnetic healing.

It is little wonder they did not comprehend the operational healing mechanism of the Bordeaux cancer-curing machine of Antoine Priore!

A New View of the Nature of Mind and Thought

The reason that Western science has not discovered what mind and thought are is simple: They have only built instruments and tools to look where the mind and thought *are not to be found.*

Let's look where they are to be found.

For example, consider the ionic discharges in and across the tremendous numbers of synapses of the human nervous system, and the slower discharge and migration of ions across cellular membranes, etc.

Considered as a single biological ensemble, these are much like a vast array of continual and continuing spark discharge vectors, slow charge current vectors, etc.

Overall, within the macroscopic space occupied by the body, these electromagnetic vectors sum almost entirely to a zero vector resultant. Only a tiny nonzero vector residue remains.

However, this vector zero summation has incredibly rich infolded signals, channels, and dynamic relationships (structure) within it.

Modern science/medicine measures the small nonzero electromagnetic residue (the remaining weak E and H fields) and tries to ascertain where and how mind and thought are accomplished, by studying that residue.

However, the residue E and H field remainders are simply the "garbage thrown out" of the glorious engines dynamically operating inside the vector zero summations (and multiplications).

The E and H field residues are the wastes or exhaust byproducts. They are not the functions of the mind/thought process itself; instead, they are the spillage or leakage from those functions.

Take a "frozen time" snapshot of the components of the zero vector summation. Regard the highly complex, infolded structure or pattern these components form.

Now take a second "frozen time" snapshot of the components of the zero vector summation, a very, very short time later. Subtract the previous "frozen pattern" from this second "frozen pattern."*

The difference or "delta" between the two patterns represents a myriad of thoughts, hence it represents the contents of the "thinking mind," in the most general sense.

The "mind" is the overall functioning and changing of the entire pattern's substructure, and the ability of an organism to have such and do such. The "ability of the organism to do such" requires at least

*Similar to the magnificient "double exposure holography" work of Dr. Robert Powell.

two more nested levels of virtual state — two more hyperdimensions.

In simplest Kaluza-Klein theory, all those electromagnetic component vectors are in the fifth dimension. Hence they are hyperdimensional.

The zero-vector system may well have further infolded, internested levels of zero-vector systems. Systems within systems. These are hyperspatial, going into the 6th, 7th, 8th, etc. dimensions. Rife's microscope, for example, could reveal some of these levels; using evanescent waves, it could resolve some 16 ever-deeper levels of dynamic energy structure.

Everything driving the component vectors themselves is higher dimensional.

"A thought" is the exact change of a localized pattern (localized

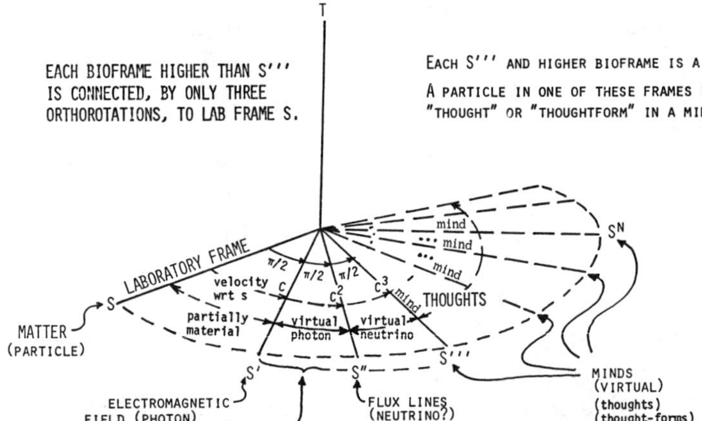

Figure 76. Hyperframes, vacuum, virtual state, minds and thoughts.

zero vector summation whose components are changing but remaining zero summed) from one moment to the next.

Thought is always a pattern change, of the components inside an EM vector zero summation.

Most thoughts are totally "unconscious" (multiple simultaneous or "parallel" thoughts). A few are conscious (serially ordered, singularly considered and processed).

The unconscious mind is totally a parallel processor (many things/thoughts at once).

The conscious mind is totally a serial processor (only one thing/ thought at a time).

Most persons never take the time and trouble to reflect and notice that, consciously, they only can perceive one single thing at a time. Of course, the conscious mind is so rapid that by habit they assume they can perceive many things at once.

Since the conscious mind cannot discriminate the "multiple images in the slide projector at once" of the unconscious mind, that's what makes it unable to "be conscious" of the contents of the "unconscious."

In fact, the unconscious mind is totally conscious — it's just **multiply conscious "simultaneously."** (Which sheds some interesting light on why one can develop multiple personalities, for instance).

When the conscious mind "regards" the unconscious contents, it sees "something" which has "multiple meanings at once."

That's what we call *symbolic*. A symbol is something which can have many meanings at once.

That's why the unconscious content always "symbolizes" something when it's trying to communicate to the conscious mind. It's necessary to interpret the symbols to understand what the message being communicated is.

That's why dreams, for instance, are symbolic. And why it usually takes a trained psychiatrist or psychologist to properly interpret the symbolic representations manifested in mental disorder, and get at the underlying cause being symbolized.

With deliberately constructed scalar EM, any or all of the conscious/unconscious portions of the mind can be available for engineering and control/change. Eventually you will be able to put contents of the mind and memory on a video screen if you wish to.

It will also be possible to interact with the mind's contents electromagnetically. Mental illness will be treated directly, on an engineering basis.

Of course this opens up the frightening possibility of hostile misuse to the detriment of an individual. It will even be possible to change or erase his or her very personality itself. We pray, of course, that such a powerful tool will not be utilized this way, but will be used to heal humans, not hurt or kill them.

Unfortunately, Lisitsyn's work reveals that the Soviet Union has long since applied energetics (scalar electromagnetics) to mind control and mind engineering, including deciphering the genetic code operation. Controlled induction of images and sensations inside the brain — where they are processed as if self-originated — has been reported by the Soviets. Indeed, they have reported being able to control whether or not the induced material should rise to conscious awareness, as well as when it should rise to consciousness.

For years, U.S. intelligence analysts and U.S. scientists simply did not believe that electromagnetic signals could directly influence consciousness.

However, they were forced to reevaluate that position when a Soviet medical machine — the LIDA device — was openly obtained and evaluated.

The LIDA machine — a small unit somewhat larger than a briefcase — has been used in Soviet medical facilities to treat humans for decades.

The device uses a 40 megahertz EM carrier and very complex waveforms (signal modulations with complex mixtures of frequencies, phases, etc.)

When exposed to it, a person is caused to gradually fall into a trance-like, catatonic-like state within a few minutes. That person becomes very still and very quiet.

It was reported that the machine was tested upon a cat and had the same effect upon it.

One American scientist stated that the device had actually been used in North Korean "brainwashing" of U.S. prisoners of war in the early 1950's during the Korean War!

If so, one can see just how long the Soviets have achieved success with electromagnetic biological warfare/medical treatment techniques.

Reportedly, prisoners exposed to the machine were rendered

unable to psychologically resist their harsh brainwashing interrogation.

But to return to the brain activity, with its innumerable, zero-summed minute EM vectors, and its extremely rich and complex deterministic substructure.

Note that the ensemble of sum-zeroed vectors forms potentials. These potentials — i.e., the scalar EM — penetrate to the atomic nuclei in the brain and body. Internal changes in the potentials' substructures (i.e., thoughts) also penetrate to the nuclei.

The nuclei continually "charge up" (the particles change their states) to these impressed potentials, including the "potential" or "charge" of each component of the impressed potential. That is, the nuclei charge up with both dynamic overall potential (mind) and thought (individual substructure changes).

Notice that **mind, thought, and memory reside in, and are recorded in, the atomic nuclei. At many virtual state levels. In many hyperdimensions.**

Thus the functioning mind and bio-control systems — including Popp's master cellular communication system, the immune control system, the acquisition control system, and the repair control system — all "reside" in the nuclei as dynamically interacting, patterned potentials or "patterned charge," complete with resonances and frequencies, etc.

We can regard the mind and its interactions as physical, in the extended sense we have briefly developed here.

Everything "mental" can be directly interfaced with and engineered.

One day, for example, "education" will be by direct loading of patterns into the brain/body/cellular biopotentials, much as we now place a diskette in a disk drive and load the computer memory. And then everyone can be educated, in the widest range of skills and to the highest degree ever dreamed of.

Kindling, Life, Mind, and Negentropy

The mass of the atomic nucleus can be charged up with a particular dynamically structured biopotential.

In scalar electromagnetics, I use the term **kindling** to refer to the effect of charging up mass by a specific structured charge pattern to form such a structured potential in the nuclei.

Note that we are actually and physically restructuring the nucleus itself. That is because, if the structure of the potential in the nucleus is changed, local spacetime of the nucleus is polarized in complex electromagnetic structures. The electromagnetic currents, actions, and charges of the affected nucleus adjust automatically to this structure or "grid." *

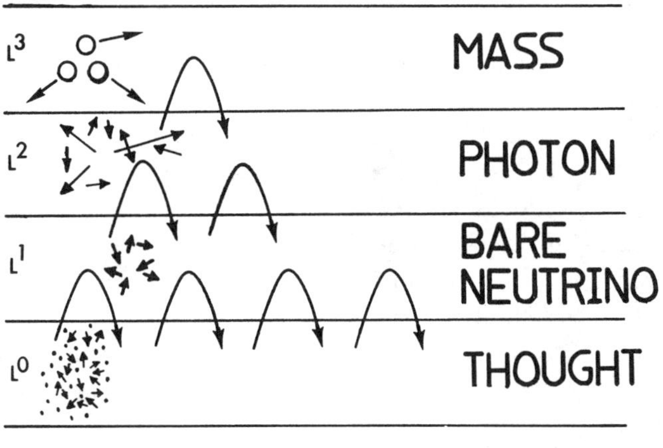

Figure 77. Internested levels of virtual state vacuum contain mind and thought. The vacuum also contains their interaction toward and upon mass.

*See Richard E. Prange and Peter Strance, "The semiconducting vacuum," **Am. J. Phy**. 52(1), Jan. 1984, p. 19-21. The vacuum may be regarded as a semiconductor. This semiconductor, particularly in the region close to the nucleus, may be manipulated by subjecting it to external fields, doping, etc. Extra energy density can even be extracted; see H. Paul and R. Fischer, "Comment on 'How can a particle absorb more than the light incident on it?' " **Am. J. Phy**. 51(4), Apr. 1983, p. 327. For the involvement of negative time/negative energy, see C.W. Rietdijk, "How do 'virtual' photons and mesons transmit forces between charged particles and nucleons?" **Found. Phy**. 7(5-6), June 1977, p. 351-374.

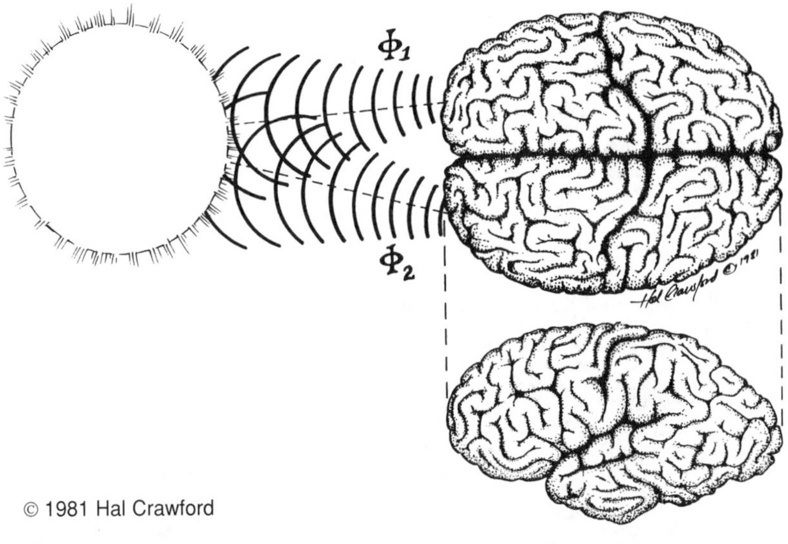

© 1981 Hal Crawford

Figure 78. The human cerebral cortex is a natural scalar interferometer. It is a virtual state tuner, processor, and transmitter-receiver. It also can produce...and control to some extent...phase conjugate energy and phase conjugate waves.

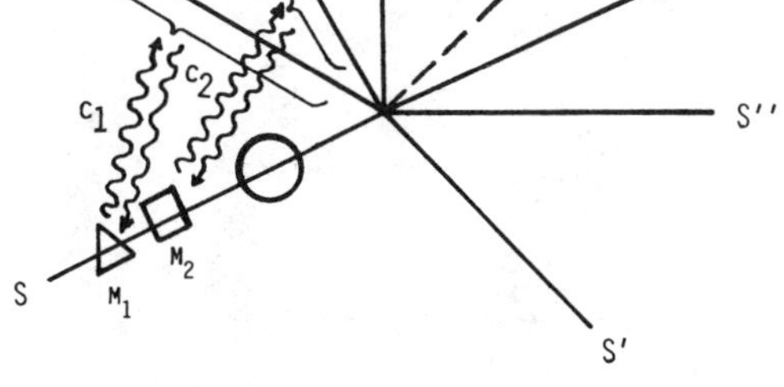

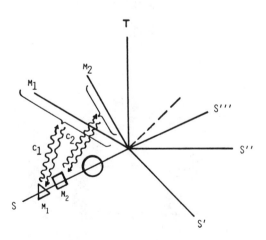

Figure 79. Consciousness and life. These phenomena refer to/constitute a deterministic hyperspatial (virtual state) coupling between mass and an ordered hyperworld.

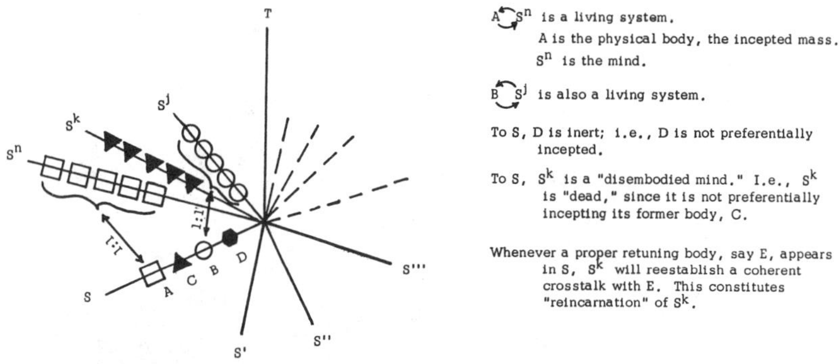

T
S^k
S^j
S^n
1:1
1:1
A
C
B
D
S
S'
S''
S'''
A S^n is a living system.
A is the physical body, the incepted mass.
S^n is the mind.
B S^j is also a living system.
To S, D is inert; i.e., D is not preferentially incepted.
To S, S^k is a "disembodied mind." I.e., S^k is "dead," since it is not preferentially incepting its former body, C.
Whenever a proper retuning body, say E, appears in S, S^k will reestablish a coherent crosstalk with E. This constitutes "reincarnation" of S^k.

Figure 80. Life and death. If the tuning or coupling between the mindworld and the tuned, structured mass body is broken, that is physical "death." Discharge of the structured cellular potentials then produces "death photons." Discharge of the overall, structured biopotential of the body constitutes discharge of the "living spirit."

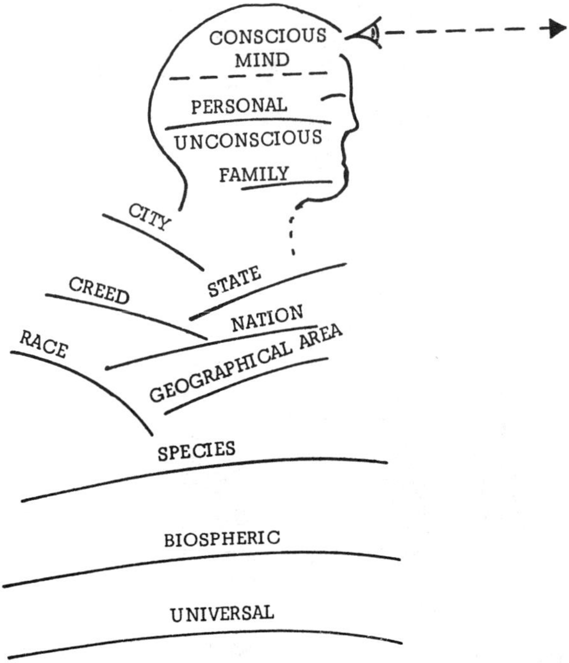

Figure 81. Layers of unconsciousness intersect hyperspatially.

© Hal Crawford 1979

Figure 82. Scalar electromagnetics can directly interact with the various levels of human mind and personality.

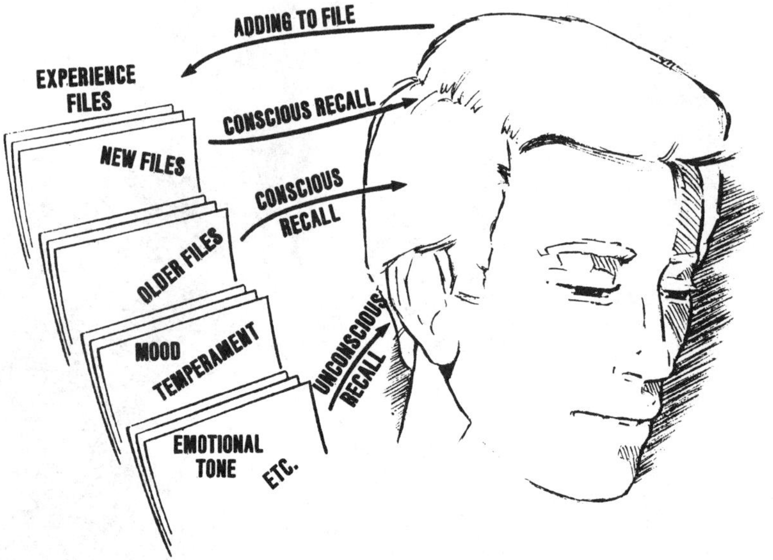

Fgure 83. What personality is.

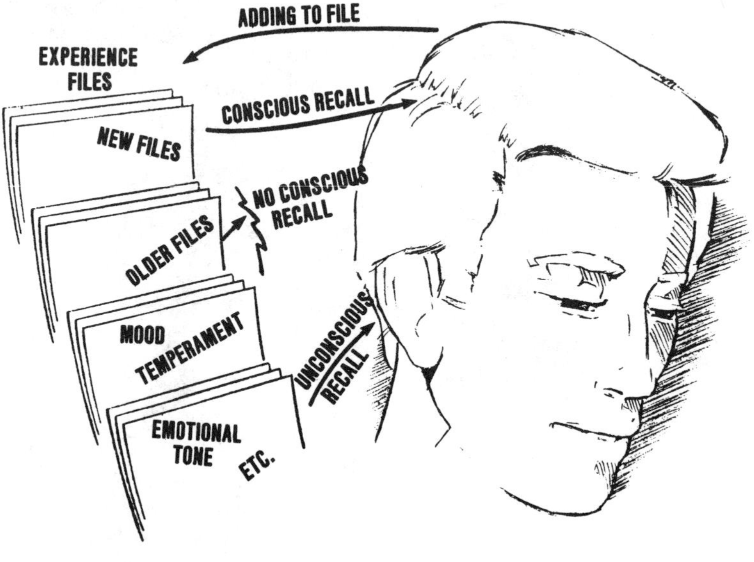

Figure 84. Jamming the "older files recall" process produces simple amnesia. If the recall process is then restored, the person regains his or her former memories.

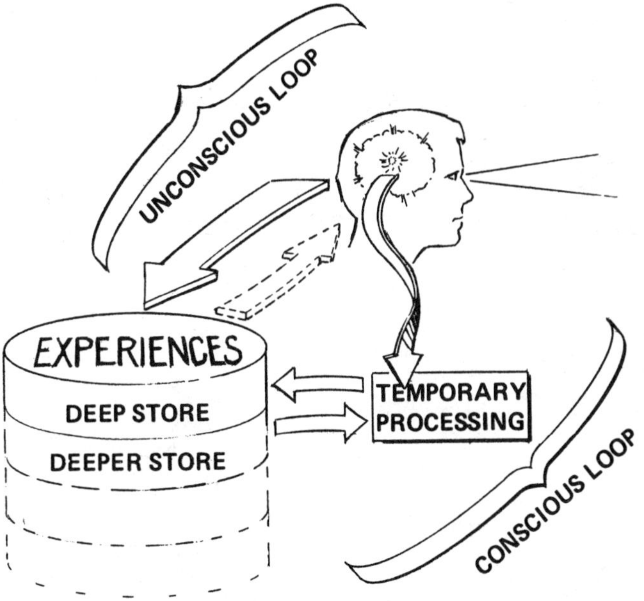

Figure 85. To sustain one's personality, continual functioning is required. All channels must be functioning.

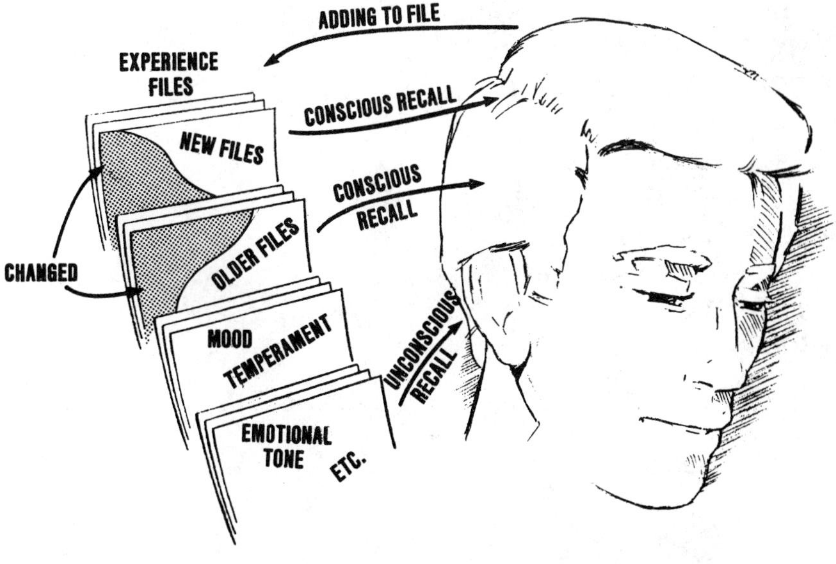

Figure 86. If the files themselves are changed, the personality itself is changed. It is possible to alter who or what a living person is.

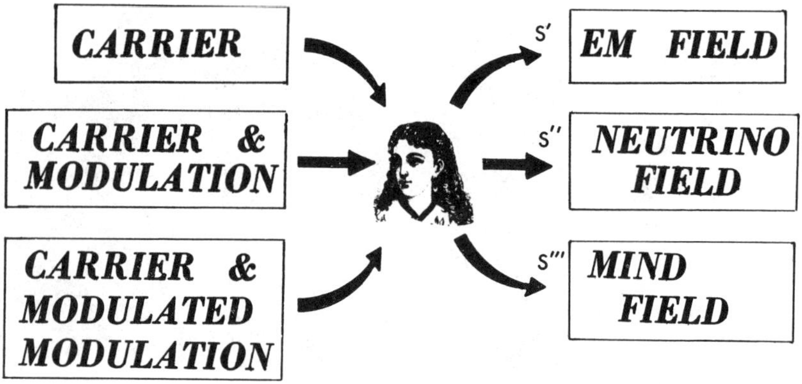

Figure 87. The mind and personality can be affected — and changed or controlled — from a distance. The Soviets have developed at least a substantial part of this technology.

Table 44. LISITSYN'S REPORT

- **THEORY DEVELOPED & FITTED**
- **HYSTERESIS MEMORY LOOP**
- **CONTROLLED INDUCTION**
  - **IMAGES**
  - **SENSATIONS**
  - **PREDETERMINED EMERGENCE**
- **23 EEG BANDS**
  - **UP TO 8.1 X 10^{20} HZ**
- **11 INDEPENDENT CHANNELS**
- **BRAIN CODE BROKEN**
- **44 DIGITS OR LESS**

Thus by tailoring the specific scalar waveform and wave substructure with which we irradiate a mass, and utilizing phase conjugate (time reversed) waves, we can directly engineer the nucleus itself when sufficient charge structure has been built up in it to form a structured potential that is powerful enough to alter/shape the nuclear processes.

We can, for example, transmute the nucleus into another form. Here an isomer form is the easiest. An isomer for an atomic nucleus (a specific isotope) has the same number of nucleons (protons and neutrons) overall as that isotope does, but a different number of protons. So it's a different element, but very specially related to its isomeric "brother."

All that it takes to change a neutron into a proton or vice versa, is to "flip" a single quark (subparticle of the nucleon).

Living systems can do that and transmute elements, to a small degree.

For example, living systems must use phase conjugation, negative time, and negative energy. To do so, they must function nonlinearly. That is the only way they can defeat the otherwise inexorable second law of thermodynamics: that all (linear) processes continue to more and more disorder as time passes. (That's called "increasing the entropy (disorder)." Unless a biosystem could defeat that law, its genetic pattern would inevitably be disordered in a few generations, and the species would disappear.

By using phase conjugation and time reversal, the living system is able to reverse the law of entropy in its time-reversed channel. That is, in that channel things go in reverse: from disorder back to order! That's called "negative entropy" or negentropy" for short.*

It follows a priori that, to do this, the living system of necessity possesses phase conjugate energy systems (negative energy, negative time systems) that are rooted in the atomic nuclei of its body. Further, it must deterministically manipulate these phase conju-

*To show how fully one can integrate physics and metaphysics, we point out that, since the vacuum **imprints** with every change, **nothing is ever lost!** Death, where is thy sting?

gate systems.

This allows the precise definition of a living or nonliving system. **If the system deliberately utilizes and manipulates phase conjugate energy/time in its atomic nuclei, it is a living system. If it does not deliberately use this, it is an inert or nonliving system.**

For example, this sheds a great deal of light on the nature of a virus.

A virus is a single molecule. Ordinarily it clouds the distinction between life and death. Viruses can be crystalized out of solution, formed into "rock-like" crystals, and placed on the shelf, so to speak. There they can remain for many years or centuries, seemingly an inert rock. Then when placed back into their "preferred medium," so to speak, the virus crystals dissolve, separate, and "come back to life" and resume their living function. Yet the virus can be killed, in which case it is just a "hunk of rock," sitting on the shelf. In that case, it won't come back to life when placed back into its preferred medium.

In one case its "deterministic phase conjugate energy system" — its mind, to put it simply — remained in the nuclei of the atoms of the crystaline form. In the other case its "mind" was destroyed or disconnected from the crystalline form.*

A somewhat similar effect can be demonstrated in bacteria.

You can "kill" bacteria, for example, with UV radiation, then hold them in the dark for 24 hours (say, for 12 generations, since a nominal bacterial generation is about 2 hours.) They will remain absolutely "lifeless" and static, with no movement or cell division.

Then if you place them in the sunlight, you will be astounded to see them revive by the hundreds of thousands. In the "special kill" case here, the virtual state substructure of the UV photons just totally "jammed" the biopotential substructure functioning of the

*In the living case, the atomic nuclei remained patterned by the structured biopotential. In the case of true death, the structured biopotential is lost and the nuclei revert to their "inert" form.

"minds" of the bacteria on one key channel. It didn't physically damage their bodies or "physical tuners." Then when placed in the sunlight, the broad frequency spectrum of the virtual substructure of the photons "dithered" and stimulated the bacteria's body-tuners, much like a "frequency massage" in all the bands. This set the physical tuners vibrating — and therefore responding once again to the biopotential substructure changes of the mind. Hence the bacteria "revived" and swam about — fat, dumb, and happy.

We have stated that **the mind is a physical thing, albeit a virtual or hyperspatial thing. In virtual/hyperspatial reality, it is a functioning, hyperspatial thing.** Interchanges be-

© Hal Crawford 1978

Figure 88. The mind and personality are physical things, albeit hyperspatial and virtual.

tween it and an otherwise inert, functional, 4-dimensional ordinary physical system (a "body") comprise life functions, "thought," cellular control, etc. Those interchanges in a living system occur in the biopotentials residing in the atomic nuclei of the physical body, in the higher levels of biopotential in the body structures such as cells, membranes, and organs, and in the overall biopotential of the entire mass of the body.

We accent that this is not mysticism, but physics.

But now let us return to phase conjugation and the Priore machine.

The Priore Machine and Phase Conjugation

In the 1960's and 1970's, in France Antoine Priore built and tested electromagnetic healing machines of startling effectiveness.

In hundreds and hundreds of rigorous tests with laboratory animals, Priore's machine cured a wide variety of the most difficult kinds of terminal, fatal diseases known today.

Funded by the French government in the amount of several million dollars, **Priore's machines concretely demonstrated a nearly 100% cure of all kinds of terminal cancers and leukemias, in thousands of rigorous laboratory tests with animals. These results were shown to medical scientists as early as 1960.**

Many of the experiments and tests were done by prestigious members of the French Academy of Sciences. Robert Courrier, head of the Biology Section and Secretaire Perpetuel, personally introduced Priore's astounding results to the French Academy.

The operation of the Priore machine was seemingly incomprehensible. Many orthodox French scientists — some of them world renowned — were outraged at the success of such a machine, shrilling that science had nothing to do with "black boxes."

They loudly called upon the inventor to explain the mechanism utilized by his machine, but the inventor either wouldn't or couldn't explain the curative mechanism.

Priore certainly knew how to build the machine and make it

work. It is debatable to this day whether anyone — Priore included — actually understood its principle of operation.

Neither the French Academy nor Antoine Priore knew anything of phase conjugation at the time.

In fact, the entire Western World knew nothing of phase conjugation in the 1960's when Priore was getting his finest results. At that time, only the Soviets knew of time-reversed waves.

Certainly Priore's machine was impressive.

Into a tube containing a plasma of mercury and neon gas, a pulsed 9.4 gigahertz wave modulated upon a carrier frequency of 17 megahertz was introduced. These waves were produced by radio emitters and magnetrons in the presence of a 1,000 gauss magnetic field. Experimental animals were exposed to this magnetic field during irradiation, and the mixture of waves (some 17 or so) coming from the plasma tube and modulating and riding the magnetic field passed through the animals' bodies.

Amongst other things, a plasma can convert a transverse wave to a longitudinal wave. Also, phase conjugate (time-reversed) waves

Figure 89. One of Priore's intermediate devices. This device cured terminal cancers and leukemias in thousands of laboratory animals. (Courtesy Bob Whitney)

can be produced by plasmas. Priore's apparatus produced a scalar EM wave/signal with deliberately constructed, infolded components including phase conjugate waves.

One may roughly view a cancer cell as a normal human cell gone "awry" and out of control of the body's master cellular control system. The cancerous cells, viewed as a sort of separate, parasitic group of cells, form a special kind of organism having its own master cellular control system "level," immersed in the host's biopotential.*

There is thus a specific, constant electromagnetic "delta" that differentiates the parasitic cancerous "organism" from the normal human cellular organism.

This "delta" can be considered a sort of constant, complex-structured charge existing in the body's atomic nuclei. It's exactly as if the body biopotential had been charged up by Kaznacheyev's "death photons" for that specific cancer condition.

If this cancerous "delta" (which may be rather like a complex intermodulation mix of waves) — or a frequency shifted "transform" of it to a different frequency band — is phase conjugated, a specific healing delta frequency pattern results.

If phase conjugate replicas of a cancer's cell's specific "delta" frequencies are fed into the body having that cancer, the deviation of the cancer cell's master cellular control system will be "time-reversed."

That will return the cancer cell to control of the animal's proper master cellular control system. The cancerous cell will be immediately destroyed, or reverted back to a normal cell of the animal.

A very similar process exists for just about every disease bacterium and infectious agent that attacks the body.

Phase Conjugates of "Death Photons" are "Healing Photons"

The Kaznacheyev experiments in the Soviet Union proved that any cellular death and disease pattern can be induced by a specific electromagnetic pattern carried on an electromagnetic signal, if the

*One strongly points out the relevance of Dr. Robert Becker's epochal experiments proving that cells can be dedifferentiated and redifferentiated electrically. Those experiments are strong indicators that the cancer cell should be capable of being reverted to its more primitive state — that of the normal cell — by electromagnetic means.

target cells are bombarded with the pattern-carrying carrier signals for a length of time.What was not published of Kaznacheyev's work was the correspondent work showing electromagnetic reversal of cellular death and disease conditions by irradiating the diseased cell cultures by phase conjugate replicas of the pattern-carrying induction signal.

In simplified terms, if an action in forward time induces a condition, then the time-reversal of that action will reverse the condition.

The concept is almost laughably simple. **The time-reversal of an electromagnetic disease process is a specific healing process for that disease.**

In his device, Priore internally structured the carrier photons themselves — making them **vacuum engines**. He phase conjugated his vacuum engines, and then passed these time-reversed vacuum engines down and through a strong magnetic field which thoroughly penetrated all cells of the biological organism being treated.

The scalar components (structured photons) representing the time-reversal of the disease were absorbed and reradiated in all the cells, "charging up" the nuclei of the atoms in the organism to some potential level of the exact "healing and reversing pattern."

In the process, the cancer/leukemia pattern/charge also destroyed the cancer cells, or converted them back to normal cells as appropriate.

As a highly simplified analogy, the complex signal — viewed as a scalar Fourier expansion — represented a "stress" against any abnormal cellular control system encountered and returned it to the normal cell's master cellular control system of the body.

Encountering the normal control system in normal cells, it produced zero stress.

Encountering the abnormal control system in tumerous cells, it produced great stress on it, reverting it to the normal control system of the body's normal cells.

Thus to a normal cell the Priore signal pattern acted somewhat as a comb passing through one's hair.

No interference occurred with the normal cell (one whose scalar control pattern is phase-locked to the body's master cellular control system and in phase with it).

The Priore signal stimulated and "stroked" the normal cell, but did not hurt it at all.

On the other hand, the scalar control pattern in and of an abnormal (cancerous) cell is out of phase with the body's master cellular control system, and is not phase-locked to it.

Hence the Priore signal caused direct interference with the abnormal cell's independent scalar control system. The interference pattern constituted the reconstruction of normal energy directly in the cancerous cell, and also jammed its abnormal scalar life signal.

This destroyed the cancerous cell by two mechanisms: (1) physical energy was kindled directly in the abnormal cell, causing direct mechanical damage, and (2) the cancerous cell, being an "independent living critter," had its scalar life channel (connecting its primitive "mind" to its "body") jammed and stopped.

If the cancerous cell was reverted to a normal cell by the Priore stress before being destroyed, it became just a normal cell and the Priore stress had no further effect upon it.

The Effect is Universally Applicable

Any disease with cellular, biochemical, or genetic basis can be cured in like fashion.

Priore's method, for example, was clearly shown to be able to completely reverse clogging of the arteries with fatty deposits, and to be able to lower the cholesterol level to normal, even in the presence of an abnormally high cholesterol diet.

His method also showed complete mastery and cure of sleeping sickness and trypanosome-induced illnesses.

Often Priore found that every cell of the body — even the hair — must be irradiated and treated ("charged up") with the signal, for the disease pattern was in every cell. The master cellular control system is holographic — the pattern (substructured potential with its dynamic, oscillating components) is in each component (each atomic nucleus, hence in each cell.)

Every structural level of the body larger than the cell also has its own correlated pattern, or modulation, on the overall.

A biological organism can regenerate lost limbs, for example, if it can utilize its natural recovery process in a Priore manner.

Even though Priore's work was presented to the French Academy of Sciences by Robert Courrier, the prestigious head of the Biology Section, the Academy could not understand the device and its functioning.

That was because the Academicians knew nothing of scalar electromagnetics, and phase conjugation, and the Priore machine was a scalar electromagnetic device using phase conjugation.

In the Mid-70's It Ended

In 1974, a change of local government lost Priore his government supporters. His support and funding were lost.

Ironically, Priore was just completing a 4-stories-tall apparatus capable of radiating and treating entire human bodies. It would have been capable of curing cancer and leukemia in humans rather than just in laboratory rats. (His previous machines were much

Figure 90. The large, special, phase-conjugating plasma tube for Priore's giant device. The final machine would have treated humans "whole-body." (Courtesy Bob Whitney)

Courtesy Bob Whitney

Figure 91. Capping assembly for the top of Priore's giant plasma tube device. The last device would have treated human patients "whole-body." The cap assembly was on the third floor of the device.

smaller, and only a small animal could be irradiated whole-body.)

In that machine Priore used a "lamp," a special section, in which 17 specific frequencies were mixed and modulated upon the 9.4 gigahertz carrier.

The machine was large enough to irradiate humans over their whole body. **It should have been capable of curing cancer and leukemia in two five-minute irradiations, one week apart.**

While Priore was still alive, with my associates I spent nearly two years of my life in an effort to bring the Priore device to market and into the mainstream of medical research and development.

Robert Whitney, Frank Golden, and Tony Gideon played the major role, going to France and negotiating directly with the Priore group and the French government.

Verbal agreements with both the Priore group and with the French government were obtained. The machines were to be built, assembled, and tested in Bordeaux. Then they were to be dismantled and shipped to the purchasers — large medical research and development laboratories where they would be reassembled on site.

A group of wealthy backers was going to provide the necessary millions to fund the effort. Final contracts were being drawn.

Mysteriously, all funding for the project was suddenly withdrawn. Our backers were "leaned on" very hard and strongly threatened. Nothing we could do could revive the project.

Priore never again recovered his funding, and later died. The machine fell into disarray and was disassembled.

However, the proof that the requisite time-reversed signal can be produced, and will ride down a magnetic field, to penetrate every cell and every atomic nucleus in the body, is already in the present hard-core physics literature, if one knows where to look and how to properly interpret the work.

The fact that such signals can reverse nearly every major cellular illness condition of the body also has been proven by Priore and the scientists who worked with him, and it is in the French scientific literature.

The Priore-type cure for AIDS and other diseases only requires the necessary funding and personnel to be redeveloped and re-established.

Work of Australians Reed and Barsamian, and the American G. Wilbanks

At the University of Sydney, Department of Obstetrics and Gynaecology, some magnificent work of great importance to our thesis has been accomplished. Indeed, this Australian research may well be some of the most important work going on in the Western world today.

Dr. B. L. Reid, Dr. S. Barsamian, and their colleagues have produced experimental studies that positively verify pattern and form transmission at a distance, even through Faraday shielding. They have directly shown the reaction to, and results of, an unexplored information field on both living cells and inert crystalline matter.

In addition, they have replicated — and extended — the published results of Kaznacheyev on the cytopathogenic effect. In fact, they have obtained the effect at over 100 meters.

This shows, of course, that the effect is not just mesoscopic, but also macroscopic. Whether we like it or not, structural patterns of cellular disease can positively be transmitted electromagnetically, and kindled in target cell structures at a distance.

Dr. Reid has been interested in the origins of cancer since at least 1958. After much work in the standard models, by the late 1970's he was convinced that the present approach of medical science is wrong. He reasoned that we should pay stricter attention to the nature of growth before examining new growth, i.e., cancer. Growth, of course, is creation — and so the problem became, what is creation?

As a metaphor for biological growth to work with, he and his colleagues chose the growth of crystals. With keen foresight and intuition, they directed their inquiry so as to expose the complicity of some force — if any — external to solute and solvent.

Their work began to show that such a force existed, and it was a type that was unaffected by interposition of a Faraday cage. In other words, *it was not a conventional electrical force.**

Dr. Reid and his colleagues then included biological subjects in the form of living cells. They were familiar with Kaznacheyev's work in Alma Ata, Kazakstan on the subject of long range transmission of pathological (viral) effects on cells. In addition, they were familiar with the seminal studies of Gurwitsch on transmissions by onion roots cells, in the 1920's.

Most of their basic studies on the nature of the new force, however, were made with common salt, drying from aqueous solution, Some of their major results were as follows:

1. The familiar cubic symmetry is altered toward a higher energy form of dendrite crystals when biopolymers such as protein are included in the solvent.
2. A mass of lead 12-20 kg in the crystal space (up to 1 meter distant) causes an interference pattern in the salt crystal display.
3. A prospective dendrite pattern is not realized when a prospective cubic-pattern of the salt is dried in the local space (up to

*For one related possible scalar EM (electrogravitation) interaction, see Ya. B. Zel'dovich, "Electromagnetic current and charge due to interaction between a gravitational and a free electromagnetic field," **J. Exper. and Elec. Phy**. (Soviet translation), 16(7), Oct. 5, 1972, p. 302-303.

1 meter). The latter by its presence in space is able to prevent the dendrite expression and enhance the cubic symmetry expression. **A photograph of crystals of cubic symmetry when moved by a vibrating holder (2 cps) has the same effect on the real crystals drying from the solvent.**

4. Dendrite forms of salt crystal result when certain chemical reactions involving proton or ion movement occur up to 30 meters away, separated by brick walls, glass, etc. These reactions were detailed by Dr. Reid and his colleagues. If the mother solution is examined by ac capacitance on a sensitive bridge, variations in capacitance of over 300% accompany the receipt of the signal.

5. If such a transmission from 30 meters distance is regarded as a carrier wave which is modulated by a foreign — and thus detectable — chemical, **the chemical can be detected in the distant atmosphere some 3 months later in the form of a discrete or adiabatic 'cloud' which contaminates sodium chloride drying at the same time.** In this way, copper sulfate dissolved at a site A in June 1985 could be repeatably detected at site B, 30 meters distant and separated by walls, screens etc., by a drying solution of sodium chloride solution in September 1985. Serial dryings of the sodium chloride solution on glass slides showed that each day, the cloud hovered over a space of 1-2 cm at the end of a venturi tube for several hours before 3 p.m., and then moved off at 1 meter per hour in a NW direction. The copper content of the cloud was discernible by crystal structure and chemical means from the adjacent sodium chloride.

6. All of the above crystal forms required ambient oxygen for their manifestation. Atmospheres of nitrogen and argon prevented their display. At the time, the researchers suspected that the effects may have been carried by orbital electrons of oxygen showing unpaired spin which had interchanged with electrons of the copper solution. They then

developed an information-carrying device which could 'infect' the electron cloud of a target molecule sufficient for the chemical display of properties of the infecting electron's parent atom. This concept seemed to explain the experiment of the following paragraph.

7. Two beakers of sodium chloride solution were connected in series with a small voltage source (say a 1.5V dry cell) to provide a transfer of electrons through each beaker. The second beaker in series was sampled for subsequent drying and display of the crystal form. A crystal form of cubic symmetry resulted. When the solvent of the first beaker was altered by the addition of a protein solution (such as albumen or globulin), the crystal pattern of the second beaker was altered from cubic to dendrite pattern as though protein were present in the second solution.

8. During attempts to stabilize salt crystals on glass by means of thin plastic films drying from appropriate solvents (in order to stain the salt with aqueous solutions of dyestuff), it was discovered by chance that the crystalizing process is accompanied by structural patterns on the plastic film so exposed. These patterns were of two major types: (a) vortices, or spirals in the film plane, of 0.1 to 1.0 mm diameter, and (b) smaller curled structures into which the spiral could be seen to merge or grade. From a concurrent mathematical study of vorticeal interaction as designed by Barsamian, the similarity of the curl structures in plastic films (the researchers usually used 0.25% polystyrene in benzol) to computer simulations of vorticeal vectors was shown to be remarkable.

9. The researchers then dispensed with the underlying crystals and exposed the drying polymer film to a variety of spaces where the field, thought to be responsible for many of these tele-effects, was operative. With this technical advance, the team has made rapid progress over the last year or so. They have come to have a more comprehensive grasp of the ether

field than was possible by less direct methods involving formation of crystals.

10. On the biological side, they repeated the Russian studies done at Alma Ata with transmission of the cytopathogenic effect of viruses on animal cells. They used the cytopathogenic effect of colchicine and its relative vinblastine on cells with the following differences from the published Russian work: (a) The effect can be transmitted at least 100 meters between campus buildings, (b) it is not necessary to use a magnetic field for the propagation, (c) it is not necessary to use quartz vessels; glass is quite effective. These experiments came to the attention of a colleague, Dr. G. Wilbanks, Head, Department of Obstetrics and Gynaecology, Medical School, University of Chicago in 1983. Dr. Wilbanks was able to repeat them with similar results. However, in a more faithful copy of the Russian experiments, he used quartz vessels with cells placed in a magnetic field, with the vessels separated by no more than 1 mm. Both the Australian researchers and Dr. Wilbanks shared another thing in common: their uniform inability to interest the editors of several scientific journals such as **Science**, **Nature**, **Naturewissenchaften**, and others in publishing papers describing these fundamental experiments and results.

11. Experience with interference of a lead mass in the crystal work prompted the use of several metals in the ambient field of growing cells. Only lead (and to a lesser extent tin) showed the following properties: (a) Cell growth with 0.5-5 Kg lead in the ambient field is depressed sometimes to one third normal. (b) The cells die (dye exclusion test) but then can be revived by placing a small bar magnet in the local space with its poles in an E-W orientation. At least in Sydney, a N-S orientation of the bar magnet does not revive the stricken cells.

12. The effects of energy flowing through living matter have been documented by Kirlian's method. It was therefore of interest

to the Australian researchers to expose living systems to drying films of polystyrene. They found that the staining properties of the ambient-derived image on plastic films parallel those of the real organism.

13. By appropriate use of an imposed potential on living cells, it proved possible to match the field strength and show the actual imposition of the ambient (scalar) field on the biopolymer content of the material during the permeation process. The traces obtained are not unlike noise and would be so regarded by the casual investigator. The design of this apparatus and associated experiments was the work of Dr. Barsamian.

Concepts of Dr. Reid and Associates

Dr. Reid has kindly shared with me some of the concepts he and his colleagues have formulated. These concepts, it is stressed, are consonant with direct physical results they have obtained in the laboratory.

Note that any errors in this explanation are strictly the fault of this author, and not of Dr. Reid and his colleagues.

1. Matter is bathed in an energy sea familiar to quantum theorists. The Australian team prefers to call this sea of energy **ether**, as a relatively bland term, perhaps in a way to rescue it from the oblivion where Einstein banished it. The key to the silence of this sea is its "fractional-charge" charged particle status and low energy values. The former conceals it from physics, while the latter conceals it from chemistry and thermodynamics.

2. The differing energy levels of this sea, combined with its enduring motion, are theoretically and practically best expressed as a **vortex**. Dr. Reid and associates have detailed this theory to explain the creativity of biology. The incipient creativity of the vortex is given material expression by its association (as part of the EM field) with an electron which it

now endows with equivalent novel properties. There is no intuitive reason why the energetic rearrangements of the electron cloud cannot proceed to the nucleus, there to set up a quark or proton rearrangement — or, as the quantum theorist would say, a virtual particle exchange — leading to transmutation. Kervran's work on biological transmutations is relevant; the literature of such effects goes back to 1798 at least! The team suspects that some such mechanism may underlie their experimental result of the transition of sodium to copper.

3. **A further prime property of vorticeal interaction is its proclivity for amplification**, wherein the atomic-size vortex can be built up to the meteorological hurricane by such adherence or affinity. The team has noted the affinity of ambient field vortices to those produced by an electric current in a metallic conductor, with particular reference to the ill-defined boundary between the two. This parasitism was the reason behind the team's use of "carrier waves" from chemical reactions as transporters of fields whose identity of origin were sufficiently specific to trace the field subsequently. It is at least conceivable that the whole process could be amplified and used to parasitize (modulate) a radar beam as carrier. The affinity property of fields may be exhibited by the experience of mariners with what they loosely term "magnetic phenomena" thought to be derived from luminescent plankton. In the South China and Arabian Gulf seas, giant "wheels" of light, 5-15 km in diameter and containing spiraling spokes, revolve about the ship at night, reversing their direction of rotation as they pass the midpoint of the vessel. The key observation in the context of the field affinity concept is that the luminescence is manifoldly enhanced when the ship's radar is switched on. There could thus exist a chain, scalar-EM/plankton-optical, the first leg (scalar EM) of which can be amplified by radar EM.

4. The property of affinity means that **a scalar field's transform or copy, of the energy disposition imposed on it by the experience of matter last permeated, may persist as**

a memory in space, as many of the Australian observations attest. The team found that recall was not all that difficult technically. **The energy transform for copper sulfate existing as a non-dissipated cloud with marked adiabatic properties could be recalled five months after its formation. There is no reason why informationally more elaborate spatial configurations of energy, including human thoughts, will not behave in precisely the same way.** The cell nucleus could conceivably be the candidate for the first site for storage of such energy. The nucleus has a highly ordered structure and an associated high permittivity, and this would make it a real target. In the human subject, there is experimental evidence that the mongoloid polymer constitution will have a higher activity for storage of the ambient field than will the Caucasian.

Other Important Ideas

Dr. Reid also shared other important insights:

Lavoisier in 1748 advanced the concept that matter itself (chemicals) is inert. The activity of all chemicals, according to Lavoisier, resided in their associated ether — and God sent the ether!

Taken to its limit, this suggests that the source of the energy which we call *thought* is a property of the scalar field. Matter (say, the nervous system) interacting with these fields, would be incapable of discerning the source of the field as presented, whether of self or external origin.

In his book **Hidden Variables in Quantum Theory**, Dr. David Bohm felt that in 'elevating' (his word) matter (as particles) from the sea, it might be possible to consider the idea as containing even more elaborate energy transforms such as biological shapes, these transforms themselves undergoing metamorphosis. [Comment by this author: Rife's microscope, using evanescent waves, actually allowed one to directly see and photograph such forms, proving the thesis.]

The ability of the Australian researchers to rescue these transforms on films together with evidence that they could be seeing the results of the exclusively space interaction of virtual forms (say microbe and antibiotic), is also a direct technical step toward validating Bohm's important idea.

Wider Implications of Structured Field Information

As T.D. Lee points out in his important book, **Particle Physics and Introduction to Field Theory**, particle physicists have not attempted to use the structure of the vacuum nor the structure of potentials.

Dr. Barsamian has shared other wider implications of the structured ether.

Over the ages a phenomenon which, as discussed, can have no representation in real (that is, electromagnetic or thermodynamic) terms can hardly have been thought of as possessing specific structure or function. Instead, it signaled its undoubted presence to generations of philosophers and physicists before Einstein, solely through statistical effects.

The writings of Helmholtz, James Clerk Maxwell, and Neils Bohr are examples. The more recent Dirac and Fermi statistics are a continuation of the process.

If an alternative definition of science is the continuing refinement of that which we partially knew or took for granted, then the refinement of these statistical approaches -- with their obligatory uncertainty as defined by Heisenberg — is a worthy goal.

In this sense, a more articulate description of the anatomy of the field is a logical progression from the beginnings of the ether concept in Classical Greece through to the statistics of the nineteenth to the early twentieth century.

A hundred years ago, this orderly progression even reached the concept of a vorticeal atom at the hands of J.J. Thompson. However, it was interrupted very effectively by Einstein's publication of the special theory of relativity.

Einstein was fortunate in that he had chosen for his mathematics a pivotal feature of the ether field, its elasticity. The mathematics of elasticity had been evolving — through the developments of Hooke, Young, invariance, and the calculus — to handle its historically increasing complexity (by tensors). This mathematics of elasticity was then available to Einstein. The wisdom of this choice was vindicated by the remarkable special relativity predictions which were born out in subsequent observation and experiment.

There was seemingly no need to suspect, let alone probe, any special properties of the medium underlying the mathematics.*

The success of these predictions effectively blocked any chance of a return to the ether field concept . Indeed, it was seen as an arrogance to despoil the "elegance" of the mathematics. Nor was the success of quantum mechanics — the other leg of the Western World statistical approach to the nature of reality — able to get the physicists to heed Bohm's 1958 ideas on the hidden variables in its fabric or Dirac's 1952 ideas on a lesser uncertainty of the particle-field relationship than Heisenberg had formulated.

Recently Dr. Barsamian has originated the concept of an **alienation of the electron from its field**. The full expression of this could see the field so alienated that it is well-nigh autonomous, and some kind of fundamental entity in its own right.

In this sense, the freed autonomous field — at least conceptually — could proceed with its creativity by hybridization with other fields and so return the product of these asides to the particle. In atoms of the next fragment of matter with which the particle then associates, this product could create novel properties derived from the interchange.

The multiple properties of such a field allow it to be resolved in EM (electrostatics and electrodynamics), in atomic structure (electrons and nucleons), and in pressure (gravity) terms. This universality makes a new concept possible, long beloved of the GUT (Grand Unified Theory) theorists: that there is only one energy.

It is also quite possible that this ubiquity need not be confined to physics. It may penetrate the biological imponderables of growth, new growth and consciousness.

In view of the work of Dr. Reid and his associates, and other work — such as that of Hines and Chimonas showing atmospheric gravity waves launched by auroral currents — the prospect of amplification and transmission of transforms and patterns over long distances,

*As, for example, whether or not the concept of an abstract vector space in vector mathematics must be modified to correspond to what we know about the vacuum medium. If the vectors are to correspond to the movements of physical things in the *vacuum medium,* then the vector medium must correspond to the vacuum.

through affinity with long distance carriers, is indicated.

Dr. Reid stated that it would be surprising if other laboratories outside Russia had not progressed as far, if not further, than he and his associates had. Obviously the lack of similar publication indicates the nearly impenetrable editorial curtain confronting Western researchers in this and related areas.

Dr. Barsamian's Important Theoretical Insights

Dr. Barsamian has formulated a theory in relation to the development of cancer that is of great importance.

In his theory, he is developing the approach of classical mechanics to electromagnetic interactions between charged particles and between dipoles. The field associated with the primary moving particle is not neglected in his theory, and this part of it differs from Dirac's "new electromagnetic theory."

The field associated with the primary moving particle, in Dr. Barsamian's approach, is viewed as an important part of the particle's interactions. This field is stressed in the sense that diverse phenomena — from Maxwell's EM field radiating from the remotest regions of the universe to the controlled charge flow in the matter medium — are viewed as manifestations of EM forces.

This of course is unlike the traditional relativity view of EM force action on moving charges.

In Dr. Barsamian's view, the potential vectors (derived by a treatment from fluid mechanics theory) form an EM field and are positioned on a vortex curve. All parameters of such a field can be treated mathematically, and Dr. Barsamian has one or more papers presently in publication.

The duality of such potential vectors (gradients) is to conduct the motion of particles (which are always either charged or dipolar) appearing in nonmatter, which is taken as an incompressible continuum — the "void." Because the final results of these forces are always movement of matter, Dr. Barsamian prefers not to classify them by their origin.

Such a field may persist with great permanence. There are some limitations in summation (triplet conditions) and selectivity (periodicity) of the vortices themselves. Part of these limitations takes the form of particle characteristics. Presently he is rather sure that the formation of patterns of organic, inorganic and liquid crystals (typical to living biomatter) are partially responsive to the effect of the described field.

Dr. Barsamian is attempting to synthesize his own experimental findings on the dielectric behavior of biosystems as they enter the cancer process with the data that Dr. Reid is producing with respect to action at a distance.

With respect to living systems, he has slowly been approaching the conclusion that existing physical laws are just not applicable concerning (1) entropy, or (2) energy breakdown, or (3) random collisions of particles in quantum terms, or (4) electron-ion exchanges in bioelectrochemistry terms.

Under such circumstances, it is difficult to find a referee who sincerely understands the related experiments and their underlying theory. This presents a nearly impenetrable barrier to publication in leading scientific journals.

This is tragic, because these considerations and experimental results at least provide an entry into more fundamental experiments with present lethal diseases such as cancer and AIDS which annually take large numbers of human lives.

The present state of the art is telling everyone loud and clear that something fundamental is wrong with present theory, and that we should come to terms with more novel views.

Comment by the present author: In his prophetic insights, Dr. Barsamian has placed his finger squarely on the fundamental struggle of living systems against the "positive energy/time" laws of present physics. In its struggle, the living system must use negative energy/time, to correct from disorder to order and provide the extra free energy to do so. Otherwise, the steady progress toward increasing disorder in all its actions, would very shortly reduce the living system to such a disordered state that it could no longer reproduce the clear genetic pattern of its own kind. We have already pointed out the hitherto unexpected role that phase conjugation plays in allowing the living system to violate and break the iron dictates of conservation, nontransmutation, entropy, and raw statistics.

To live and survive, a living system must have access to other functional levels and other mechanisms beyond those contained in our present physics, electromagnetics, and biochemistry.

The incredibly productive and important work of Drs. Reid, Barsamian, and associates is of the utmost importance. Their work clearly moves everything in biochemistry and the knowledge of cellular functioning a major step forward.

It is a betrayal of the scientific method that such vital work goes so largely unreported in the leading journals. Indeed, the work of these Australian scientists should be galvanized and well-staffed and funded. They can literally usher in a new science, given the chance to further exploit and develop their results.

Royal Raymond Rife

In the 1930's and 1940's, Royal Raymond Rife revolutionized everything that has been done before or since in high resolution optical microscopy.

He also revolutionized everything before or since in cellular biology. He carried cellular structure far beyond anything ever dreamed of at the time or presently. He revealed the direct connection between organized living energy forms and organized biological systems. He revealed that life itself is organized and dynamic, to a far finer level than anything in the textbooks today. **He revealed that our present theory of disease is fundamentally very, very wrong.**

He produced direct, economical, electromagnetic cures of cancer, leukemia, and other such debilitating diseases. His work presages a future mankind could have had, where most debilitating diseases were quickly and economically corrected, and where no poisonous drugs, violent nuclear irradiation, and harsh chemotherapeutic "burning" of the patient would be necessary.

For such epochal work, he was ostracized, essentially imprisoned in a medical treatment facility, broken, condemned, and rejected by his peers. His findings, though printed in reputable publications and journals, were discredited and ridiculed.

He literally was reduced to a non-person by the power of the medical cartel.

Finally escaping from his enforced confinement, he lived out his remaining years and died quietly and unknown.

Rife's Universal Microscope

With his universal microscope, Rife achieved optical resolution of up to 31,000 diameters and magnification up to 60,000 diameters. His microscope could examine living viruses, living bacteria, and other as-yet-undiscovered living organisms and living energy forms that no other microscope before or since could see.

Even today, only the electron microscope furnishes such resolution, and it zaps-to-death the objects that are being examined. Further, it will not at all detect or see the "living energy forms" revealed by Rife's microscope.

To appreciate Rife's accomplishment, let's briefly summarize some of the performance factors of an optical microscope.*

Several factors are important in the functioning of a microscope: Resolution, magnification, and contrast lead the list.

By **resolution** we refer to the ability of the instrument to distinguish a small object. In other words, something like looking at a medical doctor's eye chart, and specifying the smallest print one can clearly see. Resolution is often referred to as resolving power.

By "magnification" or **magnifying power** we mean the ability of the instrument to "blow up" or enlarge the image produced. Roughly, it's the ratio of the apparent size of the object seen through the microscope to the apparent size of the same object seen without the instrument.

Magnifying power is exactly like enlarging a photograph. It won't improve the resolution or make the photograph any clearer, but may make whatever was captured (resolved) easier for the human operator to see. If you just keep enlarging the photograph, it will get more and more grainy, until no further details can be seen with higher magnification.

Contrast refers to the distinctness by which the various parts of the object can be distinguished from one another. To enhance contrast of objects under the microscope, staining of the objects is often used. Very often the act of staining will itself kill the living organisms — such as bacteria — that are being examined.

*The electron microscope reveals only the "dead carnage" of the battlefield after everything is destroyed. With it, one is observing physical residuals, not the living players. For some encouraging modern work, however, see Michael Hercher, "Virometer — an instrument for the measurement of the size of viruses using an optical microscope," **SPIE Seminar Proc.**, 1977, p. 17-22.

Figure 92. Royal Raymond Rife in his laboratory. Courtesy Christopher Bird

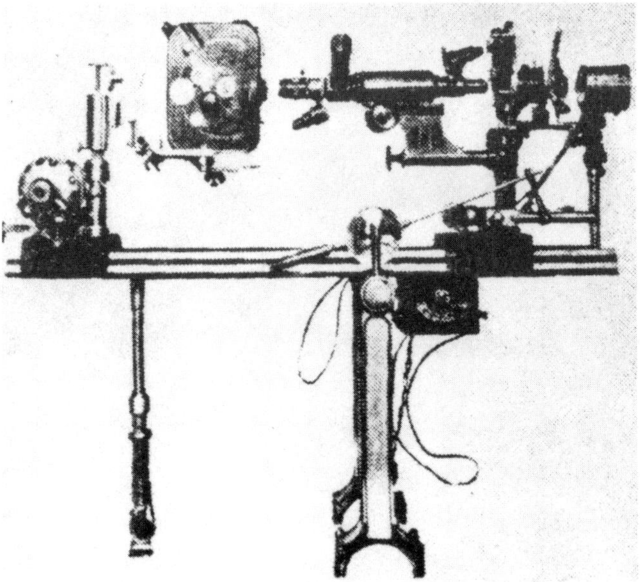

Figure 93. Rife's first virus microscope. Courtesy Christopher Bird

Figure 94. Side view of Royal R. Rife's prismatic universal microscope. Largest and most powerful of five Rife microscopes. With it, living filterable viruses could be observed. Courtesy Christopher Bird.

Figure 95. Front view of Royal R. Rife's prismatic universal microscope. Built in 1933 in Rife's San Diego, California laboratory. Courtesy Chris Bird.

We may state the resolution of an optical microscope in terms of the diameter of the smallest object resolved: for example, so many nanometers. Or we may just simply and loosely speak of so many thousands of diameters.

The resolution of an optical microscope depends upon the illumination conditions, its optical system, and the fact that the object viewed diffracts and spreads the light. A wide variety of mechanisms for illuminating, resolving, contrasting, etc. are used in optical microscopes.

According to standard Rayleigh theory, normal optical microscopes are limited in resolution to about half a wavelength. That corresponds to about 250 nanometers for visible light illumination. One can do a little better than that by using ultraviolet light and quartz optics. The UV has a higher frequency than visible light and hence a shorter wavelength. However, beyond 240 nanometers the resolution of an optical microscope quickly disappears.

A few researchers — notably in the 30's and 40's — remarked about other factors, such as "quality of the lenses," affecting resolution. Some of them reported results to about a tenth of a wavelength. Loosely, that translated to somewhere in the order of 5,000 to 6,000 diameters. The dependable upper limit seemed to be — and still is — about 3,000 diameters, however.

Normal optical microscopes simply are almost useless for trying to look at viruses. They will not resolve any but the very largest viruses, and will not resolve the internal features of even those few giants.

Much of today's knowledge of virus structures and shapes comes from the use of electron microscopes. They bombard the object viewed with a fierce rain of energetic electrons. These instruments see nothing of the *functioning* of the virus, for they kill it instantly in trying to view it.

With Rife's universal microscope, the dynamic living functions of the virus could be observed without killing it.

With Rife's microscope, a whole range of complex organisms and structures below the size of bacteria was revealed. Many of these organisms are still not known to present science, even though some of them were written about at the time. Filterable forms of bacteria

— forms which readily passed through filters supposed to easily block their passage — were discovered and reported by Rife and his medical colleagues.

In addition, Rife's microscope — which contained block-quartz prisms and lenses and interference stages — revealed halos around living organisms that other microscopes could not see, even though the object was within their resolving power. Further, it revealed the existence of entire organisms and forms which other microscopes could not see — even though, again, the size of the organisms was within their resolving power.

In other words, Rife's microscope not only revealed smaller physical forms than any other microscope could see, but it also revealed sizeable "living energy" forms which no other microscope could see.

Rife Proved That Everything Is Alive

The degree of smallness to which Rife's microscope would resolve, and the extraordinary energy forms it could detect, showed that direct detection of the virtual state organization of the living organism was accomplished by the instrument.

The science of the day was only just groping its way toward any sort of physics that could explain such an astounding instrumental result. Today, however, in the hard-core literature there is demonstrated proof that the optical limit of resolution can be drastically overcome, using evanescent waves.*

Shortly we will briefly give an "ad hoc" explanation of such evanescent waves.

Electromagnetism has been shown by Kaluza-Klein theory to actually exist in the fifth dimension. In other words, EM itself is hyperdimensional. It flows in the fifth dimension, which is "wrapped around" each point in our ordinary space. It is — to the first approximation — the external environment of every normal point in

*E.g., see T. Sato et al, "Application of evanescent waves to microscopic observation," **Bull. Tokyo Inst. Technol.** (Japan), No. 125, 1974. p. 35-41. See also G.A. Massey, "Microscopy and pattern generation with scanned evanescent waves," **Appl. Opt.** (Poland), 13(3), 1983. p. 247-255.

our 3-space.

Let's say that again.

The electromagnetics "medium" itself is totally external to each point in our space. Each of our points is surrounded in higher space by the electromagnetic medium.

We live inside a totally electromagnetic medium. It's not just an "electromagnetic environment" in our own space; instead, it's an electromagnetic environment in hyperspace.

Everything already is just the internal structure of the electromagnetic medium!

That's what the "vacuum" is.
That's what "spacetime" is.
That's what the "virtual state" is.
That's what physical matter is.

And it's all alive. Totally and completely alive. Everything is alive. There is nothing but life. The electromagnetic medium is alive.

Except within a locally-organized biopotential area, it's just "equally alive in all directions." So it appears inert, where by "inert" *we mean not singly preferential.*

Every biopotential change, at any level in a biopotential, extends "decaying-expotential-wise" to infinity, by standard theory. Part of that potential change exists at every point in the entire spatial universe. And there at that point, so do the biopotential changes for every other biosystem in the universe.

Everything's alive. There is nothing but life. Anywhere. Anytime.

An interchange between this "living, surrounding electromagnetic medium" and each particle of mass in our 3-space continually occurs. This exchange involves the so-called virtual particle flux.

If we model higher dimensions, such as are necessary to include the "particle zoo" discovered by modern particle physics, each of these "higher dimensions" corresponds to a "successively deeper" internested level of virtual particle flux—of the vacuum, or of this electromagnetic medium that surrounds us.

The living system orders, structures, and dynamically functions and interchanges electromagnetically throughout many higher "dimensions" — throughout many such internested levels of virtual-state/vacuum/spacetime.

Except for the first layer of virtual state (the 5th dimension in Kaluza-Klein theory), gross (classical) electromagnetic theory totally ignores the infolded, ordered deeper structure of electromagnetism (of the EM medium).

Using such gross electromagnetics, orthodox science thus can only detect and grasp the gross results of the living organism's functioning. Further, it can only detect and grasp those gross results that actually move 3-space matter — observable particles.

So it only detects the grossest interchanges between "mind" or "life" and matter. Specifically, it only detects the final results of that interchange — the gross movement of material particles themselves.

The first hypernumber — "i," the square root of minus 1 — is used to model another dimension at right angles to our normal three. An electromagnetic wave thus is modeled to have two parts: the first is the part that affects or moves a material particle, and that's called the "real" part or "observable" part. The second part of the EM wave is the component that lies in this "imaginary" (unfortunate standard term!) dimension. That imaginary part does not of itself move charged particles, so it is considered to be "something other than real."

Note that what's really done in this sort of orthodox modeling is to define observation as the movement of observable charged particles.

The human "conscious mind" is a functioning part of the overall human mind that has been specifically fitted to function almost totally with our gross bodily detection of the photon interaction.

We thus consciously detect and "are aware of" only the first level of reality: the interface between the first layer of virtual-state/ vacuum/spacetime/ and the 3-space of observable particles of mass.

Since the physicist must be "conscious" of his observation or instrumental detection, the detection process ultimately has to have a final stage that produces a photoelectric interaction with his body — for that is all the conscious mind detects and processes.

Everything chemical, electrical, etc. — according to quantum mechanics — will involve at its root level only the photoelectric effect.

Rife's Microscope Used Evanescent Waves

However, it is certainly possible to build an instrument which is multi-staged, and one in which higher stages interact primarily with deeper internested levels of vacuum virtual state. That is, an instrument that interacts with higher dimensional phenomena. That is, one that interacts with deeper internested levels of electromagnetics. If these stages interact causally in a vertical manner, then the final interaction with the human body and nervous system can still be "normal electromagnetics" and yet indicate a higher dimensional phenomenon, event, or function.

That is precisely what Rife did: His universal microscope penetrated to a much finer level of reality because its multiple stages used **evanescent waves.**

Here's what we mean by that.

An electromagnetic wave consists of a "real" part and an "imaginary" part, as we have discussed. It's possible, however, to have the real part become zero, and still have the "imaginary" part remain and dynamically vary.

This sort of wave — containing only the "imaginary" part — is said to be one type of **complex wave**, or an **evanescent wave**.

In advanced EM waveguide and optical theory, such evanescent waves can function to guide or determine the real parts of the EM waves. That "real part" is the part that is then going to interact with electrons and move them, and give us a "detection."

In other words, the "real" part of the EM wave will be moved and guided by the "higher dimensional" or evanescent part, or even by separated evenescent parts — pure evanescent waves.

So one can build a device or instrument that utilizes such an effect to reveal what's going on in a whole dimension beyond what we normally see. Waveguides in certain RF radars already do that.

Such instruments are not limited to the resolution determined by the "real" part of the EM wave (such as the "real part" of light).

Such a microscope would not necessarily be limited in resolution by the wavelength of the light it used to illustrate the observed object.

Indeed, if one uses a higher dimensional Kaluza-Klein model (which particle physics of necessity has to consider), one could build a "repetitive stages" instrument which could view many more higher dimensions. That's exactly the same thing as viewing many more deeper internested levels of virtual state.

That is precisely what Royal R. Rife did: **He developed a microscope using multiple stages, special interferences, etc. He built a multistaged evanescent wave instrument that could see into higher dimensions and deeper levels of virtual state.**

Rife's microscopes were thus startlingly different from normal microscopes. That is why he could see phenomena and organisms, ostensibly within the size capability of normal microscopic resolution, which ordinary microscopes could not see.*

Evanescent waves penetrate the virtual state (hyperdimensions) and interact with what to us is "dimensionless" (what does not spatially intersect our 3-space). Interfering multiple evanescent waves reflected from/having interacted with these (to us) nonphysical forms can again reproduce ordinary electromagnetic "light." Thus the evanescent wave microscope, if properly built, allows one to directly "see" (and photograph) what is to us living forms of energy, nonphysical, and without 3-space matter bodies.**

The same scheme can be used to develop instruments capable of directly revealing the living nonphysical world around us — such as the human biopotentials, their internal structures (including

*However, Rife's microscope was extraordinarily difficult to focus. Rife often spent 24 hours straight at his universal microscope, just in focusing it.

**If one is going to accept the many-dimensional theories necessary to explain particle physics, one must accept the possibility of higher dimensional living things, which we would "see" as living energy forms or as thought forms. These would appear nonphysical to us -- as is time itself -- but would be real and interactive nonetheless.

"thought forms"), etc. What the Soviets call **bioplasma** can be directly observed and photographed in this fashion. We have only to develop the necessary instruments; the science required is difficult, but it is already in the literature.

That is what Rife's microscope did. It was a forerunner of the instruments we need to develop in electromagnetic healing, and Rife was a truly great and unappreciated pioneer.

In one swoop medical science could have jumped a century ahead. The ruthless suppression of Rife and his fantastic scientific breakthrough was one of the most dastardly deeds ever perpetuated by the orthodox scientific establishment.

Rife Revealed a Far More Fundamental, Living Biology

With Rife's powerful universal microscope, it was also possible to view the interiors of the so-called "pinpoint" cells situated between normal tissue cells and just barely visible to ordinary microscopes.

Here is the astonishing living world inside those "pinpoint" cells, as revealed under Rife's powerful instrument: When one of the "pinpoint" cells was magnified, still smaller cells were revealed within its structure. When one of these still-smaller cells, in turn, was magnified, it too was seen to be composed of even smaller cells.

With Rife's microscope, this process could be repeated 16 times. An astonishing internested series of organized levels of a living cell was revealed, far more fundamental than anything that exists in present biological theory.

The present author points out most strongly that these levels correspond electrically to, and are in virtual particle flux pattern exchange with, the electromagnetic potentials of their environment. This includes their own biopotentials that are centered in the atomic nuclei of the atoms comprising the physical material of the cells, and that charge up with specific internal patterns.

The biopotential itself is organized into a corresponding virtual-state series of internested levels and functions. **The structured biopotential of the cell is a living, organized, functioning thing, and its internal functioning literally constitutes the "spirit" or "true nonmaterial deep mind" of the organism.**

All the internested levels are in constant electromagnetic exchange "up and down" with each other, particularly with respect to organized virtual particle flux patterns.

In addition, all the cells are in constant electromagnetic exchange "across" with each other, at all levels. This provides a dynamic, structured, living biopotential for the entire bio-organism (the entire body). Within this potential, dynamic interchange on all levels is continually occurring. This is the basis for the master cellular communication system that Dr. Fritz Albert Popp discovered.

Rife's powerful microscope had revealed nonmaterial functioning life forms (structured, dynamic, living biopotentials) connected to material bodies.

He could follow "filterable" forms of bacteria — actual living biopotential forms of the organisms that could not be separated out by filters, but which would easily pass through any filter.* He could observe interactions of these forms, changes of forms, translations and transmissions of forms, etc. — none of which is detectable by present biological theory or medical science.

Rife had advanced biology and biophysics a century in one jump. As always, orthodox scientists — most of whom in their scientific paradigm are self-admitted materialists — were quite unready to tolerate such heresy.

Obviously the materialistic dogma of the science of his day — and of the science of today — reacted most hostilely to such hogwash. Contrary to the prevailing mystique, most scientists are dogmatically attached to materialism and to the dogma of their present paradigm. Faced with a conflict provided by experiment, most will uphold the dogma and reject the experiment — the exact opposite of the scientific method they espouse.

Rife's revolutionary work was no exception. He incurred the unending, total opposition of powerful individuals controlling the direction of biology and medical science for their own personal gains.

Rife was hounded into court on trumped up charges. Though he was acquitted, he emerged a shaken, broken man and an alcoholic.

*More precisely, they would easily flow *around* the 3-dimensional filter, since they were hyperdimensional.

His work was suppressed. His equipment was left to gather dust. He was also forcibly committed to a medical treatment facility.

Finally escaping from his "prison," Rife lived out his remaining years quietly. He died without ever being vindicated for his marvelous, world-shaking discoveries.

But at least he left us a legacy. Persons are still alive who knew Rife and his work, to one degree or another. Some of his microscopes are still in existence, though non-operable due to missing or stolen parts. With proper funding, an enlightened team of scientists and researchers can be assembled to quickly repair Rife's remaining instruments and duplicate his incredible work.

With concentrated effort, Rife's work will yet play a primary role in the development of a direct electromagnetic cure for AIDS. As a byproduct, it will play a role in rapid development of cures for cancer and other debilitating diseases.

Royal R. Rife's contributions may yet help save half of humanity, and prevent a Soviet takeover of the world.

CHAPTER 6

DEVELOPING THE ELECTROMAGNETIC CURE FOR AIDS

By now, how one goes about developing a electromagnetic cure for AIDS — and for cancer and other killer diseases — should be apparent.

One must set up a modern research laboratory and assemble as many of the "dirty dozen" together as is possible. One then tackles the problem head-on, adding the necessary support staff and special consultants.

First the Kaznacheyev effect for AIDS must be isolated and determined. Then it must be reversed, to yield the precise "curative" signal.

Transforms for these Kaznacheyev IR/UV "death photons" and their phase conjugated "healing photons" must be obtained for a lower electromagnetic frequency band — such as, say, 10 to 20 gigahertz.

A way must be found to irradiate the whole human body with the curative signal. The ideal way is to utilize a scalar EM curative transform so that the atomic nuclei of the body — and hence its entire master cellular control system and immune control system — will be "charged up" with the correctly structured "AIDS cancellation message."

The entire procedure and apparatus must be as simple and small as possible. My colleagues have already achieved very promising — even remarkable — progress in this respect.

Reversing the Kaznacheyev Effect

The "Kaznacheyev effect" for AIDS virus condition must be stimulated between cell cultures, so that the disease condition is electromagnetically transferred from one to another. The actual electromagnetic "delta" constituting the contribution of the AIDS infection must then be isolated electronically. The best way to do this is probably to subtract the normal cell radiation pattern from the "cell plus AIDS" radiation pattern.*

With the "AIDS delta" determined, the delta is then fed into the appropriate phase conjugating mirror system, so that its time reversed replica is produced.

The new phase conjugated signal is then the required *AIDS reversal signal* to reverse the effects of the AIDS virus itself, inside the cell where it resides dormant. This " time-reversed" signal will reverse the genetic change in the cell, not just kill the HIV virus.

In a crude way, one is making an **electromagnetic anti-virus.**

For ease of development and treatment, microwave technology is most attractive. Obtaining transforms of the signals in the radar band is ideal, since a wide variety of techniques, instruments, and electronic parts are available for that region. Millimeter waves would be most attractive, for the equipment could then be highly miniaturized.

One can regard it another way also: energy forms (critters) are involved. The action of the AIDS virus in its host cell, upon the DNA of the host, is underlaid by manipulation of energy critters. If one makes the electromagnetic anti-virus form, one is also manipulating the energy critters in their virtual state substrata.

The net result is that essentially the virus pattern — even the virus itself — can be phase conjugated by the energy critters. The result can be to turn the actual virus in the cell into a negative virus, accomplishing recombinant DNA procedures in reverse.

Remember that the signal we seek to use involves negative energy and negative time. We are also engineering the virtual state directly. The ordinary positive energy/positive time/ observable state rules and limitations do not necessarily apply. And the "fixed form" first order physical reality as we normally conceive it need not

*Procedures along the lines of the extraordinary double-exposure holographic work of Dr. Robert Powell will probably be necessary. His work on biologically significant spatial frequency spectroscopy has blazed the trail as to how to obtain the specific delta patterns desired. It is hoped that Powell will shortly publish the remarkable results of his 15 years' work.

be so fixed at all.

Physical reality itself can be directly engineered.

The engineering we seek to accomplish is directly upon the probability states propagated by the Schroedinger equation, before observation and collapse of the wave function occurs. **We seek to engineer physical reality before it is born, while it is yet forming.**

Only at such a level can the previous action of the AIDS virus — that in which it combined its genetic material with the genetic material of the host cell — be reversed and undone.

Only at such a level can we convert the infected human body from an "AIDS virus factory" back to an uninfected normal human body without AIDS.

The Proof: Priore's Work

Antoine Priore's pioneering work largely proves that it can be done. Cancers, leukemias, and many other virulent diseases yielded to his phase conjugated signals passed down through a powerful magnetic field to totally penetrate every cell in the treated patient's body.

And Royal R. Rife's work proved that a virus and a bacterium are not at all the "rigidly fixed" physical forms that our normal science has led us to believe they are. Instead, both the organisms and their biochemical and genetic actions can be addressed — and changed — on a much finer level of reality.

Of course, it would be enormously helpful if one had a working Rife microscope.

My colleagues are attempting to rebuild one of the original Rife microscopes, which has parts that were missing from it. They have every hope of having the microscope in action in the future.

Another angle of attack is also possible.

One of my colleagues has discovered a very peculiar, weak electromagnetic signal that will kill viruses, harmful bacteria, toxic protozoa, etc. but not harm living human cells. Only a few volts and a few milliamps are used.

However, there exists a major problem in getting any such very weak signal into every cell in the body — which is required if one is to heal blood diseases such as AIDS and leukemia. After all, that was the reason that Priore utilized a powerful magnetic field of thousands of gauss. The magnetic field penetrated every cell in the body — even those in the bone marrow where all the blood cells are manufactured. By using the all-penetrating field as the carrier, the phase conjugated healing signal pattern could thus be introduced into every cell in the body, bathing it completely, inside and out, with the restorative signal.

Remember, one must not just get the signal into the cells themselves — instead, one must get the restorative signals directly into, and absorbed in, the atomic nuclei.

Again, that is why Antoine Priore found it necessary to employ a "rippling" magnetic field. The "ripple" was actually a magnetic wave, and nuclear resonance then provided the magic mechanism to penetrate all the atomic nuclei.

So the initial problem is, how does one provide a mechanism to carry the desired signals into and through each and every cell of the body and into each and every atomic nucleus of the matter of the body?

Obviously one can utilize nuclear magnetic resonance, after the fashion of Priore. If so, the resulting apparatus is going to be extremely large and expensive. It would be highly desirable to do it a different, simpler, much cheaper way.

After many hundreds of back-breaking experiments, one of my colleagues appears to have discovered a completely unique and direct way of introducing the desired EM restorative signals into and completely through every cell of the body, and into every atomic nucleus. Though much additional work to confirm this still remains, the initial results are marvelously encouraging.

Another colleague has succeeded in developing a peculiar sort of detector that should prove adaptable to detecting the actual "biopotential structural patterns" themselves, directly in and out of the atomic nuclei. Though obviously much more work is necessary before the final instrumentation is ready, the preliminary results are again most encouraging.

As I write these words on paper, this work is proceeding, but very, very slowly due to lack of the necessary funds to attack the research problems in force.

What is Needed

Time is running out —most conventional science appears to be driven by special interest groups/Drug Manufacturers who are unable and/or unwilling to counter the AIDS epidemic with anything other than extensive "Addict Style" symptom-reducing drugs that generate dollars, not cures. Though this is not universal, it *is* the conventional norm.

Unconventional disorders or diseases require *unconventional* science for *unconventional* cures.

Immediate funding is required if this awesome threat to humanity is to be stopped. An American public alerted in time to this desperate situation can demand that the government and/or private business immediately address and act on this life-threatening issue in a different, unconventional manner.

Encouraging Preliminary Work

One of my associates, already familiar with scalar EM devices, has exerted every effort to try to reduce the scope of the problem. In literally hundreds of experiments, he has been able to narrow down the search, and obtain at least some very promising results.

He has obtained an initial candidate phase conjugated signal for further test and trial.

He may well have succeeded in discovering a new and unique method to communicate signals directly into the atomic nuclei inside the matter in the human body. This signal presently appears to directly interact with the cellular biopotential and with the body's master cellular communication system.

Remember, however, these are preliminary results. They still must be fully substantiated in a great many more tests. Undoubtedly a great deal more research, analysis, and adaptation is necessary. We certainly cannot presently say we have any sort of "cure" — for the AIDS virus or anything else — or that these results are to be considered as proven in any fashion.

But what we can say is that my colleague has been able to derive a very complicated phase-conjugated signal, which produces negative energy and negative time of the general sort required. And he may just have made a most marvelous discovery that will point the way to eventual equipment much, much smaller than the 4-stories high machine with which Priore intended to treat terminal human cancer patients.

The initial signal discovered by my colleague, when applied to the body at miniscule voltage, seems to zap all sorts of "bad things" — viruses, harmful bacteria, dangerous protozoa, microworms, you name it — without harming the blood cells, the normal body cells, or the hosted friendly bacteria.

The signal does this at miniscule voltage and amperage.

It can be applied directly to the body through special electrodes. Through a special feature, my colleague has been able to get the signal to reverberate the entire body, all cells, all parts, and even penetrate the atomic nuclei and establish scalar resonance therein.

There turned out to be some extremely strange things that have to be done to the phase conjugated signal before it will accomplish what is being sought. At least some of these "strange things" have been uncovered by my colleague.

One of the peculiarities is that the entire electrical apparatus is part of the input "form" (that conditions the potential wave structure) being phase conjugated and sent to the organism. If a lead-acid battery is included in the apparatus to power it, one will inject the electromagnetic form for the battery acid directly into the organism,* destroying it. This includes destroying the host's cells. In this case the signal is lethal, not curative. Substitution of a dry cell battery with no liquid electrolyte eliminates the problem. Exactly why a liquid electrolyte has a toxic effect and a "sludge" or solid electrolyte does not, is not understood at this time.

Other such anomalies in the tentative process have been discovered and compensated for.

However, the way ahead is exciting. It suggests that the body

*Via a mechanism similar to that found by Reid and Barsamian.

(atomic nuclei) can literally be "charged up" (i.e., the living biopotentials can be "charged up" with the signal structure) so that the "disease-proofing" is very lasting, possibly for many years or even for a lifetime.

At least my colleague has pressed this to the point of demonstrating a long-lasting charge being acquired by the body.

For example, at one time his body became so "charged" from his lengthy experiments that a one-inch blue spark often leaped from his fingers when he reached out for something metallic. The discharge was cool, negative energy — living energy, if you will. It should be negentropic, not entropic. It was definitely not the type of energy the orthodox scientific community is accustomed to. And normal electricity will definitely not charge up the body in such a continuing fashion, so far as is known.

Let me clearly state again that we have not yet produced the specific anti-pattern per se. What my colleagues have discovered appears to be a broad-band signal that appears to act hyperspatially, analogous to the manner in which a broad-band drug such as penicillin acts biochemically. Even this much remains to be clearly established.

However, it is a most encouraging and promising first step.

Much more work, and a great deal of experiments to substantiate or adapt these tentative results, still need to be done. Now there is no substitute for rigor and thoroughness — and there is no substitute for clearly and scientifically demonstrating the proof of the concept in the laboratory.

It is not just good intentions that we seek, but solid, concrete, proven results substantiated by proper scientific procedures. Much work remains to be done.

But the preliminary results are very encouraging indeed.

Let me briefly share with you some of the things we foresee, if this present line of successful development continues.

We foresee being able to eventually develop and set up — legally and under proper medical auspices, of course — tested and proven devices that can easily treat up to two or three hundred persons at once. A treatment of about 45 minutes to one hour is all that would be required. Several repetitive treatments a week or so apart, might prove advisory.

In addition,once the entire gamut of the treatment process is validated and proven, and shown to be completely harmless and safe in accordance with legal medical requirements, if need arises we foresee simply adding the signal to ordinary radio and television transmitters — perhaps as simply as modulating the electrical ground. If so, a "maintenance" signal could be established to negate the AIDS virus (or other disease such as cancer and leukemia) in an entire area, and keep out other diseases such as malaria, sleeping sickness, etc.

Another advantage of such machines would be their portability in time of conflict. Also, they would be most useful indeed as defensive measures against biological warfare. For example, the inhalation of only a relative minor amount of anthrax agent is sufficient for 100 percent certain death unless treatment begins promptly. With the portable machines, however, this would be easily negated in any troops exposed to the agent, even before the lethal disease is evidenced. For a totally new agent, a "phase-conjugate delta signal" could be rather quickly ascertained and developed, and the proper settings made on the machines for immediate treatment and immunizing.

And even later, when we proceed to the direct engineering of the living energy form strata themselves, we shall see remarkable cures and remissions of diseases for which medical science offers little hope today. Arthritis, multiple schlerosis, lupus, and other such debilitating diseases come readily to mind. **Even reversal of the aging process should be possible.***

*Two other promising approaches have recently been discovered. First, an electrolyte compound has recently been approved by the FDA for clinical testing. This compound has the remarkable property of raising the cellular electrical potential back to that of a strong, healthy cell. In several years of lab animal testing, this alone was indicated to be over 80% effective against cancer. It may also prove effective against diseases such as arthritis, where the body's immune system attacks body tissue with lowered cellular potentials, since it fails to recognize the weakened cells as those of the body. Second, Baylor University reseachers have found that treating blood with certain laser EM radiation kills the AIDS virus, but does not harm the blood cells. This means that it will be possible to assure that blood used in transfusions will be AIDS – free, eliminating one source of AIDS transmission.

Conclusion

We have now come to the end of our road, literally and figuratively.

All of us have been struck a mortal blow by the Soviet AIDS first strike.

Make no mistake, this is **real**. We and our children are already as good as dead unless we move as we have never moved before.

We have a chance. A slim chance.

Americans have always come through when the chips are down. We can conquer this thing. We can overcome this mighty death blow that has been launched against us. We can defeat the others yet to come.

But we've got to move. *Now.*

Remember, Pandora's box has already been spilled. Even without the Soviet biological warfare strike, hosts of new viruses and different strains of old ones are going to be, and are now being, dumped into the biosphere by our own culture. It is also only a matter of time before terrorists and meglomaniacs turn to the use of this potent weapon against a wide-open society such as ours.

Both our Armed Forces and our civilian populace are totally defenseless against electromagnetic biological warfare. Now. At this moment.

Even without the Soviet BW strike implication, it is only a matter of time until we perish, unless we develop electromagnetic healing and electromagnetic biological warfare countermeasures.

We've come to one of those profound momentary pauses in history that determine the fate of the entire world henceforth.

It's like the parable of the lady or the tiger.

We're facing, so to speak, two doors.

Behind one is the most fearsome and hungry tiger of all time. If we delay, that door will open and we'll get the tiger full upon us. We shall be utterly destroyed. That mighty tiger will consume half the world in his roaring frenzy. Our children, and our children's children — what few of them will be left — will wear the hammer and sickle yoke for eons.

Those few future survivors will be taught strange things. How you and I were the real enemy. How we were absolutely destroyed for the good of all mankind. How glorious and necessary it was to unleash the great plagues upon us. And how heroic were those who performed the "noble deed."

Our own distant children will curse us and revile us, and they will be taught to worship at the throne of a false prophet.

The world will descend into a new "Dark Ages" far more frightful than George Orwell ever envisioned.

On the other hand, behind the second door is the most beautiful lady of all history. Literally all of humanity's dreams of health, beauty, and vitality lie behind that door.

If we open it, we achieve a freedom from disease and a measure of bountiful health for all mankind that has heretofore only been dreamed of. *Even reversal of the aging process itself lies beyond the second door. Health and youth — the dream of the ages — can be ours.*

But we have only a moment to open the second door. It is firmly shut, and we must exert ourselves to the fullest if we are to open it at all.

On the human stage, the first door is already slowly opening, inexorably. In only a few moments it will be open and the tiger will be upon us.

We must move quickly.

Which will it be for mankind, the lady or the tiger?

The next few moments in the human play will most assuredly tell.

SELECTED BIBLIOGRAPHY

Note: An extended bibliography for this book would consist of literally thousands of references. Since there has not been time for that, a few key references on most substantive matters are listed. Where possible, one or more of the listed references will direct the interested reader to the pertinent literature on that subject.

References Related to Chapters 1 and 2

1. Pearce Wright, Science Editor: "Smallpox vaccine 'triggered Aids virus'," **The Times** of London, Mon. May 11, 1987, p. 1, 18.

2. Jon Rappoport, "News blackout on pox vaccine link to AIDS protecting WHO?", **Easy Reader**, June 4, 1987, p. 12.

3. Jonathan Tennenbaum, "Parameters for a research mobilization against AIDS," **Executive Intelligence Review (EIR)**, Science & Technology, Mar. 6, 1987. p. 38-45.

4. Steve Connor, "AIDS: mystery of the missing data," **New Scientist**, Feb. 12, 1987, p. 19.

5. Steve Connor, "AIDS: Science stands on trial," **New Scientist**, Feb. 1987, p. 49-54.

6. "The virus reveals the naked truth," **New Scientist**, Feb. 12, 1987, p. 55-58.

7. Michael Gold, "Cancer Cover-up: How honest scientists evaded the issue of renegade cells that contaminated research labs worldwide," **Science Digest**, May 1986, p. 64-67, 80-81.

8. Michael Gold, **A conspiracy of Cells**, State University of New York Press, Albany, New York, 1985.

9. Kenneth J. McLeod, Raphael C. Lee, and H. Paul Ehrlich, "Frequency Dependence on Electric Field Modulation of Fibroblast Protein Synthesis," **Science**, Vol. 236, Jun. 12, 1987, p. 1465-1468.

10. "Leukemia Virus Linked to Nerve Disease," **Science**, Vol.236, May 29, 1987, p. 1059-1061.

11. R.C. Desrosiers, "Origin of the human AIDS virus," **Nature**, vol. 319, 1986, p. 728.

12. R.B. Strecker, "AIDS virus infection," **J.R. Soc. Med.**, Vol 79, 1986, p. 559-560.

13. S.A. Aaronson, "Common Genetic Alterations of RNA Tumor Viruses grown in Human Cells," **Nature**, Vol. 230, 1971, p. 445-447.

14. A. Chandra et al, "Serological relationship between reverse transcriptase from human T-cell lymphotropic viruses defined by monoclonal antibodies," **FEBS Lett.**, Vol. 200, 1986, 327-332.

15. E. Dermott, J.K. Clarke and J. Samuels, "The Morphogenesis and Classification of Bovine Syncytial Virus," **J. Gen. Virol**. 1971; 12:105-119.

16. G. Corneo and L.C. Nelli, "Could Bovine Leukemia Virus be a possible Agent of Some Human Lymphatic Leukemias?", **Acta Haemat**. 72; 1984:65-66.

17. C.A. Mims, "Vertical Transmission of Viruses," **Microbiol. Rev**. 45; 1981:267-286.

18. C.W. Molander et al, "Isolation and Characterization of Viruses from Fetal Calf Serum," **In Vitro** 1972; 7:168-173.

19. P. Legrain, B. Goud and B. Buttin, "Increase of Retroviral Infection in Vitro by the Binding of Antiretroviral Antibodies," **J. Virol**. 1986; 60:1141-1144.

20. S. Kennedy -Stoskopf and O. Narayan, "Neutralizing Antibodies to Visna Lentivirus: Mechanism of Action and Possible Role in Virus Persistence," **J. Virol.** 1986; 59:37-44.

21. E.K. Knott, "Development of Ultraviolet Blood Irradiation, **Am. J. Surg**. 1948; 76:165-171.

22. Dr. John Seale, "The Origins of AIDS," Mar. 15, 1987.

23. R.B. Strecker and T.A. Strecker, "The Bioattack Alert (on AIDS)," Los Angeles, California, 1986.

24. R.B. Strecker, "Aids Virus Infection," **J.R. Soc. Med.**, vol. 79, Summer 1986, p. 559-560.

25. T.E. Bearden, "AIDS: Urgent Comments on Mankind's Greatest Threat," June 1987. Privately printed and circulated. "Aids: Urgent Comments on Mankind's Greatest Threat; and the Secrets of Electromagnetic Healing," presented in absentia at the U.S.P.A. Annual Symposium, July 30-Aug. 2, 1987, Golden, Colorado.

26. **Executive Intelligence Review (EIR)** Special Report, "Global Showdown: The Russian Imperial War Plan for 1988," July 24, 1985.

27. **Executive Intelligence Review (EIR)** Special Report, "The Soviet role in covering up the deadly threat of AIDS," 12(42), Oct. 25, 1985. Charges that Soviet infectious-disease experts control the Communicable Diseases Division of the World Health Organization. Nearly hysterical responses were stimulated by this report: for example, less than a week later, **Literaturnaya Gazeta**, Oct. 30, 1985 published a counter, and claimed the AIDS virus may have been produced in U.S. laboratories by the CIA and the Pentagon.

28. Jeanne Toal, "Supervaccines," **Omni**, July 1987, p. 20, 122.

29. The Kaznacheyev work. See appropriate section for references.

30. The Priore work. See appropriate section for references.

31. William Kucewicz, "The gates slam shut on a microbiologist," "Beyond Yellow Rain: The Threat of Soviet Genetic Engineering," Sixth of a Series, **Wall Street Journal**, May 8, 1984. p. 34.

32. Department of Defense, **Soviet Military Power**, 1987.

33. William Kucewicz, "A non-stop Russian response to WWI," "Beyond Yellow Rain: The Threat of Soviet Genetic Engineering," Seventh of a Series, **Wall Street Journal**, May 10, 1984. p. 34.

34. Lewin, Leonard C., **Report from Iron Mountain on the**

Possibility and Desirability of Peace. The Dial Press, New York, 1967. If you want to read something that will curdle your blood, take a look at this book. There exists a surprising body of material where intelligentsia and "think tank" mentalities have grappled with the idea of non-warfare types of "control mechanisms" for humanity — including induction of biological disease on a mass scale, subtle forms of slavery, etc.

35. Bennett, William and Joel, Gurin, "Science that Frightens Scientists," **Atlantic Monthly**, Feb. 1977. Millions of persons in this country were inadvertently injected with a widely-used substance called simian virus 40, or SV40. Tests proved that SV40 caused cancerous cell growth when injected into animals. SV40 was an unrecognized contamination of polio vaccines given before 1962 and of some cold shots given about the same time. The authors conclude by stating: "The ultimate question is not whether bacteria can be contained in special laboratories, but whether scientists can be contained in an ordinary society."

36. Letter, Lynn M. Draft, White House Policy Staff, to Dick Gregory, April 11, 1977. Quoting: "It is true that the SV40 virus was discovered in the early 1960's. It is also true that the virus was found in certain viral vaccines prepared from virus pools grown in monkey kidney cell cultures. However, the virus had not been recognized as a contaminant prior to that time, although millions of people have received the vaccine during the 1950's."
"... contamination of the vaccine was unintentional due to lack of knowledge."

37. Snead, Dr. Eva Lee, M.D. "AIDS - Immunization related syndrome," **Health Freedom News**, July 1987, p. 14-17, 22, 44-45. Strongly and rigorously points out just now little we actually know, even today, about the cause of AIDS and some of the anomalies connected with it. Specifically, SV40 does not appear to have been searched for in AIDS victims. Lack of detection has little meaning, since SV-40 may disappear and not reappear until triggered or promoted by another virus or chemical. Yet SV-40 has been shown to be one of the activators of the HIV or AIDS virus, as reported by Howard E. Gendelman et.al, in an article published in the **Proceedings of the National Academy of the United States of America**, vol. 83, p. 9759-9763, Dec. 1986. Also, SV-40 carries other viruses

"piggyback" and may have that type of role in AIDS disease. SV-40 may predispose one to a secondary infection by nullifying the immune system. SV40 is ideally suited for genetic manipulation, splicing, and the creation of hybrids or mutants. Dr. Snead rigorously points out that no one has proved as yet that any virus positively causes AIDS. What has been proven is that HTLV-III is present in large percentages of the AIDS victims. Dr. Snead raises many excellent issues which cry out for answers.

38. Pearl Ma and Donald Armstrong, **The Acquired Immune Deficiency Syndrome and Infections of Homosexual Men**, Yorke Medical Books, 1984.

39. Ostrow, David G; Terri A. Sandholzer and Yehudi M. Felman, Eds., **Sexually Transmitted Diseases in Homosexual Men**, Plenum books, 1984.

40. Snead, Dr. Eva Lee, M.D., **aids-update**, Jun. 15, 1987. In this incisive summary, Dr. Snead "tells it like it is" about Salk vaccine, how vaccines are made, the lack of sufficient scientific accuracy and safety in making vaccines, the nearly general contamination of vaccines by at least some viruses, some macabre details of the constitution of the vaccine 'soups." etc.

41. Gallo, Robert C., "The AIDS Virus," **Scientific American**, 256 (1), Jan. 1987, p. 46-56.

42. **Institut Pasteur v. United States of America**, United States Court of Claims, Civ. A. No. 730-85. See also Steve Connor, "AIDS: Science Stands On Trial," **New Scientist**, Feb. 12, 1987, p. 49-58. Reveals some direct monetary interests involved in discovery of the AIDS virus, and in royalties for the blood test which detects the antibody to the virus. Extended litigation occurred between French scientists at the Pasteur Institute and Robert Gallo regarding who should receive credit for discovery of the virus causing AIDS. The two sides eventually agreed to share the credit for the discovery, and donate royalties to an AIDS research foundation. Note that Dr. Gallo is head of the Laboratory of Tumor Cell Biology at the National Cancer Institute.

43. Curran, James W. et al, "The Epidemiology of AIDS: Current Status and Future Prospects," **Science**, vol. 229, Sep.27,

1985, p. 1352-57. Among other things, this report downplays the role of non-viral agents in causing AIDS.

44. Duesberg, Peter H., "Retroviruses as Carcinogens and Pathogens: Expectations and Reality," **Cancer Research**, vol. 47, Mar. 1, 1987, p. 1199-1220. Cites 278 references. Duesburg is a pioneer in the study of retroviruses and a professor in the Department of Molecular Biology and Virus Laboratory, University of California at Berkeley. To show some of the scientific disagreement as to the cause of AIDS, we quote from Dr. Duesberg's article: "AIDS virus is not sufficient to cause AIDS and ... there is no evidence, besides its presence in a latent form, that it is necessary for AIDS." Dr. Duesberg presents an impressive set of technical objections to the present theory that the accepted AIDS virus actually causes AIDS.

45. **Steadman's Medical Dictionary**, Williams and Wilkins, Baltimore, 1966. p. 874. A German bacteriologist named Robert Koch established three "laws" to determine whether a certain micro-organism is the cause of a specific disease. These laws provide a basis for scientifically investigating infection and its causes. Koch's laws are: (1) Whether it be a bacterium, protozoan, or virus, the micro-organism must be present in all cases of the disease. (2) Inoculating animals with pure cultures of the micro-organism must produce the same disease in them. (3) It must be possible to obtain the micro-organism from these animals and further propagate the micro-organism in pure cultures. (Note that this leaves a real problem with any disease caused by complexes of different organisms, rather than just one.)

46. Altman, Lawrence K., "Aids Development in Infection; Data Suggest AIDS Rises Yearly After Infection," **New York Times**, Mar. 3, 1987, p. C1. Among other things, points out that the AIDS seropositivity rate rose from 4 percent in 1978 to 68 percent in 1984 among 6,875 members of a San Francisco hepatitis B study group.

47. Moyo, "Fighting AIDS in Africa," **AfricAsia**, May 1987, p. 55.

48. Altman, Lawrence K., "AIDS in Africa," **New York Times**, Nov. 1, 1986, p. A1, A8.

49. Krieger, Nancy, "The Epidemiology of AIDS Riddle," **Science for the People**, Jan./Feb. 1987, p. 18.

50. Nordheimer, Jan, "Florida Pig Farm Poses AIDS Riddle," **New York Times**, May. 2, 1986, p. A7.

51. Saul, Stephanie, "A Focus for the AIDS Mystery," **Newsday**, Jan. 26, 1986, p. 7.

52. Segal, Jakob and Lilli, **AIDS: USA Home-Made Evil: Not Imported from Africa**, date unknown (believed 1986). Pamphlet widely circulated in Africa. The two scientists are a biologist and a biophysicist, affiliated with the Humbolt University of Berlin. In the pamphlet the authors charge that the AIDS virus was manmade, and suggest that it may have been created at Fort Detrick, Maryland. This and other such literature, plus deliberate Soviet propaganda releases charging that "U.S. biological warfare" is responsible for the AIDS pandemic, have significantly influenced widespread belief in Africa that the U.S. government is responsible. Our own thesis is that this merely shows how clever and coordinated the Soviet BW strike really is: the deception plan was complete and ready made. The viruses were made elsewhere (in cancer research labs), someone else unwittingly injected the contaminated vaccines (World Health Organization), and a good cover story was immediately at hand (simply blame the U.S.).

53. Pearce Wright and Thompson Prentice, "WHO seeks evidence over vaccine link to Aids virus," **The Times** of London, May 12, 1987.

54. "Near disaster with the Salk vaccine," **Science Digest**, Dec. 1963.

55. Bernard Fields, Malcolm A. Martin, and Daphne Kamely, Eds., "Genetically Altered Viruses and the Environment," **Banbury Report**, Cold Spring Harbor Laboratory, 1985.

56. The following summary articles are in Science, 239 (4948), Feb. 5, 1988: (1) Peter Piot et al, "AIDS: An International Perspective," p. 573-579; (2) Anthony S. Fauci, "The Human Immunodeficiency Virus: Infectivity and Mechanisms of Pathogenesis, " p. 617-622; (3) James W. Curran et al, "Epidemiology of HIV Infection and AIDS in the United States," p. 610-616; and (4) Richard W. Price et al, "The Brain in AIDS: Central Nervous System HIV-1 Infection and AIDS Dementia Complex," p. 586-592.

References Related to Chapter 3

1. Publications by T.E. Bearden:

   a. **Fer-de-Lance: A Briefing on Soviet Scalar Electromagnetic Weapons**. Tesla Book Co., POB 1649, Greenville, Texas 75401, 1986. Extensive coverage of Soviet scalar EM weapons and their testing. Heavily documented and illustrated. See a review of **Fer-de-Lance** in **Defense Science & Electronics**, June 1987, p. 80.

   b. **Excalibur Briefing**. Foreword by John White. Strawberry Hill Press, San Francisco, California 1980. An updated second edition, jointly published by Strawberry Hill Press and Tesla Book Co., 1988.

   c. **Tesla's Secret and The Soviet Tesla Weapons**. 1 hr. 40 min. videotape. 1981. Available from Tesla Book Co. Generally poor quality; lots of information.

   d. "Soviet Psychotronic Weapons: A Condensed Background." **Specula**, Journal of the AAMS, POB 1182, Huntsville Alabama 35807. 1(2), Mar.-June 1978. pp. 18-32. (Journal is now defunct).

   e. **Star Wars Now! The Bohm-Aharonov Effect, Scalar Interferometry, and Soviet Weaponization**. Tesla Book Co., 1984.

   f. **Soviet Weather Engineering Over North America**. 1-hr. videotape, 1985. Available from Tesla Book Co. Excellent quality; a great deal of information.

   g. **Solutions to Tesla's Secrets and the Soviet Tesla Weapons**. John T. Ratzlaff, ed. **Part II: Reference Articles for Solutions to Tesla's Secrets**. Tesla Book Co., 1981.

   h. "Tesla's Electromagnetics and Its Soviet Weaponization," **Proceedings of the 1984 Tesla Centennial Symposium**, International Tesla Society, Colorado Springs, Colorado 1984.

   i. USSR: New Beam Energy Possible?", **Defense & For-**

eign Affairs Daily, 13 (111), June 12, 1984, p. 1-2.

j. T.E. Bearden and Andrew Michrowski, eds., The **Emerging Energy Science**, Planetary Association for Clean Energy, Ottawa, Canada, 1985.

k. "AIDS: Urgent Comments on Man's Greatest Threat; and the Secrets of Electromagnetic Healing," presented in absentia at the U.S.P.A. Annual Symposium, July 30-Aug. 2, 1987, Golden, Colorado.

l. "Soviet Phase Conjugate Weapons: Weapons that use Time-Reversed Electromagnetic Waves," **Bulletin**, Committee to Restore the Constitution, POB 986, Ft. Collins, Colorado 80522, Jan. 1988.

m. "Tesla Electromagnetics: Weapons or Healing?" Presented at the Whole Life Expo, Los Angeles Airport Hilton Hotel, Los Angeles, California, Oct. 3, 1987.

2. William C. Douglass, **The Cutting Edge**, Nov. 1987, p. 3.

3. Stefan T. Possony, "Psy-War: Soviet Device Experiment," **Defense & Foreign Affairs Daily**, 12(104), June 7, 1983, p. 1-2. Reports on Dr. Ross Adey's investigation of the Soviet LIDA device which is used to bombard human brains with radio waves of complex waveform in the 40 MHz region. Also reports on work by A.S. Davydov of the Ukranian Academy of Sciences, who discovered how the blood-brain barrier can be penetrated by low-frequency radio waves so that brain cells are affected.

4. Stefan T. Possony, "The Tesla Connection," **Defense & Foreign Affairs**, Aug. 1984, p. 12-14, 27. Highly recommended.

5. David Jones, "Israel's Secret Weapon," **Weekend Magazine**, Dec. 17, 1977.

6. Daniel A. Walker, Charles S. McCreery, and Fermin J. Oliveira, "Kaitoky Seamount and the Mystery Cloud of 9 April, 1984," **Science**, 227(4584), Feb. 8, 1985, p. 607-611. See also Daniel L. McKenna and Daniel A. Walker, "Mystery Cloud: Additional Observations," **Science**, 234(4775), Oct. 24, 1986, p. 412-413 for update to the information in the first article.

7. Robert J. Durant, "An Underwater Explosion — or What?",

Pursuit, 5(2), April 1972, p. 30-31.

8. Gwynne Roberts, "Witness to a Superweapon?", The **Sunday Times**, London, England, Aug. 17, 1980.

9. Central Intelligence Agency (CIA) Information Report No. CO-B-321/15354-66, "Sighting of Unusual Phenomenon on Horizon Near Iranian/USSR Border," Sep. 8, 1966, released on 15 Dec. 1978 under the Freedom of Information Act (FOIA).

10. CIA Foreign Intelligence Information Report CO B-324/ 33601-76, "Aerial Observation of intense Source of Light," Nov. 18, 1976, released on 15 Dec.1978 under the FOIA.

11. Max Frankel, "Khrushchev Says Soviet Will Cut Forces a Third; Sees 'Fantastic Weapon' ", **New York Times**, Jan. 15, 1960, p. 1.

12. Christopher S. Wren, "Brezhnev Calls for Accord against 'Terrifying Arms," **New York Times**, June 14, 1975, p. 1,11.

13. Malcolm W. Browne, "Senatorial Group Received by Brezhnev," **New York Times**, July 3, 1975, p. 2.

14. Christopher S. Wren, "Moscow Now Pressing Disarmament," **New York Times**, Aug. 12, 1975, p. 6.

15. Draft agreement introduced by Andrei A. Gromyko to the United Nations' thirtieth session of the General Assembly on Sept. 23, 1975: "Prohibition of the Development and Manufacture of New Types of Weapons of Mass Annihilation and of New Systems of Such Weapons." The first article provided that the types of these new weapons would be "specified through negotiations on the subject."

16. "Secret Speech: Did Brezhnev Come Clean?", **National Review**, 29(8), Mar. 4, 1977, p. 248, 250.

17. William Beecher, "Brezhnev termed detente a ruse, 1973 report said," **Boston Globe**, Feb. 11, 1975, p. 1, 12.

18. See a series of articles by C.B. Baker in **Youth Action News**,

POB 312, Alexandria, Virginia 22313: "Soviet Weather Mayhem." Nov., 1983; "Diabolic Soviet Warfare," Nov. 1984; "The Soviet Zapping of America," Dec. 1986; "Fifth Column Treachery," May 1987; and others.

19. "Jetliner drops 32,000 feet; 400 aboard; 50 are injured," Associated Press (AP) Release, **Huntsville (Alabama) Times**, Feb. 20, 1985, p. 1. Also "China Airlines Pilot Denies Cockpit Error," AP Release, **Huntsville (Alabama) Times**, Feb. 21, 1985, p. A-9.

20. Paul Brodeur, **The Zapping of America**, W.W. Norton & Co., New York, 1977.

21. "Navy sabotages traffic lights, TV sets," United Press International (UPI), PM cycle, Jan. 11, 1985; "Power blackout blamed on anti-radar particles," UPI, AM cycle, Jan 11, 1985; "Power Disrupted Briefly After Navy Plane Drops Metallic Strands," AP, AM cycle, Jan. 16 1985.

22. Bradley Wells, "The Russian woodpecker: a continuing nuisance," **CQ Magazine**, Nov. 1984.

23. "Explosive Events Seen on Soviet Island," **Aviation Week & Space Technology**, Sept. 26, 1983, p. 31. Also Letter John M. Miller, Geophysical Institute, University of Alaska, Jan. 41985 with attachment, "Bennett Island plume cases recently found." Incredibly, the U.S. State Department is now attempting to **give away**, to the Soviet Union, the five-island chain of Wrangel, Herald, Bennett, Henrietta and Jeannette Islands and an outer continental shelf portion of Alaska twice the size of California! If this happens, the Bering Sea will become a Soviet pond.

24. Sam Bishop, "UA photos show Soviets break ice for missiles," **Fairbanks Daily News-Miner**, Dec. 15 1984, p. 1,3. See also Craig Covault, "Soviet ability to fire through ice creates new SLBM basing mode," **Aviation Week & Space Technology**, Dec. 10, 1984. See also "Wrangel over Wrangel and the Weather War," Don Bell Reports, 32(9), Mar. 8, 1985. See also, "Wrangel Giveaway Imminent," **The Spotlight**, Jan. 18, 1988, p. 1, 3.

25. Philip J. Klass, "Anti-Satellite Laser Use Suspected," **Avia-**

tion Week & Space Technology, Dec. 8, 1975, p. 12-13.

26. Joe Schwartz, **Nature**, 280, July 12, 1979, p. 95.

27. V.D. Sokolovskiy, **Soviet Military Strategy**, third edition 1968, p. 298.

28. T.T. Wu, "Electromagnetic Missiles," **J. Appl. Phys**. 57, 1985, p. 2370-2373. See also "Filter Center," article on SDI, **Aviation Week & Space Technology,** Feb. 29, 1988, p. 55.

29. Michael McClelland, "State officials bend an ear to boom talk in Panhandle," **News Tribune**, Fort Pierce, Florida, Apr. 22, 1984.

30. Susan Burgess, "NASA officials stumped by strange light, boom," **News Tribune**, Fort Pierce, Florida, Nov. 28, 1985.

31. Bernie Woodall, "Residents are baffled by boom," **News Tribune**, Fort Pierce, Florida, Nov. 27, 1985.

32. Julie Enders, "Star of wonder: booming, bright," **News Tribune**, Fort Pierce, Florida, Dec. 6, 1985.

33. April 8, 1986 Canadian Broadcast Network television news interview of three eyewitnesses to the crash of the Arrow Air DC-8 jet liner at Gander Air Force Base, Newfoundland on Dec. 8, 1985. A yellow light was seen on the aircraft.

34. "Arrow Air was absolutely safe, FAA official says," UPI release, **Birmingham (Alabama) Post-Herald**, Apr. 17, 1986.

35. "Titan Explosion Cripples U.S. Launch, Surveillance Capability," **Aviation Week & Space Technology**, 124(17), Apr. 28, 1986, p. 16-19.

36. Zhores A. Medvedev, **Nuclear Disaster in the Urals**, Translated by George Saunders, W.W. Norton & Co., 1979, p. 150.

37. Gary North, "Electronic Aids (Parts 1 & 2)," **Remnant Review**, 12 (20), Nov. 1, 1985, p. 1-8; 12 (21), Nov. 15, 1985, p. 1-8. POB 8204, Fort Worth, Texas 76124.

38. Captain John D. LaMothe, **Controlled Offensive Behavior**

— **USSR**, Defense Intelligence Agency (DIA) Report ST-CS-01-169-72, 1972 (Released under FOIA).

39. Captain John D. LaMothe and Mr. Louis Maire, **Soviet and Czechoslovakian Parapsychology Research**, DIA Report DST-1810S-387-75, 1975. (Released under FOIA).

40. John Bentley, **The Thresher Disaster: The Most Tragic Dive in Submarine History**, Doubleday & Co., Garden City, New York, 1975.

41. Canadian Aviation Safety Board (CASB), **Public Inquiry Into the Aircraft Accident Which Occurred Near Gander Airport, Gander NFLD. December 12, 1985**, Vol. 1, Apr. 8, 1986. Hull, Quebec, Canada.

42. Department of Defense, **Soviet Military Power**, 1987.

43. "America's Space Program Sabotaged?" Robert Herzberg, **International Combat Arms**, Mar. 1987. p. 12.

44. Pearce Wright, Science Editor: "Smallpox vaccine 'triggered Aids virus'," **The Times** of London, Mon. May 11, 1987. p. 2.

45. Jon Rappoport, "News blackout on pox vaccine link to AIDS protecting WHO?", **Easy Reader**, June 4, 1987, p. 12.

46. R.B Strecker and T.A. Strecker, "The Bioattack Alert (on AIDS)," Los Angeles, California, 1986.

47. EIR Special Report, "The Soviet role in covering up the deadly threat of AIDS," 12(42), Oct. 25, 1986.

48. Dr. John Seale, "The Origins of AIDS," Mar. 15, 1987.

49. Martin Ebon, **Psychic Warfare: Threat or Illusion**, McGraw Hill Book Co., New York, 1983.

50. For details of mysterious, instant deaths in Afghanistan, see Yossef Bodansky, "Soviets testing chemical agents in Afghanistan," **Jane's Defense Weekly**, 1(13), Apr. 7, 1984, p. 508.

51. " 'Observers' at the August Minuteman Shot?", **The INFO**

Journal, 2(1), Fall 1968, p. 35.

52. Dietrick E. Thomsen, "The Mystery of the Cosmic Gamma-Ray Zaps," **Science News**, 105 (22), June 1, 1974, p. 357-358.

References Related to Phase Conjugation (Time Reversal)

1. Amnon Yariv, **Optical Electronics**. Third Edition. Holt, Rinehart and Winston: New York, 1985. See particularly Chapter 16: "Phase Conjugate Optics — Theory and Applications."

2. Robert A. Fisher, Ed., **Optical Phase Conjugation**. Academic Press, New York, 1983. Collection of papers. An extensive bibliography is given at the end of the book. Note that Fisher's introduction to the phase conjugation effect was as a result of two Russian visitors who briefed scientists at Lawrence Livermore Laboratory on optical phase conjugation. Also note (p.xv, p. 20) that almost any nonlinear optical effect can phase conjugate an incoming beam.

3. B. Ya Zel'dovich and V.V. Shkunov, "Spatial-Polarization Wavefront Reversal in Four-Photon Interaction," **Soviet Journal of Quantum Electronics**, Vol. 9, 1979. p. 379.

4. B. Ya Zel'dovich et al, "Connection between the wave fronts of the reflected and exciting light in stimulated Mandel'shtam-Brillouin scattering," English translation, **Sov. Phys. JETP** 15, 109 (1972).

5. B. Ya Zel'dovich, N.F. Pilipetsky, and V.V. Shkunov, **Principles of Phase Conjugation**, Vol. 42, Springer Series in Optical Sciences, Theodor Tamir, Ed., Springer-Verlag, New York, 1985.

6. J.P. Woerdman, "Formation of a transient free carrier hologram in Si," **Opt. Commun.**, vol. 2, 1971. p. 212.

7. B.I. Stepanov, E.B. Ivakin, and A.S. Rubanov, "Recording two-dimensional and three--dimensional dynamic holograms in bleachable substances," Translation: **Soviet Physics-Doklady–Technical Physics**, vol. 16, 1971. p. 46.

8. A. Yariv, "Three-dimensional pictorial transmission in optical

fibers," **Appl. Phys. Lett.**, vol. 28, 1976. p. 88.

9. A. Yariv, "On Transmission and recovery of three-dimensional image information in optical waveguides," **J. Opt. Soc. Amer.**, vol. 66, 1976. p. 301.

10. R.W. Hellwarth, "Generation of time-reversed wave fronts by nonlinear refraction," **J. Opt. Soc. Amer.**, vol. 67, 1977. p. 1.

11. A. Yariv and D.M. Pepper, "Amplified reflection, phase conjugation, and oscillation in degenerate four-wave mixing," **Opt. Lett.**, vol. 1, 1977. p. 16.

12. R.L. Abrams and R.C. Lind, "Degenerate four-wave mixing in absorbing media," **Opt. Lett.**, vol 2, 1978, p. 94. Erratum is contained in **Opt. Lett.**, vol 3, 1978, p. 205.

13. P.F. Liao, D.M.Bloom, and N.P. Economou, "CW optical wavefront conjugation by saturated absorption in atomic sodium vapor, "**Appl. Phys. Lett.**, vol. 32, 1978, p. 813.

14. A. Yariv, "Compensation for atmospheric degradation of optical beam transmission," **Opt. Commun.**, vol. 21, 1977. p. 49.

15. R.W. Hellwarth, "Third order susceptibilities of liquids and gases," **Progress in Quantum Electronics**, vol. 5, 1977. p. 1.

16. J. Auyeung et al, "A theoretical and experimental investigation of the modes of optical resonators with phase-conjugate mirrors," **IEEE J. Quant. Electr.**, vol. 9, 1979. p. 1198.

17. I.M. Beldyugin and E.M. Zemskov, "Theory of resonators with wave-front reversing mirrors," **Sov. J. Quant. Elect.**, vol. 9, 1979. p. 1198.

18. A. Yariv and T.L. Koch, "One way coherent imaging through a distorting medium using four-wave mixing," **Opt. Lett.**, vol. 7, 1982. p. 113.

19. J.O. White and A. Yariv, "Real time image processing via four-wave-mixing in a photorefractive medium," **Appl. Phys. Lett.**, vol. 37, 1980. p. 5.

20. N.V. Kukhtarev et al, "Holographic storage in electrooptic crystals," **Ferroelectrics**, vol. 22, 1979. p. 949.

21. M. Cronin-Golomb et al, "Theory and applications of four-wave mixing in photorefractive media," **IEEE J. Quant. Elec.**, vol. 20, 1984. p. 12.

22. J.P. Huignard, J.P. Herriot and G. Rivet, "Phase conjugation and spatial frequency dependence of wavefront reflectivity in $Bi_{12}SiO_{20}$(BSO) crystals," **Opt. Lett.**, vol. 5, 1980. p. 102.

23. J.O. White et al, "Coherent oscillation by self-induced gratings in the photorefractive crystal $BaTiO_3$," **Appl. Phys. Lett.**, vol. 40, No. 6, 1982. p. 450-452.

24. J.W. Haus, C.M. Bowden, and C.C. Sung, "Optical phase conjugation with smooth pump profiles," **Phys. Rev. A, General Physics**, vol. 35, No. 8, Third Series, Apr. 15, 1987. p. 3398-3405.

25. Mary J. Miller et al, "Time response of a cerium-doped $Sr_{0.75}Ba_{0.25}Nb_2 0_6$ self-pumped phase-conjugate mirror," **Opt Lett.**, vol. 12, No. 5, May 1987. p. 340-342.

26. Mark Cronin-Golomb et al, "Passive (self-pumped) phase conjugate mirror: Theoretical and experimental investigation," **Appl. Phys. Lett.**, vol. 41, No. 8, Oct. 15, 1982. p. 689-691.

27. Philip S. Brody and Richard P. Leavitt, "Dynamic holographic method of imaging phase objects," **Applied Optics**, vol. 26, No. 5, Mar. 1, 1987. p. 913-916.

28. J. Feinberg, "Self-pumped, continuous-wave phase conjugator using internal reflection," **Opt. Lett.**, vol. 7, 1982. p. 486.

29. T.Y. Chang and R.W. Hellwarth, "Optical phase conjugation by backscattering in barium titanate," **Opt. Lett.**, vol. 10, 1985. p. 408.

30. J.P. Huignard et al, "Phase-conjugate wavefront generation via real-time holography in $Bi_{12}Si0_{20}$ Crystals," **Opt. Lett.**, vol. 4, 1979. p. 21.

31. David M. Pepper, "Nonlinear optical phase conjugation," guest editorial, **Optical Engineering**, vol. 21, no. 2, Mar./Apr. 1982. p. 155. One of the leaders of the field of nonlinear optical phase conjugation (NOPC) tells one in clear English what all the excitement is about. He also points out that the conceptual extension of these techniques to other portions of the electromagnetic spectrum should follow.

32. David M. Pepper, "Nonlinear optical phase conjugation," **Optical Engineering**, vol. 21, no. 2, Mar./ Apr. 1982. p.156-183. This paper is the best introduction to, and summary of, nonlinear optical phase conjugation (NOPC) in the English language. Also, on p. 156 the author specifically notes that "...these processing techniques can, in principle, be extended to other portions of the EM spectrum (e.g.,, rt, radio, microwave, radars, UV, etc.); and can also involve other fields (e.g., acoustic waves), given the proper nonlinear medium." In other words, phase conjugation is a universal nonlinear phenomenon, unknown until recently. An extensive bibliography of over 200 references is included.

33. Jeffrey O. White and Amnon Yariv, "Spatial information processing and distortion correction via four-wave mixing," **Optical Engineering**, vol. 21, no. 2, Mar./Apr. 1982. p. 224-230.

34. R.W. Hellwarth, "Optical beam phase conjugation by four-wave mixing in a waveguide," **Optical Engineering**, vol. 21, no. 2, Mar./Apr. 1982. p. 263-265.

35. I.M. Bel'dyugin, V.N. Seminogov, and E.M. Zemskov, "Possible wavefront reversal of fields using nonlinear-optics methods," **Sov. J. Quantum Electron**., vol 9, no. 3, Mar. 1979. p. 385-387.

36. I.M. Bel'dyugin, M.G. Galushkin, and E.M. Zemskov, "Properties of resonators with wavefront-reversing mirrors," **Sov. J. Quantum Electron**., vol 9, no. 1, Jan. 1979. p. 20-23.

37. G.S. Agarwal, Ari T. Friberg, and E. Wolf, "Elimination of distortions by phase conjugation without losses or gains," **Opt. Commun.** 43(6), Nov. 15, 1982. p. 446-450. Using scalar wave theory, the authors show the conditions for complete cancellation of distortion by phase conjugation: (1) scatterer is non-absorbing, (2) infinite phase conjugate mirror, (3) conjugate

wave generated without losses, (4) effects of evanescent waves are negligible outside the scatterer. Comment: By reflecting upon this paper, one can grasp that essentially the same approach can be used to show that phase conjugation generates Newton's third law of motion.

38. G.S. Agarwal and Emil Wolf, "Theory of phase conjugation with weak scatterers," **J. Opt. Soc. Am.**, 72(3), Mar. 1982. p. 321-326. The effect of a distorting medium on an incident wave is eliminated by phase conjugation if certain conditions are satisfied: (1) the incident wave contains no evanescent components, (2) the transmitting medium is a weak, nonabsorbing scatterer, (3) backscattering of incident waves and of conjugate waves is negligible, (4) effects of scattered evanescent waves are negligible. Comment: A similar approach can be used to show that phase conjugation generates Newton's third law of motion.

39. T. Sato et al, "Application of evanescent waves to microscopic observation," **Bull. Tokyo Inst. Technol. (Japan)**, No. 125, 1974. p. 35-41. Evanescent wave illumination for microscopy can be used for recognizing higher frequency components impossible to recognize by conventional illumination.

40. S. Twareque Ali. "Evanescent waves in quantum electrodynamics with unquantized sources," **Phys. Rev. D**, 7(6), Mar. 15, 1973. p. 1668-1675. An identity between evanescent waves and virtual photons is established.

41. J.D. Lawson, "Some attributes of real and virtual photons," **Contemp. Phys. (Great Britain)**, 11(6), Nov. 1970. p. 575-580.

42. J.L. Agudin et al, "The behaviour of evanescent waves under Lorentz transformation," **Lett. Nuovo Cimento (Italy)**, vol. 23, ser. 2, no. 15, Dec. 9, 1978. p. 547-551. Two linear combinations of transverse magnetic and electrical evanescent waves (the left-and right-handed circularly polarized modes) remain the same in all systems under Lorentz transformation.

43. M. Hercher, "virometer — an instrument for the measurement of the size of viruses using an optical microscope." **Proc. Soc. Photo-Opt. Instrumentation Engineers**, vol. 126, 1978. p. 17-22.

44. G.A. Massey, "Microscopy and pattern generation with scanned evanescent waves," **Appl. Opt. (Poland)**, 13 (3), 1983. p. 247-255. This article shows how to materially violate the usual "wavelength limitation" of optical systems. Much better resolution can be obtained, and very sharp images can be performed. Comment: This mechanism may be the secret of the Rife microscope, which could see viruses and other small organisms otherwise quite beyond normal optical microscopy's wavelength resolution.

45. H.J. Gerritsen, "Nonlinear effects in image formation," **Appl. Phys. Lett**., vol. 10, 1967. p. 237.

46. D. Gabor, U.S. patent No. 2,770,166.

47. H.W. Kogelnik, "Controlled transmission of waves through inhomogeneous media," U.S. Patent 3,449, 577.

48. V.I. Bespalov. Ed., **Optical Phase Conjugation in Nonlinear Media**, IPF AN SSR, Gorky, USSR, 1979 (in Russian).

49. B. Ya. Zel'dovich et al, "Phase conjugation by a surface," **Dok. Akad. Nauk SSSR** 252, 1980, p. 92. English translation: **Sov. Phys. Dokl**. 25, 1980, p. 377.

50. F.V. Bunkin, D.V. Vlasov and Yu. A. Kravtzov, "On sound phase conjugation with amplification of phase-conjugated wave," **Kvantovaya Elektron**. 8, 1981, p. 1144. English translation: **Sov. J. Quant. Electron**. 11, 1980, p. 687.

51. A.G. Gyulamiryan et al, "Tunable nonlinear four-wave filter," **Opt. Spektrosk**. 52, 1982, p. 387. (In Russian).

52. R.Y. Chiao et al, "Stimulated Brillouin scattering and coherent generation of intense hypersonic waves," **Phys. Rev. Lett**. 12, 1964, p. 592.

53. S.A. Akhumanov et al, **Problems in Nonlinear Optics (Electromagnetic Waves in Nonlinear Dispersive Media)**, INI AN SSSR, Moscow, 1964. (In Russian).

54. N.B. Baranova and B.Ya. Zel'dovich, "Wavefront dislocations and zeros of the amplitude," **Zh. Eksp. Teor. Fiz**. 80, 1981, p. 1789. English translation: **Sov. Phys. - JETP** 54, 1981, p. 925. Might one infer from this paper a cautious hint (and

probe) at "do you Westerners know of scalar EM?"

55. V.I. Bespalov, Ed., **Phase Conjugation in Nonlinear Media**, IPF AN SSSR, Gorky, USSR, 1982. (In Russian).

56. D. Gabor, "A new microscopic principle," **Nature** 161, 1958, p. 777.

57. Yu F. Kir'yanov et al, "Four-wave mixing in resonantly amplifying media under inversion saturation," **Kvantovaya Elektron**. 8, 1981, p. 1734. English translation: **Sov. J. Quant. Electron**. 11, 1981, p. 1047.

58. V.L. Vinetsky et al, "Amplification of coherent beams by dynamic holograms in ferroelectric crystals," **Izv. Akad. Nauk. SSSR** 41, 1977. p. 811.

59. V.P. Kondilenko, G.G. Odulov and M.S. Soskin, "Amplified reflection of phase-conjugate waves in crystals with the linear electrooptical effect in an external electrical field," **Izv. Akad. Nauk. SSSR, Ser. Fiz**. 45, 1981, p. 958.

60. Yu. I. Kucherov et al, "Copropagating four-beam interaction in slowly-responding media," in **Phase Conjugation in Nonlinear Media**, ed. by V.I. Bespalov, IPF AN SSSR, Gorky, USSR, 1982, p. 111.

61. A.P. Brysev et al, "Model realization of a NbLi parametric phase-conjugating sound amplifier," **Pis'ma Zh. Tokhn. Fiz**. 1, 1982, p. 546.

References Related to William J. Hooper's Work

1. William J. Hooper, "Apparatus for generating motional electric field." U.S. patent #3,656,013, Apr. 11, 1972.

2. William J. Hooper, "New horizons in electric, magnetic and gravitational field theory," presented at a meeting of the Particles and Fields Division of American Physical Societies, University of Colorado, Boulder, Colorado, Aug. 21, 1969.

3. William J. Hooper. "New horizons for the BxV theory of gravity," undated, unpublished.

4. William J. Hooper, "Equivalence of the gravitational field and

a motional electric field," Session S6, American Physical Society Meeting, Chicago, Illinois Nov. 28-29, 1958.

5. William J. Hooper, "Equivalence of the gravitational field and a motional electric field," **Proceedings of the Boulder Conference on High Energy Physics**, Colo. Assoc. Univ. Press, 1970. p. 483.

6. William J. Hooper, "The motional electric field generator," **Bull. of the Am. Phys. Soc.**, Series II, 15(2), Feb. 1970. p. 209.

7. J.H. Jeans, **The mathematical theory of electricity and magnetism**, 4th edn., Cambridge University Press, 1923. p. 125, 606.

8. Henry W. Kendall and Wolfgang Panofsky, "The structure of the proton and the neutron," **Scientific American**, June 1971.

9. William J. Hooper, "All-electric motional electric field generator." U.S. Patent #3,610,971, Oct. 5, 1971.

10. William J. Hooper, "Similarities of the motional electric and gravitational fields," undated, unpublished.

11. P. Moon and D.E. Spencer, "Some electromagnetic paradoxes," **Journal of the Franklin Institute**, vol. 260, 2955. p. 373.

12. Leigh Page and Norman I. Adams, **Electrodynamics**, D. Van Nostrand Co., 1940.

13. William J. Hooper, **New horizons in field theory**, revised 1965, unpublished. Chapter 1, "Fundamental Fields," is particularly important.

14. G.I. Cohn, **Electrical Engineering** 68, 1969. p.441. Pointed out difference between flux linking law and flux cutting law of induction. Comment: Recently the Lorentz force law has been proven false. A modified version of Ampere's law results and saves the day.

15. G.I. Cohn, **Paradoxes of Electromagnetic Induction**, thesis, Illinois Institute of Technology library.

16. Pharis E. Williams, "The Possible unifying effect of the dy-

namic theory," Los Alamos National Laboratory report LA-9623-MS, Los Alamos, New Mexico, May 1983 .

17. Pharis E. Williams, **On a possible formulation of particle dynamics in terms of thermodynamic conceptualizations and the role of entropy in it**, thesis, U.S. Naval Postgraduate School, 1976.

18. Pharis E. Williams "The Principles of the dynamic theory," Research Report EW-77-4, U.S. Naval Academy, 1977.

19. Pharis E. Williams, "The Dynamic theory: A new view of space, time, and matter," Los Alamos Scientific Laboratory report LA-8370-MS, Dec. 1980.

20. Pharis E. Williams, "The Arrow of time in the dynamic theory," Los Alamos Scientific Laboratory report LA-8690-MS, Feb. 1981.

21. Pharis E. Williams, "The Dynamic theory: Some shockwave and energy implications," Los Alamos Scientific Laboratory report LA-8402-MS, Feb. 1981.

22. Dan C. Ross, "Plane electromagnetic waves in the dynamic theory," Los Alamos National Laboratory report, date unk.

23. Dan C. Ross, "Speed of light in the dynamic theory," Los Alamos National Laboratory, date unk.

24. G. Gilbert and B. McClain, "Fermions and stability in quantum Kaluza-Klein theories," **Nuc. Phys. B, Part. Phys. (Netherlands)**, B244 (1), Sept. 24, 1984. p. 173-185. Oscillations of the internal space produce conformal gravity waves in the four-dimensional space.

25. M. J. Perry, "Magnetic monopoles and the Kaluza-Klein theory," **Am. Inst. Phys. Conf. Proc**. No. 116, 1984. p. 121-125. Kaluza-Klein theory admits soliton solutions which constitute magnetic monopoles. These monopoles have inertial mass, but no gravitational mass.

26. M.W. Kalinowski, "The nonsymmetric Kaluza-Klein theory." **J. Math. Phys**. 24(7), July 1983. p. 1835-1845.

27. D.J. Toms, "Induced Einstein-Maxwell action in Kaluza-Klein

theory," **Phys. Lett. B (Netherlands)**, 129B(1-2), Sept. 15., 1983. p. 31-35.

References Related to Ehrenhaft's Work

1. Alden P. Armagnac, "Magic with magnetism," **Popular Science** Magazine, June 1944. p. 130-133, 222, 226.

2. "Ehrenhaft discovery confirmed by new experiments," **Popular Science** Magazine, date unk., p. 208. [Comment: Later than June 1944, and still during WWII.]

3. "Magnetic current — discovery of the age?", **Radio-Craft** Magazine, Mar., 1944. p. 332.

4. "Discovery of the age?" **Radio-Electronics** Magazine, date unknown, p. 58.

5. Felix Ehrenhaft and Emanuel Wasser, "New evidence of the existence of charges smaller than the electron," **Philosophical Magazine and Journal of Science**, Seventh Series, 5(28), Feb. 1928. p. 225-241.

6. Felix Ehrenhaft, "The microcoulomb experiment. Charges smaller than the electronic charge." **Philosophy of Science**, 8(3), July 1941. p. 403-457.

7. Felix Ehrenhaft and Leo Banet, "Is there 'true magnetism' or not?", **Philosophy of Science**, 8(3), July 1941. p. 458-462.

8. Felix Ehrenhaft and Leo Banet, "Magnetization of matter by light," Nature, Mar. 8, 1941. p. 297.

9. Felix Ehrenhaft, J. Franklin Inst., vol. 230, 1940. p. 381.

10. Felix Ehrenhaft, **Nature**, vol. 146, 1941. p. 25.

11. D. Morichini, **Gilberts Ann. Phys.**, vol. 43, 1813. p. 212.

12. D. Morichini, **Gilberts Ann. Phys.**, vol. 46, 1814. p. 367.

13. M. Sommerville, **Gilberts Ann. Phys.**, vol 52, 1826. p. 493.

14. F. Zantejeschi, **Gilberts Ann. Phys.**, vol. unk. 1829, p.187.

15. V. Baumgartner, **Gilberts Ann. Phys.**, vol. unk., 1827. p. 508.

16. Felix Ehrenhaft, "Rotating action on matter in a beam of light," **Science**, 101(2635), June 29, 1945. p. 676-677.

17. Gordon Ferrie Hull, "The torque or rotating action in a beam of light," **Science**, vol. 101, 1945. p. 220.

18. F. Ehrenhaft, **Wiener Akad. Anz.**, vol. VII, Mar. 4, 1909.

19. F. Ehrenhaft, **Wiener Akad. Anz.**, vol. X, Apr. 21, 1910.

20. F. Ehrenhaft, **Wiener Berichte**, vol. 119, 1910. p. 815.

21. F. Ehrenhaft, **Physik. Ztschr.**, vol. 11, 1910. p. 619.

22. F. Ehrenhaft, **Physik. Ztschr.**, vol. 39, 1938. p. 673.

23. F. Ehrenhaft, **Ann. der Physik.**, vol. 56, 1918. p. 81.

24. F. Ehrenhaft, **Comp. Rend.**, vol. 190, 1930. p. 263.

25. F. Ehrenhaft, **Ann. der Physik.**, vol. 13, 1940. p. 151.

26. F. Ehrenhaft, **Jour. Frank. Inst.**, vol. 233, 1942. p. 235.

27. F. Ehrenhaft, **Nature**, vol. 154, 1944. p. 426.

28. F. Ehrenhaft, **Phys. Rev.**, vol. 65, 1944. p. 287.

29. F. Ehrenhaft, **Bull. Am. Phys. Soc.** (New York Meeting), vol. 6, 1945.

30. H.S. Renue, **Radio Electronic Engineering (Radio News)**, vol. 4, 1945. p. 22.

31. Woldemar Voigt, **Festschrift fuer Heinrich Weber**, 1912.

32. P.A.M. Dirac, "Development of the physicist's conception of nature," **Symposium on the Development of the Physicist's Conception of Nature**, ed. Jagdish Merha, D. Reidel Pub. Co., Boston, 1973. p. 12-14.

33. Olof Alexandersson, **Living Water: Viktor Schauberger**

and the Secrets of Natural Energy, translated by Kit and Charles Zweigbergk, Turnstone Press Limited, Willingborough, Northamptonshire, England, 1982. An excellent bibliography is included in the book.

34. O. Alexandersson, "Implosion contra explosion," **Seklet**, vol. 4, 1965.

References Related to Louis Kervran's Work

1. Publications by Louis Kervran:

   a. **Biological Transmutations**. Crosby Lockwood, London, 1972.

   b. **A la Decouverte des Transmutations Biologiques, une Explication des Phenomenes Biologiques Aberrants**. Le Courrier du Livre, Paris, 1966.

   c. **Preuves Relatives a L'existence de Transmutations Biologiques, Echecs en Biologie a la loi de Lavoisier d'invariance de la Matiere**, Maloine, Paris, 1968.

   d. **Transmutations Biologiques; Metabolismes Aberrants de L'azote, le Potassium et el Magnesium**, Librairie Maloine, Paris, 1962.

   e. "Les Transmutations Biologiques en Agronomie," Maloine, Paris, 1970.

   f. **Biological Transmutations**, Swan House Publishing Co., Binghamton, New York, 1972.

   g. "Alchimie d'hier et d'aujourd'hui," **L'Alchimie, Reve ou Realite**, Revue des Ingenieurs do L'Institut National Superieur de Rouen, 1972-73.

   h. **Transmutations biologiques et physique moderne**. Paris: Maloine S.A., 1982.

   i. **Transmutations a faible energie (naturelles et biologiques)**. Paris: Librairie Maloine, 1972.

j. **Transmutations biologiques**. Rue de l'Ecole-de-Medecine, Paris: Librairie Maloine S.A., 1963.

k. **Transmutations naturelles**. Librairie Maloine S.A., Rue de l'Ecole-de-Medecine, Paris VIe, 1963.

2. Rudolf Hauschka, **The Nature of Substance**, Vincent Stuart Ltd., London, 1966.

3. V.B. Neiman. ed., **Problems of Transmutations in Nature: Concentration and Dissipation**. (Collection of papers in Russian), Aiastan Pub. House, Erevan, Armenia, USSR, 1971.

4. Peter Tompkins and Christopher Bird, **The Secret Life of Plants**, Harper & Row, New York, 1973.

5. The Kaznacheyev work and references. See appropriate sections.

6. Dr. Fritz Albert Popp's work and references. See appropriate sections.

7. The Australian work of Reid and Barsamian. See appropriate sections.

8. Fritz Albert Popp et al, eds. **Electromagnetic Bio-Information**. Proceedings of the Symposium, Marburg, September 5, 1977. Urban & Schwarzenberg, Baltimore, 1979.

9. Thomas E. Bearden, **The Excalibur Briefing**, Second edition, Strawberry Hill Press, San Francisco, 1988.

10. N.A. Kozyrev, "Possibility of the Experimental Study of the Properties of Time," Sep. 1967. English translation JPRS 45328, May 1968, p. 1-49.

11. Captain John D. LaMothe and Mr. Louis Maire, **Soviet and Czechoslovakian Parapsychology Research**, DST-1810S-387-75, Defense Intelligency Agency, Washington, D.C., 1975. Released under the Freedom of Information Act.

12. Jeff Hecht, "IBM Reports on Dark-Pulse Solitons," **Lasers & Optronics**, 7(3), Mar. 1988, p. 42 -44.

References Related to Popp's Master Cellular Communication System

1. Fritz Albert Popp, Gunther Becker, Herbert L. Konig, and Walter Peschka, Eds., **Electromagnetic Bio-Information: Proceedings of the Symposium**, Marburg, September 5, 1977, Urban & Schwarzenberg, Baltimore, 1979.

2. V.P. Kaznacheyev et al, "On distant intercellular interactions in a system of two tissue cultures connected by optical contact," **Transactions of the Moscow Society of Naturalists**, Vol. XXXIX, 1972. p. 224-227.

3. F.A. Popp, **Biophotonen. Ein neuer Weg zur Losung des Krebsproblems**. Verlag fur Medizin, Heidelberg, 1976.

4. F.A. Popp et al, "Biosignale zur Steuerung des Zellstoffwechsels. Eine Resonanzhypothese der Karzinogenese (vorl. Mitt.)" **Munch. med. Wschr**, vol. 116, 1974. p. 381-384.

5. F.A. Popp, "Molecular aspects of carcinogenesis, in Deutsch et al, eds.: **Molecular Base of Malignancy**, Stuttgart, 1976.

6. A. Gurwitsch, "Die mitogenetische Strahlung der Optischen Bahn bei adaquater Erreguns." **Pfluger Arch. ges. Physiol.**, vol. 231, 1932. p. 254-264.

7. A. Gurwitsch, "Die mitogenetische Strahlung des markhaltigen Nerven," **Pflugers Arch. ges. Physiol.**, vol. 231, 1932. p. 234-237.

8. A.A. Gurwitsch, "The problem of mitogenetic radiation as an aspect of molecular biology." (in Russian), Leningrad, 1968.

9. A.A. Gurwitsch, V.F. Eremeiev, and Yu. A. Karabchievsky, "Energy bases of the mitogenetic radiation and its registration on photoelectron multipiers," **Medicina**, Moskva, 1974.

10. J.W. Hastings, "Bioluminescence," **Ann. Rev. Biochem.**, vol. 37, 1968. p. 597-630.

11. L.W. Latmanisowa, "Die mitogenetische Sekundar-strahlung des Nerven," **Pflugers Arch. ges. physiol.**, vol. 231, 1932. p. 265-279.

12. H. Ninnemann et al, "Inhibition of respiration in yeast by light," **Biochim. Biophys. Acta**, vol. 205, 1970. p. 499-506.

13. T.I. Quickenden and S.S. Que Hee, "Weak luminescence from the yeast saccharomyces cerevisiae and the existence of mitogenetic radiation," **Biochem. Biophys. Res. Comm.**, vol. 60, 1974. p. 764-770.

14. A. Babloyantz, "Self-organization phenomena resulting from cell-cell contact," **J. Theor. Biol.**, vol. 68, 1977. p. 551-561.

15. R.M. Benolken, "Reversal of photoreceptor polarity recorded during the graded receptor potential response to light in the eye of limulus," **Biophys. J.**, vol. 1961. p. 551-564.

16. H. Breithaupt, "Biological rhythms and communication," in Fritz Albert Popp, Gunther Becker, Herbert L. Konig, and Walter Peschka, Eds., **Electromagnetic Bio-Information: Proceedings of the Symposium**, Marburg, September 5, 1977, Urban & Schwarzenberg, Baltimore 1979. p. 1-23.

17. Herbert L. Konig, "Bioinformation - Electrophysical Aspects," in Fritz Albert Popp, Gunther Becker, Herbert L. Konig, and Walter Peschka, Eds., **Electromagnetic Bio-Information: Proceedings of the Symposium**, Marburg, September 5, 1977, Urban & Schwarzenberg, Baltimore, 1979. p. 25-55.

18. Ulrich Warnke, "Information transmission by means of electrical biofields," in Fritz Albert Popp, Gunther Becker, Herbert L. Konig, and Walter Peschka, Eds.., **Electromagnetic Bio-Information: Proceedings of the Symposium**, Marburg, September 5, 1977, Urban & Schwarzenberg, Baltimore, 1979. p. 55-79.

19. Walter Peschka, "On kinetobaric effects and bioinformational transfer by electromagnetic fields," in Fritz Albert Popp, Gunther Becker, Herbert L. Konig, and Walter Peschka, Eds., **Electromagnetic Bio-Information: Proceedings of the Symposium**, Marburg, September 5, 1977, Urban & Schwarzenberg, Baltimore, 1979. p. 81-94.

20. Gunther Becker, "Communication between termites by means of biofields and the influence of magnetic and electric fields on termites," in Fritz Albert Popp, Gunther Becker, Herbert L. Konig, and Walter Peschka, Eds., **Electromagnetic Bio-In-**

formation: Proceedings of the Symposium, Marburg, September 5, 1977, Urban & Schwarzenberg, Baltimore, 1979. p. 95-106.

21. Bernhard Ruth, Experimental investigations on ultraweak photon emission," in Fritz Albert Popp, Gunther Becker, Herbert L. Konig, and Walter Peschka, Eds., **Electromagnetic Bio-Information: Proceedings of the Symposium**, Marburg, September 5, 1977, Urban & Schwarzenberg, Baltimore, 1979. p. 107-122.

22. Fritz Albert Popp, "Photon storage in biological systems," in Fritz Albert Popp, Gunther Becker, Herbert L. Konig, and Walter Peschka, Eds., **Electromagnetic Bio-Information: Proceedings of the Symposium**, Marburg September 5, 1977, Urban & Schwarzenberg, Baltimore, 1979. p. 123-149. A most important paper, presenting what I have been calling the master cellular communication system. Ruth has confirmed the existence of the "degradation radiation," ("death photons"). Experimental results of Ruth and others have led Popp to postulate that biological systems generally have the capacity to store coherent photons which come from the external world, and that ultraweak photon emission from biological systems is governed by photon storage ("charge up") within the cell population.

23. S.S. Sung, "A possible biophotochemical mechanism for cell communication," in Fritz Albert Popp, Gunther Becker, Herbert L. Konig, and Walter Peschka, Eds., **Electromagnetic Bio-Information: Proceedings of the Symposium**, Marburg, September 5, 1977, Urban & Schwarzenberg, Baltimore, 1979. p. 151-174.

24. Helmut A. Fischer, "Photons as transmitter for intra- and inter-cellular biological and biochemical communication — the construction of a hypothesis," in Fritz Albert Popp, Gunther Becker, Herbert L. Konig, and Walter Peschka, Eds., **Electromagnetic Bio-Information: Proceedings of the Symposium**, Marburg, September 5, 1977, Urban & Schwarzenberg, Baltimore, 1979. p. 174-180.

25. Walter Kroy, "The use of optical radiation for stimulation therapy," in Fritz Albert Popp, Gunther Becker, Herbert L. Konig, and Walter Peschka, Eds., **Electromagnetic Bio-In-**

formation: Proceedings of the Symposium, Marburg, September 5, 1977, Urban & Schwarzenberg, Baltimore, 1979. p. 181-193.

26. Ulrich Warnke and Fritz Albert Popp, "Some aspects of magnetic influences on biological systems," in Fritz Albert Popp, Gunther Becker, Herbert L. Konig, and Walter Peschka, Eds., **Electromagnetic Bio-Information: Proceedings of the Symposium**, Marburg, September 5, 1977, Urban & Schwarzenberg, Baltimore, 1979. p. 195-199.

27. A.S. Presman, **Electromagnetic Fields and Life**, Plenum Press, New York, 1964.

28. F.A. Popp and B. Ruth, "Untersuchungen zur ultraschwachen Lumineszenz aus biologischen Systemen unter Berrucksichtig ung der Bedeutung fur die Arzneimittelforchung," **Arzneimittel-Forsch**, vol. 27 (I), 1977. p. 933.

29. B.Ruth and F.A. Popp, "Experimentelle Untersuchungen zur ultraschwachen Photonenemission biologischer Systeme," Z. **Naturforsch**, vol. 31c, 1976. p. 741.

References Related to Kaznacheyev's Experiments

1. V.P. Kaznacheyev et al, "Apparent information transfer between two groups of cells," **Psychoenergetic Systems**, 1(1), Dec. 1974.

2. V.P. Kazacheyev et al, "Distant intercellular interactions in a system of two tissue cultures," **Psychoenergetic Systems**, 1(3), Mar. 1976.

3. Captain John D. LaMothe, **Controlled offensive behavior — USSR**, Report ST-CS-01-169-72, Defense Intelligence Agency, Washington, D.C. (Released under F0IA).

4. Captain John D. LaMothe and Mr. Louis Maire, **Soviet and Czechoslovakian Parapsychology Research**, Report DST-1810S-387-75, Defense Intelligence Agency, Washington, D.C. (Released under F0IA).

5. Trevor James Constable, **The Cosmic Pulse of Life**, Merlin

Press, Santa Ana, California, 1976.

6. John White and Stanley Krippner, eds., **Future Science**, Anchor, 1977.

7. B. Ruth, "Experimental Investigations on Ultraweak Photon Emission," in **Electromagnetic Bioinformation, Proceedings of the Symposium**, Marburg, September 5, 1977 (Munchen-Wien-Baltimore, 1979). p. 107-122

8. H. Fischer, "Photons as Transmitters for Intra- and Intercellular Biological and Biochemical Communication — the Construction of a Hypothesis," in **Electromagnetic Bioinformation, Proceedings of the Symposium**, Marburg, September 5, 1977 (Munchen-Wien-Baltimore, 1979). p. 175-180.

9. F.A. Popp, "Photon Storage in biological systems," in **Electromagnetic Bioinformation, Proceedings of the Symposium**, Marburg, September 5, 1977 (Munchen-Wien-Baltimore, 1979). p. 123-149.

10. A.G. Gurvitsch, **Theory of Biological Field**, Moscow, 1944 (in Russian).

11. A.G. Gurvitsch,"A Concept of 'the Whole' in the Frame of Biological Field Theory," in **Works on Mitogenesis and Theory of Biological Field**, Moscow, 1974, p. 141-147 (in Russian).

12. E.S. Bauer, "General Theory of Living Substance. The Problem of 'Living Protein'," **Archives Biol. Sci**., Vol. 35, Ser. A, Issue 1, 1934, p. 1-36 (in Russian).

13. E.S. Bauer, "Contradictions between the Inner and Outer Work of Living Systems," **Archives Biol. Sci**., Vol. 35, Ser. A, Issue 1, 1934, p. 37-52 (in Russian).

14. E.S. Bauer, **Theoretical Biology**, Moscow, 1935 (in Russian).

15. S.V. Konev, "On the Question of Nature and Biological Significance of Ultraweak Luminescence of Cells," in **Bioluminescence**, Moscow, 1965, p. 181-183 (in Russian).

16. B.N. Tarusov, A.I. Pllivoda, and A.I. Zhuravlev, "Study of Ultraweak Spontaneous Luminescence of Animal Cells," **Biofzika**, Vol. 6, No. 4, 1961. p. 490-492 (in Russian).

17. M. Rottemeyer, "Modelle zur Interpretation der Ultraschwachen Photone-emission aus Biologischen Systemen," **Diplomarbeit** (Marburg, 1978), (in German).

18. Yu. A. Vladimirov, "Ultraweak Luminescence of Subcellular Structures," **Ultraweak Luminescence in Biology, Proceedings of the Symposium**, Moscow, 1969 (in Russian).

19. I.S. Marchenko, **Biofield of Forest Ecological Systems**, Bryansk, 1973 (in Russian).

20. S.S. Sung, "A Possible Biophotochemical Mechanism for Cell Communication," in **Electromagnetic Bioinformation, Proceedings of the Symposium**, , Marburg, September 5, 1977 (Munchen-Wien-Baltimore, 1971). p. 151-174.

21. F.A.Popp and B. Ruth, "Untersuchungen zur Ultraschwachen Luminiszenz aus Biologischen Systemen uter Berucksichtig ung der Bedeutung fur die Arznei-mittelforschung," **Arzneimit. Forsch**. (Drug Research), Vol. 27, No. 5, 1977 (in German).

22. V.P. Kaznacheyev, "Informational Function of Ultraweak Flows of Light in Biological Systems," in **Materials of Scientific Conference: Physical and Mathematical Methods of Research in Biology and Medicine**, Novosibirsk, 1965, pp. 38-41 (in Russian).

23. V.P. Kaznacheyev, N.V. Ignatovich, and S.P. Shurin, "Intercellular Distant Interactions in a System of Two Tissue Cultures Connected by Optical Contact," in **Ultraweak Luminescence in Biology**, Moscow, 1969 (in Russian).

24. V.P. Kaznacheyev, L.P. Mikhailova, and S.B. Stephanov, "Studies on Cellular Monolayer and Cellular Distant Interaction in High Latitude Conditions," in **Technical-Scientific Progress and Circumpolar Medicine**, Novosibirsk, 1978, p. 133-134 (in Russian).

25. V.P. Kaznacheyev, L.P. Mikhailova, V.N. Sudarev, and S.P.

Shurin, "Studies on the Biological Role of Electromagnetic Emission as a Factor of Adaptive Behavior of Cells under Conditions of Latitude Changes," in **Abstracts of the Second All-Union Conference Devoted to the Problem of Human Adaptation to Different Geographical, Climatic, and Labor conditions**, Novosibirsk, 1977, p. 101-104 (in Russian).

26. V.P. Kaznacheyev, L.P. Mikhailova, V.N. Sudarev, and S.P. Shurin, "Distant Intercellular Interactions Caused by UV-radiation," in **Photobiology of a Living Cell**, Leningrad, 1979, p. 221-223 (in Russian).

27. V.P. Kaznacheyev, L.P. Mikhailova, D.G. Kadayeva, and M.P. Dranova, "Conditions Necessary for Appearance of distant Intercellular Interactions after UV-radiation," **Bulleten Experimentalnoy Biologii i Meditsiny**., No. 5. 1979, p. 468-471 (in Russian).

28. V.P. Kaznacheyev, L.P. Mikhailova, and S.P. Shurin, "Distant Intercellular Interactions in a System of Two Tissue Cultures Connected by Optical Contact," in **Regulation of Biosynthesis and Biophysics of Populations**, Krasnoyarsk, 1969, p. 372-374 (in Russian).

29. V.P. Kaznacheyev, S.P. Shurin, and L.P. Mikhailova, Discovery No. 122, "Distant Intercellular Interactions in a System of Two Tissue Cultures," **Official Bulletin of the Committee on Inventions and Discoveries Affiliated to the Council of Ministers of the USSR**, No. 19, 1973, p. 3.

30. V.P. Kaznacheyev, S.P. Shurin, L.P. Mikhailova, and N.V. Ignatovich, "Distant Intercellular Interactions in a System of Two Tissue Cultures Connected by Optical Contact," in **Ultraweak Luminescence in Biology**, Moscow, 1972, p. 224-227 (in Russian).

31. V.M. Inyushin, "The Concept of Biological Plasma and Some Questions of Photoenergetics," in **Questions of Bioenergetics**, Alma-Alta, 1968 (in Russian).

32. E. Makovsky, **Nature and Structure of Living Matter**, Bucharest, 1976 (in Russian).

33. A.L. Chizhevsky and Yu. Shishina, **In the Rhythm of the Sun**, Moscow, 1969.

34. Stefan T. Passony, "Psy-War: Soviet device experiment," **Defense and Foriegn Affairs Daily**, 12 (104), June 7, 1983, p. 1-2.

35. V.I. Vernadsky, **Collected Works**, Moscow, 1960, (in Russian).

36. A.L. Chizhesvsky, **The Earth's Echo of the Sun Storms**, Moscow, 1973.

37. A.S. Pressman, **Electromagnetic Fields and Living Nature**, Moscow, 1968, English translation: **Electromagnetic Fields and Life**, Plenum, New York, 1970.

38. H.Z. Konig, "Bioinformation. Electrophysical Aspects," in **Electromagnetic Bioinformation, Proceedings of the Symposium**, Marburg, September 5, 1977 (Munchen-Wien-Baltimore, 1979). p. 25-54.

39. V.P. Kaznacheyev, "Information Function of Ultraweak Light Flows in Biological Systems," in **Problems in Biophysics**, Novosibirsk, 1967, p. 7-18 (in Russian).

40. V.P. Kaznacheyev and L.P. Mikhailova, "Ultraweak Radiations in Intercellular Interactions," Novosibirsk, 1981 (in Russian); English Translation: San Francisco: Washington Research Center, 1982.

41. John F. Gilbey, "The delayed death touch," **Secret Fighting Arts of the World**, Charles E. Tuttle Co., Rutland, Vermont, 1963. p. 13-22.

42. Edward W. Russell, **Report on Radionics: Science of the Future**, Neville Spearman, London, 1973.

43. Paul Brodeur, **The Zapping of America**, W.W. Norton & Co., New York, 1977.

44. Waldemar Kaempffert, " 'Dead' organisms revived," Science in the News: **Science Digest**, May 1950, p. 77-78.

45 "Rejuvenating light," **Scientific American**, May 1949.

46. Death-rays and life-rays discovered," **Science Digest**, Feb. 1950, p. 56. A "death" frequency seems to be at 2,537 angstroms, while a "life" frequency seems to be at 3,659 angstroms.

47. Lewis R. Koller, **Ultraviolet Radiation**, 2nd edn., John Wiley & Sons, New York, 1965. p. 236-237.

48. T.E. Bearden, Appendix: "Theory of Pulsor(R) operation," and "A partial glossary for scalar electromagnetics and subtle phenomena," in George T.F. Yao, **Pulsor(r): Miracle of Microcrystals**, Gyro Industries, Newport Beach, California, 1986.

49. The Antoine Priore material.

50. The Louis Kervran material.

51. Thomas E. Bearden, **The Excalibur Briefing**, Strawberry Hill Press, San Francisco, 2nd Edition, 1988.

52. Martin Ebon, "Moscow, June 11, 1977," in his **Psychic Warfare: Threat or Illusion**, McGraw-Hill Book Co., New York, 1983, p. 1-11.

References Related to the New View of the Nature of Mind and Thought

Author's Note: So far as I can find, there are no available references other than my own that deal precisely with my particular approach to the nature of mind and thought. There is, however, a serious debate over whether (a) the mind is simply the physical brain, similar to a computer (the prevailing materialist view of orthodox science), or (b) the mind is something else altogether, and metaphysical — at least with respect to the level of scientific knowledge today. My own approach utilizes a non-Aristotlean fourth law of logic (included in an appendix to this book) by means of which the dichotomy between mind and matter is removed. In that fashion, one can model the mind as material, or model matter as mind.

Some references that have influenced my thinking are given below.

Selected Bibliography

1. Publications by Thomas E. Bearden:

a. "A Conditional Criterion for Identity, Leading to a Fourth Law of Logic," **Pursuit**, 13(1), Winter 1980. p. 6-10. (Appendix III to this present book.).

b. "A mind/brain/matter model consistent with quantum physics and UFO phenomena," **Mutual UFO Network Annual UFO Symposium Proceedings**, 1979. Also available through the National Technical Information System, Port Royal Road, Springfield, Virginia 22161. Report AD-A068988.

c. "An approach to understanding psychotronics." Paper delivered to 1977 Annual Symposium of the U.S. Psychotronics Association. Oglethorpe University, Atlanta, Georgia. 1977. Available through the National Technical Information System (NTIS), Port Royal Road, Springfield, Virginia 22161. Report AD-A027866. (This report is mostly rough notes).

d. **Excalibur Briefing: Understanding Paranormal Phenomena**. Second edition. Foreword by John White. Strawberry Hill Press, San Francisco, 1988.

e. "Hyperspace (virtual state) engineering." presented at the 11th MUFON UFO Symposium, Clear Lake City, Texas, June 6-8. 1980. Published in **UFO technology: a detailed examination: 1980 MUFON UFO Symposium Proceedings**. Edited by Walter H. Andrus, Jr. and Dennis W. Stacy. Mutual UFO Network, Seguin, Texas, 1980.

f. "Photon quenching of the paranormal (time) channel: a brief note." Paper presented in absentia at the Third International Psychotronics Congress, Tokyo, 1977. Available through the NTIS, Port Royal Road, Springfield, Virginia 22161. Report AD-A038588.

g. **Quiton/Perceptron Physics: A Theory of Existence, Perception, and Physical Phenomena." NTIS, 1973. Report AD-763210.**

h. "The Boundary Identity of Exact Opposites: A simple Solution to the Age-old Philosophical Problem of Change." NTIS, Oct. 1975. Report AD-020798.

i. "The fourth law of logic." NTIS, 1979. Report AD-A068987.

j. **Field, Formon, Superspace, and Inceptive Cyborg: A Paraphysical Theory of Noncausal Phenomena**. U.S. Army Medical Intelligence and Information Agency, Report MIIA-1-74, Dec. 1974. Available from the Defense Documentation Center (DDC), Report AD A-005579/8GI.

k. "The One Human Problem, Its Solution, and Its relation to UFO Phenomena." **Pursuit**, January 1976. Available from NTIS, Report AD-A034236.

l. "Writing the Observer Back Into the Equation," Address given to the Princeton Center for Alternative Futures, Princeton, New Jersey, Mar. 5, 1976, published in June, 1976. Available from NTIS, Report AD-A027867.

m. "Species Metapsychology, UFO Waves, and Cattle Mutilations, May 23, 1977. Privately published.

n. "The Holography of Being," 1975. Unpublished.

o. **Yoseikan Aikido**, 1973. Privately published.

p. "AIDS: Urgent comments on mankind's greatest threat; and the secrets of electromagnetic healing," presented in absentia at the annual USPA Symposium in Golden, Colorado 30 July-2 Aug. 1987.

2. Mike Costello, "Without a Brain," letter, Fortean Times, 96 Mansfield Road, London NW 8 2HX, England, Spring 1987, p. 78. Information on hydrancephaly, persons with normal intelligence but with large cavities in the area normally occupied by cortical tissue. Most of the data on these anomalous cases is buried in obscure medical journals. (Hydrocephaly — an excess of fluid in the cerebral/spinal system — is much more widely known.). See also Anthony Smith, **The Mind**, Hodder & Stoughton, 1984 for additional information on hydrancephaly.

Quoting from Costello: "Actually cases of this kind have been turning up at autopsies for years, and reported in the appropriate medical journals, but have been disregarded, perhaps because they are so destructive of established beliefs about the relationship between consciousness and the human brain."

Costello goes on to point out that a group at Sheffield University has collected a great deal of data on this subject, from case studies of 253 hydrocephalics and hydrancephalics. There seems to be no correlation between the IQ of these individuals and the amount of residual brain tissue.

One living subject, Roger, has an IQ of 126 and a First Class degree in Mathematics, yet has no more than 5% of the normal amount of brain tissue.

A Swedish documentary on the subject was shown on ITV in 1982.

Fortean Times 38, p. 30 also contains an item on surviving adults with no detectable brains.

3. Hugh Everett, III, The **Many-Worlds Interpretation of Quantum Mechanics: A Fundamental Exposition**, with papers by J.A. Wheeler, B.S. DeWitt and Neill Graham, Princeton Series in Physics, Princeton University Press, 1973.

4. Louise and Galen Hieronymus, **Tracking the Astronauts in Apollo 11, With Data From Apollo 8 Included**," Advanced Sciences Research and Development Corporation, Fort Lauderdale, Florida, 1969.

5. Vlail Kaznacheyev's work and publications related to it (see Kaznacheyev references).

6. Antoine Priore's work and publications related to it (see Priore references).

7. Charles Muses and Arthur M. Young, eds, **Consciousness and Reality**. Outerbridge & Lazard, 1972.

8. George Meek, **Healers and the Healing Process**, Theosophical Publishing House, 1977.

9. Harold Puthoff and Russell Targ, **Mindreach**, Delacorte, 1977.

10. Harold Puthoff and Russell Targ, "A Perceptual Channel for Information Transfer Over Kilometer Distances: Historical Perspective and Recent Research," **Proceedings of the IEEE**, 64(3), March 1976.

11. Edward W. Russell, **Report on Radionics**, Neville Spearman, London, 1973.

12. John White and Stanley Krippner, eds., **Future Science**, Anchor, 1977.

13. C. Louis Wiedemann, "Results of the N.J. 'Spook Light' Study," **Vestigia Newsletter**, Stanhope, New Jersey, May 1977.

14. David Bohm, **Wholeness and the Implicate Order**, Routledge, Kegan Paul, 1980.

15. Renee Weber, "Reflections on David Bohm's Holomovement: A Physicist's Model of Cosmos and Consciousness," in Valle and von Eckartsberg, editors, **The Metaphors of Consciousness**, Plenum Press, 1981.

16. "The Physicist and the Mystic: Is a Dialogue Between Them Possible?" A Conversation with David Bohm, conducted by Renee Weber, edited by Emily Sellon, **ReVision**, 4(1), Spring 1981, p. 22-35.

17. "The Tao of Physics Revisited," A Conversation with Fritjof Capra, conducted by Renee Weber, **ReVision**, 4(1), Spring 1981, p. 36-52.

18. "Reflections on the New Age Paradigm," an Interview with Ken Wilber, **ReVision**, 4(1), Spring 1981, p. 36-52.

19. Fritjof Capra, **The Tao of Physics**, Shambhala, Boulder, Colorado, 1975.

20. Fritjof Capra, **The Turning Point**, Simon & Schuster, New York, 1982.

21. Ken Wilbur, **Up From Eden**, Doubleday, 1981.

22. G. Spencer, **Laws of Form**, Julian Press, New York, 1972.

23. Bernard D'Espagnat, **Conceptual Foundations of Quantum Mechanics**, W.A. Benjamin, Menlo Park, California, 1971.

24. Robert Linssen, **Zen: The Art of Life**, Pyramid, New York, 1969.

25. E.P. Wigner, "Remarks on the Mind-Body Question," **The Scientist Speculates**, I.J. Good ed., W. Heinemann Ltd., London, 1961.

26. Thomas G. Hieronymus, U.S. Patent No. 2,482,773, Sept. 27, 1949.

27. Langston Day and George De La Warr, **New Worlds Beyond the Atom**, Vincent Stuart Publishers Ltd., London, 1973.

28. Jule Eisenbud, M.D., **The World of Ted Serios**, Pocket Books, Simon and Schuster, New York, 1968.

29. Sheila Ostrander and Lynn Schroeder, **Psychic Discoveries Behind the Iron Curtain**, Prentice-Hall, 1970.

30. Carl G. Jung, **Man and His Symbols**, ed. by Carl G. Jung and after his death by M.S. von Franz, Aldus Books Ltd., London, 1964.

31. **The Unfathomed Mind: A Handbook of Unusual Mental Phenomena**, compiled by William R. Corliss, The Sourcebook Project, Glen Arm, Maryland, 1982.

32. Charles Panati, ed., **The Geller Papers: Scientific observations on the paranormal powers of Uri Geller**, Houghton Mifflin Company, Boston, Massachusetts, 1976.

33. Ken Wilbur, **The Spectrum of Consciousness**, The Theosophical Publishing House, Wheaton, Illinois, 1977.

34. "Godel's proof," **Scientific American**, June 1965, p. 81-86. As Ken Wilbur puts it, "Thus logically as well as physically verification is not an absolute mark of reality. If all is to be verified, how do you verify the verifier, since he is part of the all?"

35. Erwin Schroedinger, **What is Life? and Mind and Matter**, Cambridge University Press, London, 1969.

36. Teilhard de Chardin, **The Phenomenon of Man**, Harper Torchbooks, New York, 1965.

37. D.T. Suzuki, **The Zen Doctrine of No Mind**, Rider, London, 1970.

38. Frederick S. Perls, **Gestalt Therapy Verbatim**, Real People Press, Lafayette, Indiana, 1969.

39. Frederick S. Perls, Ralf F. Hefferline, and Paul Goodman, **Gestalt therapy**, Dell, New York, 1951.

40. John White, ed., **The Highest State of Consciousness**, Anchor, New York, 1972.

41. J. Blofeld, trans., **The Zen Teaching of Huang Po**, Grove Press, New York, 1958.

42. R.E. Ornstein, **The Psychology of Consciousness**, W.H. Freeman and Company, San Francisco, California, 1972.

43. Joseph C. Pearce, **The Crack in the Cosmic Egg**, Julian, New York,

44. Andrija Puharich, **Beyond Telepathy**, Anchor Press, Doubleday & Company, Garden City, New York, 1973.

45. Jacques Vallee, **Passport to Magonia: From Folklore to Flying Saucers**, Henry Regnery Company, Chicago, Illinois, 1969.

46. Robert Bruce Lindsay and Henry Margenau, **Foundations of Physics**, Dover publications, New York, 1957. See p. 2-3 for the blunt statement that physics has nothing at all to say about a possible real world lying behind its concepts and equations. That is, physics is simply a model, and the assumption of a kind of reality is an interpretation and an hypothesis.

47. Ted Bastin, ed., **Quantum Theory and Beyond**, Cambridge University Press, 1971.

48. Edgar D. Mitchell, **Psychic Exploration: A Challenge for Science**, edited by John White, G.P. Putnam's Sons, New York, 1974.

49. Hector Hawton, **Philosophy for Pleasure**, Fawcett Publications, 1956, Fifth printing, June 1970. (A real gem.)

50. Jiro Kikkawa and Malcom J. Thorne, **The Behavior of Animals**, Plume, The New American Library Inc., New York, 1974.

51. Helena Curtis, **Biology**, Worth Publishers, Inc., New York, 1968 (fourth printing); p. 614-637 contains a good discussion of instinct, learning, and memory.

52. John Cunningham Lilly, **The Mind of the Dolphin: A Nonhuman Intelligence**, Avon, New York, Mar. 1969.

53. Isaac Asimov, **The Human Brain: Its Capacities and Functions**, Signet Science Library, The New American Library, Inc., New York, 1963.

54. R.W. Sperry, "The Great Cerebral Commissure," **Scientific American**, Jan. 1964, p. 42-52.

55. Michael S. Gazzaniga, "The Split Brain in Man," **Scientific American**, Aug. 1967, p. 24-29.

56. Roger Sperry, "Problems Outstanding in the Evolution of Brain Function," James Arthur Lecture, American Museum of Natural History, New York, 1964.

57. Jose M.R. Delgado, **Physical Control of the Mind: Toward a Psycho-Civilized Society**, Harper Colophon Books, Harper & Row, New York, 1971.

58. B.B. Kazhinskiy, **Biological Radio Communications**, Izdatel'stvo Akademii nauk Ukrainskey SSR, Kiev. 1962. Trans. available through DDC, AD 415676.

59. S.K. Lisitsyn "New Approach to the Analysis of Electroencephalograms," in **Problems of Bionics (Selected Articles)**, p. 16-25, DDC Report AD 730045.

60. Evert W. Beth, **The Foundations of Mathematics**, Harper Torchbooks, Harper & Row, New York, 1966. p. 481-518 contains a discussion of the "contradictions" of logic painfully noted by mathematicians shortly after the turn of the century.

61. Stanley Krippner and James Hickman, "West Meets East: A Parapsychological Detente," **Psychic**, May/June 1974, p. 51-55.

62. G.G. Globus, ed., **Consciousness and the Brain**, Plenum, New York, 1976.

63. Karl Pribram, **Emotion: the Search for Control**, McGraw Hill, New York, 1968.

64. Karl Pribram, **Languages of the Brain**, Prentice Hall, Englewood Cliffs, 1971.

65. Charles Hampden-Turner, **Maps of the Mind: Charts and Concepts of the Mind and Its Labyrinths**, Collier Books, Macmillan Publishing Co., New York, 1981.

66. Adam Smith, **Powers of the Mind**, Random House, New York, 1975.

67. Peter Tompkins and Christopher Bird, **The Secret Life of Plants**, Harper & Row, New York, 1973. (a real gem.)

68. The Louis Kervran material.

69. The Antoine Priore material.

70. Langston Day and George De La Warr, **Matter in the Making**, Vincent Stuart, London, 1966.

71. Sister Justa Smith, "Paranormal Effects on Enzyme Activity," Professional Paper No. 2, **Human Dimensions**, 1(2), 1972.

72. John Pierrakos, **The Energy Field in Man and Nature**, Institute of Bioenergetic Analysis, New York, 1971.

73. Jeffrey Mishlove, **The Roots of Consciousness**, Random House, New York, 1975.

74. Andrija Puharich, "Psychic Research and the Healing Process," in **Psychic Exploration**, ed. John White, Putnam, New York, 1975.

75. Andrija Puharich, **Beyond Telepathy**, Darton, Longman and Todd, London, 1962.

76. Lyall Watson, **Supernature**, Hodder & Stoughton, London, 1973.

77. Jule Eisenbud, "The Mind-Matter Interface," **Journal of American Society for Psychical Research**, 69(2), Apr., 1975.

78. George W. Meek, **From Enigma to Science**, Samuel Weiser, New York, 1973.

References Related to Antoine Priore's Work

1. Antoine Priore. "Procede et dispositif de production de rayonnements utilisables notamment pour le traitement de cellules vivantes." Republique Francais: Brevet d'Invention P.V. No. 899.414, No.1.342.772, 1963. For the U.S. patent, see Antoine Priore, "Method of producing radiations for penetrating living cells," U.S. patent No. 3,280, 816. Oct. 25, 1966.

2. Letter, R. Pautrizel to his colleagues at the University of Bordeaux, Sept. 11, 1979.

3. Letter, R. Pautrizel to his colleagues, Mar. 26, 1969.

4. Jacques Sylvain and Jean-Michel Graille, "Depuis quinze ans le "rayon Priore" divise le monde scientifique." [For fifteen years the "Priore Ray" has divided the world of science.]. **Sud-Ouest Dimanche**, Jan. 27, 1980.

5. "Affaire Priore: L'armee va trancher? [The Priore Affair: Will the Army resolve it?] **Sud-Ouest Dimanche**, May 20, 1980.

6. "Affaire Priore: L'armee va tranchera." [The Priore Affair: The Army will resolve it.]. **Sud-Ouest Dimanche**, Apr. 12, 1981.

7. M.R. Riviere, A. Priore, F. Berlureau, M. Fournier and M. Guerin, "Action de champs electromagnetiques sur les greffes de la tumeur T8 chez le Rat." [Action of the electromagnetic fields on the graftings of the TB tumor on the rat.]. **Compt. Rend. Acad. Sci.** (Paris), 1964, **259**, 4895-4897.

8. M.R. Riviere, A. Priore, F. Berlureau, M. Fournier and M. Guerin, "Effets de champs electromagnetiques sur un lymphosarcome lymphoblastique transplantable du Rat." [Effects of Electromagnetic fields on lympheuplastic lymphosarcoma transplantable from a rat.]. **Compt. Rend. Acad. Sci.** (Paris), 1965, **260**, 2099-2102.

9. M.R. Riviere, A. Priore, F. Berlureau, M. Fournier and M. Guerin, "Phenomenes de regression observes sur les greffes d'un lymphosarcome chez des souris exposees a des champs electromagnetiques." **Compt. Rend. Acad. Sci**. (Paris), 1965, 260, 2639-2643.

10. G. Delmon and J. Biraben,"la croissance du carcinome de Guerin sous l'action de champs electromagnetiques." **Rev. Path. comp.**, 1966, **3**, no. 2, 85-88.

11. M.R. Riviere and M. Guerin, "Nouvelles recherches effectuees chez des rats porteurs d'un lymphosarcome lymphoblastique soumis a l'action d'ondes electromagnetiques associees a des champs magnetiques." **Compt. Rend. Acad. Sci**. (Paris), 1966, **262**, 2669-2672.

12. R. Pautrizel, M.R. Riviere, A. Priore, and F. Berlureau, "Influence d'ondes electromagnetiques et de champs manetiques associes sur l'immunite de la souris infestee par **Trypanosoma equiperdum**." [Influence of electromagnetic waves and associated magnetic fields on the immunity of the mouse infected with the Trypanosoma equiperdum.]. **Compt. Rend. Acad. Sci**. (Paris), 1966, **263**; 579-582.

13. R. Pautrizel, A. Priore, and F. Berlureau, and A.N. Pautrizel, "Stimulation par des moyens physiques des defenses de la Souris et du Rat contre la trypanosomiase experimentale." [Stimulation, by physical means, of defenses of the mouse and of the rat against the experimental Trypanosoma.]. **Compt. Rend. Acad. Sci**. (Paris), 1969, **268**, 1889-1892.

14. R. Pautrizel, A. Priore, F. Berlureau, and A.N. Pautrizel, "Action de champs magnetiques combines a des ondes electromagnetiques sur la trypanosomiase experimentale du Lapin" [Action of magnetic waves combined with electromagnetic waves on the experimental trypanosoma on the rabbit.]. **Compt. Rend. Acad. Sci**. (Paris), 1970, **271**, 877-880.

15. A.J. Berteaud, A.M. Bottreau, A. Priore, A.N. Pautrizel, F. Berlureau, and R. Pautrizel, "Essai de correlation entre l'evolution d'une affection par **Trypanosoma equiperdum** et l'action d'une onde electromagnetique pulsee et modulee." [Trial of the correlation between the evolution of a disease by Trypanosoma equiperdum and the action of a pulsating and modulated electromagnetic wave.]. **Compt. Rend. Acad. Sci**. (Paris), 1971, **272**, 1003-1006.

16. R. Pautrizel, P. Mattern, A. Priore, A.N. Pautrizel, and D. Bernard, "Etat de protection vis-a-vis de **Trypanosoma equiperdum** chex des souris splenectomisees et soumises a une stimulation physique." **ler Multicolloque Europeen de Parasitologie**, Rennes, l au 4 Septembre 1971.

17. R. Pautrizel, A. Priore, M. Dallochio and R. Crockett, "Action d'ondes electromagetiques et de champs magnetiques sur les modifications lipidiques chez le Lapin par l'administration d'un regime alimentaire hypercholesterole." [Action of electromagnetic waves and magnetic fields on provoked lipidic modiications in the rabbit by the administration of an alimentary hyperchloresterol diet.]. **Compt. Rend. Acad. Sci**. (Paris), 1972, **274**, 488-491.

18. G. Mayer, A. Priore, G. Mayer and R. Pautrizel, "Action de champs magnetiques associes a des ondes electromagnetiques sur l' orchite trypanosomienne du lapin." [Action of the magnetic fields associated with electromagnetic waves on the trypanosomian orchitis of the rabbit.]. **Compt. Rend. Acad. Sci**. (Paris), 1972, **274**, 3011-3014.

19. R. Pautrizel, A. Priore, P. Mattern, and A.N. Pautrizel, "Stimulation des defenses de la souris trypanosomee par l'action d'un rayonnement associant de champ magnetique et ondes electromagnetiques." [Stimulation of the defenses of the trypanosomized mouse by the action of a ray associated with a magnetic field and electromagnetic waves.]. **Compt. Rend. Acad. Sci**. (Paris), 1975, **280**, 1915-1918.

20. R. Pautrizel, A. Priore, P. Mattern, A.N. Pautrizel, and A. Capbern, "Guerison de la trypanosomiase chronique du Lapin a **Trypanosoma equiperdum** par l'action combinee de champs magnetiques et d'ondes electromagnetiques modules." **J. Protozool.**, 1975, **22**, no. 3, A 84.

21. R. Pautrizel, "La trypanosomiase experimentale: stimulation des defenses de L'organisme par des moyens physiques." **XVIIth Seminar on Trypanosomiasis Research**, Londres, 22-23 Septembre 1976.

22. R. Pautrizel, P. Mattern, A.N. Pautrizel, and A. Priore, "Effets des champs magnetiques et des ondes electromagnetiques modules sur la trypanosomiase experimentale." [Effect of magnetic fields and modulated electromagnetic waves on the experimental trypansomiasmis.]. **Ann. Soc. Belge Med. trop.**, 1977, **57**, 501-523.

23. R. Pautrizel, P. Mattern, A. Priore, A.N. Pautrizel, A. Capbern and T. Baltz, "Importance des mecanismes immunitaires dan la guerison de la trypanosomiase experimentale par stimulation physique." [Importance of immune mechanisms in the cure of the experimental trypanosomias by physical stimulation.]. **Compt. Rend. Acad. Sci**. (Paris), 1978, **286**, 1487-1492.

24. R. Pautrizel, and A. Priore, "Un aspect spectaculaire du bioelectromagnetisme: permettre a l'organisme de se debarrasser d'une infection aig ue ou chronique sans l'aide d'aucune substance medicamentese." [A spectacular aspect of bioelectromagnetism: permitting the organism to rid itself of an old chronic infection without the aid of any medical substance.] **Communication presented to the 104 eme Congres National des Societes Savantes**, Bordeaux, 17-21 Avril 1979 — section Sciences, p. 112.

25. R. Pautrizel, and A. Priore, "Guerison de la trypanosomiase experimentale par association de champs magnetiques et d'ondes electromagnetiques," [Cure of the trypanosomias by associated magnetic fields and electromagnetic waves.]. **Communication presented to the Symposium International des Therapeutiques Ondulatoires**, Versailles 19-20 Mai 1979, p. 9.

26. R. Pautrizel, A. Priore, A.N. Pautrizel and P. Chateau-reynaud-Duprat, "Guerison de la trypanosomiase experimentale par l'association de champs magnetiques et d'ondes electromagnetiques: une stimulation des defenses de l'organisme." [Cure of the trypanosomias by associated magnetic fields and electromagnetic waves: a stimulation of the organism's defenses.]. **Communication presented to the Journees Nationales Microondes - Colloque Hertzienne et Dielectriques**, Lille 26-29 juin 1979, p. 31.

27. David M. Rorvik, "Do the French have a Cure for Cancer?" **Esquire** Magazine, July 1975, p. 110-111, 142-149. Excellent summary of the Priore Affair, with some details of the working of the machine.

28. J.B. Bateman, "A Biologically Active Combination of Modulated Magnetic and Microwave Fields: The Priore Machine," Office of Naval Research, London Report R-5-78, Aug. 1978. Comes very close when he states that "The possibility that some hitherto unrecognized feature of the radiation from a rotating plasma may be responsible for the Priore effects should not be dismissed out of hand..." Indeed, none of the persons who checked the machine or pondered over it knew anything about phase conjugation — which plasmas can do.

29. J.B. Bateman, "Microwave Magic." Office of Naval Research London Conference Report, ONRL C-14-77, 1977.

30. D.S. Greenburg. "The French Concoction." **Saturday Rev. Sci.**, May, 1978. p. 36-44.

31. Lord Zuckerman, "The great Bordeaux magnetic mystery machine." **Sunday Times Weekly Review**, Jan. 7, 1973.

32. Lord Zuckerman, "Pride and Prejudice in Science. William Randolph Lovelace Commemorative Lecture. **Aerospace Medicine**, 1974, **45**, 638-647.

33. L.B. Bateman, "Staging the perils of non-ionizing waves." Office of Naval Research London, **European Scientific Notes**, ESN 32-3: 85-88.

34. R. Courrier, 1977. "Expose de M. le professeur R. Courrier secretaire perpetuel de l'Academie des Sciences fait au cours d'une reunion a l'Institut sur les effets de la machine de M.A. Priore le 26 Avril 1977.

35. M. Riviere, A. Priore, F. Berlureau, M. Fournier and M. Guerin, "Phenomena of regression observed on the graftings of a lymphosarcome in mice exposed to electromagnetic fields." Mar. 1, 1965.

36. Jean-Michel Graille, **Le Dossier Priore**: De Noel, Paris, 1984. Published in France.

37. G. Lakhovsky, "Apparatus with circuits oscillating under multiple wave lengths," U.S. Patent No. 1,962,565. June 12, 1934.

38. G. Lakhovsky, "Tube for producing multiple wave lengths." U.S. Patent No. 2,351,055. June 13, 1944.

39. Thomas H. Moray, "Electrotherapeutic apparatus," U.S. Patent No. 2,400,707. Feb. 1, 1949.

40. Robert C. Beck, "Extremely low frequency magnetic fields and EEG entrainment: A psychotronic warfare possibility?" Audiotape; presentation at the 1978 U.S. Psychotronics Association (USPA) Conference, Atlanta, Georgia.

41. T.G. Hieronymus, "History of radionics. Parts 1 and 2." Audiotape; presentation at the 1979 USPA Conference, University of Houston, Texas.

42. Robert C. Beck, "Extreme low frequency magnetic pulses and E.E.G. entrainment: Soviet Psychotronic Weapon?" Audiotape; presentation at the 1979 USPA Conference, University of Houston, Texas.

43. Al Bielek and William Bise, "A magnetic pacer." Audiotape; presentation at the 1980 USPA Conference, Dayton, Ohio.

44. Thomas E. Bearden, "Mind and matter interaction." Audiotape; presentation at the 1980 USPA Conference, Dayton, Ohio.

45. John Moray, "Sea of energy." Audiotape; presentation at the 1980 USPA Conference, Dayton, Ohio.

46. T. Galen Hieronymus, "Sunspots trigger earthquakes." Audiotape; presentation at the 1981 USPA Conference. Available from USPA, 3459 Montrose Ave., Chicago, IL 60618.

47. Al Bielek and Bill Bise, "Measurements of ELF and its parameters." Audiotape; presentation at the 1981 USPA Conference.

48. Martin Ruderfer, "Misconceptions in established science and their relevance to psychotronics." Audiotape; presentation at the 1981 USPA Conference.

49. Material on the Kaznacheyev experiments. See Kaznacheyev section for references.

50. Material on phase conjugation. See phase conjugation section for references.

51. Material on Ehrenhaft experiments. See Ehrenhaft section reverences.

52. Material on Kervran's work. See Kervran section for references.

53. Extensive proprietary scalar electromagnetics experiments by Frank Golden and John Bedini.

54. Material on Royal Raymond Rife's work. See Rife section for references.

References Related to the Australian Work

1. Private correspondence, Dr. B.L. Reid.

2. Private correspondence, Dr. S. Barsamian.

3. B.L. Reid, "Propagation of properties of chemical reactions over long distance in the atmosphere as seen by crystal growth pattern changes," **Australian Journal of Medical Laboratory Science**, Vol. 7, Feb. 1986. p. 30-35.

4. H.E. Anderson and B.I. Reid, "Vicinal Long Range and Extremely Long Range effects on growth of sodium chloride crystals from aqueous solutions containing protein," **App. Phys. Comm.**, vol. 4, 1984. p. 217.

5. W.H. Campbell and J.M. Young, "Auroral zone observations of infrasonic pressure waves related to ionosopheric disturbances and geomagnetic activity," **J. Geophys. Res.**, vol. 68, 1963. p. 5909.

6. G. Chimonas and C. Hines, "Atmospheric gravity waves launched by auroral currents," **Planet Space Sci.**, vol. 18, 1970. p. 565.

7. F.B. Abeles, **Ethylene in Plant Biology**, Academic Press, New York, 1973.

8. G.I. Distler, **Jour. Cryst. Growth**, Vol. 3 & 4, 1968. p. 175.

9. G.I. Distler and V.P. Vlasov, **Thin Solid Films**, vol. 3, 1969. p. 333.

10. G.I. Distler, **Jour. Cryst. Growth**, Vol. 9, 1971, p. 76.

11. B. DeWitt, **Phys. Rev.**, 19C, 1975, p. 297.

12. W. Greiner and J. Hamitton. **Amer. Sci.**, vol. 68, 1980, p. 154.

13. P. Davies and T. Birrell, **Quantum Fields in Curved Space**, Cambridge University Press, Cambridge, 1982.

14. P. Mitchell, **Nature**,vol. 191, 1961. p. 144.

15. A Rothen. **Proc. Nat. Acad. Sci.** (U.S.), vol. 72, 1975. p. 2462.

16. L. Niemeyer, L. Betroniero, and H.J. Weismann, **Phys. Rev. Lett.**, vol. 52, 1984. p. 1033.

17. T.A. Witten and L.M. Sander, **Phys. Rev. B.**, vol. 27, 1983. p. 5686.

18. T.D. Lee, **Particle Physics and Introduction to Field Theory**, Harwood Academic Publishers, New York, 1981. See particularly Chapter 16, "Vacuum as the source of asymmetry."

References Related to Royal R. Rife's Work

1. Royal R. Rife, "Bacteria," Apr. 28, 1939.

2. Royal R. Rife, "The filterable virus of carcinoma," Apr. 26, 1939.

3. Royal R. Rife, "The Rife microscopes," Apr. 28, 1939.

4. Royal R. Rife, "History of the development of a successful treatment for cancer and other viruses, bacteria and fungi." Allied Industries, Dec. 1, 1953.

5. Arthur Isaac Kendall and Royal Raymond Rife, "Observations on Bacillus Typhosus in its filterable state," **California and Western Medicine**, California Medical Association, Dec. 1931.

6. Arthur Isaac Kendall, "Filtration of bacteria; studies in bacterial metabolism," **Science 75**, Mar. 18, 1932. p. 295-301.

7. Arthur Isaac Kendall, "The filtration of bacteria," **Science**, Mar. 18, 1932.

8. E.C. Rosenow, "Observations on filter-passing forms...," **Proceedings of the Staff Meeting of the Mayo Clinic**, July 13, 1932.

9. E.C. Rosenow, "Observations with the Rife Microscope of Filter-passing forms of micro-organisms," **Science**, n.s., vol. 76, Aug 26, 1932. p. 192-193.

10. E.C. Rosenow, "Microdiplococci in filtrates of natural and experimental poliomyelitic virus compared under the electron and light microscopes," **Proceeding of the Staff Meeting of the Mayo Clinic**, 17(7), Feb. 18, 1942. p. 99-106.

11. E.C. Rosenow, "Observations of filter-passing forms of Eberthella Typhi (Bacillus Typhosus) and of the Streptococcus from Poliomyelitis," **Proc. Staff. Meet. Mayo Clinic** 7, July 13. 1932. p. 408-413.

12. E.C. Rosenow, "Transmutations within the Streptococcus-Pneumonococcus Group," **Journal of Infective Diseases**, vol. 14, 1914.

13. "Powerful microscope makes very tiny objects visible," **Science Newsletter**, vol. 33, Jan. 22, 1938. p. 55.

14. "The Rife microscope or "facts and their fate'," Reprint No. 47, The Lee Foundation for Nutritional Research, Milwaukee, Wisconsin.

15. R.E. Seidel, M.D. and M. Elizabeth Winter, "The new microscopes," **Journal of the Franklin Institute**," Feb., 1944. p. 103-129.

16. R.E. Seidel, M.D. and M. Elizabeth Winter, "Filterable bodies seen with the Rife microscope," Science Supplement, **Science**, Dec. 11, 1931. p. 10-11.

17. "Is a new field about to be opened in the science of bacteriology?" Editorial, **California and Western Medicine**, California Medical Association, Dec. 1931.

18. Christopher Bird, "What has become of the Rife microscope?", **New Age Journal**, Mar. 1976.

19. Peter Tompkins and Christopher Bird, **The Secret Life of Plants**, Harper & Row, New York, 1973.

20. Lida H. Mattman, **Cell Wall Deficient Forms**," CRC Press, Cleveland, Ohio. 1974.

21. Georges Lakhovsky, **La Cabal: Histoire d'une Decouverte L'oscillation Cellulaire**," G. Doin, Paris, 1934.

22. Georges Lakhovsky, "Apparatus with circuits oscillating under multiple wave lengths," U.S. Patent no. 1,962,565. June 12, 1934. See also G. Lakhovsky, " Tube for producing multiple wave lengths," U.S. Patent No. 2,351,055. June 13, 1944.

23. Georges Lakhovsky, **"L'oscillation Cellulaire," Ensemble des Recherches Experimentales**, G. Doin, Paris, 1931.

24. Harold Saxton Burr, **Blueprint for Immortality: The Electric Patterns of Life**, Neville Spearman Ltd., London, 1972.

25. George De La Warr and Douglas Baker, **Biomagnetism**, De La Warr Laboratories, Oxford, 1967.

26. Ruth Beymer Drown, **The Theory and Technique of the Drown H.V.R. and Radiovision Instruments**. (Private printing.). Artists' Press, Los Angeles, 1939.

27. Ruth Beymer Drown, **The Science and Philosophy of the Drown Radio Therapy**. Los Angeles, 1938.

28. Albert Abrams, **New Concepts in Diagnosis and Treatment**. Philopolis Press, San Francisco, 1916.

29. Albert Abrams, **Iconography: Electronic Reactions of Abrams**. San Francisco, 1923.

30. Jagadis Chandra Bose, **Response in the Living and Non-Living**, Longmans, Green & Co.; New York, 1902.

31. Jagadis Chandra Bose, **The Physiology of Photosynthesis**, Longmans, Green & Co.; New York, 1924.

32. D.M. Bose, "J.C. Bose's Plant Physiological Investigation Relating to Modern Biological Knowledge," **Transactions of the Bose Research Institute**, Vol. 37, Bose Research Institute, Calcutta, 1947-48.

33. "Invisible ultra-violet life frequencies made visible," **New Light on Therapeutic Energies**, Source/data unk., p. 51-55.

34. Wilheim Reich, **The Cancer Biopathy**. Orgone Press, New York, 1948.

35. V.M. Inyushin and P.R. Chekorov, "Biostimulation through laser radiation and bioplasma," Kazakh State University, U.S.S.R.

36. Philip Medley et al, "The filterable forms of bacteria," **Journal of Infectious Diseases**, vol. 48, 1931.

37. Gianni A. Dotto, "Method for constructing a thermionic pile," U.S. Patent no. 3,839,771. Oct. 8, 1974.

38. Gianni A. Dotto, "Story of the Dotto Ring." notarized in Montgomery County, Ohio on Feb. 8, 1972. Certain parts of Dotto's theory, apparatus, and recommended treatment method suggest potential effects on recombinant genetic structures.

39. Gianni A. Dotto, "Electrostatic Wand," U.S. Patent No. 3,785,383. Jan. 15, 1974.

40. T.H. Moray, **The Sea of Energy**. 5th Edition. History and biography by John E. Moray. Foreword by Thomas E. Bearden. Cosray Research Institute, 2505 South 4th East, Salt Lake City, Utah 84115. 1978.

41. T.H. Moray, "Electrotherapeutic Apparatus," U.S. Patent no. 2,460,707. Feb. 1, 1949.

42. John Moray, "Radiant Energy," in **1st International Symposium on Non-Conventional Energy Technology**, Toronto, Canada. Planetary Association for Clean Energy, 1981. p. 316-319.

43. Antoine Priore's research and devices.

44. Wilheim Reich's orgone energy work and devices.

45. Radionics researchers' work and devices.

46. Jonathan Tennenbaum, "Soviet Work on Electromagnetic Pulse Weapons," EIR Special Report, **"Electromagnetic-Effect Weapons: The Technology and the Strategic Implications,"** Wiesbaden, Federal Republic of Germany, 1988.

47. Ron Iscoff, "Dye Lasers Used to Treat Blood," **Lasers & Optronics,** 7(3), Mar. 1988, p. 26-28.

APPENDIX I

The Case of Antoine Priore and His Therapeutic Machine: A Scandal in the Politics of Science

© 1984, 1988 Christopher Bird (Used by permission)

Forty- four years ago, in 1944, an Italian engineer working as a prisoner and forced laborer for the Germans in the huge submarine base in Bordeaux, approached a French police agent to plead for his life. He would be killed when the Germans left Bordeaux, he said, and since they were by that time obviously losing the war, the day of his execution was at hand.

The police officer, who also worked clandestinely for the French underground, told the engineer to get in his car, then simply drove him out of the base and introduced him to the 7th battalion of underground resistance fighters, in the nearby province of Dordogne. There he so distinguished himself in military operations that he was ultimately decorated by the French government.

It was due to his thankfulness to his savior, and his loyalty to his companions-in-arms, that Antoine Priore decided after the war's end to live out the rest of his life in Bordeaux. Thus he became the focus of one of the strangest, and most scandalous, chapters in the scientific history of France or any other nation.

Antoine Priore had earlier graduated from a small provincial school for electricity in Trieste, Italy and become a radar operator in the Italian Navy. During this period he observed what to him was an exciting anomaly: some oranges left in a room filled with electrical bric-a-brac had fallen into an assemblage where they seemed to have been preserved in the same fresh state they had enjoyed when bought off a fruit stand. Other oranges in the room, bought at the same time, were rotten and putrid.

Stunned by his observation, Priore dreamed throughout the war of one day working out an electrical means of conserving foods in their fresh state based on what he surmised was a new, and wholly unexplained, principle. Newton's apple had become Priore's orange.

Occupied during the day as a humble electrical repairman — and projectionist in a movie theater — the almost wholly self-taught Priore devoted all his free time and his meager resources to research. With the help of his war-time companions, some of whom had attained high rank in the Bordeaux police force, he was able to beg, borrow, steal, scrounge, or otherwise acquire a mini-warehouse of electrical and electronic components and parts. With these he put together a device worthy of Rube Goldberg. Exposing lentil seeds to a magnetic field of 225 gauss and electromagnetic frequencies of 80,

32, 3 and 10 Hertz, Priore's device caused the lentil plants which sprouted from them to grow 12-15 centimeters in length, as against only 5 centimeters for controls not subjected to the same treatment. He got similar results for tulips, asparagus and other plants.

Shifting his focus, he next irradiated fertilized hens' eggs, only to see the chicks hatch in 19 days, instead of the normal 21. Though he could not explain these astonishing results, he realized he had stumbled upon a process basic to the enhancement, or speeding up, of cellular growth.

It was at this point that one of his police friends introduced him to Francis Berlureau, the former Director of Studies at the School for Veterinary Medicine in Toulouse and, at the time of their meeting, director of the Bordeaux abbatoir. Priore asked Berlureau to supply him with various animal tissues for experimentation. For 10 years they worked together, Priore's free time allowing, during which Priore noticed he could get no electrical measurement from a cancerous bull's testicles. Since he realized that, in some way, his newly constructed device (no trace of which remains today, except for a snapshot of it) affected the electrical properties of cells, he put two and two together and his sum of four led him to believe that he might be onto an electromagnetic cure for cancer. Newton's gravity had become Priore's cancer cure.

Berlureau next allowed him to expose a cat with cancer of the mammary glands to radiation of his machine. To make absolutely sure that he was not exposing himself to mockery, the veterinarian had all the histological work done by his friend and colleague, a Professor Drieux at the famous Veterinarian School of Maisons-Allfort, near Paris. Drieux wrote a technical report proving that a tumor taken from a cat had, before treatment, started to become cancerous and, after treatment, had become benign.

By 1953, with the help of a doctor of general medicine, Maurice Fournier, Priore began treating human patients whose cancers had been judged hopeless. The huge file of cases maintained by Fournier, and filed with a notary until after his death, was subsequently mysteriously lost. But a few details were preserved in letters discovered in an old dog-eared file.

Some of these dating to the year 1954 concerned a 12-year old boy, Alain B., whose diagnosis wavered between one of reticulo-histio-sarcoma and a malignant form of Hodgkin's disease. The boy was taken by his parents to Priore, who irradiated him. Though the exact nature of the radiation was not known, 12 years later a Bordeaux physician, after a medical examination, certified that the boy, now become a man of 24, was free of disease.

A second case unearthed from the old file indicated that a patient with cancer of the larynx was able to avoid a laryngectomy and be totally cured after Priore's new ministration.

Fascinated by the principle which he suspected must lie behind the strange Priore Ray, Dr. Berlureau tried to get some Bordeaux University physicists interested in the problem but was laughed out of their offices. He next turned to cancer specialists, beginning with Professor Lachapele, the Director of the Bergonie Foundation, a prestigious center for cancer research, to whom he proposed animal experiments to prove the efficacy of Priore's methodology. His plea met with a stony affirmation on Lachapele's part to the effect that he and his colleagues had no need of the new discovery, inasmuch as "all the patients treated in his hospital were cured and departed in perfect health." As if bound in the chains of his curt reply, years later Lachapele was to become one of the bitter adversaries of Priore's pioneering research.

Only somewhat discouraged, Priore kept up his momentum. He went on to build a new and more complicated version of his treatment device, called the P-1, over the next year. When it was finished he secretly and unofficially began to treat dozens of cancer patients who had been given up by their doctors as incurable. At his funeral in March of last year, among the crowd of mourners was, it is said, a small platoon of older people who had been cured of their terrible afflictions by Priore in the 1950s.

While his findings excited him, he nevertheless felt tremendously frustrated that he could apparently get no one in the world of medicine or science to pay attention to them. Undaunted by his previous rebuffs, his friend Berlureau next introduced the Italian at the end of 1959 or the beginning of 1960 to Professor Tayeau, vice dean of Bordeaux's Medical Faculty. Unlike Lachapele, Tayeau behaved as a true physician and scientist. He sent Priore to two researchers, Biraben, head of the Faculty's Department of Pathological Anatomy, and his assistant, Delmon. The two had been working together on cancerous rats for two years--specifically on animals grafted with T-8 tumors, discovered by the internationally famous team of Guerin and Oberling in Paris, which had proven to be intractable to any form of treatment yet known. To their utter surprise, the tumors in the rats treated with Priore's machine were reduced in volume by 60%, marking the first time in the history of cancerology that the virulent T-8 tumor had in any way been affected by any form of treatment.

Knowing that the mayor of Bordeaux, Jacques Chabans--Delmas--who has kept his post until this day, and was soon to become prime minister of France-- was most interested in the work of Priore (who, he too, had known as a fellow resistance fighter), they also informed Chaban.

Promptly Chaban convoked not one, but two, commissions made up of Bordeaux and Parisian scientists to study the Biraben-Delmon results in detail. Both commissions rejected Priore and his machine out of hand, and without appeal. It is curious that, in the science of our day, a result, undeniable though it may be, seems to have no hearing unless and until all means to effect it can be adequately explained. It was for this ostensible reason that the two commissions decided to so adamantly reject the research: Biraben and Delmon could not explain the nature of the radiation engendered by the Priore device.

One can stress the word *ostensible* here because the principal reason for the rejection lay elsewhere. The decision by the first commission was, in fact, hardly unanimous. But among its members was the same Professor Lachapele who had refused Berlureau's plea for assistance. His opinion was that even the results themselves were of little value because they were obtained, not on spontaneously arising, but on grafted, cancers. The fact that no treatment whatsoever had ever affected a T-8 tumor was totally discounted. As the sole cancerologist on the commission, Lachapele's dictum was preponderant.

When he learned that the rejection of the first commission had actually been a split decision, the Bordeaux mayor asked for the formation of a second commission to re-examine the problem. Fearing a reversal, Lachapele was able to get one of his colleagues, Professor Courtial, director of the Radium Institute in Paris, and one of the so-called top authorities of French cancer research, named to it. It was all but impossible for the other physicians on the new commission now to outvote not one, but two, cancer specialists, so again the antagonists won the day.

At no time did either of the commissions bother to interview Priore himself or to run a supplementary experiment under their own control.

This seemingly incomprehensible attitude on the part of scientific authority was only a foretaste of what was to come, again and again, over the years. Biraben and Delmon went on to do new experiments. They modified either the time after grafting that the radiation was applied, or the length of its duration. This time their efforts were crowned with unequivocal and complete success. The tumors stopped growing and, when still living cells were excised from them and implanted in healthy control animals, none of them became malignant.

Though these results should normally have fascinated any academy of medicine or sciences, the two researchers did not publish them. Why? The reasons horrify or disgust. It seemed that Biraben was simultaneously preparing an examination for the *agregation*, the highest French academic degree leading to a senior university teaching post. In charge of the committee to pass on, and award, this degree was none other than that same Professor Lachapele who told him: "Either you get the degree, necessary to your professional advancement, or you publish your research paper. But not both!" Discouraged, Biraben ceded to this demand but nevertheless continued to work on the research that looked so exciting and promising.

Most mystifying to him was how the machine operated to achieve its startling results. At the 3rd Congress of Biometerology held in 1963 in the Pyrennees mountains, a New York City researcher by the name of Kenneth McLean reported he had been able to obtain regressions on tumors and improve the health of cancer patients by using a magnetic field of a strength of 3000 gauss or more. Acting on this hint, Biraben and Delmon made an electromagnet that put out a field of 4,500 gauss and tried it out on the T-8 tumors but without the slightest success. Obviously, something other than a simple magnetic field was at issue.

In 1966, after others had had the same success with the T-8 tumor by irradiating it with the "Priore Ray," the two scientists finally published a memoir in the **Revue of Comparative Pathology** in which they stated that neither magnetic fields nor X-rays had any effect on the T-8s and that "only certain devices associating a magnetic field with high frequency waves seem at present to reveal therapeutic properties..."

Their conclusions were too late for, by that time, a campaign to stamp out Priore and his electromagnetic approach to cancer cure was well underway, a campaign that has lasted right up to the present moment.

The all-powerful Lachapele had sealed the fate of the Priore device as far as the local Bordeaux medical community was concerned. Veterinarian Berlureau and Priore next decided to carry their case to Paris. They contacted Professor Guerin at the cancer institute at Villejuif, the leading French center for cancer research and the equivalent of the American National Cancer Institute in Bethesda, Maryland. Guerin, one of the discoverers of the T-8 tumor, which for the first time had been stopped in its tracks by the Priore device, courteously received his guests and heard them relate the whole story of how the device had come into being, starting at the point when Priore had seen the oranges strangely preserved by some unaccountable electromagnetic effect.

Guerin was sufficiently impressed that he assigned his colleague, Marcel-Rene Riviere, to delve into the whole question. For two years, Riviere, who also had teaching responsibilities at the University of Rennes in Brittany, unremittingly worked to corroborate the Biraben-Delmon findings. On 9 December 1964 a note was sent for publication in the **Proceedings** of the French Academy of Sciences detailing the research and modestly concluding: "... as of now, one may already state that our first observations show that electromagnetic fields used can lead to most interesting data from a point of view of the biological behavior of grafts and their therapeutic action on experimental tumors."

Riviere next decided to see if the Priore Ray could affect another tumoral form that had never been affected by any therapeutic method, the 347 lymphoblastic lymphosarcoma. The results were even more spectacular than for the T-8 tumor. The effects produced were of broader scope and took place more rapidly. A second note was sent to the Academy for publication. The conclusion read: "We can now already affirm that our research offers proof that electromagnetic fields are capable of producing effects on quite different types of neoplasms."

At this point one of the key characters in this extraordinary drama must be introduced. There might have been no drama at all without his appearance on stage. This personage was Robert Courrier, an eminent endocrinologist, who had been named, while still in his 30s, a full professor. Courrier was now perpetual secretary of the Academy of Sciences and later would become President of the Academy of Medicine. Because no scientific paper can be accepted by an academy unless introduced by one of its members, Riviere would have had no chance to see his work so prestigiously published had not Courrier, who knew Riviere well, since he had shepherded him through the winning of his doctorate, taken the responsibility for its introduction.

It was Courrier who, at this point, also took up the cudgel to interest various highly placed French organizations responsible for the administration of scientific projects and their funding. Thus, he sent a personal letter to the French Minister for Scientific Atomic and Space Research, who immediately offered to try to make funds available for further research on and with the Priore Ray. He also personally asked the Director of the CNRS (National Center for Scientific Research, which coordinates and oversees all such activity in France) to receive Priore and Riviere.

That this meeting was, in its way, somewhat of a disaster, can be explained in part only by a brief resume of the complex character of Priore himself. Priore throughout his life had great difficulty making himself understood in the French language and, as the years went by, he even forgot how adequately to speak his own mother tongue, Italian. Added to these twin impediments was his lifelong fear that his discoveries and inventions were prone to being stolen, a fear which led him never to fully explain the exact nature of the complex radiation emitted from his machine, far less the settings which controlled its various parameters. Whether Priore would not, or could not, exactly explain the functioning of his invention (which, as we shall see, went through several increasingly complex generations) is a question to which no precise answer has been given. It would appear that Priore was an excellent engineer gifted more with a God-given intuition than with school-book reasoning and logic. In short, Priore had a combination of talents that could remind one of the same enigmatic personality that was Nikola Tesla, the deductive reasoning behind some of whose discoveries has never fully been unravelled.

Highly placed scientific administrators are neither comfortable with, nor sympathetic to, what they see as self-appointed geniuses who have not run the same academic gauntlet through which they themselves had to pass. Thus the CNRS director took aversion to Priore's somewhat incomprehensible, yet fairly prolix explanations of his technology and only recommended that a physicist be sent to look over his device to properly decipher its working. At the same time, the Minister, together with the head of the general delegation for Scientific Research (DGRST) — still another key body in the administration of the French scientific decision-making process — let it be known to Robert Courrier that they had not understood a single thing about Priore's invention despite his best efforts to present it.

Advancing one more step into what was to become for him a 20 year-long expedition into a jungle of scientific intrigue, Courrier next resolutely decided to send to Bordeaux one of his most trusted laboratory workers, Madame Colonge, to repeat Riviere's experiments under her personal supervision. The DGRST director fully concurred with Courrier's decision, while letting slip his admission that he strongly suspected that Riviere might well have been duped in some manner by Priore. When Courrier asked the minister for travel funds for Madame Colonge, he was refused with the dry remark that such a request was "premature." The now angry Courrier telephoned to reply: "You've been spending millions for programs and hypotheses about the cancer problem. Riviere has been presenting you with facts!"

The physicist who had been sent to try to elucidate the functioning principles of Priore's device, reported that he could make neither "head nor tail" of the machine.

Madame Colonge's experimentation was as prolonged as necessary. She was so meticulous that, in order not to take her eyes off the experimental animals for an instant, she limited her lunches to sandwiches eaten in the laboratory. She returned, profoundly impressed, to Paris.

Nor was Riviere idle during this period. He decided to experiment with the L-52 lymphosarcoma, a tumor similar to, but even more malignant than the 347. This time, he used not rats, but mice, as hosts for the grafts. So successful were his results that, this time, Courrier decided to bar no holds. Instead of simply having a note published in the Academy Proceedings on the quiet, he decided to present it personally, orally, and in all solemnity, before his fellow academicians at an official meeting scheduled for 1 May 1965.

That date was, and is, a turning point in what came to be known in France as the "Priore Affair." From then on the whole French, and even the international, scientific community could be divided into a minority and a majority group, the first that believed in the research, the second that did not know enough details about it, did not or would not believe, or simply didn't give a damn.

Before Courrier could make his presentation, its scheduling and subject were inadvertently and prematurely leaked to the press. Immediately thereafter, a horde of journalists arrived in Bordeaux. After one or two of them managed to all but force entry into his lab, Priore closed its doors and, with the help of his friends, wrote a printed press release that stressed his thankfulness to the many people who had helped him over the years rather than providing any comprehensible details about the machine he had brought to birth. Stymied, many of the newsmen travelled across town to seek an explanation from its leading cancerologist, Professor Lachapele, who informed them acidly that the machine was all but useless and unworthy of their attention or their time.

The journalists' reports, founded as they were on rumor of outright lies, roiled the pages of their newspapers and magazines in such a way that they either over-exaggerated the potential or a forthcoming cancer cure, or came close to billing Priore as just one more cancer-cure charlatan. All of which so alarmed, among many others, Dr. Wilhelm Bernhard, world specialist in electron microscopy, that he called his friend Courrier to warn him that his forthcoming presentation to the academy might put his hard-won reputation at risk as well as those of Guerin, Riviere and the Villejuif cancer institute itself.

In the journalistic melee, no one had bothered to read the declaration carefully issued by Riviere from Rennes, where he was occupied with his university courses, which formally stated: "Our experiments are of real interest. Much more experimental research has of course to be done before any therapeutic application on human cancer victims can even be considered. It goes without saying that this will take a certain time and no little effort of many types, both scientific and financial. Our work, as fascinating a perspective as it might hold, in no way, therefore, allows anyone to offer the public hope which could only lead to deception at the present time."

On May Day, Courrier gave his report to an Academy assembly hall crowded with scientists, newspapers and television reporters, photographers and an unusual number of curious bystanders. Accompanied with slides showing histological details, and animals before and after treatment, his lecture was heard out in almost tomb-like silence. When the lights came on again, he announced that he had personally checked the validity of Riviere's findings through the offices of his personal assistant, Madame Colonge. He then went on to say that he had taken the responsibility of presenting three notes to the Academy for two reasons. The first was a ringing declaration and a challenge to critics and skeptics of every stamp. It reads "When it is a question of a problem as serious as that of cancer and when one sees a little light beginning to dawn, one has the obligation to see what this light might represent. One has no right to snuff it out before learning what it may be worth."

The second was a tribute to his colleagues who had done the pioneering work, particularly Guerin, Riviere and Madame Colonge, and a statement of the essence of the problem to be faced down the road. It read: "Attention must naturally be given to the apparatus which Monsieur Priore has conceived and constructed. It has apparently already been examined by several physicists. It is found to be too complicated. While that may be possible, it is nevertheless a fact that Guerin and Riviere have obtained results with it that had to be made public. What is emitted from such an apparatus? I hope Monsieur Priore will allow disinterested physicists to study it at their leisure, for Science cannot tolerate apparatuses enveloped in mystery." Then, as almost a footnote to the history of the moment: "The biological action of magnetic fields is the object of intense research in the United States. In specialized institutes, the influence of these fields on tissue cultures, microbes, plant forms, diastases and certain tumors is under study. Up to now, the results obtained on grafted tumors seem less significant than those which have here been presented."

After Courrier sat down, a leading cancer specialist, Professor Lacassagne, rose to ask snidely why the notes had included no bibliographical references on work done on the bio-effects on tumors from electromagnetic fields, and criticized the experimentation as "impromptu." When Courrier denied this allegation as ludicrous,

Lacassagne stalked out of the assembly hall in full view of the audience.

The meeting caused a new eruption of media reports which unfortunately accented one of three aspects of the problem at the expense of the other two. These were 1) the hope that a miraculous cure for cancer was in the offing 2) the contradictory, not to say discordant, reception of the data by various academics and 3) the enigma of Priore's personality.

Remarkably, no serious discussion among the scientists present at the meeting ever took place. This led a foreign scientist, present in Paris at the time, to remark: *"I don't understand. Here is a report given to the most authoritative scientific body in France by one of the most respected and eminent of its members and it is publicly subject to doubt without that leading to any reaction whatsoever."*

The General Delegation for Scientific Research was at this point still open to the idea of providing funds for more research with the Priore Ray. The big stumbling block, however, was one related to niceties involved in relations up and down the scientific hierarchy. To open the way to the allocation of such funds required the approval of the Delegation's own section for cancer research and that section was headed by none other than the same Professor Lacassagne who had so rudely walked out of the Academy's assembly hall.

At the same time the General Delegate diplomatically covered himself by suggesting to Robert Courrier that he had to have more information underscoring the potential importance of the research accomplished. Courrier told him to simply re-read the three notes he had presented to the academy. His matter-of-fact, yet terse, come-back then elicited his invitation to a full-dress meeting of scientific experts at the Institute for Scientific Cancer Research.

In this short historical account we obviously cannot go into the ins and outs of what transpired at this meeting or any of the many similar meetings which followed it. A paragraph in a brilliant book, four years in the writing, by the courageous Bordeaux journalist, Jean-Michel Graille and entitled: **Dossier Priore, A New Pasteur Affair** (of which this account is but a tenuous synopsis) must suffice to pointedly characterize the nature of the problem in its most general sense.

Writes Graille: "To read what follows in this chapter might well seem tedious: an enumeration of names and titles, the content of a debate held at an administrative meeting, personal remarks by one ranking personage or another, exchanges of letters following the meeting itself and the official report which came out of it. Tedious but indispensible for not a few reasons. It is important to know who were the participants at this meeting and what of these participants each was trying to represent. It is important to know how such scientific meetings go about their business at the 'top level,' And, finally, it is important to learn about and to understand, in the particular case of the Priore Affair, the behavior and reactions of all concerned. A reading of all this could be difficult (and it won't be the only such passage in this book) yet it is necessary to understand the essence of the dossier in order to be able to create for oneself as clear and well-motivated a personal opinion about it as to subsequently be able to discuss it, or to hear it discussed, with a thorough knowledge of the facts."

In this single paragraph, Jean-Michel Graille has, in my opinion, pointed to both the nub and the difficulty in getting at the essence of the real facts behind a case such as that of Priore's that are so important to its proper understanding, an understanding which can be painted against the backdrop of the history of science and the backdrop of human pettiness and maliciousness or human courage and magnanimity.

One of the participants, Professor Andre Lwoff, soon to become a Nobel Laureate for his work in virology, was violently against the meeting's central issue: namely, whether or not funds should be spent to build a new and better Priore machine. Not only did Lwoff aver that the three notes presented to the Academy never should have been published, but he also opined that since all the work was done, not on spontaneously generated but on grafted cancers, the effects of the machine were hardly impressive. He later added in writing that 1) the patents issued to Priore for his device were nothing but a web of nonsense, 2) the machine itself could never be duplicated based on any description given for it by its inventor and, in a repetition of his oral remarks, 3) the fact that only cancer grafts were experimented with was nothing to shout about. He strangely added that because the animals who had been irradiated subsequently were able to entirely reject new grafts, the whole phenomenon offered no proof that cancer cells could be killed while healthy cells were not. The whole thing came down to a question of immunity, he said, as if that were not of the greatest possible importance.

To which, in due course, Guerin and Riviere replied: "It has been claimed that our experiments are valueless because they were carried out on grafted tumors and that other therapeutic measures were known to get rid of such tumors and their metastases. *We defy those persons who have made such affirmations* to prove, *with the use of such other measures, that animals infected with T-8 tumors can be cured at a percentage rate identical to those obtained by using the device which Monsieur Priore has developed."*

Not a soul has responded to this challenge, then or since.

A second cancer expert at the meeting, a woman of great influence, resorted only to the cavil that the experiments had been of doubtful quality since none of the animals had been *weighed*. The fact that those same animals had survived normally lethal cancers seemed not to have *weighed* with her.

There were many more observations of the same ilk. They seem atrociously paltry, trifling and picayune coming from professionals who, if they no longer believed in the Hippocratic oath to which they once swore, are considered by the public in general, and by cancer patients in particular, at least to be concerned with seeing what a little light on the problem might reveal before extinguishing it, as Professor Courrier expressed it.

At the same time, we must not forget Priore's decidedly difficult personality. He was an inventor determined at all costs that his invention be developed for the benefit of humanity, yet anxious that that same humanity not steal it from him. As author Graille puts it, "His conceptions and attitude directly or indirectly conditioned the overall essence of this affair. Full of enthusiasm, from the very day he discovered that the ray he had developed had a curative effect on a cancerous cat, he developed a single-minded fixation on cancer. One could understand and sympathize with him on this score. Here he is, a little Italian immigrant without money or means, and he is going to offer the world a cancer cure. He is so convinced that he wants to move ahead to doing just that. He will never understand or accept the exigencies of Science or Medicine. For him, experiments, controls, verifications and parallel research are a waste of precious time. 'I've made machines which cure cancer. Take them and treat cancer patients. Don't bother with the rest.' Such would be a summation of his point of view."

Through the efforts of persons kindly disposed to the inventor, this point of view was softened and he came finally to understand the necessity for what has been called scientific rigor, on the other hand, another aspect of his character never changed an iota. This was his determination to preserve the secret of his invention, motivated first of all by his unshakeable desire that it be developed in Bordeaux, the city of his adoption, for the citizens of that city. Deeply rooted was his belief that if he made his secret public, the machine would be taken from the Bordeaux region and further developed by Parisians, those who considered themselves to be in the penthouse of the scientific edifice. Once this was accomplished, he would likely not have one more word to say about the matter. Therefore he continued jealously to conserve his secret and put confidence in nobody.

As Graille generously concedes, he may well have been right, and adds: "All his life he had to go up against men, whether scientists or industrialists, who had but one idea in their heads: to get to the bottom of the inventor's secret in order to build for themselves a machine which they then could exploit for their own account, for their own glory. Many such 'Priore Machines' were to be actually built more or less surreptitiously or clandestinely. Not one of them ever worked."

While one might easily accuse Priore of a limited view, the horizons of the researchers themselves were certainly not as broad as they might have been. Those involved in bio-medicine were content with the results produced by the machine, the workings of which were of no concern to them. A black box, as it were, emitted a ray that definitely affected experimental animals. At the same time, as researchers specifically interested in the cancer problem, they never gave a thought to what the Priore Ray might accomplish in the wider clinical domain of other afflictions.

As for the physicists, they were seemingly not up to the task of comprehending a complex radiation that had miraculously sprung, as from the head of Zeus, out of the intuition of a man they considered to be an undereducated and all but illiterate gadgeteer. Still others, whether physicists, biologists, doctors of medicine or specialists in a dozen other fields, were willing to throw the baby out even before it went into the bath water. In their eyes Priore was just a nobody.

Behind the scenes, many of these scientists resorted to using the press to achieve their own ends. Thus, the chief medical chronicler for **Le Monde** (the French **New York Times**), herself a doctor of medicine, was led to write outright lies about the Priore Affair--specifically and falsely stating that cancer patients had been treated with the Priore Ray in the clinic of Professor Lachapele in Bordeaux with not only negative, but disastrous, results.

On the other hand, a journalist for another leading Paris daily, **Le Figaro**, scrupulously conscious of his responsibility to fairly report what was going on, aptly wrote: "We would like to see at least one thorny point clarified as soon as possible. Several years ago Professor Biraben of the Bordeaux Medical Faculty (who at that time had not become a ranking professor) was involved with the Priore device. According to certain reports from medical circles, his results seemed, even at that time, to have been already quite positive on small animals and he seems to have written a report to that effect. He was advised by highly placed authorities "to keep quiet" and stop talking about this affair. If this turns out to be true, it would be a veritable medical scandal to be judged in the harshest terms."

Could one have put it more succinctly?

The foregoing is to present something of the flavor of what was transpiring in the wide world far removed from the laboratory of

Priore who, at the time unaware of it, was revelling in the fact that his machine had been successfully used by high-ranking French cancerologists and its results reported in three separate notes to the Academy of Sciences.

His courage was also more than buoyed by the arrival on the scene of the commercial director of a large French industrial firm specializing in the intricacies of manufacturing glass components. This man had heard that Priore needed a large tube that was beyond all existing norms and perhaps did not exist anywhere in the world. This tube, it can be stated, contained a rare gas, neon, which when excited into a plasma, seemed somehow to convert the various electromagnetic inputs into a single Priore Ray which surged from the business end of the tube. In the tube were an anode and cathode. Peculiar to the anode was that it had to *rotate* to produce the desired biological effects and this is but one of the anomalies in Priore's equipment which physicists and bio-physicists have to this day been unable to explain.

The manufacturing company, a subsidiary of the internationally known company, Saint Gobain, was looking for a new product. The commercial director thought the new tube might fill the bill, particularly if it could be adapted to a machine that might ultimately cure cancer, a product that indubitably would have an enormous market across the world. There were plenty of problems with regard to the tube, notably those of its large dimension, its resistance and its conductability. When the tube was finally made, it now seemed that Priore would have to explain his discoveries to the scientists of the company that had made it. One of these was sent to elicit such an explanation but was, so to speak, "shot down in flames" by Priore. So a second attempt was made by Ivan Peyches, a senior executive of the company, and president of the Society of Civil Engineers of France, who made a detailed investigation of the device. His reports were subsequently lost, but there remained an article he published in a leading French journal, **Sciences and Technics**, a short time before his death in 1978. It bore the intriguing title: "What Are So-Called Paranormal Phenomena?"

In it the engineer wrote: "There was so great an accumulation of components capable of having some kind of action, and being unable to work separately, that the results of measurement were limited to proving that there were no specific rays that issued from the tube (Priore talked about canal rays), no more than there were any X rays. On the other hand one could detect a magnetic field which was the end result of a field proper to the tube and of the magnetic field of a solenoid that constituted the experimental chamber, an electromagnetic field with a frequency of 16 megacycles (19 meters) and a high frequency field (metric waves), the whole being pulsed at a very low frequency of an order of one per second. It was impossible, in such an imbroglio, to determine what was necessary and what was sufficient. Priore maintained that the simultaneous action of his various generators was indispensible to achieving his effect."

Peyches then went on to relate how he tried to persuade Priore to offer a more precise definition of his thinking about the workings of his device. He wrote the inventor: "At this point, I would say that all reticence on your part, which in your eyes would be justified by the fear of seeing yourself partially dispossessed of your work, would be of far greater detriment to you than any safeguard of your interests. Moreover, since it has become a question involved in public health, you are no longer entirely your own boss...you absolutely must bring all this to the clear light of day and I don't believe you can do it alone...You must supply all the characteristics so that third parties can reproduce your results." Then, he concluded by citing the words of an academician: "Many phenomena are rejected by the scientific world because they are considered irrational: But it is not a proof of scientific honesty to refuse **a priori** to try, out of homage to truth, to have a look at them and perhaps to understand them. Will Science one day be able to abandon its taboos?"

It was Peyches' final conclusion that, in the end, Priore was a man of genius who knew absolutely nothing about what occurred in his machine from the scientific point of view. The company which he represented no longer exists since it was bought out by the American firm of Corning Glass.

Industrial interest in the Priore device was not limited to the Saint Gobain subsidiary. Next into the lists was a company in Anguouleme, Leroy-Somer, which specialized in electric motors, generators and later was to branch out into solar power. Its president, Georges Chavanes, took the initiative to write to Priore in 1965 that his company was interested in providing some of the complex electrical equipment needed by the inventor, more particularly high-powered generators, on the condition that Priore move his operation to the company seat at Anguouleme. When the inventor categorically refused, Chavanes tentatively agreed to build a factory to manufacture the Priore device in Bordeaux itself.

The alliance between Leroy-Somer and Priore, shaky at best, lasted two years and blew up on Holy Thursday of 1967. The period was a stormy one for both parties to the agreement. Priore did his best to convince Chavanes to commit himself to building a huge machine with a magnetic gauss strength of 10,000 gauss. In the end he got one that put out only 920 gauss, not much stronger than the machine he had already built which put out 620 gauss. Since the field of action increased with the gauss strength, Priore reasoned that a machine of literally behemoth size would be able to irradiate the whole, or every part, of a human cancer victim lying on a stretcher, whereas the smaller machines had been effective only for small animals or for treating a limited portion of the human body.

Chavanes and his company were aware that it would be a tremendous financial burden to contemplate building the larger machine. So they went ahead with plans for the smaller one while at the same time putting great pressure on Priore himself to make him feel that he was the least important cog in a new gear, in fact that his status was reduced to being a simple employee of Leroy-Somer. In Graille's estimation, this lack of psychological finesse on Chavanes' part constituted what he called "the blackest pages in the Dossier Priore."

Even the smaller machine was to cost about half a million dollars, a price which today, due to inflation, could be tripled or quadrupled. During a stage in which an intermediate machine was designed by the chief Leroy-Somer engineer, Ribeau, a machine that never did function properly, Chavanes all but forced Priore, who was heavily in debt, to sign a contract which was falsified. The falsification was a matter of one word which was changed in the contract. In a phrase reading that an exclusive license of patents, and subsequent patent modifications, would accrue to the company "for all countries solely for therapy on cancers concerning animals and humans," a word was inserted by hand so that the phrase read: "concerning *particularly* animals and humans" implying that other uses of the machine, whatever they might turn out to be, would also accrue to the company. This one word change was amended on Priore's copy of the contract by calling the word "particularly" a "nullified word," but on Chavanes' copy it was called an "added word."

Leroy-Somer believed it was sufficiently well positioned in the driver's seat to be able to deal on behalf of Priore himself with the French governmental institutions, mainly the General Delegation, concerned with the funding of the new machine. When Priore learned of Chavanes' contact with the General Delegation he wrote a letter informing it that no one had the right to deal in his name. Nor did Chavanes even attempt to cut the Saint Gobain subsidiary, which alone could supply the tube, key to the device's functioning, in on the government funding.

In the meantime, no less a figure than Professor Kastler, soon to win the Nobel Prize in Physics, came down from Paris to inspect the existing Priore device. He brought with him Delmon, who, we recall, had worked with Berlureau on the first animal experiments and who now, it turned out, was trying to build his own version of a Priore device on the sly without telling Priore. Kastler's bringing Delmon with him to Priore's lab so angered Robert Courrier that he told the physicist he had committed a real gaffe. He also convinced Kastler that Leroy-Somer should build a machine with a power of at least 5000 gauss, but Chavanes refused. There seemed to be no harmony of outlook between the leading industrialist concerned, on the one hand, and the top physical and biological scientists on the other.

While all these, and many more, peripatetics were proceeding, Priore's sister in Italy came down with cancer. Beside himself with grief, Priore informed all concerned to commit themselves either to building an intermediate machine correctly, under his supervision or, better, the 5000-gauss machine, and to do this in time to save his sister, or he would wash his hands of the entire matter. Confronted with this ultimatum, the company began to work round the clock to perfect the intermediate machine but engineers involved, believing themselves to be more adroit with respect to its design than Priore, left out a host of what, to them, were unnecessary components. The result was that when the machine was first put to trial, most of the components burned out or otherwise failed, and the machine itself became a useless pile of rubble.

Shortly thereafter, Priore's sister died of cancer. Her grief-stricken brother went into what amounted to total isolation, unwilling to talk to a soul.

The whole Priore affair might have ended at that point, in the early part of 1967, were it not for the entry onto the scene of a key figure, Professor Raymond Pautrizel. Born on 3 June 1916 in Basseterre, capital of the French Carribean island of Guadeloupe, at forty years of age he was on the Faculty of Medicine at Bordeaux. He soon became known, world-wide, as the "father of parasitological immunity," a title he never accepted, saying that, if others had awarded it, it was simply because "he had searched through old scientific publications to find ideas that were as valid for modern research as they were forgotten by modern researchers." And he later was quoted as adding: "It is really too bad that researchers today don't pause from time to tome to dig into studies made by their predecessors, some of which were performed even decades ago!"

Professor Pautrizel was awarded the first academic chair in France for immunology, and later a special unit was created for him for parasitological immunology, a subject which is both simple and complex. The simple part involves the fact that various immunological techniques can be applied to diagnosing specific parasites that have invaded an organism in order to develop preventative actions against them via vaccines, or curative actions via serums.

When invaded by parasites, organisms react by creating antibodies, specific substances aimed at killing the invaders also known as antigens. These antibodies are liberated, like an attacking army, into the blood. Simple enough so far. The complexity arises because the defending army, the parasites, don't just lie down and die under the attack. They are capable of modifying their "personalities, " as it were, and of changing various of their characteristics such that the mechanisms that the host uses to recognize, or detect, the invaders are invalidated. Thus, the substance which an organism would secrete to destroy an invader A becomes incapable of recognizing A, now become A-1, and therefore incapable of destroying it.

The organism at this point seems to realize it has to create a different substance to rid itself of its antagonist but, in the meantime, the metamorphized parasite is getting on with its assigned destructive task. Alternatively, the parasite has another capability: that of itself liberating substances which can annul or annihilate the organism's overall defense system. A sort of "in the blood" version of Star Wars is going on at the microscopic level.

The study and classification of the substances - - call them weapons - - emitted by parasite-attacked organisms allows for the establishment, in turn, of batteries of tests to define the exact nature of the parasites themselves in order to come up with an appropriate therapy or counter-weapon.

This then, is the essence of parisitological immunology, Raymond Pautrizel's area of research. He specialized on a particularly lethal parasite known as trypanosome, the scourge of tropical third-world countries where, in one form, it causes sleeping sickness in animals and humans, in another, equine syphillis, in still others, other afflications. Over the years, during which he produced a small library of literature on the problem (known mostly to specialists in countries where that problem is acute), Pautrizel and his team discovered, among other things, that the trypanosome can modify itself, again and again, up to 101 times over a period as short as only three weeks.

Even before his work on trypanosomes, Pautrizel, back in 1949, was one of the first researchers to discover what is known as *ambivalence* in drugs, notably histamine. Histamine is a substance which is secreted by an organism as a defense mechanism but if oversecreted by certain cells circulating in the blood, it becomes virulently noxious, mainly by overdialating blood vessels, thus making them permeable to water and leading to edema and even death. This process occurs, for instance, in some human beings who are highly susceptible and over-reactive to bee or wasp stings.

Pautrizel's research on the noxious aspects of histamine led to his finding that the same substance, applied in requisite small doses, is extremely important to the defense system of the organism. Today he stresses the notion of *ambivalence* in many areas of his work and characterizes it as "a key to the biology of the day after tomorrow."

To finish with the background on Pautrizel, before bringing him on stage in the Priore drama, it may be added that only a few years ago, at a formal reception for him attended by the medical elite of France, he was given a Basque *makila*, an iron-bound honorific cane of sculptured wood, in tribute to his work. On it was the incised inscription: "Sometimes to heal, often to alleviate, always to console," an epithet that perfectly characterizes a medical doctor imbued with that kind of rare compassion that marked Pautrizel's character.

When Robert Courrier sent Madame Colonge to Bordeaux, it was Pautrizel whom he asked to provide her with every assistance. In this way, Pautrizel was first introduced to Priore and his device. After witnessing the results obtained with it he was to say: "What stupified me, and led me to ponder the question, was to see the control animals die from their tumors in 3 weeks, while at the same time I could observe that the tumors in the animals under treatment were literally melting away and the same animals were taken back to Courrier's lab at the College de France in Paris in perfect health." As a result of his thinking about the problem, Pautrizel came to the belief that the machine, however it worked, did not exert any action at all to kill cancer cells but, through as yet unexplained mechanisms, stimulated the afflicted organisms to provide themselves with new immunological weapons that could overpower the cancer cells.

To shed light on this problem, Pautrizel proposed the simple expedient of experimenting, not on cancer-infested animals, but on *in vitro* cultures of cancer cells. He made this proposition to both French and British cancerologists but they were convinced that the Priore device *had to be actually killing cancer cells themselves*,. They could not see the point that, if the machine did not kill cancer cells, then it was doing something else to the body to allow it, and not the machine, to do that job.

Pautrizel's involvement with the British was the result of a team being sent from England to experiment with cancer mice with the Priore Ray. What happened cannot be related in this brief resume except to say that, out of a lack of understanding on the part of certain British cancer experts and malicious conniving on the part of one member of the cancer "aristocracy" in Paris, the experiments were put under a cloud. It was alleged that mice had been substituted somewhere during their long round-trip voyage between

England and Bordeaux to make it look as if a failed experiment had been successful. This did not prevent Sir Alexander Haddow, chief of the prestigious Chester Beatty Research Institute for Cancer from stating, at a meeting in Paris, that the Priore machine had been indubitably effective on the English mice and supporting Pautrizel's idea that experiments should forthwith be done to see if the Priore Ray had any effect on cancer cells *in vitro.* Haddow's suggestion backing Pautrizel's recommendation fell on deaf ears.

Because of the emotional turmoil and rancor with respect to cancer that had so long surrounded Priore and the workings of his machine, Pautrizel suggested that it be tried in a completely new area, one he knew so well, namely on afflictions caused by the trypanosomic pathogen. Before these could get underway, however, someone had to persuade the still desolate Priore to return to work. Pautrizel, known to those really concerned with and knowledgeable about the potential of the Italian's invention, at last was able to convince the inventor to cooperate and get back into harness. This he did with that rare combination of diplomatic tact and warm human sympathy with which only the Pautrizels of this world are gifted.

In the meantime, Riviere had gone on to implant new 347 tumor grafts in rats previously cured of 347 tumors. When none of the tumors developed, that result added one more argument to back Pautrizel's idea that the machine was, in fact, affecting the immunological defense system of the animals. However, when Riviere tried the same procedure with the T-8 tumors, his animals died. This lead to the conclusion that the immunity acquired by the animals to lymphoblastic lymphosarcoma 347 was specific to that tumor. When a note on this research was sent, again through Courrier's good offices, to the Academy, for the first time, it strangely omitted from the listing of the participating researchers the name of Antoine Priore. It seemed that Riviere had been taken to task by fellow cancerologists who believed that Priore was nothing but a naive bumpkin or, worse, a swindler. They had warned him against publishing any papers with which Priore's name would be associated. This rank injustice and lack of fair play again sent Priore into a fit of despondency and depression from which he could only be withdrawn by those subtleties involved in Pautrizel's sympathetic and friendly counsel.

On 25 July 1966, another note was sent to the Academy filed for the first time not under the rubric **Cancerology** but under the rubric **Immunology**. It was entitled "Influence of Associated Electromagnetic and Magnetic Fields on the Immunity of Mice Infected with Trypanosoma equiperdum." The conclusion read: "The treatment allows the organism to rid itself of parasites even when these have invaded it in a most intensive way.... There is an enhancement of both the specific and aspecific factors of immunity."

Thus, for the first time, the field of research shifted from the narrower field of cancer to the much vaster domain of immunology. And, for the first time, Pautrizel's name appeared as the senior author on the paper. It also appeared that, for the first time, there should no longer be any problem about experimenting with the Priore machine. Such was not the case.

Still complicating the whole issue was the fact that Priore himself was using different setting to produce different varieties of radiation depending upon his own intuitive evaluation of the particular biological experiments being run with his machine. He would never reveal the nature of these settings.

At this point there appeared on the scene a new researcher who became Pautrizel's loyal ally, a young woman, Pierette Chateau-Reynaud Duprat. During her work in Paris, she had learned of the Priore controversy, and, against the stern advice of mentors senior by many years to her in the cancer hierarchy, she came to Bordeaux to meet Pautrizel and learn more about the research.

Her work, performed over many years, is too detailed for presentation here but it led to important conclusions. One was that the Priore Ray had no direct effect on the trypanosomes themselves but stimulated and reinforced the defense mechanism of the infested organisms, allowing them to reject the parasitical influence with an effect so durable that they were no longer subject to this influence even after treatment stopped.

Another conclusion was even more important and involved, in part, British research. It pertained to the effects of the machine on both *allografts* or those made between two different individuals of the same species, and *isografts*, or those made between two different individuals of the same genetic line having in common antigens that were characterized by what is called the same histocompatability. The conclusion was that not only was the rejection of *allografts* accelerated by the Priore Ray but that *isografts* were also rejected. This meant, in sum, that the ray stimulated not only the *defense* mechanisms of the organism but also, and more importantly, its *recognition* mechanisms. In the case of an isograft, this allowed the recognition of weak antigens that were not recognized in non-irradiated animals. In other terms, where at first the anti-aircraft batteries could not shoot down the aircraft because they could not see them, now they could shoot them down because they could see them. In immunological terms, the ray affected both humoral and cellural, both specific and aspecific, immunity.

Here we must return to the mystery of the settings on the device.

As a result of the new experimentation it seemed that, depending on those very settings, the active ray, complex as it was, could have either similar, totally different, or diametrically opposed effects. Thus it was not a question of a ray having universal effects — a kind of magic bullet capable of killing any target ---- but of multiple radiations which, due to the complexities in Priore's personal makeup, have unfortunately yet to be sorted out and explained.

Thus, the machine originally designed by Priore, called the P-1 when it put out a wave length of from 19-21 meters, had a radical effect on certain animal cancers, on *cellular* defense mechanisms, and finally, but not universally, on organisms infested with **Trypanosoma equiperum**, (hereinafter called T.e.).

A second machine, dubbed the P-2, was at first not able to produce these frequencies. What it did put out was a frequency of 17 meters that *was* universally effective against T.e. and seemed to act not on the cellular, but the *humoral*, defense mechanisms. The rejection of grafts depends on the cellular defense mechanisms, which partially explains why Pautrizel when using the P-2 machine, selected the T.e. vector, as it is called in microbiology, just because this creature is fought by the organism's humoral defense system.

Consequently, the bio-effects that were successfully attained depend on the varying, not to say quixotic, nature of the radiation. At one point Pautrizel actually did experiments on animals infected with *plasmodia* — the vector for malaria which attacks red cells — and found that the settings used were effective while never learning exactly what they were or the exact nature of the radiation. Furthermore, Priore himself maintained that over the years he had successfully treated cases of human tuberculosis but, again, never revealed which frequencies had been used to achieve this.

Several more notes were sent to the academy on the successful work performed with the Priore Ray on animals affected with T.e. But the central issue remained: how to find out exactly how the machine worked. It fell, not to civilian scientists, but to those in the French army service to attempt, at this point, to work out the problem. The army service brought into the picture was the DRME (an acronym which translates as Administration for Research and Test Methods), to which Pautrizel had sent a request for funds in 1968.

This request was the subject of a meeting at which were present three of the top names in French science, one representing biology, the second physics and the third, medical physics. The latter two turned in extremely unfavorable reports recommending that no money be wasted on the problem. The biologist, however, turned in a most favorable report and, despite the fact that he was in the minority, his opinion won the day.

As remarkable as was this victory, it was even more stunning and incredible given the fact that this biologist was the same Andre Lwoff who had so adamantly opposed the Priore research a couple of years previously. Lwoff had summoned the courage to completely reverse himself only after he sent one of his most trusted colleagues to do secret experiments with the Priore Ray on mice injected with peroxydase (an antigenic solution) to see if they would produce a higher level of antibodies than non-irradiated animals. This they did so well that Lwoff became convinced that the Priore Ray caused an extremely important increase in immune reactions. These results were never published because, before the experiments could be repeated to be absolutely sure of their results, the machine suffered one of its many interminable breakdowns.

The DRME report was at length, and in length, issued but not publicly since it was protected by a military classification. However, a synthesis of it was finally published in November 1979 by Herbert Gossot, Secretary General for the French Association for Bioelectromagnetism, under the title: "A Scientific Balance Sheet on the Priore Ray." Its contents were as follows:

"The two physicists assigned by the army made a complete analysis of the electromagnetic radiations and magnetic fields activated by the Priore device. They thus determined the spectrum of frequencies which the device emitted. They showed particularly that frequencies in the visible light and infrared range had no biological effect; that there were no X-rays or Y-rays; and that the pulsed ultra-high frequency electromagnetic wave was modulated in amplitude to that of a high-frequency wave. They did a topographic survey of the respective intensities of the various magnetic and electromagnetic fields in the experimental plane of the device. In particular, they determined the spatial repartition in this plane of the density of the strength of the ultra-high frequency wave. They showed that its value was very weak and that it could not produce any kind of overall significant thermal effect imputable to the hyperfrequency ray.

Finally, and most importantly, by using what they had learned about these repartitions, they demonstrated a clear correlation between the biological effects obtained and the intensity of the hyperfrequency ray. What they actually observed was that, on the biological model used, i.e. experimental trypanosomosis of the mouse, there was a diminution of the rate of evolution of the parasitemia that was proportional to the strength of the hyperfrequency wave. To quote them: *'These experiments of correlation are of certain interest: they confirm, if there is still any need of so doing, the biological efficacy of this device."*

The two physicists, Bottreau and Berteaus, are still interested in rebuilding a Priore device with which additional biological research could go forward. At the same time they suggested to administrative bodies in French science the creation of a special laboratory for bioelectromagnetism to fund more work, a suggestion in which Professor Pautrizel concurred. No action was taken and their report was kept under wraps. In a note they presented to the Academy of Sciences on their investigation, they were not allowed to include the names of the laboratories where they worked: in the case of one, the CNRS Magnetic Laboratory at Bellevue near Paris, and of the other, the Laboratory of Ultra-Hertzian Optics and Talence near Bordeaux. Why? Because the directors of these laboratories did not want any mud in the Priore affair to be spattered on them.

The next experiment done by Pautrizel was on rabbits whose testicles had been so seriously affected by trypanosomes as to be almost entirely destroyed. After radiation the same testicles took on their normal histological appearance and the rabbits, able to procreate again, in no way abstained from their newly regained ability. **This implied the complete regeneration of an organ that had all but completely degenerated.**

Yet journalists, who sought out truths about the Priore affair in Paris from high officials they believed would know best about what was going on, continued to be led astray. For example, an American scientific reporter, writing in the **Saturday Review of Science** in 1973 saw fit to state: "It is really a question of a mystical problem that has little to do with science." He was quoting Professor Bader, a man who for 15 years held top administrative posts in science that could have allowed him to back the Priore research with all the funding necessary to its accomplishment. At the time Graille's book came out, Bader issued a book of his own about the Priore affair which offers no real idea of what was involved. When I asked several people in France why Bader had written the book, they were unaware of Bader's inmost motivation.

Machinations continued to swirl about the case over the next several years. Behind-the-scenes intrigues, distorted accounts in the press, lethargic attitudes on the part of administrative officials who would not take responsibility to cut an increasingly tight Gordian knot, outright fear of various personalities to become too deeply implicated lest they lose their jobs - - all these, and more, continued their daily round in an atmosphere of "Business As Usual," and "Don't Risk Your Neck."

To get to the nexus of the situation, we have but to cite the observation of one of the few perspicacious journalists who, in the prestigious scientific monthly, **Sciences and Life**, wrote: "The physicists are convinced that the effective Priore Ray is very complex but to analyze this further some things first have to be made clear. One is to raise the suspicion that has surrounded Monsieur Priore with a fabulous acretion of misunderstandings, insults and accusations of being a swindler over many years. What is needed is a veritable national effort to act effectively and to act rapidly."

Over the next two years the decision-making process of the French government lumbered its way along until it was finally decided to back the construction of a powerful machine. This decision was not favorably accepted in many quarters. As **Le Monde** would comment: "The decision was made in spite of the disapproval of many scientists. When money is tight, one should pay particular attention to how it is being spent. Such seems not always to be the case. A credit of some $3.5 million francs (or about a million dollars) has just been accorded to finance the construction of a new Priore machine."

The scientists to whom the article referred were in a rage. They understood, at this juncture, that the only way to put an end to the affair was to eliminate Pautrizel who, because of the very success he was having with his research, was seen as a dangerous competitor that might even become one of the top figures in medicine and science on a national, or perhaps, on a world scale. Indeed, it was learned that Professor Courrier had gone to the length of sending a report on Pautrizel's behalf to the Nobel Committee in 1979.

To make a long story short, the large powerful machine, the M-600, was built but a huge tube in it, after functioning for about a week, exploded. Due to the galloping inflation of the 1970's, to replace it would have cost another million dollars. The money was not forthcoming.

In the meantime Pautrizel, ever experimenting with the still functioning smaller machine, was to discover new facts. Mice with their spleens cut out, for example, also could survive injections of T.e. The Priore Ray had important implications for Arterio-sclerosis, since it effected lipid modifications in rabbits given a dietary regime high in cholesterol. This research, published in another note in the Academy **Proceedings**, instead of being warmly received, only irritated the cardiological fraternity which felt, as some of its members put it, "trapped" by Pautrizel's efforts.

One particularly virulent opponent was Professor Bricault, Dean of the Bordeaux Medical School who, as late as 1980, was telling his own students that the published results were a farce and had never been obtained. The students, who carried out a special investigation of the matter on their own, were able to judge what a farce their own medical dean might represent.

L'Express, the **Time** magazine of France, read by at least half the population of French intellectuals, had the gall to compare the results of the Priore research to those of the infamous Trofim Lysenko of the Russia of Stalin's day. Haughtily **L'Express** added: "Today Priore's defenders explain that his machine has not only cured cancer but, in all probability, altered the immunological characteristics of mice. Were this, in fact, so, all the immunologists, all the geneticists of the world would unite to affirm that a machine capable of changing the genetic patrimony is the discovery of the century, far more important than the atomic bomb or the conquest of the moon. Unfortunately, the history of the whole thing has never been properly elucidated." The article was illustrated with photos distortedly selected to convince viewers that the Priore machine was as serious and effective as the one that purportedly brought Frankenstein to life.

In this poisonous atmosphere the slow work of building the M-600 went forward. To give anyone who was not there a feeling for this endeavor we may now cite verbatim a passage from Graille's book: "The construction and assembly of the prototype —theM-600, that of highest power and variable parameters — were fraught with many uncertainties and delays on the one hand and, on the other, were marked by the stamp of Antoine Priore's sparkling genius.

"To go from an apparatus that developed 1,240 gauss applied over an effective area of some 20 centimeters, to one developing 5000 gauss over an area of 60 centimeters means to take on an extremely risky technical and technological wager. Electrical, mechanical and glass-blowing specialists plunged into the unknown. They had to conceive, make, adapt and put together all the various myriad components almost haphazardly with no precise technical study being previously available. Priore's stubbornness forced them to take on a trial-and-error manufacturing "gimmickry" without precedent. As the thing was put together and preliminary tests made, it became clear that many of the components were unsuitable and that they would have to be modified or replaced. The tube itself, made of pyrex, 60 centimeters in diameter, and 6 meters tall, had to be replaced twice after it imploded. In fact, practically everything had to be reconsidered or readapted. "Everything" meant the parts going to make up a generator of 50 tons in weight. For example, the coil which created the magnetic field: 5.5 tons with 11 miles of copper wire. For example, the numerous cooling circuits which stabilized the thermal equilibrium of the generator and its environment or, additionally, the circuits governing command, control regulation and selection — 6 tons of electrical cables of which 15 miles were of tele-command wiring.

"Priore astonished everyone. Breakdown after breakdown, incident after incident, it was he alone who showed what to do next, indicated the proper steps to take, the right settings to adopt, the right way to assemble the components: He was virtually building his machine by himself, nursing its construction along day after day, all the engineers' studies and efforts actually, and ultimately, serving only as a preliminary attempt, a sketch as it were. When Priore made his presence felt, things began working."

Then.... after the machine was built: "The part of the entire apparatus to generate electricity was set up on a provisional basis. It was so noisy that, while functioning, it woke up the whole neighborhood. The number of experiments had therefore to be curtailed so that the machine would not be used at night. And, all at once, everything came to a halt. The Faraday cage, shielding and isolating Priore's apparatus, was torn and fissured by the shock of the cement pilings that were being sunk into the ground all around to hold up the building under construction. This allowed high-frequency waves to escape which disturbed radio broadcasts emitted by local radio stations, the army, and civilian aircraft for miles around."

Nevertheless during the week or ten days that the machine was in good operation the results of experiments performed with it were more than formidable. First of all, it allowed for as many as forty experiments to be performed on some 280 animals in a remarkably short period of time. Among the discoveries made were: The ray emitted provided the treated animals with an extremely strong immunitary response. Animals whose immune defenses had been attentuated by an immuno-depressant were able to overcome the effects of injected parasites but relapsed a few days later. One could therefore conclude their immune response was much weaker than those normally infested and treated.

Newborn animals, whether treated or not, developed a marked parasitemia leading to their deaths. At the time of death, the parasites had the same antigenic structure as those of the innoculum which thus implied that they had met with no defense at all in the infected organisms. This also proved that the Priore Ray did not act directly on the parasites themselves but only by way of an increase in the immune defense system of the organisms. The newborn animals succumbed to their parasitemia because their immune system was not yet sufficiently developed to be stimulated by the P-Ray. The phenomenon of a stimulation of the immune defenses was demonstrated by the fact that animals which had received soluble antigens developed, after being irradiated, a level of antibodies far superior to the controls.

These and other conclusions were the object of notes presented to the Academy of Sciences by Pautrizel and his team in 1978. Even before, at a colloquium held in Antwerp, Belgium devoted to African human trypanosomiasis, the same team had offered the conclusion that the stimulation of the immune defense system that allowed organisms to throw off the effects of trypanosomiasis had to be very significant in that all attempts to try to effect such stimulation through immuno-stimulants as well known as B.C.G., or Corynebacterium granulosum, had led neither to the cure produced by the Priore Ray, nor to any prolongation of the infected animals' lives, nor even to the slightest modification in the evolution of the Trypanosomiasis.

These three scientific papers did little for the cancerologists who read them except to exacerbate their urge to oppose the Priore research, if not to arouse their outright hatred for the principal experimenter, Raymond Pautrizel. Could this have been because, for over 20 years, the same cancerologists had been working in vain to provoke in cancerous organisms immuno-stimulative reactions by intensively and successively vaccinating them with B.C.G.? Many others had been life-long apostles of chemotherapeutic cocktails of all sorts, or life-destroying ionizing radiations, or, what more recently has become the fashion, of applying the two methods in endless combination.

For this reason, they saw Priore and Pautrizel as nothing more than spoil-sports who had to be destroyed.

One of the opening shots in this campaign was a letter received by Pautrizel to inform him that his request for funds to continue his research through Unit-89, a unit that had been specially set up for him to direct, had been denied. It took many months of investigation for Pautrizel to learn that the real reason for the refusal was because of his work with Priore.

Next Pautrizel was informed that his appointment as director of the same research unit would be extended for only two years, whereas the normal extension for similar units was five years. A third insult came when Pautrizel tried to win a post within his unit for a high-ranking military physician, who had been his student and who had decided to quit the military in order to participate in the fascinating research prosecuted by his mentor. Pautrizel's request for funds to pay this physician, who all his life had been working on tropical medicine closely associated with problems of trypanosomiasis, were refused four times in a row with no cogent reason given. The physician, who in the meantime had volunteered his time without pay, finally became so emotionally overwrought that he gave up his medical career and retired to the countryside where he gave himself over to alcohol. Then Pautrizel tried to get a salaried post for another of his brilliant collaborators (who still works with him). He was told that this man could take up his new functions only if he left Bordeaux. One could go on with many other shocking stories but we will leave it to Graille to conclude: "Everything possible was done to isolate Pautrizel, to separate him from his collaborators. Every single one of these collaborators saw their careers put in jeopardy, compromised, or broken."

As a final insult, when the time came again to renew Pautrizel as director of Unit 89, those responsible, not daring to overstep what even they knew to be decent limits by not extending him, simply abolished the unit. And to add injury to that insult, a doctoral thesis that had now been prepared by Priore, and backed not only by Pautrizel but by Nobel Laureate Andre Lwoff himself, was summarily refused by the President of the University of Bordeaux.

It is perhaps unnecessary to state that the details behind all of this skulduggery could, and did, fill up two chapters of a book and make for the most heart-rending reading imaginable.

So what happened next? In the autumn of 1977, Professor Georges Dubourg, one of the leading lights in Bordeaux's company of surgeons and a friend and admirer of Pautrizel's, came to him to say openly and baldly: "My friend, at the point you've reached, there is only one more way to jolt medical opinion and that is to treat human cancer patients." Pautrizel was hesitant, believing his role to be one of continuing with his animal experiments but where would the funds for that come from now? He therefore asked his old mentor, Robert Courrier's advice. Courrier gave the green light. The treatments were restricted to terminal cancer patients whose immune defense systems had been disastrously weakened by chemotherapy or radiation or both. At least one of them was totally cured. The other lived, without pain, for a period many times longer than predicted by prognosis. Dubourg, Pautrizel and their collaborators wrote up the results and sent them as an official communication to the French Academy of Medicine for publication.

The reply they received from that Academy's perpetual secretary reads: "Experts whom we consulted consider that your work does not fall within the jurisdiction of our members and that it would doubtless find an audience more worthy of its purpose in a more specialized society."

To which Pautrizel formally replied: "Since two of the four signatories of our note are corresponding members of your Academy, could we not benefit from the remarks and comments made by the committee which saw fit to refuse our paper? And even, if this is not too indiscreet a request, to learn the names of the expert members who were consulted which would allow us to get into contact with them directly and to benefit from their singular competence?"

His letter has remained unanswered for four years.

There was nothing more to do except one thing which Raymond Pautrizel, as a man of science, had always been careful to avoid: Get a responsible journalist interested in the case, inform him of all possible details, and let him carry the Priore Affair in all its harrowingly loathsome aspects to the broad reading public. That journalist was Jean-Michel Graille.

For four years, Graille went about his task, publishing three consecutive long articles in his newspaper **Sud-Ouest France** and finally the book to which we have referred and of which this presentation is largely a resume. As early as 1980, Graille would write in his newspaper: "The Priore Affair is simple in essence. It can be reduced to a simple alternative: either the machine developed by Antoine Priore is of no interest and, having shown this, the affair can be considered at an end. Or else the machine is of real and demonstrable medical interest and, if that is officially recognized, he would be allowed to get on with the work. For this dilemma runs the risk, yet again, of being buried under delays and evasions. Beyond all the powers-that-be that have been directly connected to the affair for many years now — the power of finance, the power of medicine, the power of science — perhaps it is now political power with which responsibility lies if it can rise to meet and assume that responsibility through decision."

That was Graille's statement in 1980. His book which came out four years later ends with the sentence: "The Dossier Priore thus depends, from here on out, on a decision that must be taken on the very highest level, and imperatively. This responsibility devolves, in last resort, on the chief of state and on him alone. Will he assume it?"

Would the President of the United States?

<u>Note added by T.E.B.:</u> *Antoine Priore is now dead. His machine has been dismantled. The iron dogma and hatred of electromagnetic medicine by bureaucratic science may have doomed hundreds of millions of humans - - whom Priore's device could have saved - - to bitter, agonizing, and unnecessary deaths. Hitler, Stalin, and Mao combined were not responsible for the deaths of so many.*

APPENDIX II

PATENTS

English Translation of the French Patent No. 1,342,772 of Antoine Priore, 7 Oct. 1963.

Procedure and Assemblage for Production of Radiation Especially Serviceable for the Treatment of living cells.

Brevet d'Invention. P.V. no. 899.414 no. 1.342.772 Classification Internationale: A61 k-H 05 g

Procedure and assemblage for production of radiation especially serviceable for the treatment of living cells.

Antoine Priore
Requested 1 June 1962, 14.52 hours, Paris
Released by decree (arrete) of 7 Oct 1963

The invention deals in a general manner with radiation capable of penetrating matter. More exactly, it aims at a procedure and an apparatus making it possible to obtain a combination of radiations of different types able to penetrate matter and especially to penetrate intimately living organic tissues in order to produce in them certain effects, particularly in human tissues with a view to a therapeutic effect without destroying essential elements such as the enzymes.

In conformity with the present invention, one emits in a cavity a stream (rayonnement) of electrically charged particles upon which one superposes electromagnetic radiation of the centimeter wavelength range, the wavelength of which is preferably between 3 cm and 80 cm, and one directs the resulting radiation emerging from the cavity on to the object to be irradiated.

This applicant has shown that the penetration and, in particular, the curative effects are very distinctly improved when one gives the electromagnetic radiation a frequency determined as a function of the organ or the tissue to be penetrated or to be treated. For example, a wavelength of 14 cm is suitable for the liver and a wavelength of 19.5 cm for the spleen.

Preferably, the stream of charged particles is accelerated in a particle accelerator in such a way as to increase the force of penetration.

The resulting radiation is advantageously applied and directed upon the target, that is to say, upon the tissue to be penetrated, by the intermediary of a tube which is the site of electric fields and of magnetic fields for acceleration and control, the said radiation being preferably guided and/or reflected by a rotary deflector placed in the tube.

It is often advantageous to modulate or impose rhythm on this stream of particles by means of variable magnetic and/or electric fields so as to augment still more the force of penetration. This rhythm is preferably consistent, especially in medical applications, with the intrinsic period of the tissue to be penetrated or of the neighboring tissues, for example, muscle. These intrinsic periods are well-known in medicine and are applied, particularly, for diathermy: they are situated in the wavelength range from 1 m to 50 m and more especially from 1 m to 18 m.

Preferably, one arranges to modulate the emission of radiation, the accelerating magnetic and electric fields, and perhaps also the rotatory deflector, to the cardiac rhythm of the subject.

It seems that the result obtained by the invention in the treatment of maladies of living cells (vegetable or animal) are due to certain phenomena which will be described, it being understood that this exposition will not circumscribe the invention.

As a function of its electro-physico-chemical constitution, the cellular pair nucleus-protoplasm is endowed with electric conductivity in direct relationship with ion exchange processes provoked by metabolic phenomena. One finds in tissues the presence of an accumulation of electricity at different potentials according to the different cellular densities of the tissues.

The work of Renshaw, Forbes, Morison, Amassian, de Vito, Ruset, Albe-Fessard, Tauc, Adrian, etc. has shown with the aid of micro-electrodes the existence of slowly oscillating elementary electric activity in the interior of cells; it can be thought that the *rythmeur* (or pace-maker) is achieved by the oscillatory electromagnetic system comprising the cell nucleus. This nucleus, in effect, is made up essentially of tubular filaments of insulating material (related to chitin) containing in its interior an electrically conducting saline liquid, and these filaments, coiled upon themselves, can be considered to constitute real little oscillatory circuits.

The recent work of Warson (sic) in America, as well as that of French scientists, including a communication from Polonsky, Donzon and Sadron presented to the **Academie des Sciences** by Prof. Francis Perrin on 16 May 1960 (**Rec. comptes rend. heb.**, 250 No. 20, 3414-3416) making it clear that experimental samples of solid DNA manifest properties analogous to those known in ferroelectric materials, makes plausible the hypothesis that a potential difference may exist between nucleus and periphery of cells. Certain recent theories go even further and liken the cell to an electronic receiver-emitter device normally functioning in harmony with the ambient media. The oscillatory system of demand waves, constituted by the cell nucleus, would behave in accordance with the laws governing semi-conducting materials.

The applicant is led to the conviction that in a normal state of physico-electric equilibrium, the cell nucleus is positively charged, but can acquire a negative surcharge following phenomena analogous to polarization.

The invention, especially, enables organs afflicted by this inversion of their electric potential, particularly in the case of the pathologic negative surcharge of cancerous nuclei, to recover their former equilibrium.

The following description in regard to the attached drawing, given as a non-restricting example, will make it possible to understand how the invention can be realized, the details which emerge both from the text and the drawing being, of course, part of the said invention:

Fig. 1 is a schematic section showing an apparatus for production and emission of an electromagnetic field combined according to the invention.

Fig. 2 is a frontal elevation of the cathode, taken from the right of Fig.1.

Fig. 3 is a section through III- III in Fig. 1.

Fig. 4 is the overall scheme of the electric supply.

Fig. 5 is a view analogous to Fig. 1 showing another mode of implementation.

Fig. 6 is a section through VI-VI in Fig. 5.

Fig. 7 represents schematically an apparatus for pulsing the electric current.

Fig. 8 is the circuit of an amplifier permitting activation of the apparatus of Fig. 7 at the cardiac frequency.

Fig. 9 is the circuit of an oscillator permitting modulation of the electric current according to a wavelength between 1 m and 18 m.

The assemblage of Fig. 1 contains an apparatus 1 emitting electrically charged particles 2 in a cavity or passage 3, a cyclotron 4 accelerating the particles 2 and sending them into a cavity 5 forming a tube into which merges another cavity 6 acting as waveguide for electromagnetic radiation of frequency in the centimeter range emitted by a magnetron 7. The cavity 8 formed by the joining of tube 5 and waveguide 6 leads into a tube 9 in which the resulting radiation is accelerated and aligned. The interior of the cavity-formed by the assemblage of elements 1, 3, 5, 6, 8, and 9 contains argon at a pressure of 2 mm mercury.

The particle emitter 1 consists of an electron gun comprising a plate 10 and a cathode 11.

The cathode 11 is of molybdenum and has the very special form represented in Figs. 1 and 2. It consists of a rim 11a connected by two aligned spokes 11b to a hub 11c pierced by a hole 11d with its axis along XX'. The rim 11a is in two parts (as one sees in Fig. 1) which may be held together by screws (for example) forming a cavity of revolution 11e traversed by a number of holes 11f parallel to the axis XX' and regularly spaced. The filament for heating, 12, situated in the interior of the cavity 11e and is connected to the power supply conductors 12a.

The best results are obtained with a cathode 11 of molybdenum. The applicant has obtained satisfactory, but slightly inferior, results with tungsten cathodes. It turns out that molybdenum, and to a lesser degree tungsten, are the metals whose valency is closest to the mean valency of the chemical molecules constituting living tissues and more particularly those of human beings. One might well seek to use this fact to explain scientifically the phenomena involved, but it is understood that *the invention is not limited by any scientific explanation*. Concerning, on the other hand, the gas present in the apparatus at low pressure, the best results have been obtained with argon; the applicant has also obtained satisfactory, but slightly inferior, results with other gases of the rare gas series.

Surrounding the tube which constitutes the electromagnetic chamber are arranged: an electromagnet 13 with its winding 13a, placed at the level of the accelerating coils 14 and 15. Other accelerating coils 14, 15 and 16 are similarly dispersed around the cavities 3, 5 and 8.

The two semi-circular boxes or "dees" 4a of the cyclotron 4 are placed in the usual manner between the poles of the frame around which are wound the accelerating coils 4b and 4c.

The magnetron 7 is of a familiar type and must be capable of emitting in the cavity 3 a centimeter wave of adjustable wavelength from 3 cm to 80 cm.

The lower portion of the tube 9, for acceleration and alignment, contains a cathode 17 resembling the cathode 11, with a filament 17a. This cathode 17 is supported by a hollow pillar 18 pierced by holes 18a close to its junction with the bottom of tube 9. This pillar 18 communicates with a tube 18b emerging on the axis of a rotary deflector 19 carrying at each end a "crown" of graphite plates 19a inclined at 45° to the vertical. The rotating axis 19b of the rotary deflector is mounted in a support 20 fixed to the interior of tube 19 and carries at its upper extremity magnetic bobs 19c which ensure that it will be set in motion in cooperation with the magnetic bobs 21a mounted on the shaft 21b of a motor 21. The lower extremity of the rotary deflector 19 is composed of a piece of molybdenum or of tungsten 19d in the form of a pyramid whose apex is opposite the open end of the tube 9.

The hollow base 18 and the tube 18b can be of a borosilicate glass of low coefficient of expansion such as that sold under the trademark "Pyrex." They may also be of quartz. Tube 9 itself can be of "Pyrex" as above or of another glass of the quality currently used for the manufacture of electronic tubes, but its bottom 9a, which is traversed by the radiation, is advantageously made of quartz.

The duct 8 joins the tube 9 by way of several tubulures such as 8a and 8b directed in vertical planes towards the plates 19a at a certain angle, which is advantageously about 22.5°. An electromagnet 23 analogous to the electromagnet 13 of the emitter tube 1 is placed around the cathode 7. Similarly, accelerator windings 24 are disposed around the tube 9. This tube also carries, at positions indicated in the drawing, three electrodes 25, 25a, and 25b surrounded by windings 26, 26a, and 26b, respectively. The drawing shows the supply lines, 17b, 17c of the cathode and its filament and that of the plate, 22a.

The basic plan of the electric supply is represented in Fig. 4. The part 27 feeds an initial branch with low voltage alternating current: this consists of a rectifier 28 (e.g., a Kenotron) whose rectified current is modulated at a frequency variable between 30 and 120 pulses per minute by means of a resistance 29, the control apparatus for which will be described with reference to Figs. 7 and 8. The current so modulated is passed through the electromagnets 13 and 23 in such a manner as to generate, normal to the cathodes 11 and 17, a modulated field of 10,000 to 20,000 gauss.

The part 27 also feeds a variometer (interrupter) 30 which modulates the current of this part at a variable frequency 30 to 120 pulses per minute, the current pulsed in this way serving to feed the remainder of the installation, to wit: The magnetron 7; a converter 31 whose excitation is modulated at a variable frequency *300 to 900 Hz*, yielding a doubly modulated current (first at 30-120 pulses per minute, then at 300-900 Hz) which feeds the coils 15, 16 and 26; another converter 32 producing a low voltage direct current modulated at 30-120 pulses per minute by the variometer 30. This current feeds the motor 21 as well as the motors driving the variometer 30 and the apparatus controlling the resistance 29.

The current produced by the converter 32 also feeds a voltage step-up apparatus 33 consisting of a vibrator followed by a transformer and a rectifier, and producing a direct current varied at 30 to 120 pulses per minute imposed by the variometer 30. The maximum value of the voltage produced by the apparatus 33 is, for instance, 300,000 V, but this value may vary up or down, depending on the power one wishes to operate with.

The current produced by the voltage step-up apparatus 33 feeds the coils 4b of the cyclotron and 24 of tube 9, as well as a rheostat 34 permitting regulation of voltage to the desired value between 5000 V and 70,000 V. This voltage is applied to an oscillatory circuit 35 which produces oscillations at a frequency variable at will of wavelength between 1 m and 18 m. The current available to the output terminals 35a, 35b of this oscillating circuit 35 is thus a high tension current modulated first at 30 to 120 pulses per minute (by the variometer 30) and secondly at a wavelength 1-18 m. This current feeds the coils 4c and 14; the electrodes, 25a and 25b are connected to terminals 35a and 35b, respectively, and electrode 25 is connected to the mid-point 35c.

Cathodes 11 and 17, the "dees" of the cyclotron, and the plates 10 and 22, not shown in the diagram of Fig. 4, are connected to the output of the step-up assembly 33, while the heating current for the filaments 11e and 17a is furnished by the resistance 29.

To operate the apparatus, one adjusts the controls of the resistance 29 and the variometer to the desired rhythm; in medical applications, this is advantageously the subject's cardiac rhythm: This rhythm is thus imposed upon the whole installation. The cathode 13 emits toward the left a stream of positively charged particles 2, which are concentrated by the electromagnet 13 and accelerated by the coils 14, 15 and 16 and by the cyclotron 4. Superimposed on this particle stream in the duct 8 is the electromagnetic radiation from the magnetron 7, which is adjusted to the wavelength found by experience to be most appropriate to the cells which are to be penetrated, e.g., 14 cm for the liver and 19.5 cm for the spleen. The resulting radiation is deflected, directed and accelerated in tube 9 and is directed by way of the base of this tube toward the target to be penetrated.

It must be noticed that the magnetic field of the coils 15, 16 and 26 is modulated, by means of the converter assembly 31, at a frequency adjustable *between 300 and 900 Hz*. This modulation has the effect of concentrating the particles, that is to say to detach them from the walls of the tubes, and it also permits an appreciable saving in weight of the iron cores of the coils. One chooses the highest frequencies (i.e., around 900 Hz) when one wishes to produce hard radiation at the exit of tube 9, and the lower frequencies for soft radiation.

The unidirectional magnetic fields of the coils 4c of the magnetron (sic) (cyclotron?) and the accelerator coils 14 as well as the electric field of electrodes 25, 25a, 25b, are modulated by the oscillatory circuit 35 at a chosen wavelength between 1 m and 18 m. In medical applications notably one selects the wavelength that best suits the organ to be treated or its surroundings, such as muscle. As already indicated, experience with diathermy makes it possible to determine the most suitable wavelength.

It must be noted that the resulting radiation already possesses, in tube 8 (Fig. 1) a considerable penetrating force. One could therefore use the assemblage described by omitting tube 9 and terminating the cavity at the end of tube 8 by means of a glass or quartz base, the resulting radiation being accelerated and directed, for example, immediately upstream from the base, by a final coil (not shown) surrounding tube 8. However, tube 9 appreciably improves the results.

Figs. 5 and 6 represent another mode of realizing the assemblage in accordance with the invention, in which the elements playing the same role are indicated by the same signs as in Figs. 1 and 3, modified by primes.

The arrangement of the connecting ducts of Fig. 5 in relation to tubes 1' and 9', to the magnetron 7' and the cyclotron 4', is different from that of Fig. 1 and has been used successfully by the applicant. The waveguide 6' of the magnetron 7' opens into the end of tube 1' and the duct 3', carrying the resulting radiation, divides into two branches: Branch 36, which conducts the radiation directly to tube 9', and branch 37 which conducts it to the cyclotron 4'. This blocks the electromagnetic radiation and accelerates the stream of particles which is passed by way of duct 38 to the tube 9'.

This arrangement can be used with a particle emitter and an accelerator and director tube similar to tubes 1 and 9 of the preceding figures. However, tubes 1' and 9' of Figs. 5 and 6 are constructed in a different manner with regard to their cathodes and anodes.

Tube 1' contains a first electrode 11' exactly like that of the cathode 11 of tube 1, and an identical second electrode 39 furnished with a filament 39a. Tube 9' (Fig. 6) contains in its lower part a first electrode 17' with filament 17'a and an identical second electrode 40 with its filament 40a.

In normal operation, i.e., to produce radiation identical to that described in connection with Figs. 1 to 4, electrode 11' serves as cathode and electrode 39, given a positive potential, plays the role of the plate 10 in Fig. 1, the filament 39a being unheated. Electrode 40 and its filament 40a are disconnected; cathode 17' and plate 22' are supplied as in Fig. 3.

To obtain particularly penetrating radiation, the polarities are reversed: Electrode 11' becomes an anode and its filament 11'e is disconnected, while electrode 39 receives the cathode supply and its filament 39a is heated; electrode 17' (with filament 17'a disconnected) and electrode 22' become anodes, while electrode 40 serves as cathode and its filament 40a is heated. For example, one can establish a potential difference of 250,000 V between 40 and 17', and 50,000 V between 40 and 22'. It is understood that in these conditions the cathode 39 emits to the left a stream of electrons which is concentrated, modulated and accelerated by the various coils and in the cyclotron, the polarities of which must of course be established in the proper direction. This stream of electrons is combined with the centimeter radiation emitted by the magnetron 7', resulting in tube 9' in the emission of very hard x-rays, modulated at the chosen frequencies, combined with the centimeter radiation of the desired frequency.

The assembly shown in Figs. 5 and 6 thus permits one to obtain at will either very hard x-rays or the radiation described in connection with the preceding diagrams.

The following description, referring to Figs. 7 and 9, relates to certain details of the apparatus used for modulating the electric current.

Fig. 7 represents schematically the apparatus for control of the resistance 29 and the variometer 30. The variable resistance 29 consists of a graphite helix 29a immersed in a conducting liquid 29b; another electrode 29c, also of graphite, partly immersed in the liquid, is set into up-and-down oscillations by a connecting rod 41a linked to a fly-wheel 41. The fly-wheel is set in rotation, through the intermediary of a worm transmission 41b, by an axle 42 which can be driven, thanks to a double clutch 42a, 42b, either by a motor 43, or by the shaft 30a of the variometer 30. The variometer 30 is driven by a motor 44 by way of the worm transmission 44a.

If the fly-wheel 41 is driven by the motor 43 at the proper speed, the resistance 29 causes the supply current of the electromagnets 13 and 23 (Figs. 1 and 4) to vary at the chosen rhythm which as we have seen can be between 30 and 120 pulsations per minute and which can be checked by means of a rotation counter shown schematically in 45. In this case, the motor 44 of the variometer 30 can be stopped and the remainder of the installation is then not pulsed. If, on the contrary, the fly-wheel 41 is engaged in 42b and disconnected from 42a, the motor 44 activates the variometer 30 and the resistance 29 at the chosen rhythm.

The speed of rotation of motors 43 or 44 can be regulated at the required speed, corresponding visibly to the cardiac rhythm of the subject, by acting upon the excitation of these motors by means of a manually adjustable rheostat. If one prefers to regulate the speed of motors 43 or 44 in direct accord with the cardiac rhythm of the subject, one can use an assembly such as that represented schematically in Fig. 8: At 46 there is a contact microphone which, when placed over the subject's heart, produces impulses. These are amplified in the circuit shown and applied to an electromagnet at 47 with a moving core which activates a rheostat; this in turn regulates the current running the motors 43 or 44.

Fig. 9 shows schematically the principle of the oscillating circuit 35. The rectified potential, adjustable between 5000 V and 70,000 V by means of rheostat 34 (Fig. 4) is applied between the terminals 48 and 48a. Terminal 35c (which is also connected to electrode 25, Figs. 2 and 4) is connected to the neutral point on the high tension side of the transformer which is a component of the step-up assembly 33 (Fig. 4). The terminals 49 and 49a receive the heating current produced by the resistance 29. The variable condensers 50 and 50a make it possible to regulate to the desired wavelength (which, as seen, is between 1 m and 18 m) the current available at the output terminals 25a and 25b of the oscillator shown.

The modes of implementation described gave been successfully carried out but it is self-evident that these are only examples, and that they might be modified, notably by substitution of equivalent techniques, without going beyond the bounds of the invention. In particular, the electron gun 1 or 1' could be replaced by another charged particle generator.

Resume

The invention includes especially:

1. A procedure for obtaining a combination of radiations of different kinds capable of penetrating matter, especially of

intimately penetrating living tissues in order to produce in them certain effects and more particularly in human tissues with a therapeutic effect in mind, consisting of the emission in a cavity of a stream of electrically charged particles, upon which is imposed electromagnetic radiation in the centimeter wavelength range, and the guiding of the resulting radiation emerging from the cavity toward the target to be penetrated.

2. Types of implementation exhibiting the following features taken separately or in the various possible combinations:

   a. The centimeter radiation has a wavelength between 3 cm and 80 cm;

   b. This wavelength is set at the value found by experience to be most suitable for the tissues to be penetrated, e.g., 14 cm for liver and 19.5 cm for spleen;

   c. The particle stream is accelerated by magnetic and electric fields such as those which are used in particle accelerators;

   d. The resulting radiation is accelerated and guided, before its emergence from the cavity, by means of electric and magnetic fields;

   e. The resulting radiation is guided, before its emergence from the cavity, by means of deflecting and/or reflecting surfaces;

   f. The stream of particles and/or the resulting radiation are concentrated and accelerated by means of individual magnetic fields modulated at a frequency between 300 and 900 Hz, the highest frequencies being used to produce hard rays and the lower frequencies to produce soft rays;

   g. The emission of the particle stream, as well as the acceleration and concentration of the radiation resulting at its exit from the cavity, are aided by individual magnetic fields of temporally variable intensity, advantageously pulsed at a rhythm between 30 and 120 pulsations per minute and preferably at the cardiac rhythm of the subject;

h. The assemblages for production of the resultant radiation are pulsed in their entirety at the same rhythm as the magnetic fields according to g;

i. The stream of particles and/or the resulting radiation are accelerated and concentrated by direct magnetic and/or electric fields modulated at a wavelength between 1 m and 50 m and preferably between 1 m and 18 m, this wavelength being advantageously chosen as that which is known in diathermy as suitable for the tissues to be penetrated or for the surrounding tissues.

3. An assemblage making it possible to obtain a combination of a stream of electrically charged particles and a beam of centimeter electromagnetic waves in order to penetrate intimately and to irradiate living tissues and particularly human tissues, the said assemblage comprising at least a particle emitter, means for channeling said particles in a cavity serving as waveguide for an emitter of electromagnetic radiation of which the wavelength is included in the range of centimeter waves and preferably adjustable from 3 cm to 80 cm, means for generating in the cavity magnetic field for acceleration and concentration and means for concentrating and accelerating the resulting radiation at the exit of the cavity.

4. Modes of implementation with the following details taken separately or in the various possible combinations:

a. The particle emitter is an electron gun of which the anode is at the end of the cavity and the cathode is situated further along, this cathode being hollow and placed in the magnetic field of an electromagnetic in order to ensure emission of a stream of particles towards the mouth of the cavity;

b. The cathode consists of a rim connected by two aligned spokes to a hub, the said rim being provided internally with an annular housing containing a heated filament and the said housing communicating with a number of holes arranged annularly and traversing the rim transversely;

c. The cathode is made of a metal of valency close to the

mean valency of the chemical molecules comprising the tissue to be penetrated;

d. The cathode is of tungsten or preferably of molybdenum;

e. The cavity contains a rare gas, preferably argon, under a vacuum of the order of 2 mm Hg;

f. The cavity contains a duct carrying at least part of the stream of particles to a cyclotron and a duct bringing back into the cavity the particles accelerated in the cyclotron;

g. The cavity passes through several coils, the supply current for the various coils being capable of undergoing modulation at different frequencies;

h. The downstream end of the cavity is composed of a tube containing, in the part from which the resulting radiation must emerge, a cathode and an electromagnet which may be identical to the cathode and the electromagnetic according to para. a, an anode near the other end, and a rotary deflector consisting of a number of plates arranged *en couronne* on a rotor lacing the incident radiation at such an angle that the radiation deflected and/or reflected is directed toward the cathode, several coils whose supply current can be modulated being distributed over the length of the tube;

i. This tube also contains electrodes supplied by alternating current generating an electric field at the level of the rotary deflector, each of the said electrodes being surrounded by a bobbin of which the supply current can be modulated;

j. Methods are anticipated for modulating, at an adjustable rhythm between 30 and 120 cycles per minute, the supply current of the electromagnetic according to a and h, and preferably to modulate the supply current of the rest of the assemblage at the same rhythm;

k. Methods are anticipated for modulating, at a frequency between 300 and 900 Hz, the supply current of the bobbins surrounding according to i and one or several coils according to g;

l. Methods are anticipated for modulating, at an adjustable wavelength between 1 m and 50 m and preferably between 1 m and 18 m, the supply current of the electrodes according to i, of one or several of the coils generating the magnetic field of the cyclotron;

m. The electrodes of the electron gun consist of two electrodes identical to the cathode according to a, b, c, or d, the cathode of the tube according to h is replaced by a double electrode reproducing the arrangement of the electrodes of the electron gun, and methods are anticipated for reversing at will and simultaneously the polarities of these two pairs of electrodes and the direction of flow of the current supplying the acceleratory coils, a first pattern of polarities assuring the functioning of the apparatus in the conditions which are laid down according to a, and a second pattern of polarities assuring emission in the cavity of a stream of electrons combined with the centimeter radiation and giving rise, at the exit of the said tube, to emission of very hard x-rays.

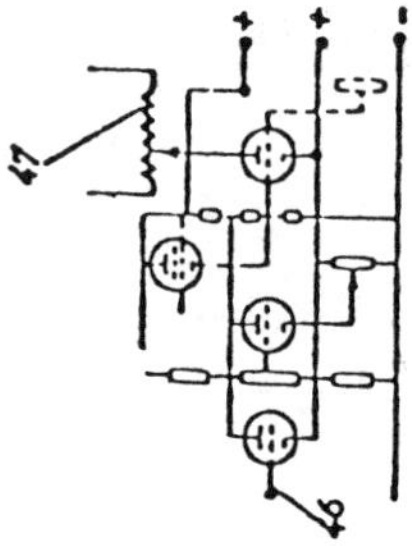

Fig. 18

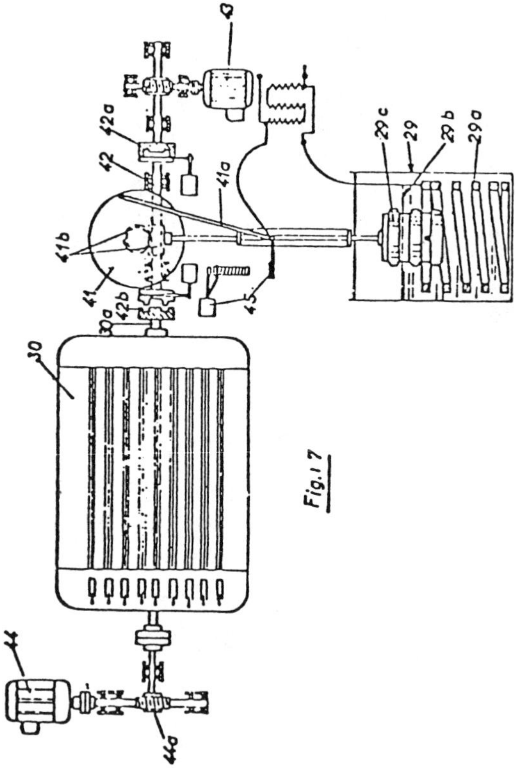

Fig. 17

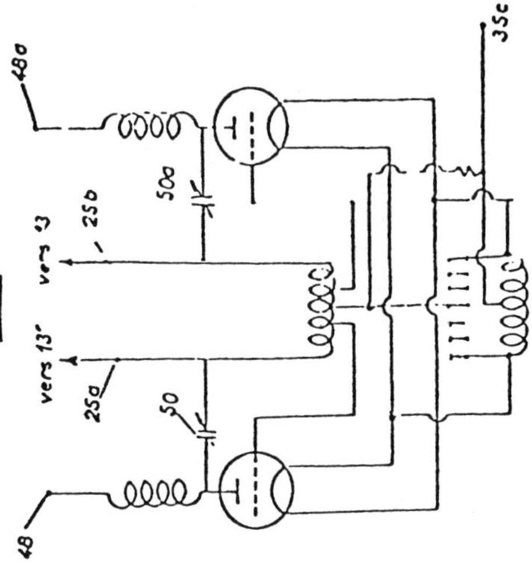
48
48a
50
50a
vers 13'
vers 13
25a
25b
35c
49
49a

Fig. 19

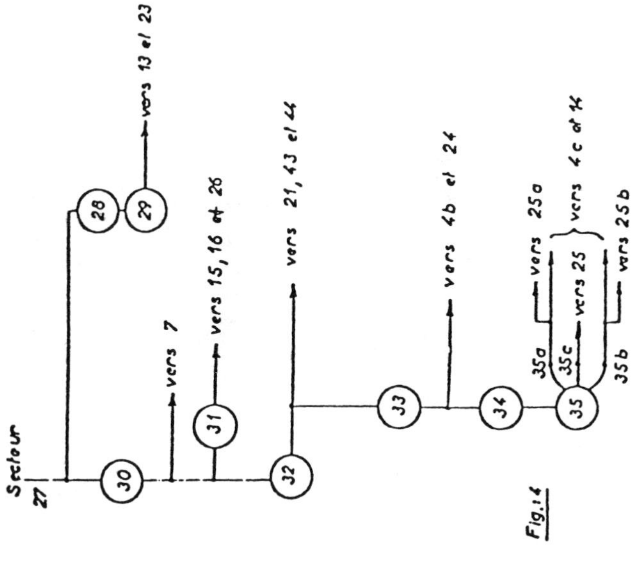
Secteur
27
28
29
30
31
32
33
34
35
vers 13 et 23
vers 7
vers 15, 16 et 26
vers 21, 43 et 44
vers 4b et 24
vers 25a
vers 25
vers 25b
vers 4c et 14
35a
35b
35c

Fig. 14

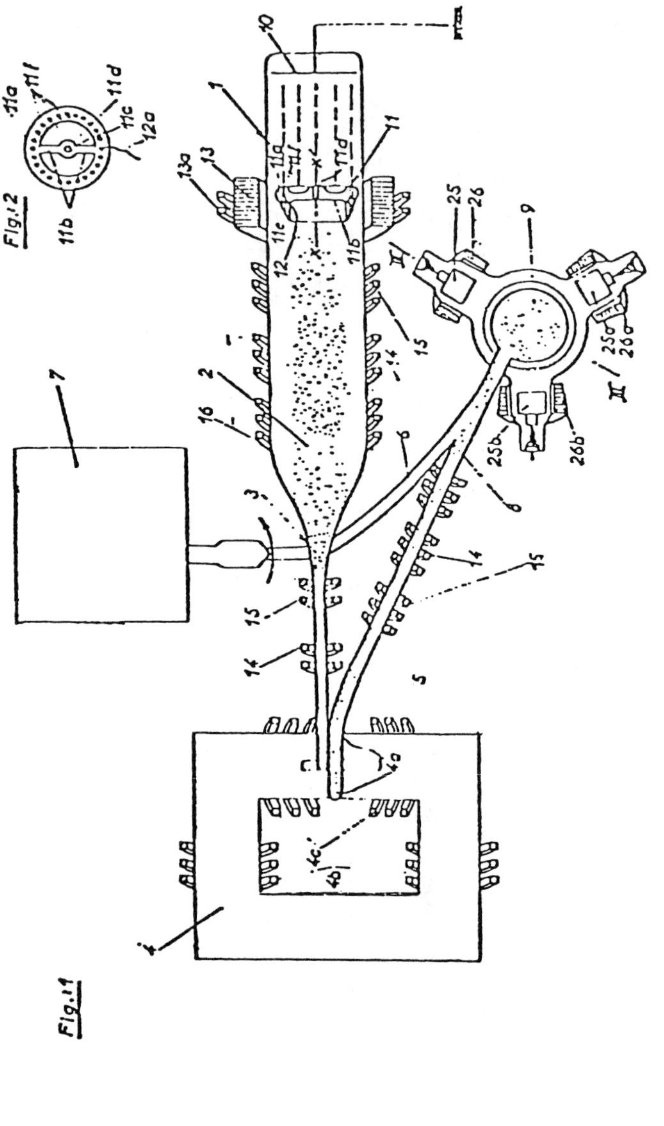

11a
11b
11c
11d
12a
1
2
3
4
4a
4b
4c
5
6
7
9
10
11
12
13
13a
14
15
16
25
25a
25b
26
26a
26b

Fig. 2

Fig. 1

Fig.: 3

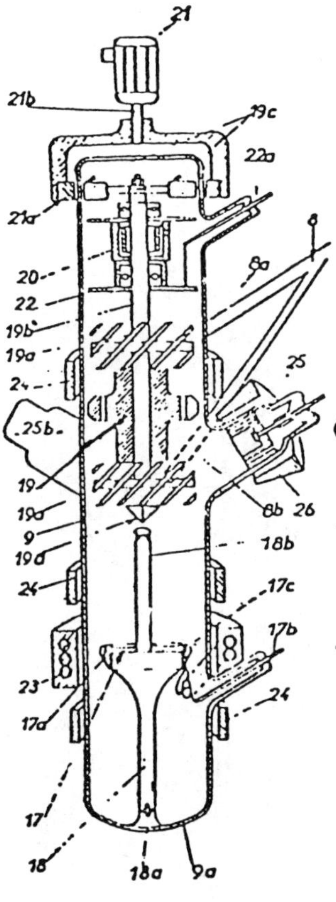
21
21b
19c
22a
21a
1
8
8a
20
22
19b
19a
24
25
25b
19
19a
9
19d
8b
26
18b
24
17c
17b
23
17a
24
17
18
18a
9a

Fig.: 6

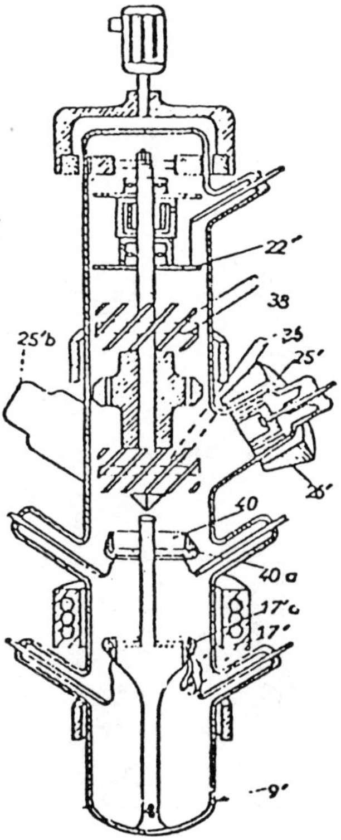
22'
38
25'b
25
25'
26'
40
40 a
17'c
17'
9'

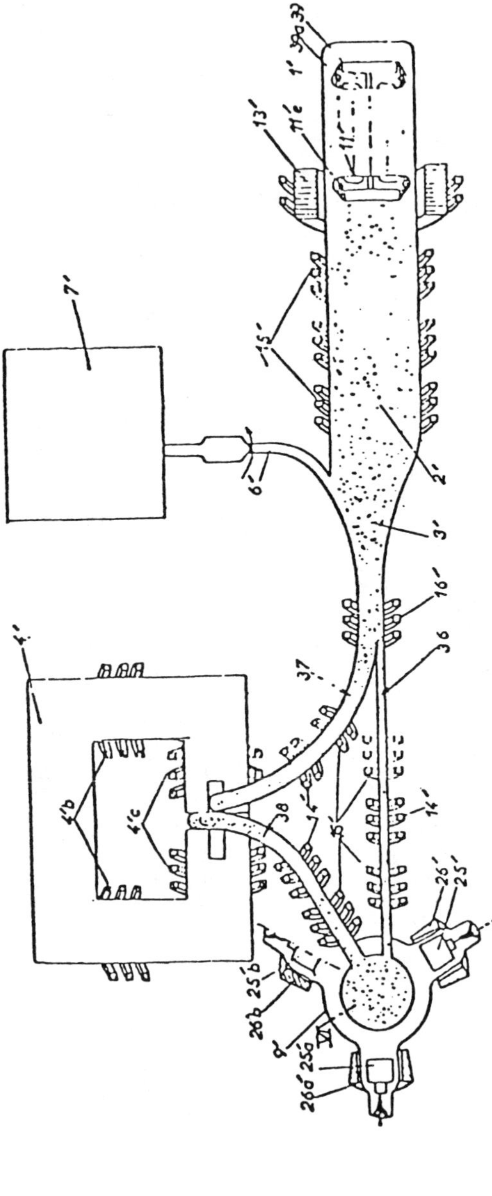

Fig. 5

Two Patents of G. Lakhousky

June 12, 1934. G. LAKHOVSKY 1,962,565

APPARATUS WITH CIRCUITS OSCILLATING UNDER MULTIPLE WAVE LENGTHS

Filed Nov. 13, 1931

Fig. 1.

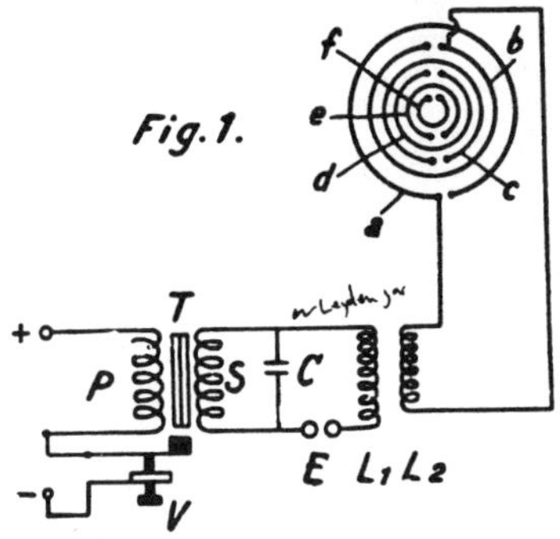

Fig. 2.

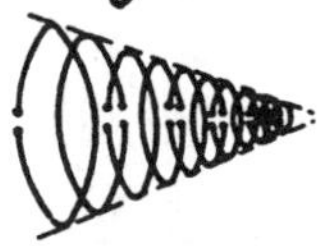

Fig. 3.

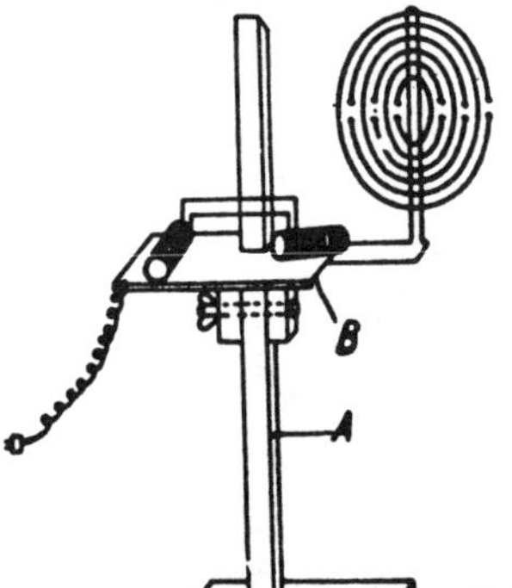

G. Lakhovsky
INVENTOR

By: Marks & Clerk
Attys.

Patented June 12, 1934 | 1,962,565

UNITED STATES PATENT OFFICE

1,962,565

APPARATUS WITH CIRCUITS OSCILLATING UNDER MULTIPLE WAVE LENGTHS

Georges Lakhovsky, Paris, France

Application November 13, 1931, Serial No. 574,967
In France May 2, 1931

7 Claims. (Cl. 250—33)

The present invention has for its object an apparatus capable of sending out simultaneously different wave lengths so that among these waves or their harmonics there is found almost always one or several capable of producing the best effect sought for any application whatever.

There is used for that purpose the property of open circuits having a fundamental or natural self induction and capacity to oscillate upon a well determined wave length if they are excited by electric impulses emanating from discharges of any source.

The radiating part of the system, producing waves of various lengths, is therefore constituted by a certain number of concentric open rings of different diameters, which are maintained insulated by any appropriate process. These rings may or may not be terminated by small spheres forming capacities.

These rings may be arranged either in the same plane or in different planes so as to form any surfaces, such as portions of cones, spheres, paraboloids, ellipsoids, etc. . . . , these surfaces being of a nature to concentrate the waves in a determined direction in the manner of a reflector, for example.

These rings may be fed by any producing device whatever of high frequency, for example, a combination comprising a trembler coil (or any other transformer) and a high frequency circuit provided with a self-induction coil and a capacity.

One or several points of this high frequency circuit is or are connected to the end of one or several of the rings forming the radiating apparatus. The other rings not connected are excited by induction.

The complete apparatus (coil, high frequency circuits, rings, etc. . . .), may be mounted in a box or upon a small board capable of sliding along a guide or rocking so as to be able to be placed in the most convenient position.

In the accompanying drawing, by way of example, not limitative, there is shown:

Fig. 1 a diagram of the system.

Fig. 2 the position of the rings in the form of a cone.

Fig. 3 the apparatus mounted upon a foot or base.

In Fig. 1 there is seen at T the transformer or coil (P the primary, S the secondary of this coil), V, the screw of the trembler, C the condenser the discharge of which across the spark gap E produces oscillations in the self-induction coil L^1, which in its turn acts by induction upon the self-induction coil L^2; this self-induction coil L^2 is connected on one side to the first exterior ring *a*, on the other side to the following ring *b*. It thus forms an electrostatic field of high frequency which induces oscillations in the other rings *c*, *d*, *e*, *f*.

As a modification, L^2 may be suppressed and the rings *a* and *b* may be connected each to one of the ends of L^1.

One of the ends, or even any point of the self-induction coils L^1 or L^2 may likewise be connected to any one of the rings.

Fig. 2 shows the arrangement of the rings in the form of a cone.

The open circuits *a*, *b*, *c*, . . . *f* can be constituted by solid conductors. They can also be tubular circuits, this being advantageous, since, for the same bulk, the radiating surface is larger. Finally, the area of the cross section of each of these various circuits can vary from one circuit to the other; for instance, this area can decrease from the periphery (ring *a*) to the center (ring *f*) of the radiating system.

Fig. 3 shows the apparatus mounted upon a foot A along which it can slide, in order to be placed at any desired height and upon a hinge B which allows it to be oriented upon the horizon.

I claim:—

1. An apparatus adapted to produce electric fields of high frequency having multiple wave lengths, comprising a high frequency producing device, a series of high frequency radiating circuits constituted by concentric insulated split rings of different diameters, the split ends being spaced from each other and terminating with small spheres.

2. An apparatus adapted to produce electric fields of high frequency having multiple wave lengths, comprising a high frequency producing device, a series of high frequency radiating circuits constituted by concentric insulated split rings of different diameters and terminated by small spheres forming capacities.

3. An apparatus adapted to produce electric fields of high frequency having multiple wave lengths, comprising a high frequency producing device, a series of high frequency radiating circuits constituted by concentric insulated split rings of different diameters and arranged in one and the same plane the split ends being spaced from each other and terminating with small spheres, in staggered position as regards adjacent rings.

4. An apparatus of the type described comprising a base, a plate slidably mounted on said

base, a support pivoted to the said plate, a series of open and insulated, high frequency radiating circuits mounted on the pivoted support, and a high frequency producing device for the excitation of the said circuits.

5. An apparatus adapted to produce electric fields of high frequency having multiple wave lengths, comprising a high frequency producing device, a series of high frequency radiating circuits, said circuits being open, insulated, and having dimensions different from each other.

6. An apparatus adapted to produce electric fields of high frequency having multiple wave lengths, comprising a high frequency producing device, a series of high frequency radiating circuits arranged in the same plane, said circuits being open, insulated, and having dimensions different from each other.

7. An apparatus of the type described comprising a transformer, a high frequency energising circuit fed by the said transformer and provided with a self-induction coil and a capacity, a series of open and insulated high-frequency radiating circuits having dimensions different from each other, an inductive connection between two of these radiating circuits and respectively each of the poles of the outgoing element of the high frequency energising circuit.

GEORGES LAKHOVSKY.

June 13, 1944. G. LAKHOVSKY 2,351,055

TUBE FOR PRODUCING MULTIPLE WAVE LENGTHS

Filed Nov. 21, 1941

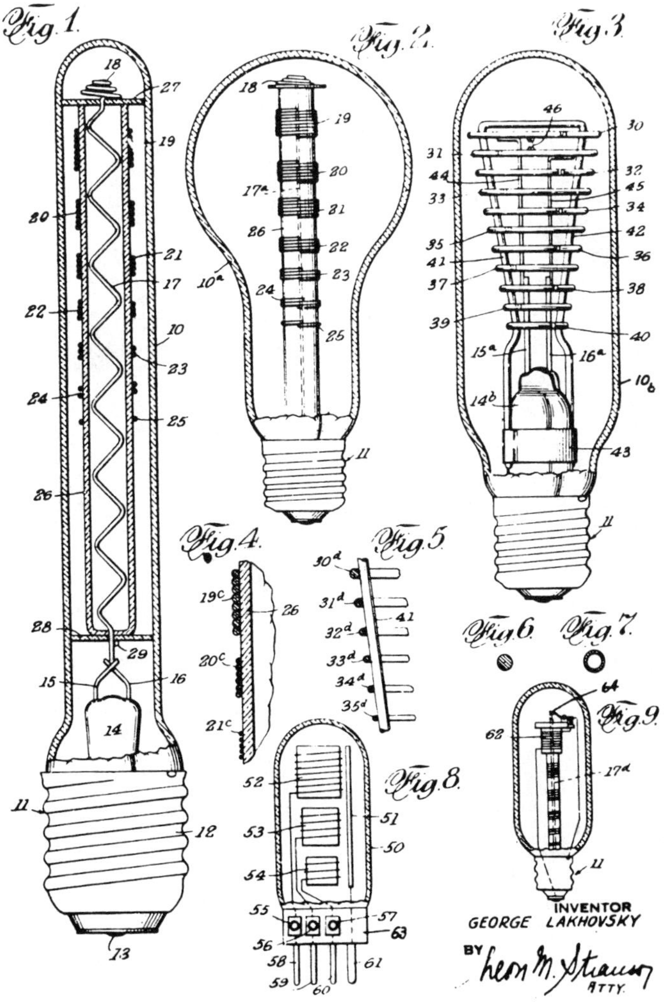

Patented June 13, 1944 2,351,055

UNITED STATES PATENT OFFICE

2,351,055

TUBE FOR PRODUCING MULTIPLE WAVE LENGTHS

George Lakhovsky, New York, N. Y.; Anne-Marie Louise Lakhovsky, administratrix of said George Lakhovsky, deceased, assignor to Henry S. Blum, Chicago, Ill.

Application November 21, 1941, Serial No. 420,006

11 Claims. (Cl. 250—33)

This invention relates generally to electric devices excited by electric impulses and more particularly to multiple wave length conducting and/or producing means. This invention has for its primary object the provision of such means disposed within a vacuum tube or a tube containing rare gas or gases.

My work over a period of more than 20 years has led me to the belief that there is great need for means conducting and/or producing multiple wave lengths which may be employed in many industrial and medical fields. Suitable apparatus for producing waves of various lengths is disclosed in my U. S. Letters Patent No. 1,962,565, dated June 12, 1934. Embodiments of this apparatus have been in use the world over. Because of the need for simplification in such apparatus so that it may be handy and easily used by persons lacking skill in electrical matters, I have concluded that by providing one unit which incorporates oscillation generating means and another in which the wave lengths are produced, the apparatus may be more universally used in the treatment of cellular life in therapy, in the aging or treating of liquids and in other industrial fields.

The present invention deals with those units, preferably combined with one another and constructed as a portable device and as stated above, has for its major object the provision of a unitary multiple wave length producing and/or conducting device in the form of a vacuum tube.

The present invention further contemplates the incorporation in such a tube, of means for varying the effect of wave lengths, or selectively employing the means therefor enclosed in or forming part of said tube.

This invention further seeks to provide a tube of the indicated type incorporating means for generating oscillations.

Another object of the invention is to provide a single unit which contains an oscillation generator, which produces waves of definite frequency, and further inductance means each permitting emanation of wave lengths of various values.

The structural features of my invention also form a material part of this disclosure, the objects and advantages being attained in structures such as shown in the accompanying drawing, which exemplifies the invention. The following specification, based on said drawing, more clearly points out the purposes and advantages of my invention.

In the drawing:

Fig. 1 is a vertical, partial sectional, partial elevational view of a tube incorporating features of my invention.

Fig. 2 is a similar view of an alternate form thereof.

Fig. 3 illustrates in a similar manner a modified form of my invention.

Fig. 4 is a fragmentary sectional view of a modification made in accordance with the invention.

Fig. 5 is a similar view of another modification.

Figs. 6 and 7 are sectional views illustrating types of wires used in either of the forms of my invention as shown in Figs. 1, 2 and 3.

Fig. 8 is a partial sectional, partial elevational view illustrating a tube incorporating a plurality of grids and selective capacity means for varying the effects of said grids.

Fig. 9 is a similar view of a tube, such as shown in Figs. 1 or 2 and incorporating oscillating or vibrating means.

In that form of my invention shown in Fig. 1, there is provided a sealed preferably transparent envelope **10** made of glass or like material affixed in the usual manner to a screw or Edison plug **11**. The latter is conventionally provided with a shell terminal **12** and a central terminal **13**. The support or seal **14** of the tube serves to hold wires such as **15** and **16** which connect to the terminals **12** and **13**.

Connected to the wires **15** and **16** is a primary inductance member in the form of a loose coil **17** which may be disposed axially of the envelope **10**, as shown. The upper end of said member **17** forms a tight wound coil **18** which serves to radiate the strongest induced wave lengths.

Surrounding the primary inductance member **17**, there are arranged a plurality of separate coils of wire each being of different length and capacity. Thus, I provide a coil **19** having greatest capacity and successive coils **20**, **21**, **22**, **23**, **24** and **25**, each having less capacity than the preceding coil. These coils **19** to **25** form secondary inductance means each permitting emanation of a wave length of different magnitude and value than the other.

I may support the secondary coils in several ways. As shown, I prefer to provide a dielectric member such as a glass sleeve **26** surrounding the primary inductance wire member **17** and to mount the secondary coils **19** to **25** on the outer surface of said sleeve, leaving the coil **18** exposed at the top thereof. In order to effectively support and centralize the glass sleeve **26**, I provide spacing washers **27** and **28** of mica or the like, top and bottom, and provide a supporting cross-piece **29** on the lower portion of the wire **17**.

The tube above described may be employed as indicated for the treatment of cellular structures by connecting it to any one of the rings in the electrostatic field of high frequency, such as shown in said U. S. Letters Patent No. 1,962,565, each of the coils **13** to **25** producing by induction a different wave length, as can be understood.

In the form of my invention shown in Fig. 2, the envelope **10a** is somewhat differently shaped, and the wire **11a** straight instead of arranged as an open coil. In other respects, the structure follows that described with reference to Fig. 1.

As shown in Fig. 3, there may be arranged a plurality of open rings **30**, **31**, **32**, **33**, **34**, **35**, **36**, **37**, **38**, **39**, and **40** in frustro-conical form, for instance, with the largest of said rings at the top and the smallest one adjacent the bottom. I have shown said rings as supported, for instance, by glass posts **41** and **42**, said posts being supported on the seal **14b**, as by a band **43**. I provide extensions for the terminal wires **15a** and **16a** and connect said extensions **44** and **45** to the upper ring **30** and the next lower ring **31**, respectively.

The rings **30** and **31** may become the primary inductance members, whereas the remaining rings constitute the secondary inductance members as before set forth. Electric current conducted to the suitably spaced rings **30**, **31** will cause a spark **46** to be drawn between the rings **30** and **31** providing oscillations emanating from electrical discharges therebetween and causing the radiation of waves of various lengths within the envelope **10b** and affecting the remaining rings.

In Figs. 1 and 2, I have shown the secondary coils as formed of wires having uniform cross-section. Fig. 4 illustrates how such wires may be made progressively smaller in the succeeding coils **19c**, **20c**, and **21c**, etc. Similarly, I have shown the rings of Fig. 3 made progressively smaller in Fig. 5, said rings being designated by numerals **30d**, **31d**, **32d**, **33d**, **34d** and **35d**, etc. In such various manners, the wave length producing effect of the secondary coils or rings may be arrived at.

The secondary coils or rings may be round or somewhat flattened wire as shown in Fig. 6 or tubular as in Fig. 7, offering a yet greater flexibility of design.

The devices of Figs. 1 and 2 above described may be incorporated in the system shown in said U. S. Letters Patent by connecting one of the rings *a*, *b*, *c*, *d*, *e*, or *f* with plug **11** of Fig. 1, since either terminal **15**, **16** is in contact with primary inductance member **17**. To this end a conductor (not shown) connects such a ring with said plug or socket.

In Fig. 8, I have shown a modification of the invention which comprises a vacuum tube **50** containing a plate **51** and a plurality of different wave lengths producing grids **52**, **53**, and **54**. I connect each grid with a variable capacity device, such as **55**, **56**, and **57** carried by said tube **50** and preferably by its base support **63**, whereby the grids may be selectively connected into an operating circuit (not shown) by means of the respective prongs **58**, **59**, and **60**, and the plate prong **61**. Heating or other exciting means may be incorporated in the tube in a well-known manner. This combination tube **50** is designed to replace a plurality of known tubes each operating with different and variable wave length effect, mere exterior manipulation at said base support brings about change of the capacities **55**, **56**, and **57** and cutting in one or more of the grids **52**, **53**, and **54**.

The effect of the spark as produced in the form of the invention depicted in Fig. 3 may be further utilized in Fig. 9 in which I also incorporate a vibrator **62** which produces electrical oscillations by a spark intermittently generated between the end of the primary inductance member **11d** and vibrator armature **64**. In other respects the structure follows that of Fig. 1.

It may be noted that any type of spark producing or oscillation generating means may be substituted for the vibrator shown. The tubes shown in Figs. 3 and 9 may be used in the manner described for Fig. 1 by connecting one terminal of the base as set forth to produce an induction effect. These tubes may be also connected across both terminals with a suitable potential to obtain the spark effect.

From the foregoing it may be seen that I have provided tubes in various forms for the purpose of generating and conducting multiple wave lengths. Other forms of the invention may be produced within the spirit and scope of the invention as claimed.

Having thus described my invention, what I claim as new and desire to be secured by Letters Patent, is:

1. A device of the character described comprising a vacuum tube having an envelope and base, primary inductance means, and a plurality of separate secondary inductance means of different length for radiating waves of various lengths extending above said primary inductance means, all said inductance means being arranged within said envelope.

2. A device of the character described comprising a vacuum tube having an envelope and base, a primary inductance member axially arranged in said envelope, and a plurality of secondary inductance members spaced apart and independent from each other each member surrounding a respective portion of said primary inductance member and within the field of influence thereof.

3. A device of the character described comprising a vacuum tube having an envelope and base, a primary inductance member axially arranged in said envelope, and a plurality of secondary inductance members each surrounding the primary inductance member and within the field of influence thereof, each of said secondary inductance members having a different wave length effect than the others.

4. A device of the character described comprising a vacuum tube having an envelope and base, a primary inductance member comprising a pair of split rings in inductive relation, and a plurality of secondary inductance members each comprising split rings.

5. A device of the character described comprising a vacuum tube having an envelope and base, a primary inductance member comprising a pair of split rings in inductive relation, and a plurality of secondary inductance members each comprising split rings, said latter rings being arranged in different planes and being of different length to produce a different wave length effect.

6. In a device of the character described, means for producing multiple wave lengths comprising a wire member, enclosing dielectric means for said member, and a plurality of separate wire coils of different lengths on said dielectric means and in the field of inductance of said wire member.

7. In a device of the character described,

means for producing multiple wave lengths comprising a wire member, enclosing dielectric means for said member, and a plurality of wire coils on said dielectric means and in the field of inductance of said wire member, each coil extending over said wire member and having a different number of convolutions than the others.

8. In a device of the character described, means for producing multiple wave lengths comprising two split rings in inductive relation, and a plurality of split rings in inductive relation to the two split rings.

9. In a device of the character described, means for producing multiple wave lengths comprising two split rings in inductive relation, and a plurality of split rings in inductive relation to the two split rings, the plurality of rings being of smaller diameter than the mentioned two rings and each progressively smaller than the others.

10. In a device of the character described means for producing multiple wave length comprising two split rings in inductive relation, and a plurality of split rings in inductive relation to the two split rings, the plurality of rings being of smaller diameter than the mentioned two rings and each progressively smaller than the others, all of the rings being arranged in frusto-conical disposition.

11. In a vacuum tube having a primary inductance member and secondary inductance members, a vibrator arranged in the field of influence of said primary inductance member and secondary inductance members, a vibrator arranged in the field of influence of said primary inductance member for affecting the induction of said secondary members.

GEORGE LAKHOVSKY.

T.H. Moray's Patent Electrotherapeutic Apparatus Feb. 1, 1949

Feb. 1, 1949. T. H. MORAY 2,460,707

ELECTROTHERAPEUTIC APPARATUS

Filed April 30, 1943 3 Sheets-Sheet 1

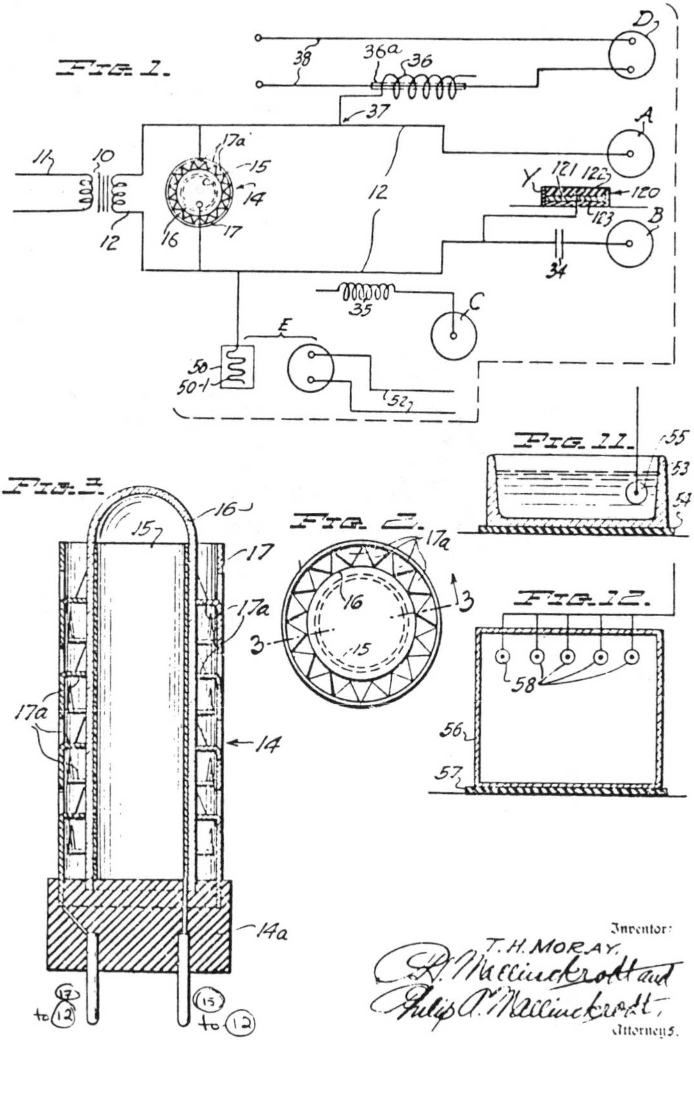

Feb. 1, 1949. T. H. MORAY 2,460,707

ELECTROTHERAPEUTIC APPARATUS

Filed April 30, 1943 3 Sheets-Sheet 2

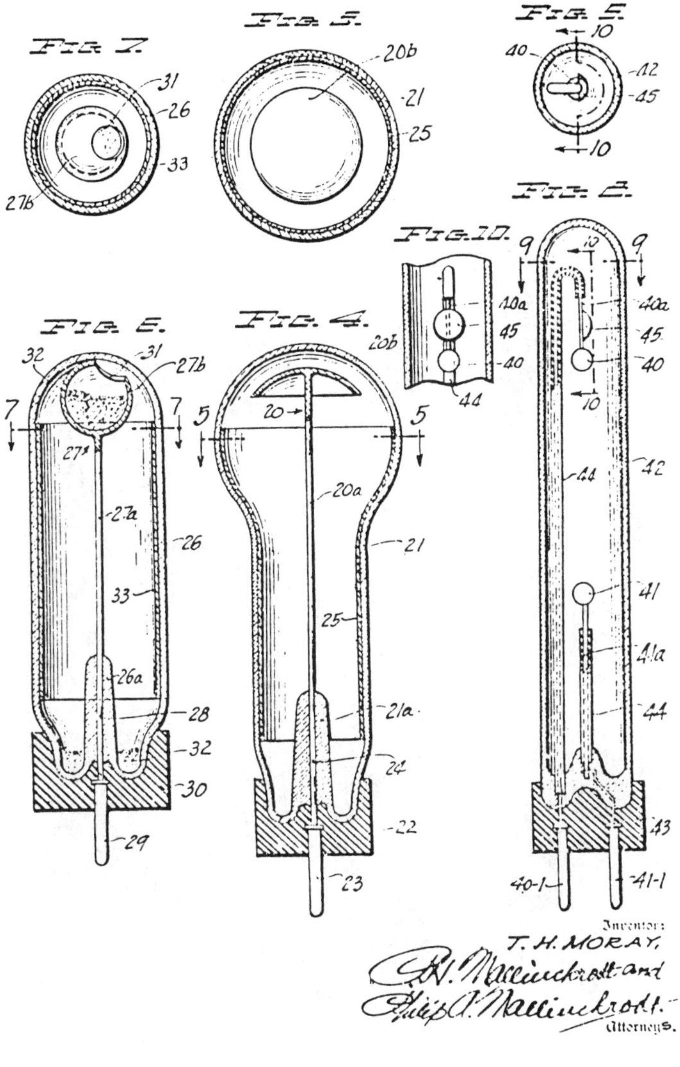

Inventor:
T. H. MORAY,

R. W. Mallinckrodt and
Philip A. Mallinckrodt.
Attorneys.

Feb. 1, 1949. T. H. MORAY 2,460,707

ELECTROTHERAPEUTIC APPARATUS

Filed April 30, 1943 3 Sheets-Sheet 3

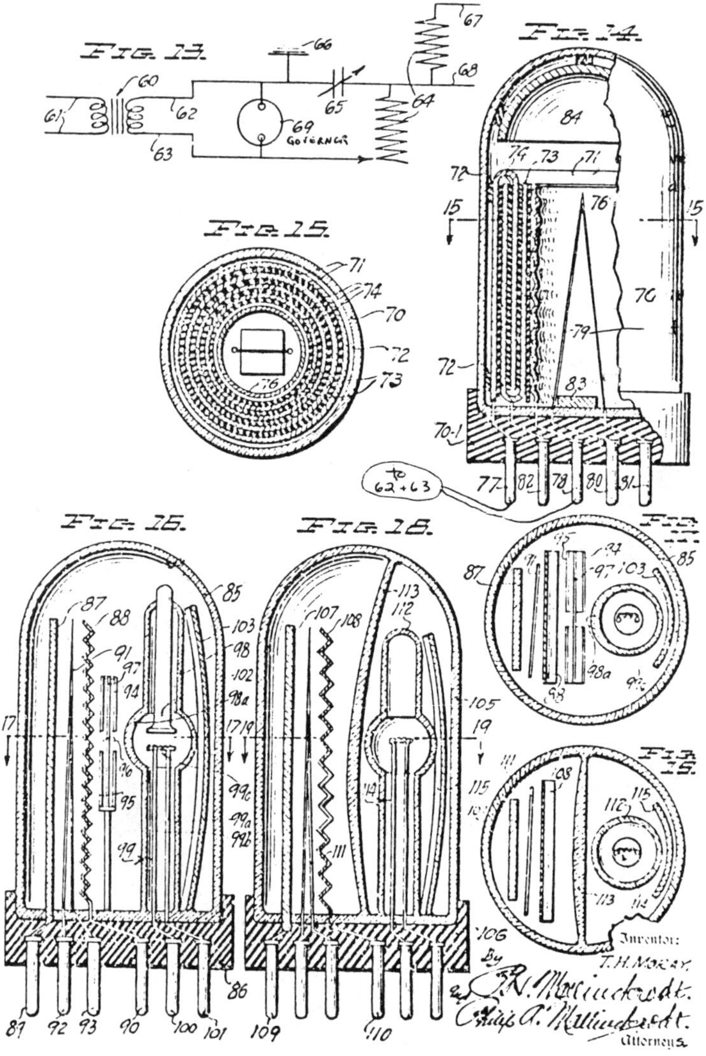

Patented Feb. 1, 1949 2,460,707

UNITED STATES PATENT OFFICE

2,460,707

ELECTROTHERAPEUTIC APPARATUS

Thomas H. Moray, Salt Lake City, Utah

Application April 30, 1943, Serial No. 485.112

8 Claims. (Cl. 128—421)

This invention relates to electrotherapeutic apparatus, and to methods of applying electrical, radioactive, and other radiant phenomena therapeutically.

The invention is primarily concerned with the use of high potential, high frequency electricity though not necessarily limited thereto, in conjunction with radioactive and other types of electronic and radiation phenomena, for therapeutic purposes.

Among the objects of the invention are the following:

First.—To render highly effective, from a therapeutic standpoint, radioactive and other types of electronic and radiation phenomena, and, likewise, to render highly effective, from a therapeutic standpoint, high potential, high frequency electricity.

Second.—To augment the therapeutic effect of radioactive and other types of electronic and radiation phenomena by the conjoint use of high potential, high frequency electricity, and, conversely, to augment the therapeutic effect of high frequency, high potential electricity by the conjoint use of radioactive and other types of electronic and radiation phenomena.

Third.—To accomplish the above without danger of burning or of otherwise harming the patient.

Fourth.—To provide apparatus for accomplishing the above, which is relatively simple in construction and operation and relatively inexpensive to produce and operate.

Fifth.—To provide novel electronic and radioactive devices especially adapted for use in conjunction with high potential, high frequency electrical therapy.

I have found that, by enveloping a patient in a high potential, high frequency electrical field in such a manner that no closed circuit is completed through his body, radioactive and other electronic and radiation phenomena can be used therapeutically with considerably greater effectiveness than if used alone. The exact reason for this is not known, nor is it known definitely which, the electric field or the radioactive phenomena, acts upon the other to produce the advantageous results. It is thought, however, that the electric field, permeating the body of the patient as it does, attracts the radioactive emanations or radiations and enables them to penetrate considerably deeper into the tissues and vital organs of the patient than would otherwise be the case. In any event, remarkable therapeutic results have been achieved by use of the invention in the treatment of malignant tumors, arthritis, sinus infections, and various other diseased conditions.

The invention contemplates the use, in therapeutics, of high potential, high frequency electricity to produce diversified forms of radiant energy, such forms being those which have been found best suited, individually, to benefit various human ailments. In accomplishing this purpose, several special discharge tubes have been developed to serve as treatment electrodes, by means of which correspondingly different curative results are obtained. Throughout the practice of the invention, a prime consideration is that only one terminal of any particular circuit shall be in contact with a patient's body at one time, so there will be no flow of current through a closed circuit of which the patient's body is a part. Such a terminal, too, is usually non-heat producing, so there is no danger of burning. In cases where there is a tendency for a tube to produce X-rays or other injurious rays, these are filtered out.

The present application constitutes a continuation in part of a copending application filed by me November 15, 1940, which bears Serial No. 365,798 and is entitled "Method of and device for the therapeutic application of electric currents and rays," and which has now become abandoned.

In the accompanying drawings, which illustrate several embodiments of apparatus preferred for carrying the method of the invention into practice:

Fig. 1 represents a wiring diagram of a preferred embodiment of apparatus for carrying out the method of the invention in general therapeutic work, several independent treatment stations being provided;

Fig. 2, a top plan view of the novel corona regulator of Fig. 1, employed in the circuit to control and adjust the current and as a governor to safeguard the transformer;

Fig. 3, a vertical section taken on the line 3—3, Fig. 2;

Fig. 4, a vertical section taken centrally through one novel type of discharge tube used as a treatment electrode in the apparatus of Fig. 1;

Fig. 5, a horizontal section taken on the line 5—5, Fig. 4;

Fig. 6, a vertical section taken centrally through another novel type of discharge tube used as a treatment electrode in the apparatus of Fig. 1;

Fig. 7, a horizontal section taken on the line 7—7, Fig. 6;

Fig. 8, a vertical section taken centrally through

a novel discharge tube used as a treating device in the apparatus of Fig. 1;

Fig. 9, a horizontal section taken on the line 9—9, Fig. 8;

Fig. 10, a fragmentary vertical section taken on the line 10—10, Figs. 8 and 9;

Fig. 11, a fragmentary view in vertical section, and drawn to a reduced scale, of a tub bath capable of use as a treatment station in the apparatus of Fig. 1;

Fig. 12, a view similar to that of Fig. 11, but showing a shower or vapor bath arrangement for the same purpose;

Fig. 13, a wiring diagram similar to that illustrated in Fig. 1, but fragmentary in nature, and of a somewhat different embodiment of apparatus;

Fig. 14, an elevation, partly in central vertical section, of a novel tube used in the apparatus of Fig. 13 in place of the corona regulator of Figs. 2 and 3;

Fig. 15, a top plan view, partly in horizontal section on the line 15—15, Fig. 14, of the tube of Fig. 14;

Fig. 16, a vertical section of another novel tube which may be used in place of the tube of Figs. 14 and 15;

Fig. 17, a vertical section taken on the line 17—17 of Fig. 16;

Fig. 18, a top plan view of still another novel tube which may be used in place of the tubes of Figs. 14 and 15 and of Figs. 16 and 17; and

Fig. 19, a vertical section taken on the line 19—19 of Fig. 18.

In accordance with the invention, provision is made for enveloping the patient in a high potential and, in certain instances, a high frequency electric field, and for applying to the patient, while so enveloped in the electric field, radiations and emanations having therapeutic value.

The apparatus of Fig. 1 is capable of administering various specific kinds of treatment, pursuant to the invention, at the several treatment stations provided. The treatment stations are indicated A, B, C, D, and E, respectively.

For supplying the high potential electric field, a suitable transformer is employed. This may be of any type capable of delivering high potential electricity, say from 10,000 to 30,000 volts. It is preferred, however, to utilize a conventional double magnetic circuit type of transformer, indicated at 10 in Fig. 1, having adjustable, laminated, magnetic shunts (not shown), the transformer being connected across an ordinary power line 11 charged with the customary 115 v. The output lines 12 from this transformer advantageously extend to the treatment stations A and B, respectively. The first secondary of the transformer 10 is preferably direct connected to the second secondary thereof. It is noted that this high potential electricity may be applied, without causing injury, direct to a patient who is not grounded. However, in order to safeguard the transformer 10 from damage by sparking across its output terminals, and to render the high potential electricity more suitable for therapeutic purposes, which is believed to include the automatic changing of the frequency to an extent which depends upon electrical characteristics of the patient's body, a governor or control device 14 is shunted across the leads 12.

This governor or control device 14 is a sparking condenser of high capacity embodying a multitude of spark gaps. A preferred embodiment of this governor or control device 14 is illustrated in detail in Figs. 2 and 3.

As illustrated, the device comprises a cylindrical, electrically conductive plate 15 surrounded by a cylindrical dielectric 16. An outer cylindrical and electrically conductive element 17 surrounds the dielectric 16 exteriorly. It is provided with a multitude (for example, 250) of inwardly extending prongs 17a, which are advantageously formed by stamping out, and inturning, triangular portions of the electrically conductive element 17. The internal plate 15 preferably contacts the interior surface of the dielectric 16, but, in any event, should lie closely adjacent thereto. Likewise, the tips of the prongs 17a preferably contact the outer surface of the dielectric. The several elements are advantageously mounted in a plug-in base 14a, which is adapted to mate with a suitable receiving socket (not shown) carrying the required electrical connections. The internal plate 15 connects with one of the electric lines 12, while the external element 17 connects with the other electric line 12, as shown diagrammatically in Fig. 1.

It is preferable that the dielectric 16 be in the form of a closed tube or envelope, as shown, and be exhausted to vacuum condition. The multitude of sparking prongs 17a product a brush discharge.

Where the dielectric 16 is not a closed tube or envelope, it is preferred that it be of quartz.

The treatment station A is a discharge tube of a novel type, exemplified by the tubes illustrated in detail in Figs. 4 and 5 and Figs. 6 and 7. Either tube is plugged into the circuit of Fig. 1 at a suitably provided, single-terminal outlet. High potential electricity is, therefore, fed directly into the tube, which serves as an electrode. The tube also embodies radioactive material, which supplies radioactive emanations to the patient simultaneously with the electrical discharge.

As illustrated in Figs. 4 and 5, the tube or electrode may comprise an electrically conductive discharge element 20, having a supporting stem 20a and a major discharge cap or head 20b, which is preferably in the form of a thin, convex-concave plate. The head 20b may be spot welded to the end of the stem 20a.

The discharge element 20 is enclosed within a tube 21 of dielectric material, preferably glass, the stem 20a being fixed in the fused tongue portion 21a of the tube. The tube or shell 21 is fitted into an insulating base 22, provided with a single plug-in terminal 23, and an electrical connector 24 extends from the terminal 23 to the stem 20a.

The inside surfaces of the side walls of the tube or shell 21 are coated with a radioactive material, as at 25. The coating is conveniently made from uranium salts or powdered carnotite or other radioactive ore. The ends of the tube or shell are left uncoated.

Air is evacuated from the tube 21, and a small quantity of mercury introduced. The mercury is preferably triple-distilled to insure great purity. It is preferred that argon or like inert gas be also introduced.

Since the tube just described is plugged into the circuit of Fig. 1, the discharge element or cathode 20 is charged with high potential electricity, and, in its capacity of a treatment station in the apparatus of Fig. 1, serves as an electrode to similarly charge the patient. The patient is insulated from the ground, and the tube is applied directly to the afflicted part of his body, preferably in close contact with the body.

Because of the construction of the tube, radiation of a radioactive nature is also directed against the patient through the uncoated top end of the tube. This radiation has been found to differ somewhat from the radioactive emanations discharging from the side walls of the tube, and is thought to comprise rays lying close to X-rays on the radiation spectrum. These rays appear to have a definite healing value, and to lack the injurious nature of X-rays. Where a predominantly radioactive emanation treatment is desired, the side walls of the tube are placed against the body of the patient.

Best results are obtained when the discharge element or cathode 20 is made of an alloy metal compounded from copper, lead, sulphur, and, if desired, aluminum. The relative percentages of the several ingredients may vary considerably, but a satisfactory mixture comprises 5.0% copper, 55.0% lead, 30.0% sulphur, and 10.0% aluminum. Should aluminum not be used, the difference may be made up by additional copper.

In preparing the alloy, the copper and aluminum are heated to a molten state, after which the sulphur is added while stirring the mixture. After cooling, the mass is again melted, and the lead, in a molten state, is mixed with it, the molten mass being thoroughly stirred. This new mass is then cooled, being later reheated, and, while hot, rolled to make it ductile, so it can be shaped into the desired forms.

The discharge tube or electrode of Figs. 6 and 7 is similar to that of Figs. 4 and 5, having an enclosing tube or shell 26 which is evacuated. A cathode discharge element 27 is positioned within the shell, being fixed in the tongue portion 26*a*. A conductor 28 connects the stem 27*a* of the element 27 with a plug-in terminal 29, which extends outwardly of the base 30. The cap or head 27*b* of the element 27 differs from the cap or head 20*b* of the electrode of Figs. 4 and 5, in that it is spherical in form and hollow. It has an opening 31 formed at its top, contiguous with the top inside surface of the tube 26. A quantity 32 of radioactive material, which may be the same as used for the coating 25 of the electrode of Figs. 4 and 5, is introduced into the tube or shell 26, along with a relatively small quantity of mercury, before the tube is sealed tight. Such material 32 is preferably powdered or granulated, and is shaken into the hollow of the head 27*b* through the opening 31 before any given treatment is commenced. The mercury is provided primarily as a getter, and does no harm if shaken into the head 27*b* along with the radioactive substance. The mercury also tends to produce a vapor in the tube, which aids in the operation thereof. As in the case of the electrode tube of Figs. 4 and 5, this tube may have a radioactive coating 33 covering the inner surfaces of its side walls.

The treatment station B of Fig. 1 differs from the treatment station A only in the fact that a condenser 34 is interposed in the electric supply line 12.

The treatment station C of Fig. 1 differs from the stations A and B only in the fact that the high potential electricity is supplied from the supply line 12 through an inductance 35.

The treatment station D utilizes a germicidal discharge tube, a preferred form of which is illustrated in detail in Figs. 8, 9, and 10. The high potential electricity is taken by induction from the particular supply line 12 concerned. For this purpose, an induction coil 36 is provided, tapping the line 12 at 37. A pair of leads 38 from an ordinary 115 v. supply source extend to a plug-in socket connection for the germicidal tube, one of the leads passing through a glass tube 36*a*, Fig. 1, which is disposed within and extends along the length of the induction coil 36. Thus, high potential electricity is impressed, by induction, upon the ordinary current flowing through the particular lead 38 concerned.

The germicidal discharge tube of Figs. 8, 9, and 10 has a pair of discharge terminals 40 and 41, respectively, positioned in an evacuated tube or envelope 42, and electrically connected with plug-in terminals 40—1 and 41—1, respectively, by means of stems 40*a* and 41*a*, respectively. The tube or envelope 42 and plug-in terminals are mounted in a conventional base 43. It is preferred that insulating material 44, such as a ceramic sleeve, cover the major portions of the stems 40*a* and 41*a*. A piece of lithium metal 45, see particularly Fig. 10, is advantageously secured to the stem 40*a* adjacent the discharge terminal 40 to act as a getter. It may, however, be placed at any other convenient location in the tube. It is preferred that the discharge terminals 40 and 41 be formed of the special alloy previously described. Argon or other suitable inert gas is preferably injected into the tube or envelope 42, as is, also, a small quantity of mercury. The mercury, by vaporizing, aids electrical arcing between the discharge terminals. As will be noted, the high potential electricity induced in the one lead 38 will manifest at the upper discharge terminal 40, and will charge the patient simultaneously with the discharge into his body of germicidal rays from the tube.

The treatment station E embodies the tube of Figs. 8, 9, and 10, as above described, but impresses the high potential electricity directly on the patient instead of passing it first through the tube. For this purpose, a discharge device 50, in the form of a soft, flexible pad in which a coil 50—1 is embedded, taps one of the high potential electric lines 12. This pad 50 is wrapped around the patient's body adjacent the afflicted portion thereof, thus charging the patient. Any other electrode capable of charging the patient with high potential electricity may be used in place of the pad 50. The germicidal tube has its terminals 40—1 and 41—1 plugged into a suitable plug-in socket connected to leads 52 which extend to an ordinary 115 v. source of supply. The high potential electricity with which the patient is charged is induced into the germicidal tube, thereby further activitating the discharge therefrom. A certain beneficial discharge from this germicidal tube will be had by induced activation alone, it being unnecessary, in such instances, to plug the tube into the 115 v. line.

Other types of germicidal and discharge tubes may be used in place of the tube of Figs. 8, 9, and 10, as, for instance, the well known infra-red and ultra-violet lamps, to produce results surpassing those ordinarily attained by the use of such infra-red or ultra-violet lamps apart from the apparatus of the invention.

It should be remembered that the patient is insulated from the ground while being treated at any of the treatment stations of the invention.

Figs. 11 and 12 show how a patient is treated, pursuant to the invention, while immersed in an electrically conductive fluid bath. In Fig. 11, a bath tub 53 is insulated from the ground by a layer of insulation 54. A treatment electrode of the type shown in any of the figure groups 4 and 5, 6 and 7, and 8, 9, and 10 is positioned to charge the fluid of the bath with high potential electricity, as well as to discharge healing radiations and emanations into the patient. The particular electrode illustrated is diagrammatic in form and is designated 55. It may be connected into the circuit of Fig. 1 as shown at any of the treatment stations A, B, C, and D. In Fig. 12, a shower or vapor stall 56 is insulated from the ground by a layer of insulation 57. A plurality of treatment electrodes are designated 58, respectively. These correspond to the treatment electrode 55 of Fig. 11. A water spray or vapor, such as steam, may be admitted to the stall 56 in any well known manner (not shown), thus enveloping the patient during treatment.

Another embodiment of apparatus, pursuant to the invention, is illustrated diagrammatically by the wiring diagram of Fig. 13. While no treatment stations are shown, those provided are identical with the several treatment stations designated A, B, C, D, and E in Fig. 1. The distinction in this embodiment of apparatus resides in the fact that a special generator of high frequency electricity is provided in the system.

A transformer 60 has its input terminals connected across an ordinary 115 v. electric power line 61. Electrical conductors 62 and 63 lead from the respective output terminals of the transformer to a high frequency generator of the Oudin coil type, indicated generally at 64, a variable condenser 65 being interposed in the line 62, and the circuit being grounded at 66. Output conductors 67 and 68, leading from the high frequency generator 64, provide connections for the several treatment stations in the same manner as illustrated in Fig. 1.

The transformer 60 may be any ordinary high voltage type. A governor or control device 69 is shunted across the conductors 62 and 63.

In the illustrated instance, the governor or control device 69 preferably takes the form of a vacuum tube, having the construction shown by Figs. 14 and 15, Figs. 16 and 17, or Figs. 18 and 19. These tubes all possess high capacity, and include elements effecting a brush discharge. They serve, as does the device 14 of Figs. 2 and 3.

The tube of Figs. 14 and 15 embodies an outer shell or envelope 70 of insulating material such as glass, a plastic, or fiber coated with shellac. Inside the shell 70 is a bi-cylindrical element 71 formed of electrically conductive material. Separating element 71 from the enclosing shell 70 are spacers 72 made of rubber, Bakelite, or other insulating material. Inter-fitting with the element 71 is a second electrically conductive, bi-cylindrical element 73, the two elements being separated by a dielectric 74. Inwardly of the element 73, and separated therefrom by a dielectric 75, is a corrugated, cylindrical element 76. The shell or envelope 70 is secured in an insulating base 70—1, provided with plug-in terminals. One of the terminals, designated 77, is electrically connected with the element 71, while another, designated 78, is electrically connected with the corrugated element 76. These two terminals connect with the conductors 62 and 63, as illustrated in Fig. 13, and the brush discharge takes place at element 76.

Under certain circumstances, it is desirable that the outer shell 70 be made of quartz glass, and that a filament 79 be provided, the filament being heated by connection, through plug-in terminals 80 and 81, with a source of low voltage heating current (not shown). Plug-in terminal 82, which is electrically connected with element 73, may be used instead of or in connection with the terminal 77, since element 73 acts in a manner similar to element 71. A getter 83 of suitable material, and an insulating and reflecting shield 84 may be provided, as shown. While the tube may have either a high or a low vacuum condition, or may be filled with an inert gas, I have also found it advantageous to fill the tube with a moist vapor. The tube acts as an oscillator for electric currents, and has an enormous capacity, a capacity many times that of a condenser of approximately equal size.

The tube of Figs. 16 and 17 comprises an outer shell or envelope 85, which may be made of metal, glass, or fused quartz. This shell is mounted in an insulating base 86. Inside the shell 85 is a metal plate 87, and, spaced apart therefrom, a corrugated metal plate 88. A plug-in terminal 89, which extends from the base, is electrically connected with the plate 87, and a second plug-in terminal 90 is electrically connected with the corrugated plate 88. These terminals are adapted to connect, through a suitable socket, with the electrical conductors 62 and 63 of Fig. 13.

Under certain conditions of use, it is desirable to have other elements in the tube. These are provided, and may be utilized or not as occasion warrants. A filament 91 is disposed between the plates 87 and 88. It is electrically connected with the two plug-in terminals 92 and 93, which are adapted to be connected to a source of low voltage heating current (not shown). A slit screen, comprising shields 94 and 95, with apertures 96 extending therethrough, is disposed adjacent that side of corrugated plate 88 which is remote from plate 87. The apertures 96 are in alignment with each other, and the shields 94 and 95 are made of lead or other material capable of screening off X-rays. Between shields 94 and 95 is a sheet 97 of material which is readily permeable to X-rays. Within the shell 85 there is also mounted a shell or envelope 98 of glass, quartz glass, or similar material, having a portion 98a which is ground like a lens and directed toward the slit screen. This shell 98 really constitutes a tube within a tube. A filament or cathode 99, comprising electrically conductive legs 99a and 99b and an electron-emitting portion 99c, is disposed within the shell 98, plug-in terminals 100 and 101 being electrically connected to the respective legs 99a and 99b. A bombardment element 102 is disposed within the shell 98 opposite the portion 99c of cathode 99. Within the shell 85, but outside the shell 98, is a reflector 103 directed toward the slit screen.

The tube of Figs. 18 and 19 is essentially the same as the tube of Figs. 16 and 17, being equipped with a shell or envelope 105, a base 106, a plate 107, and a corrugated plate 108, the two plates being connected to plug-in terminals 109 and 110, respectively, which are adapted to connect electrically with the conductors 62 and 63 of Fig. 13. There is a filament 111 and an inner shell or envelope 112, but no slit screen. Instead of a lens portion being provided on the inner shell 112, a partition 113 of lens formation is disposed between the inner shell and the corrugated plate 108. It is fused to the walls of the outer shell 105. Within the inner shell 112 is a filament or cathode 114, which corresponds to the similar element 99 of the tube of Figs. 16 and 17. A reflector 115 is directed toward the lens partition 113.

Reverting now to Fig. 1, there is another advantageous way of treating a patient pursuant to the invention. As shown at Y, a foot pedestal 120 may be provided for making the patient a part of a condenser. The pedestal comprises an electrically conductive plate element or electrode 121, connected electrically with one of the high potential lines 12, and covered by an insulating platform 122 upon which the patient rests his feet while being treated at any of the previously described treatment stations A, B, C, D, or E. The electrode 121 and insulating platform 122 are conveniently mounted in a frame 123, which insulates the plate from the ground. The insulating platform 122 is made of a high quality insulating material, such as first grade hard rubber. In certain instances it is desirable that the device be made in other than foot-pedestal form. For instance, it may be of cylindrical formation for use in a bed against any part of the patient's body.

If desired, the patient may be charged with the high potential electricity by direct contact with a metal or electrically conductive electrode in place of the pad 50 of treatment station E, or of the tube electrodes.

The invention has been described in the foregoing with sole reference to its use for therapeutic purposes. It should be noted, however, that inorganic matter may also be treated to advantage pursuant to the method and with the apparatus of the invention. It has been found that metals, for example, lead, have changed physical properties after treatment in accordance with the above. In instances where the invention is not being used therapeutically, it is not always necessary to insulate the subject from the ground.

Whereas this invention is here illustrated and described with respect to particular specific embodiments thereof, it is to be understood that various changes may be made in such specific embodiments and various other embodiments may be utilized by those skilled in the art without departing from the spirit and generic scope of the invention as set forth herein and in the claims which here follow.

Having fully described my invention, what I claim is:

1. Apparatus for applying radiant energy therapeutically, comprising means for producing high potential, high frequency electricity; a high capacity sparking condenser, and a treatment electrode connected in circuit with the foregoing, said treatment electrode including a discharge element adapted to charge the patient with said high potential, high frequency electricity, and radioactive means adapted to discharge radioactive emanations into said charged patient.

2. Apparatus in accordance with claim 2, wherein the sparking condenser is in the form of a vacuum tube of high capacity having mutually spaced capacity elements adapted to produce a corona discharge.

3. Apparatus for applying radiant energy therapeutically, comprising means for producing high potential, high frequency electricity; a high capacity sparking condenser; and a treatment device connected in circuit with the foregoing, said treatment device including discharge means adapted to charge the patient with said high potential, high frequency electricity, and radiating means adapted to discharge radiations into the charged patient.

4. Electrical treatment apparatus, comprising a high capacity sparking condenser; a treatment outlet electrically connected to said condenser; and means for electrically connecting said condenser to a source of high potential electricity.

5. Electrical treatment apparatus, comprising a transformer for producing high potential electricity; a high capacity sparking condenser electrically connected across the high potential output terminals of said transformer; and a treatment outlet electrically connected to said condenser.

6. Electrical treatment apparatus, comprising a transformer for producing high potential electricity; a high capacity sparking condenser electrically connected across the high potential output terminals of said transformer; and a plurality of treatment outlets independently electrically connected to said condenser.

7. Electrical treatment apparatus, comprising a transformer for producing high potential electricity; a treatment electrode electrically connected to one of the output terminals of said transformer; an electrical conductor sheathed by insulation electrically connected to the other of the output terminals of said transformer and disposed adjacent said treatment electrode so the subject to be treated may be placed between and in contact with the two; and a high capacity sparking condenser connected across the said outlet terminals of the transformer.

8. In electrical treatment apparatus equipped with means for the supply of high potential electricity and a treatment electrode, a high capacity sparking condenser electrically connected between the said supply means and the said treatment electrode.

THOMAS H. MORAY.

REFERENCES CITED

The following references are of record in the file of this patent:

UNITED STATES PATENTS

Number	Name	Date
628,351	O'Neill	July 4, 1899
647,687	Topham	Apr. 17, 1900
765,470	Friedlander	July 19, 1904
950,842	Davis	Mar. 1, 1910
1,156,317	Santos et al.	Oct. 12, 1915
1,193,018	Howard	Aug. 1, 1916
1,466,777	Winkelmann	Sept. 4, 1923
1,590,930	Falkenberg	June 29, 1926
1,655,783	Gallois	Jan. 10, 1928
2,010,018	Hodnette	Aug. 6, 1935
2,073,428	Schmid	Mar. 9, 1937
2,126,070	Wappler	Aug. 9, 1938
2,192,638	Dixon	Mar. 5, 1940

OTHER REFERENCES

Tousey; Medical Electricity and Roentgen Rays (1910), pp. 493 to 498. Copy in Division 55.

Two Patents of William J. Hooper

FIG. 1

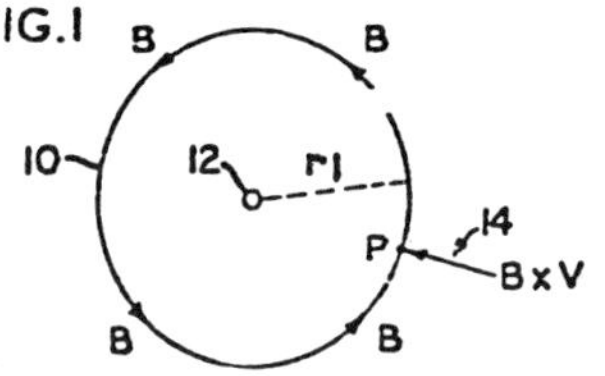

FIG. 3

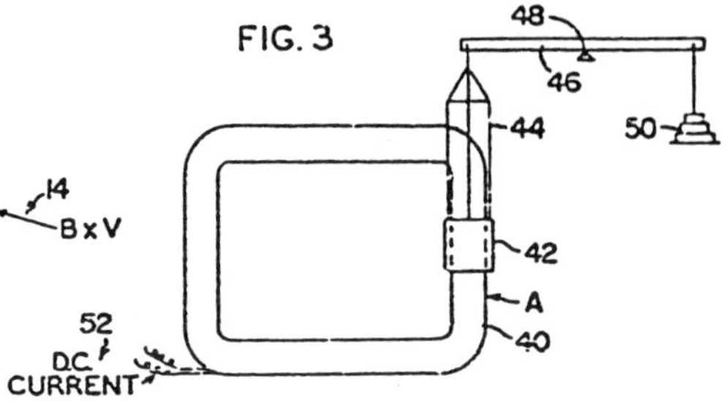

FIG. 2

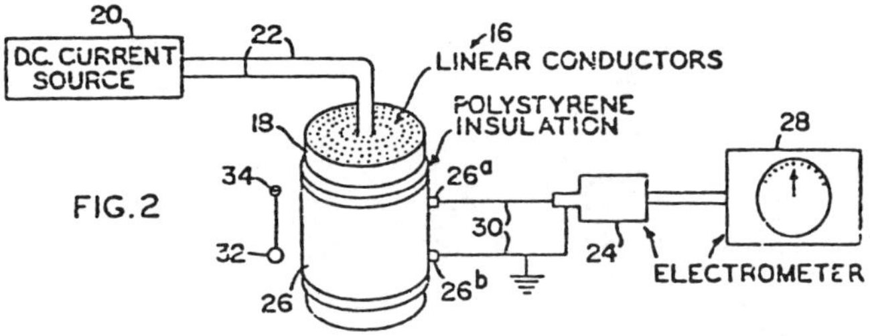

FIG. 4

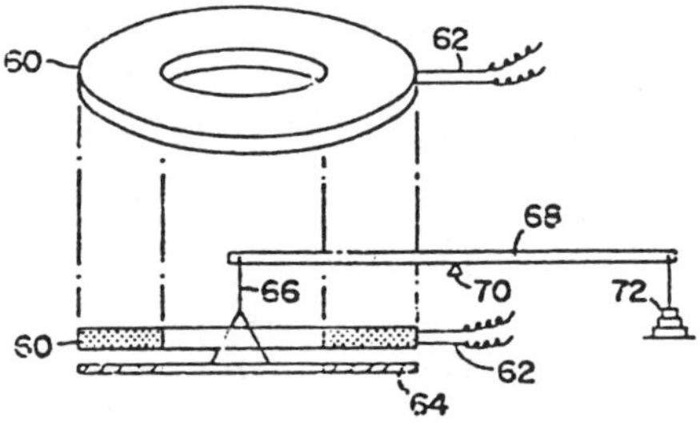

FIG. 5

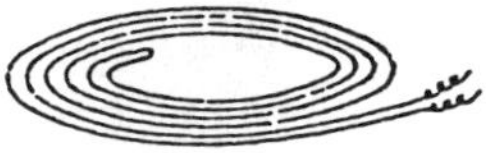

FIG. 6

FIG. 8

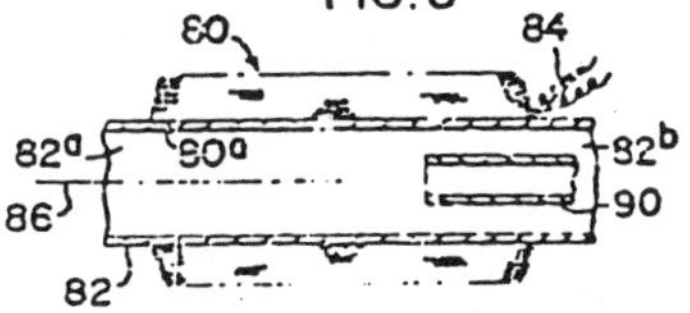

FIG. 7

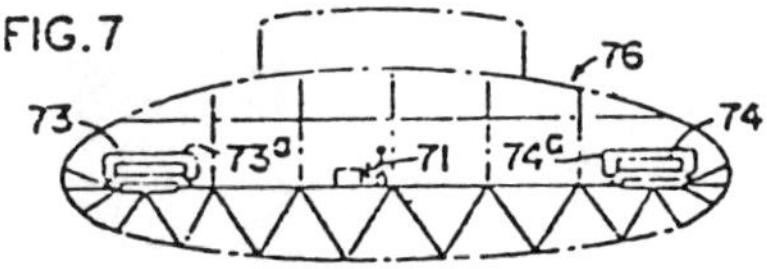

INVENTOR
WILLIAM J. HOOPER

BY *Oldham & Oldham*

ATTORNEYS.

UNITED STATES PATENT OFFICE

CERTIFICATE OF CORRECTION

Patent No. 3,610,971 Dated October 5, 1971

Inventor(s) William J. Hooper

It is certified that error appears in the above-identified patent and that said Letters Patent are hereby corrected as shown below:

Col. 1, line 14, after "conductor" insert -- with -- and delete "electric charges".

Col. 1, line 45, "10^{17}" should be -- 10^{-7} --.

Col. 2, line 4, "nd" should be -- and --.

Col. 2, line 25, "3.6×10^{12}" should read -- 3.6×10^{-2} --.

Col. 2, line 44, "motion" should be -- motional --.

Col. 4, line 7, "anitgravitational" should read -- antigravitational --.

Col. 4, line 22, "he" should be -- the --.

Col. 5, line 20, "out" should be -- our --.

Col. 6, line 26, after "conductor" delete "o" and insert -- to --.

Signed and sealed this 16th day of May 1972.

(SEAL)
Attest:

EDWARD M. FLETCHER, JR.
Attesting Officer

ROBERT GOTTSCHALK
Commissioner of Patents

United States Patent

[11] 3,610,971

[72] Inventor William J. Hooper
Sarasota, Fla.
[21] Appl. No. 816,356
[22] Filed Apr. 15, 1969
[45] Patented Oct. 5, 1971
[73] Assignee Electrodynamic Gravity, Inc.

[54] ALL-ELECTRIC MOTIONAL ELECTRIC FIELD GENERATOR
5 Claims, 8 Drawing Figs.

[52] U.S. Cl. 310/10
[51] Int. Cl. H02n 11/00
[50] Field of Search 310/10, 11; 324/109; 336/181, 225; 338/284, 297

[56] References Cited
UNITED STATES PATENTS
2,553,875 5/1951 Shaw 338/284 X
3,259,784 7/1966 Vogel 338/297 X

OTHER REFERENCES

Textbook—The Electromagnetic Field in Its Engineering Aspects by G. W. Carter, 2nd Edition, 1967, Published by Longmans—48 Grosvenor St. London W.1, pp. 168, 169, 170 (Copy in Central Library, Washington, D.C.)

The Feynman Lecture on Physics by Feynman, pages 13–6 to 13–11; Addison-Wesley Publishing Co., New York.

Primary Examiner—D. X. Sliney
Attorney—Oldham & Oldham

ABSTRACT: This invention relates to an all-electric generator yielding a motional electric field in the space surrounding the device, but requiring no mechanical movements of its parts in generating this field. The Theory underlying the production of such a field postulates that each moving electron constituting the current in a linear conductor carries with it a loop of magnetic field energy about it.

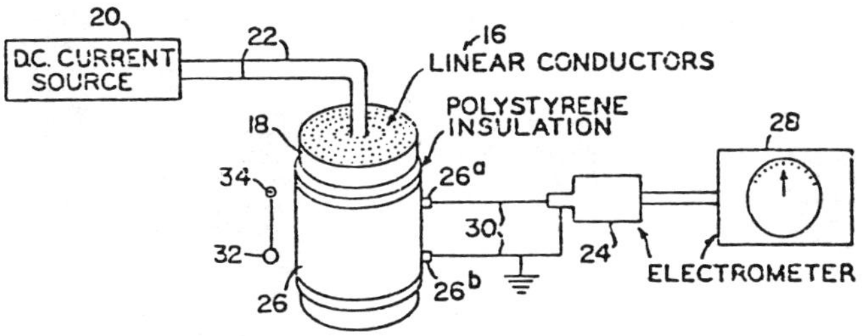

ALL-ELECTRIC MOTIONAL ELECTRIC FIELD GENERATOR

This application is an extension of the teachings presented in my earlier filed pending applications, Ser. Nos. 722,587, filed Apr. 19, 1968 and 803,187, filed Feb. 28, 1969.

PRIOR HISTORY

The detection of a magnetic flux about a current-carrying conductor was first made in 1820 by Hans Christian Oersted. This discovery unified the then separate sciences of electricity and magnetism. My experimental discovery that this magnetic flux actually moves along the conductor electric charges the electric charges constituting the current has great promise of now unifying the three known fields of electricity, magnetism and gravitation.

For a better understanding of the invention, reference should be had to the accompanying drawings wherein:

FIG. 1 is a schematic illustration of a wire containing flowing electrical current indicating the magnetic field generated with respect thereto;

FIG. 2 is a perspective block diagram schematic of a preferred embodiment of the invention;

FIGS. 3 and 4 illustrate modifications of the generator of FIG. 2 adapted to techniques for studying and utilizing gravitational and antigravitational phenomena;

FIG. 5 illustrates the winding of the wire in the device of FIG. 2;

FIG. 6 illustrates the winding of the wire in the device of FIG. 4;

FIG. 7 illustrates the incorporation of a plurality of the devices of the invention into a spacecraft where they might be appropriately utilized; and

FIG. 8 illustrates a coil wound embodiment useful for producing the separation of oppositely charged ions in gases or liquids.

BACKGROUND INFORMATION

The law of Biot and Savart yields the magnetic flux density B (webers/m.²) at a point distant *r* meters from the conductor carrying a current of I amperes and is given by

$$B=\mu_o I/2\pi r \qquad (1)$$

where $\mu_o=4\pi\times10^{-7}$ webers/amp. meter. With reference to FIG. 1 of the drawings, this flux consists of circular magnetic loops directed counterclockwise, as shown by arrow 10, for current directed in a linear conductor wire 12 at right angles to this paper and outwardly toward the reader.

Electrons producing this flux will be moving perpendicularly into the paper, carrying the flux B with them, at a velocity V meters/sec. Thus, at any point P, distant r_1 from the long linear conductor 12, there will be existent a motional electric field of intensity $E=B\times V$ volts/meter directed radially inward toward the wire in the plane of the paper, as indicated by vector arrow 14, where $B\times V$ is the vector cross product of *B* and *V*.

PREFERRED EMBODIMENT

The preferred embodiment of the invention is illustrated in FIG. 2 and consists in part of many insulated linear conductors indicated generally by numeral 16, all parallel, packed and held in close proximity, and connected in series, so as to form a solid package 18 preferably cylindrical in shape. When a constant direct current from a source 20 is caused to flow through wires 22 this device with its axis in the vertical direction, half of the linear conductors 16 will have current flowing upward and half downward. It will be a noninductive device, since surrounding it the magnetic flux due to the upward currents will be superimposed on the flux due to the downward currents, so that no magnetic flux can be measured. On the well recognized "Principle of Superposition of Fields," each one exists however, and acts as though the other was absent.

When the package 18 of linear conductors has a circular cross section there will exist two systems of circularly directed magnetic flux, one directed clockwise and the other counterclockwise as seen from above, and one set moving upward and the other set moving downward. What is of capital interest however is that each of these two systems give rise to equal radially and inwardly directed $B\times V$ motional electric fields distributed laterally in horizontal planes in the space about the cylindrical device. Here we have a field which is not magnetic, is not electrostatic, and which I have shown experimentally to be immune to electrostatic shielding. No such spacially distributed field is known to Physics today except that of gravity. I have shown theorectically that this field should act attractively on electrically neutral matter. I have shown experimentally that the intensity of this field can be measured with the aid of an electrometer system 24, 28 driven by the potential difference induced electromagnetically in the conductors 30 connecting the electrometer to the capacitor plates 26a and 26b of the capacitor 26. The electrometer head 24 actuates a visual dial indicator 28.

At cryogenic temperatures the drift velocity of the electrons in the linear conductors will be greatly enhanced. Theoretical calculations indicate that this velocity in copper at 20° C. is of the order of 3.6×10^{-2} cm./sec. in a current density of 480 amp./cm². The random velocity of free electrons in conductors is theoretically estimated at 10^8 cm./sec. At superconducting temperatures when the electrical resistance approaches zero, it is generally believed that the drift velocity of electrons approaches the value of 10^8 cm./sec. This velocity is 10^{10} times greater than the velocity at 20° C. (See "Physics," Halliday and Resnick, pages 681 and 691, J. Wiley, 1962). This indicates that the intensity of the $B\times V$ field about the device, herein described, might possible be enhanced 10^{10} times at or near the absolute zero of temperature. Hence, the invention contemplates that each of the devices described hereinafter will preferably be operated at or below the critical temperature at which the conductor used becomes superconducting. As the state of the art advances new conducting materials will undoubtedly become available with critical temperatures very considerably above the absolute zero.

Not only does the device that has been described in FIG. 2 afford apparatus hitherto unavailable for the generation of a spacial distribution of the motion electric field, but it affords means for investigating the properties of this field in connection with its relation to gravity and antigravitational phenomena. In addition, it affords for the first time, a direct experimental method for determining the electron drift velocities and mobilities in linear conductors made of different materials.

When the cylindrical capacitor 26 is charged by the $B\times V$ field and its potential difference (P.D.) measured, it is determined by the equation

$$\text{P.D. (volts)} = B\times V\cdot l \qquad (2)$$

where *l* is the distance between the thin capacitor plates. The direct measurement of V meters/sec. can then be made

$$V=\text{P. D. (volts)}/Bl\ \text{m./sec.} \qquad (3)$$

where B is in webers/m.².

This device will exhibit an attractive force on electrically neutral matter, better defined as a differential force; i.e. the difference between a pull and push, in which the pull is greater. (See reference to general theorem, page 125, The Mathematical Theory of Electricity and Magnetism, by Sir James H. Jeans) The $E\times V$ field is an electrical field acting on all the elementary charges comprising the atoms of matter, electrons, protons and even neutrons, as I believe neutrons also consist of electrons and protons in close bond. The $B\times V$ force being relatively weak does not ionize the atoms of matter, but being immune to shielding, electrically polarizes them. This causes a slight elongation of some of the electrons orbits within the atoms in the direction of the field. The positive charges move slightly into the more intense region of the converging, radially directed field while the negative charges move slightly further way from the device into the weaker portion of the field. Thus the differential force between the pull and the push upon the component parts of an atom results in the polarization of the atoms and a resultant attractive force, equivalent, I believe, to that of gravity.

A small, electrically neutral, simple pendulum 32 suspended close to one side of my device of FIG. 2, about pin 34, should thus undergo a slight measurable deflection under a fairly strong $B\times V$ motional electric field. At cryogenic temperatures this attractive force should be greatly enhanced. When the device is lying horizontally, a gravity meter placed centrally over it should give a measurable reading in milligals.

Modifications of my generator such as are shown in FIGS. 3 and 4 show diverse methods for studying gravitational and antigravitational phenomena which the invention makes possible. FIG. 3 illustrates a rectangular coil 40 made up of a single wire passed many times in the coil configuration so as to provide a large leg A preferably having a circular cross section. However, any cross-sectional configuration would meet the objects of the invention as long as the wires are parallel to each other and closely packed. About one leg of the coil, a cylindrical shell 42, made of electrically neutral, conductive or nonconductive material, is suspended by a carrier frame 44 from one end of a sensitive beam balance 46. The beam pivots about a support bar 48 and carries a load 50 to normally counterbalance the weight of the shell 42. When a fairly strong DC current I is fed through lines 52 and is built up in the coil, the flux density B is generated in the region of the cylindrical weight whose walls are a distance r from the central axis of the coil and n is the number of linear conductors in the coil.

$$B=\mu_o nI/2\pi r \text{ (webers/meter}^2\text{)} \quad (4)$$

If the current I is suddenly cut off the flux B will rapidly collapse. This flux in the act of collapsing should cross the walls of the suspended cylinder with a considerable inwardly directed horizontal velocity of V meters/sec. This should yield a very considerable vertical $B\times V$ in the walls of the cylinder directed either up or down, depending on the direction of the current in the coil.

In this device the motional electric field $B\times V$ is not convergent, but is uniformly vertical, hence the pull and push exerted on the electric components of the atoms in the cylinder will be equal. In other words the action of this field will either enhance or decrease the state of polarization already existing within the cylinder and produced by the gravitational field of the earth. If the polarization is increased, then the gravitational pull of the earth's field should be greater. If the polarization is decreased then the weight of the cylinder should be less. It is conceivable that the polarization could be reduced to zero. In this case, the object should be weightless. If the intensity of the depolarizing $B\times V$ field is still further increased, then polarization in the opposite direction to that produced by the earth's field should be achieved. In this event the earth's gravitational field would act repulsively on the cylinder. This would be antigravity in its truest sense.

The apparatus I have just been describing acts only momentarily (during the time interval in which the flux is collapsing) to change the weight of the cylinder shell 42 (shown in FIG. 3).

It is desirable to have an apparatus with which to experimentally study gravitational and antigravitational phenomena under steady continuous conditions. In FIG. 4 of the drawings is shown another modification of the device shown in FIG. 2. Here I utilize a noninductive coil wound in the form of a solid, low, thick walled, hollow, right circular cylinder, and indicated generally by numeral 60. DC current is supplied through lines 62 to the coil 60. In the region directly beneath this coil disk 60 I place a similarly shaped nonferrous disk 64, suspended by a carrier 66 to the end of a beam 68. The beam 68 is pivotal about a fulcrum 70 and is counterbalanced by a load 72. For positions of disk 64 below coil 60, the $B\times V$ field can only be directed vertically upward when a continuous DC current is flowing in the wires composing the disk 60. It should be noted that this field is practically uniform and parallel close to the disk, hence it is not attractive in its action on neutral matter. Its action on such matter can only change the state of electrical polarization in the matter. Any change thus effected in the state of polarization should cause the earth's gravitational field to act less intensely, on any object placed close to the under surface of the device, causing it to weigh less, become weightless, or to actually be accelerated upward by the anitgravitational action of the earth's field.

FIG. 5 of the drawings illustrates the manner in which the noninductive device in FIG. 2 is wound with wire 22, by turning the linear conductors back on themselves through a 180° turn. FIG. 6 illustrates the way the noninductive windings of the device illustrated in FIG. 4 is achieved. One very long insulated wire is simply turned back on itself at its midpoint and wound double into a solid coil held together in the shape illustrated.

FIG. 8 illustrates a modified embodiment of the invention which comprises a wire coil 80 either simply wound, or noninductively wound, around a hollow tube 82. Electrical current is passed to the coil 80 through wires 84, and at low temperature this coil will produce a radially, outwardly directed, internal $B\times V$ field from the axis 86 of the cylinder to he internal circumference 80a of the coil 80. The electrical wire making up coil 80 is preferably a ribbonlike conductor which is coated with any appropriate electrical insulation. A minimum space between adjacent turns with concentricity between adjacent turns is the preferred winding embodiment for coil 80. As many courses of turns as deemed appropriate to generate field strength desired will meet the objects of the invention. The tube 82 is preferably made of material having little or no magnetic permeability. Both the coil 80 and tube 82 are stationary.

An apparatus of the type illustrated in FIG. 8 might be utilized to effect separation and concentration of fluids. For example, in the desalinization of water, a $B\times V$ electric field generated by the passage of the current through the coil 80, acts upon the disassociated ions of the sodium chloride in solution. Hence, by introducing a flow saline water at end 82a of tube 82, and providing a concentric separating tube 90 at end 82b of tube 82, increments of fluid which are concentrated with chlorine and depleted of solium may be drawn off through the stationary tube 90, while the increments of fluid which are concentrated with sodium and depleted of chlorine may be drawn off through the space between the exterior walls of tube 90 and the interior walls of tube 82.

FUTURE APPLICATIONS

This country's space projects have become expensive beyond the ability of the average man to comprehend. Achieving lift by means of costly propellants will some day soon be seen as akin to primitive man's use of awkward clubs as a means of exerting force. In a very short interval of time an intense $B\times V$ field should effect the reversal of the gravitational polarization of an object. Once achieved, only a very small expenditure of energy would be required to hold the polarization. Energy from the atoms of the earth would supply the lift and propulsion through the medium of the earth's gravity field. The most formidable problem would appear to be the problem of holding the $B\times V$ generator at cryogenic temperatures. In view of the overall possibilities of this invention, this problem does not appear to be incapable of a solution. A breakthrough in finding superconducting materials or even near superconducting at slightly elevated temperatures from those presently required would greatly aid in the solution of this problem.

FIG. 7 of the drawings illustrates in outline, the future possible application of this device, obtaining regulated lift by an operator 71 adjusting the current into the coils 73 and 74 which incorporate the structural features of the devices of FIG. 4. The antigravity gravity control features of the coils 73 and 74 thus control the lift and movement of vehicle 76. Suitable cryogenic generators 73a and 74a are associated with each of the coils 73 and 74 to provide the cooling thereof to as near absolute zero as possible to give the enhanced current passage characteristics necessary to the objects of the invention.

While I have demonstrated that AC current can be used in my device, it appears at present that DC current is much to be preferred.

This invention could be uniquely adapted to a communication system from one side of a solid barrier to the other side whether this barrier be solid concrete or battleship armor, by pulsing the *BXV* generator coil with signals, Morse Code or even voice modulated signals to be picked up by a capacitor-electrometer circuit on the other side of the barrier. Secret communications could be carried on and with the electrometer circuit as shown in FIG. 2 connected to a relay radio broadcasting unit, so that one might conceivably broadcast by radio from the interior of a solid metallic enclosure.

It is conceivable that the invention might be useful in the highly specialized art of concealed detonation devices. A detonating circuit connected to the capacitor electrometer receiving circuit of my device such as shown in FIG. 2 could be actuated through a solid barrier by out *BXV* generating coil placed on the other side of such a barrier.

It is conceivable that for some specialized purposes, it might be highly desireable to transmit electrical power from one side of a fixed solid barrier, concrete or armor plate, etc. by pulsing, DC or AC, in our *BXV* coil on one side of such a barrier. A resonant LC circuit could pick up these *BXV* pulsations and supply a source of electrical power on the other side of the barrier, in a manner somewhat analogous to my electrical receiving methods outlined in U.S. Pat. Application, Ser. No. 803,187, identified above.

In accordance with the patent statutes, only the best known embodiments of the invention have been illustrated and described in detail, but it is to be understood that the invention is not limited thereto or thereby, but that the scope of the invention is defined in the appended claims.

What is claimed is:

1. Apparatus for demonstrating an electrical phenomenon comprising,

a coil made from an electrically conductive material having a very large plurality of sections compacted in close proximity arranged in substantially complementary relation around a common central axis, where the coil forms a solid cylindrical shape with the sections parallel to the axis thereof, and

means to pass current through the coil so that about half the sections will pass current in a direction opposite to the other sections to cancel magnetic flux.

2. Apparatus according to claim 1 where adjacent sections are electrically insulated from each other, and the coil comprises a single wire bent back on itself to make the sections.

3. Apparatus according to claim 1 which includes means to increase the passage of electrical current through the conductor.

4. Apparatus according to claim 3 where the means to enhance is a cryogenic generator which reduces the temperature of the conductor o or below its critical temperature at which it becomes superconductive.

5. Apparatus according to claim 1 which includes an elongated hollow tube having an axis, the conductor formed around the tube.

Patented April 11, 1972 3,656,013

4 Sheets-Sheet 1

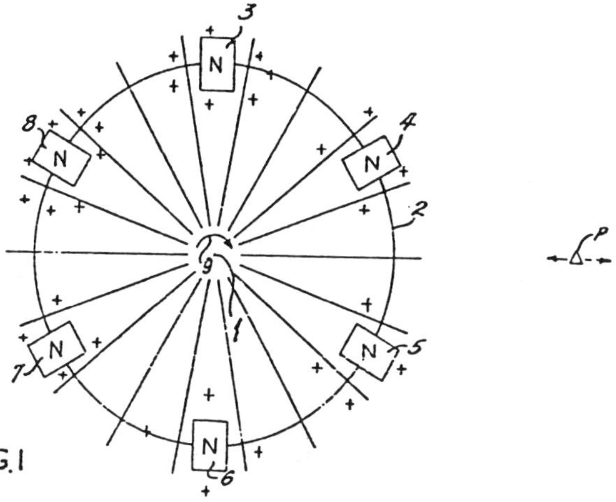

FIG. 1

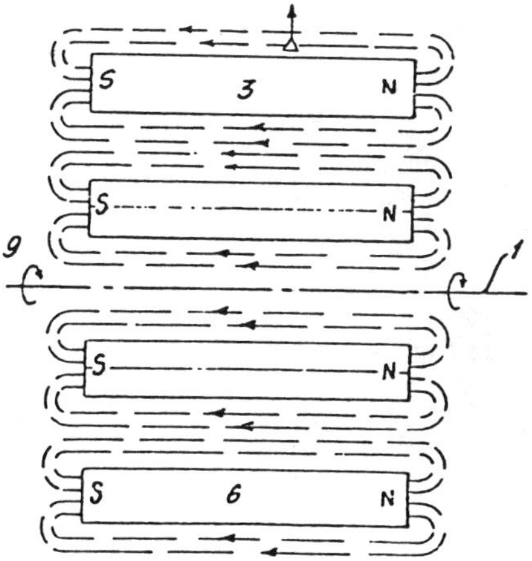

FIG. 2

INVENTOR!
WILLIAM J. HOOPER

BY Oldham & Oldham
ATTORNEY.

Patented April 11, 1972

3,656,013

4 Sheets-Sheet 2

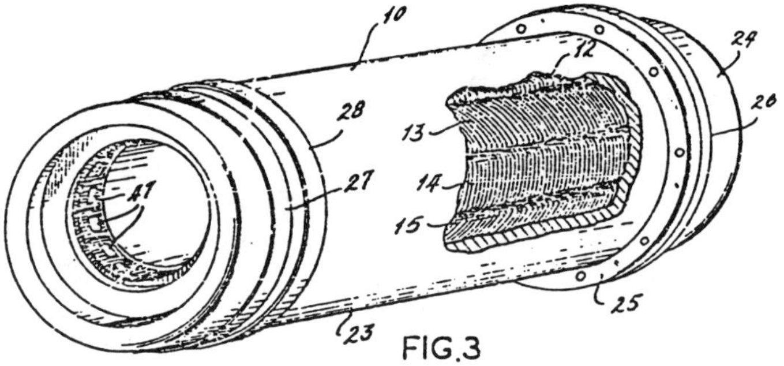

FIG.3

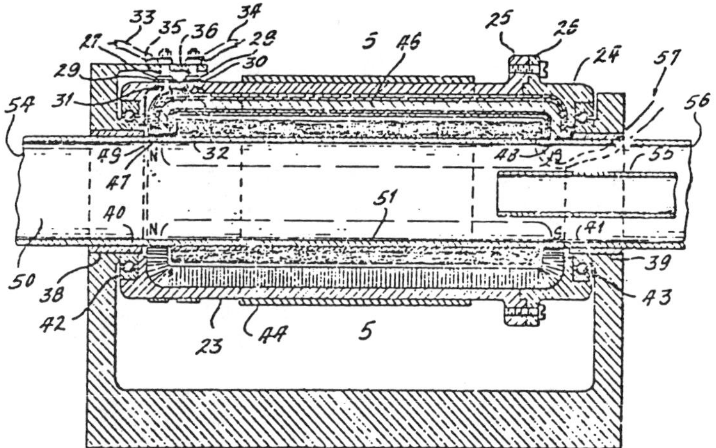

FIG.4

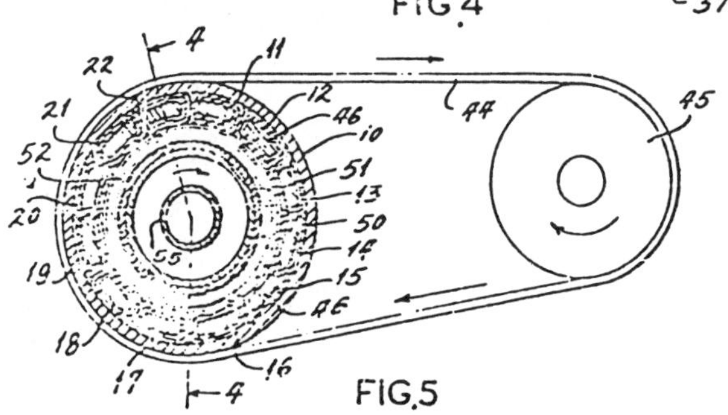

FIG.5

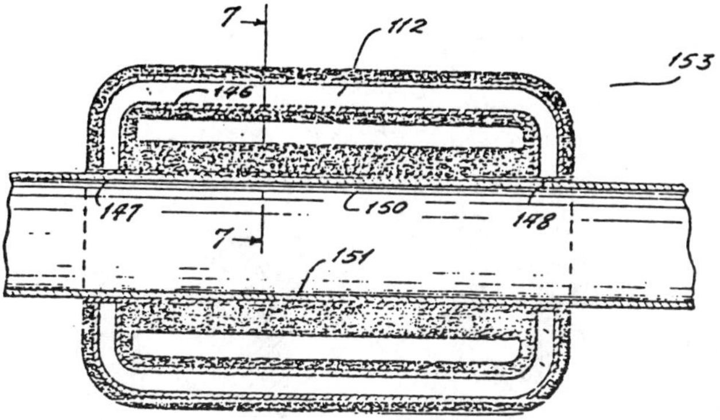

FIG.6

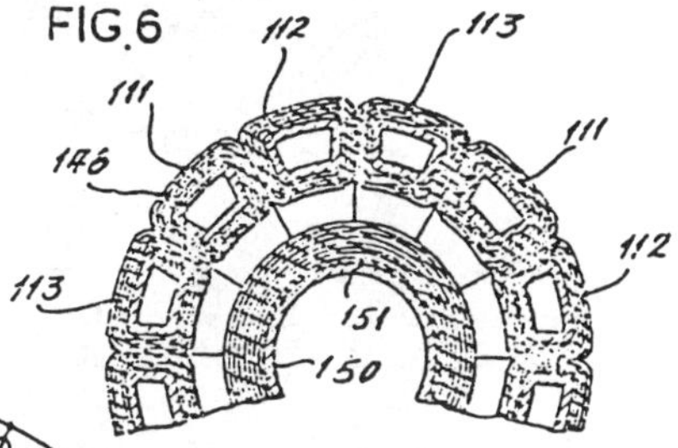

FIG.7

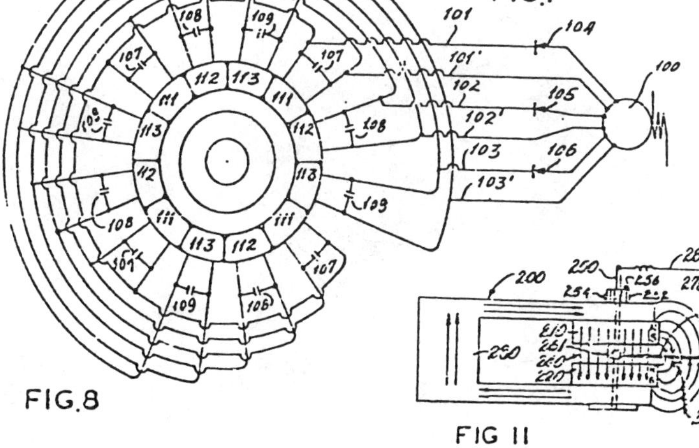

FIG.8

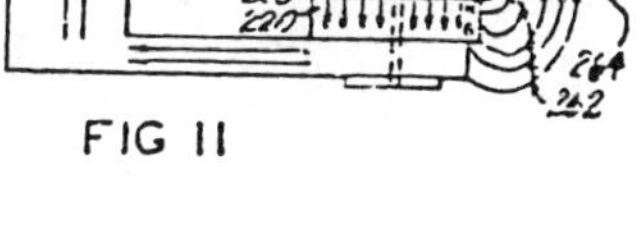

FIG 11

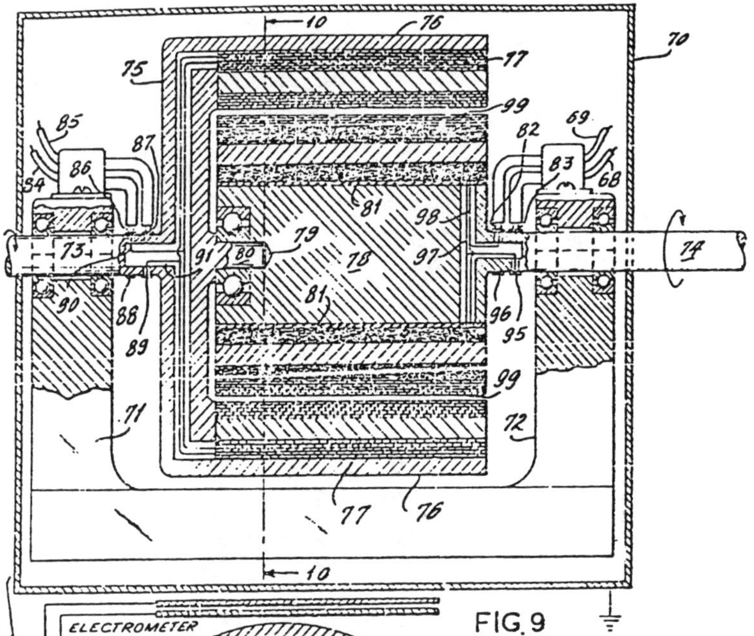
10
76
70
77
75
99
85
69
82
87
83
86
68
84
81
98
79
73
80
91
78
97
74
90
81
96
88
95
89
99
71
72
77
76
10
ELECTROMETER

FIG. 9

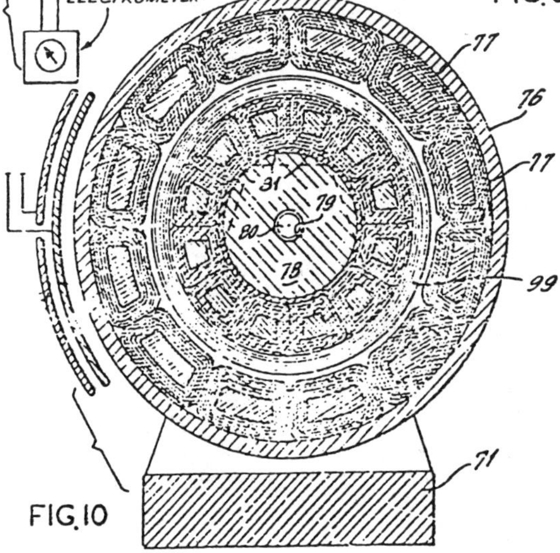
77
76
77
31
79
80
78
99
71

FIG. 10

United States Patent

Hooper

[15] **3,656,013**

[45] **Apr. 11, 1972**

[54] **APPARATUS FOR GENERATING MOTIONAL ELECTRIC FIELD**

[72] Inventor: William J. Hooper, Cuyahoga Falls, Ohio

[73] Assignee: Electrodynamic Gravity, Inc., County of Sarasota, Fla.

[22] Filed: Apr. 19, 1968

[21] Appl. No.: 722,587

[52] U.S. Cl. 310/10

[51] Int. Cl. H02k 1/00

[58] Field of Search....310/10, 11, 178, 177, 156, 310/42, 268, 211, 169, 216, 269, 259; 103/1; 55/2, 14, 101, 123, 127, 120; 73/194 EM; 328/233–238

[56] **References Cited**

UNITED STATES PATENTS

3,285,179	11/1966	Resler, Jr.	103/1
3,336,489	8/1967	Volger	310/40
3,431,441	3/1969	Shair	310/11
399,800	3/1889	Thomson	310/115
460,087	9/1891	Hewett	310/46
2,066,343	1/1937	Gillen	310/46
2,558,540	6/1951	Clos	310/46
2,705,762	4/1955	Pile	310/104
3,277,631	10/1966	Sunnen	55/3
3,385,983	5/1968	Bohn et al	310/11

OTHER PUBLICATIONS

Book–Theory and Calculation of Electrical Apparatus by C. P. Steinmetz; N.Y.– 1917.

Text Book– The Electromagnetic Field in its Engineering Aspects G. W. Carter– 2nd edition– 1967 pages 168 to 171 incl., 328, 329, 334, 335 and 336

The Feynman Lecture on Physics by Feynman, Leighton and Sands Addison– Wesley– Publishing Co., New York; pages 17–1 and 17–2

Primary Examiner—D. X. Sliney
Attorney—Oldham & Oldham

[57] **ABSTRACT**

Apparatus for producing and demonstrating properties of motional electric fields by means of rotating magnetic flux produced by a plurality of magnets extending parallel with the axis of rotation, said flux of these magnets being put into rotation about a common axis by mechanical or by electro magnetic means.

6 Claims, 11 Drawing Figures

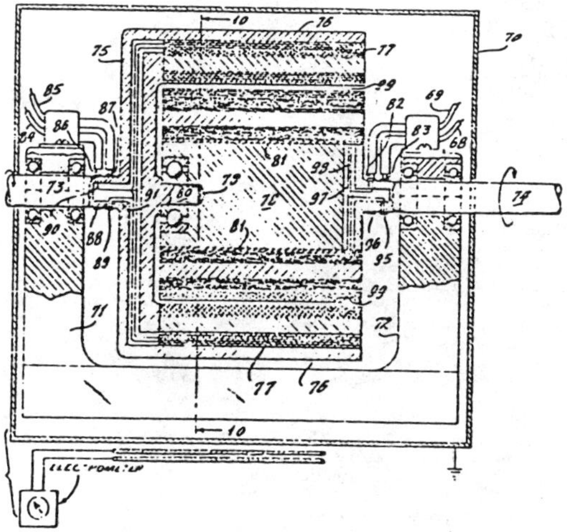

APPARATUS FOR GENERATING MOTIONAL ELECTRIC FIELD

This invention relates to the generation of motionally induced electric fields as distinct from electrostatic fields, and as distinct from the electric field (illustrated by transformer action) which is induced by the time rate of change of magnetic induction. Hence, all reference herein to a motional electric field means the electric field that is generated by the movement of magnetic flux.

The motional electric field generated by rotational motion of magnetic flux is non-uniform in both direction and radial intensity. Particles (large or small) of matter (solid, liquid or gaseous) which are within the ambit of this motional electric field are acted upon with a force which tends to accelerate them. It is well known that a particle carrying a charge Q (coulombs) in an electric field of intensity E (Newton/coulomb) will be acted upon by a force F (Newton) given by the equation $F = EQ$. The electric intensity E of a motional electric field is given by the vector equation $E = B \times V$, where B is the magnetic flux density at a point in space, expressed in webers per square meter, and V is the velocity of the moving magnetic flux at that point in space, expressed in meters per second. What is not so well known, however, is the fact that a non-uniform electric field exerts a force upon electrically neutral matter. In his celebrated text, "The Mathematical Theory of Electricity and Magnetism", Sir James H. Jeans describes, in the case of a non-uniform electrostatic field, how a "slab of dielectric will be sucked in between the plates of the condenser" thus demonstrating the mechanical force produced by such a field. He states (P. 125), "This, as will be seen later, is a particular case of a general theorem that any piece of dielectric is acted on by forces which tend to drag it from the weaker to the stronger parts of an electric field of force." According to Clerk Maxwell in "Electricity and Magnetism" (Vol. II, p. 181), Faraday discovered that the electric field due to electromagnetic induction penetrated within and throughout all materials. The motional electric field is just such a field. Apparatus for demonstrating the "general theorem", stated by Jeans, has, in the case of the non-uniform motional electric field, not heretofore been provided.

Accordingly, it is one of the objects of the present invention to provide a device for generating a non-uniform motional electric field whose force is of magnitude such that it can be sensed.

Since the motional electric field acts within and throughout all matter, such a non-uniform field will exert a physical force on any kind of electrically neutral matter, in a manner quite analogous to that of the electrostatic field with respect to dielectric material.

Another object of the invention is to provide apparatus for obtaining useful work from a non-uniform motional electric field.

The several objectives of the invention may be accomplished by rotating an elongate magnetic field about an axis which is concentric with the field and parallel with the field's elongation. For example, an array of magnets may be mounted on a rotor so that all magnets are parallel with the axis of the rotor, and all have the same polar orientation relative to the rotor. A solenoidal electro magnet, or another array of magnets, with magnetic axis concentric with the rotational axis may also be employed to enchance the flux density of the array of rotating magnets by flux linking with them. When such an array of magnets is rotated about the axis of the rotor, the magnetic field of each is rotated with it. As another example, an elongate magnetic field can be rotated about its axis, without mechanical movement, by the provision of stationary solenoidal electro magnets arrayed like the staves of a barrel and connected to a source of multi-phase alternating current (half wave rectified to prevent reversal of sign) in a manner comparable to the stator winding of a three-phase motor to produce "revolving field." While the composite magnetic field is thus in rotary motion, every charged, or uncharged particle of matter (solid, liquid, or gaseous) within the non-uniform motional electric field thus generated in the neighborhood of the rotor, will be acted upon by a force due to the electric intensity E. Positively charged particles will be forced in the direction of the vector E, negatively charged particles will be forced in the opposite direction, and electrically neutral matter will be pulled from the weaker regions of field intensity to the stronger regions. This latter mechanical force is called a differential force due to the action of the field on the internal electrical polarization of the neutral matter.

The three vectors E, B, and V are always (with a possible exception) mutually at right angles to each other. If the thumb of the right hand is pointed in the direction of the magnetic flux density vector B, and then rotated like a right-handed screw so that it points in the direction of the velocity V of the moving magnetic flux, then the forefinger of the right hand will point in the direction of the electric vector E. The rotation of the composite magnetic flux about its axis produces a motional electric field which will, except at the axial ends of the magnetic field, be quite generally directed radially with respect to the axis of rotation. The possible exception is the case of a magnet having a homogeneous electrically conductive core of perfectly circular cross-section, in which case the force of the electric field may be somewhat off radial.

With a given polar orientation of magnets relative to the axis of rotation, rotation of the magnetic field in a clockwise direction will generate a motionally induced electric field of sign (positive or negative) opposite that which is generated when the rotation is counterclockwise. For any given sense of rotation, reversing the polar orientation of the magnets relative to the axis of rotation likewise reverses the sign (positive or negative) of the motionally induced electric field. Reversing both the direction of rotation and the polar orientation of the magnets (a situation exemplified by viewing the apparatus first from one axial end, and secondly from the opposite axial end) produces no change in the sign (positive or negative) of the motionally induced electric field.

In the accompanying drawings, three embodiments of the invention are exemplified. Also, there are two model schematics to illustrate in its simplest form the principle of the invention, in which a plurality of commonplace permanent magnets are mounted upon a rotor.

The first embodiment is one in which an array of electro magnets is mounted on a rotor having a hollow center, through which particles of matter can be moved and their response to the motional electric field perceptibly demonstrated.

Second, there is an embodiment in which electro magnets are arrayed as in the first embodiment, but are stationary and their composite magnetic field is rotated electromagnetically by phase displacement.

Third, there is an embodiment in which a pair of oppositely rotating rotors, nested one within the other, are each provided, on its circumference, with an array of electro magnets oriented as aforesaid on each rotor, but oppositely oriented on the respective rotors, and wherein the effect of the motionally induced electric fields can be perceptibly demonstrated by the behavior of particles of matter externally of the rotor.

In the accompanying drawings:

FIG. 1 is a diagrammatic view illustrating the effect of rotating an array of spaced permanent magnets about an axis which is parallel with each of the magnets when all magnets have corresponding polar orientation;

FIG. 2 is a diagrammatic view representing a side elevation of the arrangement shown in FIG. 1, and illustrating the external magnetic flux paths of the several permanent magnets;

FIG. 3 is a perspective view of a rotor for generating a radially directed motional electric field in accordance with one embodiment of the invention, wherein electro magnets are arrayed within a hollow rotor with axes parallel to that of the rotor;

FIG. 4 is a sectional view taken along a diametric plane of the rotor shown in FIG. 3, together with its cooperating parts;

FIG. 5 is a sectional view along line 5—5 of FIG. 4, and showing, in addition, driving means for the rotor.

FIG. 6 is a sectional view taken along a diametric plane of a stationary form of apparatus similar to that shown in FIGS. 3, 4, and 5, but wherein the magnetic flux field is rotated electromagnetically by phase displacement;

FIG. 7 is a sectional view taken along line 7—7 of FIG. 6;

FIG. 8 is a wiring diagram for the apparatus shown in FIGS. 6 and 7.

FIG. 9 is a longitudinal sectional view of an apparatus having a plurality of rotors for generating a B × V electric field;

FIG. 10 is a sectional view taken along line 10—10 of FIG. 9; and

FIG. 11 is a diagrammatic illustration of an apparatus for exhibiting moving field phenomena.

In FIGS. 1 and 2, the principle of the invention is diagrammatically illustrated with the utmost simplicity, wherein a catena of magnetic flux fields, all with the same polar orientation, is produced by arranging an array of rod-type permanent magnets parallel with each other, and parallel with the axis about which they are to be rotated. In FIG. 1, the axis of rotation is designated 1, and may be considered as the center of a shaft of a rotor, preferably composed of material having low, if any, magnetic permeability, and low, if any, electrical conductivity. The periphery of such a rotor is designated by the circle 2. In the form shown, a series of permanent magnets 3, 4, 5, 6, 7, and 8 is appropriately secured to the periphery of the rotor with the respective magnets in equi-spaced relationship, and all with their north poles addressed in the same direction which, as shown in FIG. 1, is in the direction of the reader or, as shown in FIG. 2, to the reader's right. The external flux fields from the respective permanent magnets 3, 4, 5, and 6 are illustrated in FIG. 2, where it will be observed that the external flux path of all magnets is from right to left, a relationship designated by the plus (+) marks in FIG. 1. With such an arrangement, the flux fields of all magnets may be concurrently rotated about axis 1. Considering the rotation to be in the direction of arrows 9 and the polar orientation of the several permanent magnets to be as illustrated, a B × V motional electric field will be generated both externally and internally of rotor periphery 2 upon rotation of the rotor. The thus generated motional electric field will exert a radially directed force upon every particle of matter, neutral or charged, such as particle P, which is within the ambit of the catena of magnetic flux fields. The magnitude of the so impressed electric field intensity will depend upon the magnetic flux concentration at the particle P and the relative velocity between the flux field and particle P. While, if particle P is in motion, its velocity must be considered in arriving at the relative velocity V (in the formula $E = B \times V$) the disclosure will be simplified if the particle P be considered as stationary, and in such event V will be 2 R times S, where R is the radial displacement of particle P from axis 1, and where S is the revolutions per unit of time made by the rotor. Hence, with the particle P stationary, the magnitude of the force impressed upon it is increased when the speed of rotation of the rotor is increased at a given flux density; and is increased by an increase in the flux density at a given speed of rotation. The direction in which the force of the motionally induced electric field acts upon particle P is always perpendicular to the magnetic flux field B and to its velocity V. The sign of the electric force field may be either positive (acting radially outward from the axis of rotation) or negative (acting radially inward toward the axis of rotation), which, for any given polar orientation of the permanent magnets, may be reversed by reversing the direction of rotation of the rotor. With the polar orientation shown in FIGS. 1 and 2, and the direction of rotation indicated by arrow 9, if particle P is a proton or a positively charged molecule, the force of the $B \times V$ electric field will be radially inward as indicated by the solid line arrow attached to particle P; but if particle P is an electron or a negatively charged molecule, the particle will tend to move radially outward as shown by the broken line arrow; and if the particle P is electrically neutral, it will tend to move in the direction of increasing electrical intensity E. Increase of E requires either that both B and V be increasing or that one be increasing at a sufficiently greater rate than the other is decreasing so that the product ($B \times V$) increases. In the relationship of field and particle shown in FIG. 1, the product ($B \times V$) increases radially inward.

For practical purposes, however, commonplace permanent magnets produce insufficient flux density in their external flux paths to impress upon a particle of charged matter such as P, an electric force of sufficient magnitude that the force of the electric field can be measured with ease, at least at speeds of rotation within practical limits. Consequently, the practical embodiments of the invention, later to be described, make use of electro magnets of a form capable of producing external flux fields of vastly greater flux density B, as well as higher velocities V.

The term "unipolar induction" has been used to indicate the induction of an electric field in the vicinity of an axially symmetrical magnetic system rotating about its axis of symmetry. There has been disagreement about whether as the magnetic system is rotated the lines of magnetic induction are carried with it or remain stationary while the magnetic system rotates through them. For example, when a bar magnet is rotated about its magnetic axis, it is believed by many that the magnetic field is stationary. I have demonstrated that under certain conditions, at least, the magnetic lines can be made to move, and I have devised certain methods and apparatus for utilizing this phenomena as in the production of localized and high intensity electric fields.

Turning now to FIG. 11 of the drawings, an apparatus for demonstrating certain magnetic phenomena is illustrated in diagrammatic form. A magnetic system, indicated generally by numeral 200, includes a pair of permanent magnets 210 and 220 which are axially magnetized and mounted in axial alignment between the ends of a U-shaped yoke 230 of highly permeable magnetic material. The adjacent surfaces of magnets 210 and 220 being of opposed polarity are spaced apart, providing an air gap 240 therebetween. The lines of magnetic flux are shown in the drawing and indicated generally by numeral 262. A brass rod 250 extends axially through magnets 210 and 220. The magnetic system 200 is rotatable about rod 250. A stiff conductor 260 is electrically connected by a collar 261 at one end in rotatable or fixed relation as selectively desired, with the brass rod 250 at a point in the gap 240 between magnets 210 and 220. The other end of conductor 260 extends substantially perpendicularly from rod 250 to a distance in space away from the magnets and yoke where the magnetic field falls to approximately zero intensity. In order to complete an electrical circuit through galvanometer 270 and conductor 280 to the brass rod 250 and conductor 260, a flexible and extensible electrical wire 264 connects the end of conductor 260 to the galvanometer 270. A gear 252 locked alternatively by set screw 254 to rod 250 or by set screw 256 to yoke 230 can serve to provide driving motion to either the rod 250 or YOKE 230 as selectively desired. Normally, for the purposes of the experiment, the driving motion will be reciprocal because of the connection of wires 280 and 264.

With this apparatus, if the magnetic system 200 is held fixed and a given angular displacement imparted to conductor 260 by rotating it horizontally about or with rod 250 through the air gap at a given angular speed, a voltage is induced which provides a deflection of galvanometer 270. Furthermore, when the conductor 260 is held fixed and the magnetic system 200 rotated through the same angular displacement about rod 250, at the same given angular speed, a similar voltage of exactly the same magnitude but opposite direction is induced in the galvanometer circuit. The same deflection is obtained whether or not the magnets 210 and 220 rotate with the yoke 230 or are held stationary while the yoke alone is rotated. This indicates clearly that the lines of magnetic induction in the quantity rotate about the axis of rotation 250 as if they were rigidly attached to the magnetic system 200.

A most important aspect of the operation of the apparatus of FIG. 11 is noted when the magnets 210 and 220 are held fixed in relation to the conductor 260 and rod 250 and the yoke 230 is rotated about the rod 250. This action causes induction of current in the galvanometer circuit exactly as occurs when the entire magnetic structure or the conductor itself are moved. However, if the magnetic yoke 230 and conductor 260 are held fixed and magnets 210 and 220 rotated, there is no deflection of the galvanometer. Thus, it appears that the yoke structure plays an important part in controlling movement of the magnetic flux. Furthermore, it should be noted that the magnetic flux does not link the galvanometer circuit in the usual sense that this term is used, but that a current is induced in the galvanometer circuit through the action of the conductor 260 in merely cutting across the field extending between adjacent faces of magnets 210 and 220.

It has also been found that the permanent magnets 210 and 220 may be replaced by an electromagnet and the results described above duplicated. Furthermore, it can be demonstrated that the magnetic flux within the air core of a solenoid may be rotated about its magnetic axis. A brass tube formed in the shape of a toroidal C has a winding applied to its entire length with holes drilled in the tubing to receive a brass rod, as 250 in the structure shown in FIG. 11. With the winding energized, the above-described procedures produce similar galvanometer deflections.

This application is concerned with certain methods and apparatus which make use of the phenomena described above.

Referring now to FIGS. 3, 4, and 5 for an illustration of the second embodiment, a tubular rotor 10 is provided on its inner periphery with 12 keystone cross-sectional electro magnets 11, 12, 13, 14, 15, 16, 17, 18, 19, 20, 21, and 22 of the solenoid type. As seen in the cross-section of FIG. 5, the several electro magnets are arranged as sectors of a cylindrical annulus. While in the form shown, the several electro magnets 11–22 are shown in circumferentially wedged relationship, whereby to minimize the likelihood of relative movement radially inward as at standstill, as well as in the interest of achieving substantial uniformity of external flux density throughout the inside circular area of the rotor, it will be understood that when and if desired, the several electro magnets can be circumferentially spaced one from the other, and, if desired, a spacer of relatively low, if any, magnetic permeability interposed between them. Any suitable means may be employed for securing the several electro magnets to the shell of the rotor.

In order to facilitate the assembly of the several keystone-shaped electro magnets on the interior of the rotor as shown, the shell thereof is made of at least two pieces 23 and 24. In the form shown in FIGS. 3–5, the two pieces 23 and 24 are cup-shaped, and are respectively provided with outwardly extending flanges 25 and 26. Once the several solenoids have been positioned within the longer shell piece 23, the shorter shell piece 24 may be applied as a cap so that flanges 25 and 26 abut, and may be appropriately secured together as by riveting, bolting, welding, or cementing.

The shell pieces 23 and 24, as well as their interconnecting means, may be formed of material having little or no magnetic permeability, or in cases where it is desired to shield the exterior from the escape of magnetic flux, they may be formed of material having a high magnetic permeability. Instead of dividing the rotor shell in twain axially, it may be divided in twain radially, in which event the two halves will have axially extending joints when assembled, and may be held in such assembled position by banding or other appropriate means capable of sustaining the centrifugal force to which the rotor will be subject in use.

At the end of shell piece 23, remote from flange 25, there is provided a pair of slip rings 27 and 28 which, in the event the shell piece is formed of electrically conductive material, may be separated from the shell piece by sub-rings 29 and 30, of appropriate insulating material. The slip ring 27 is connected through a conductor 31 to the free end on the inner course of the solenoid winding for each of the electro magnets 11–22. The slip ring 28 is connected trough a conductor 32 to the free end of the outer course of winding in each of the solenoids 11–22. All 12 solenoids are connected so that the direction of electric current flow is the same in all solenoids. The energizing current is supplied from an external source through conductors 33 and 34 and brushes 35 and 36, in a manner well understood in the art.

The rotor is mounted upon an appropriate frame 37, having opposite stationary stub axles in the form of ferrules 38 and 39 which project toward each other. On the projecting portion of each of ferrules 38 and 39, there is provided an inner race 40 and 41 for each of two ball bearing sets whose outer races 42 and 43 are appropriately mounted to the respective ends of the rotor 10, so that the rotor 10 is free-running, with respect to the frame 37, about an axis concentric with the rotor 10.

In the embodiment shown, the exterior cylindrical surface of rotor 10 serves as a pulley for a drive belt 44 which connects the rotor to a source of power 45, but any other suitable means of driving the rotor in rotation may be utilized.

In the form shown in FIGS. 3–5, the apparatus is intended to concentrate the magnetic flux of the several solenoids radially inward, and to facilitate this each of the solenoids is provided with a core 46 of material having high magnetic permeability. As shown in FIG. 4, the several cores 46 are of squat U-shape, and extend, for the most part, parallel to the axis of the rotor, but at each end the cores are curved so as to provide faces 47 and 48 addressed radially inward. To minimize the radially outward escape of magnetic flux from the several solenoids, they are preferably wound of ribbon-like conductor which is coated with any appropriate electrical insulation. The first course of winding begins at 49, and proceeds in helically wound fashion with the minimum of space between adjacent turns about core 46, to the opposite end thereof, whereupon, without interrupting the continuity of the conductor, the second course is wound helically over the first course, with the pitch of the helix reversed from that in the first course. In this way, any gaps between successive turns in the first course are overlapped by turns in the second course. While the drawings show only two courses of conductor about each core 46, it will be understood that, in practice, there may be many more courses.

With the several solenoids connected through the slip rings to a source of direct current as above-described, it will be understood that all the solenoids 11–22 have the same polar orientation with respect to the axis of rotation of the rotor. For example, all core ends 47 are North poles, and all core ends 48 are South poles.

A tube 50 of circular cross-section is mounted in fixed relationship within the respective ferrules 38 and 39. The tube 50 is preferably made of material having little or no magnetic permeability. The tube 50 is stationary, but the rotor 10 rotates about the axis of the tube 50.

A stationary solenoid 51 is fixedly mounted on the exterior of tube 50 in a position such as to fit, with clearance, into the bight of the squat U-shaped solenoids 11–22. Solenoid 51 may be wound directly on tube 50, but in the form shown, it is wound on a cylindrical core 52 of material having little or no magnetic permeability, and the core 52 is telescoped on tube 50. The stationary solenoid 51 is energized through appropriate leads (not shown) from conductors 33 and 34 or other source of direct current, and is so connected that its magnetic polarity is opposite that of solenoids 11–22, that is to say that when, as aforesaid, the core ends 47 are North poles, the adjacent end of solenoid 51 will be its South pole. Thus, magnetic flux of solenoids 11–22 has an external path, through tube 50, which is coincident with, and in the same direction as, the internal path of magnetic flux in solenoid 51.

Thus, the magnetic field generated by each of the solenoids 11 through 22, as well as that generated by solenoid 51, penetrates the interior of tube 50, and when the rotor is driven in rotation, these magnetic fields rotate collectively about the axis of tube 50. During such rotation, particles of matter within the tube 50 are within the motional electric field generated by the rotating magnetic flux. Such an apparatus has a demonstrable effect in the separation and concentration of fluids. For example, in the de-salinization of water, the $B \times V$ electric field generated by the rotating magnetic fields, acts upon the disassociated ions of the sodium chloride in solution. This is explained by the fact that if the rotor 10 be rotated in the direction shown by the arrows in FIG. 5, the $B \times V$ field tends to drive the positively charged sodium cations toward the center, and tends to drive the negatively charged chlorine anions away from the center of tube 50. Hence, by introducing a flow of saline water at end 54 of tube 50, and by providing a concentric separating tube 55 at end 56 of tube 50, increments of fluid which are concentrated with sodium and depleted of chlorine may be drawn off through the stationary tube 55, while the increments of fluid which are concentrated with chlorine and depleted of sodium may be drawn off through the space between the exterior walls of tube 55 and the interior walls of tube 50.

Another utility of the apparatus shown is that of transmuting hydrogen into helium, in which event tube 55 is omitted and electrodes are provided at opposite ends 54 and 56 of tube 50, so that an electric arc may be established between them. Heretofore, difficulty has been encountered in maintaining the plasma of the arc in a relatively straight path between the electrodes as it ends to wiggle and extinguish itself when it makes contact with one of the confining walls. However, by impressing a $B \times V$ electric field upon such an arc, its path may be confined within controllable limits. The $B \times V$ electric field has the further effect of driving hydrogen protons toward the center of the tube, and driving electrons away from the center of the tube. Add one neutron to a hydrogen atom nucleus, and there is produced the isotope known as Dueterium; add one more neutron to the Dueterium nucleus, and it becomes Tritium; add one more proton to the Tritium nucleus, and it becomes Helium.

A third embodiment of the apparatus is shown in FIGS. 6, 7, and 8. With the significant exception that the embodiment of FIGS. 6, 7, and 8 has no moving mechanical parts, its organization is, in general, quite similar to that shown in FIGS. 4 and 5, and hence the last two digits of the reference characters utilized in the previous embodiment. As shown in FIG. 6, a cylindrical tube 150 has a solenoid 151 wound on the exterior thereof, and is energized with direct current from a suitable source through leads 153. A plurality of squat U-shaped solenoids 111, 112, and 113, of keystone-shaped cross-section, of which there are four each or any multiple of four, are wound as described in connection with the previous embodiment, and securely mounted in any suitable way with their pole faces 147 and 148 contiguous with, and addressed toward the axis of, tube 150. In this embodiment, however, the several squat U-shaped solenoids 111, 112, and 113, have cores which are made of material having little or not magnetic permeability, such as tubes 146 of paperboard wound to a keystone shape with hollow interior. As in the previous embodiment, the magnetic polarity of solenoid 151 is opposite that of the solenoids 111, 112, and 113, which is to say that if ends 147 of the solenoids 111–113 are the North poles thereof, the adjacent end of solenoid 151 is its South pole, so that the external magnetic flux path from solenoids 111–113 is coincident with, and in the same direction as, the internal flux path of solenoid 151.

In the embodiment shown in FIGS. 6–8, the several squat U-shaped solenoids 111, 112, and 113 are energized with non-interconnected three-phase alternating current, each phase of which has been half-wave rectified to produce direct current pulsating at alternate half cycles. One phase of the alternating current is connected to all solenoids 111; another phase of the alternating current is connected to all solenoids 112; and the third phase of the alternating current is connect to all solenoids 113, as shown in the wiring diagram of FIG. 8, where a three-phase alternator 100 is provided with six leads arranged in three pairs, to wit: leads 101 and 101' for the first phase, leads 102 and 102' for the second phase, and leads 103 and 103' for the third phase. The respective phases are not electrically interconnected. In each of leads 101, 102, and 103, there is a rectifier 104, 105, and 106, respectively. Leads 101 and 101' serve all four of solenoids 111; leads 102 and 102' serve all four of solenoids 112; and leads 103 and 103' serve all four of solenoids 113. Across leads 101 and 101', between the rectifier 104 and the respective solenoids 111, there is provided a capacitor 107. Such capacitor is to coordinate the capacity and inductance of input, and to neutralize the effect of induction in solenoids 111 by adjacent solenoids during the off half-cycle of energization. Likewise, a capacitor 108 is connected between leads 102 and 102', and a capacitor 109 is connected between leads 103 and 103'. It will be apparent to those skilled in the art that since the four solenoids of like phase are arranged in quardrature with each other, and since solenoids 111 will reach their peak of magnetic flux 120° ahead of solenoids 112 reaching their peak flux, and the latter 120° ahead of solenoids 113 reaching their peak flux, a revolving magnetic field is created. Due to the rectification of the alternating current, and the consequent utilization of the half cycles which all flow in the same direction, there will be no reversal of the direction of magnetic flux generated by any of solenoids 111, 112, and 113, and hence, as in the case of the previous embodiment, the external path of all magnetic flux generated in the solenoids 111, 112, and 113 is coincident with, and in the same direction as, the internal flux generated by direct current energization of solenoid 151. When such an arrangement is supplied with alternating current at high frequency, such as a thousand cycles per second, the same results are achievable with this embodiment as with the previous embodiment but without movement of any mechanical parts.

For the purpose of illustrating the effect of the $B \times V$ electric field, and segregating that effect from the effect of stray magnetic or electrostatic forces, reference may be had to FIGS. 9 and 10. The device there shown is intended to be encased in an electrically grounded box 70 of material which has a high magnetic permeability, and which also has the property of electrical conductivity for shielding electrostatic fields.

Within the box 70, there is a compound rotor machine, wherein the respective rotors are driven in opposite directions. In a suitable frame having spaced pedestals 71 and 72, there is mounted a shaft 73 and an independent shaft 74. Both shafts 73 and 74 may be driven from a single source of power, and are preferably driven at the same rotational speed, but in opposite senses. A yoke 75 is fixedly mounted to shaft 73 for rotation with it. The yoke is cup-shaped with cylindrical skirt 76. About the inner periphery of the skirt 76, a plurality os solenoidal electro magnets 77 are fixedly mounted thereto. The several electro magnets extend parallel with the common axis of rotation of shafts 73 and 74, and are of the same polar orientation with respect to those shafts. The several electro magnets 77 have identical solenoids wound, in the manner previously described, about identical cores of material having high magnetic permeability. The solenoids of the several electro magnets 77 are energized from a suitable source of direct current through conductors 84 and 85, brushes 86 and 87, slip rings 88 and 89, and conductors 90 and 91. The respective solenoids 76 are preferably connected in parallel circuit relationship, but, if desired, may be in series so long as uniform polar orientation is maintained.

Shaft 74 is provided with a hub 78 having a coaxial bore 79, into which is rotatably fitted a pilot 80 projecting concentrically from shaft 73. On the outer periphery of hub 78, there is fixedly mounted a plurality of electro magnets 81, each of which is an identical solenoid, and each of which has an identical core of material having high magnetic permeability. As in the previous case, the several solenoids 81 are all energized so as to have the same polar orientation with respect to their axis of rotation. Each of the solenoids is energized from a suitable source of direct current through conductors 68 and 69, brushes 82 and 83, slip rings 95 and 96, and conductors 97 and 98. All of the solenoids 81 are preferably connected in series circuit relationship, but, if desired, may be in parallel.

If desired, and as shown, the several solenoids 81 may be surrounded by a simple solenoid 59 wound helically thereabout and electrically connected in parallel or series relationship with solenoids 81 and to conductors 97–98 so that the current flow through solenoid 99 is in the same direction as through solenoids 81. Thus the winding 99 serves the dual purpose of boosting the magnetic fields generated by solenoids 81 and of mechanically binding the latter to the surface of hub 78.

When, as contemplated, the shafts 73 and 74 are driven in rotation simultaneously, but in opposite directions, the solenoids 77 which rotate with shaft 73 have opposite magnetic polar orientation to those (81) which rotate with shaft 74. The several solenoids 77 are preferably designed to create external magnetic flux fields of flux density approximately equal and opposite to those created by electro magnets 81 and 99, but by the principle of superposition ("Elec. & Mag.", by Ralph W. Winch, 1963 Ed., p. 202), each flux field acts as if the other were not present. Despite the fact that the flux fields created by the responsive series of electro magnets 77 and 81 and 89 are oppositely directed, since their rotation is in opposite senses, their resultant effect, insofar as concerns the generation of a $B \times V$ electric field, is cumulative. Accordingly, the external $B \times V$ electric field is intensified at the exterior of the device, and its effect on the outside of shielding box 70 is demonstrable, even though the resultant magnetic flux density there is approximately zero. Such demonstration might be through a capacitor and electrometer as shown in FIG. 9, for example.

In order to achieve the maximum flux density and hence the maximum $B \times V$ electric field intensity, it is desirable to take measures which keep the apparatus cool. This may involve resort to such means as: winding the several solenoids with so-called "super-conductors" such as that known commercially as "Supercon"; or refrigerating the apparatus as by immersing it in a bath of liquid helium which is capable of maintaining a temperature of approximately 4° Absolute.

While several illustrative embodiments of the invention have been disclosed in detail, it is not to be understood that the invention is limited to those embodiments. On the contrary, the principles of the invention are susceptible of application in a vast variety of forms without departing from the spirit of the invention or the scope of the appended claims. The apparatus defined in the following claims is believed by the applicant to demonstrate his unique theory disclosed above.

What is claimed is:

1. Apparatus for generating an electric field, comprising:
- a frame;
- a cylindrical rotor;
- a shaft journalled on the frame and supporting the rotor for rotation about is longitudinal axis;
- a plurality of electro magnets, each of which is an identical solenoid having a core formed of a material having a high magnetic permeability, the electro magnets being fixedly mounted on the rotor with each electromagnet extending parallel to the axis of rotation thereof,
- means to energize the solenoids of the electro magnets from a direct current source, the solenoids being energized so as to maintain a uniform polar orientation; and
- an enclosure surrounding the frame and the rotor, the enclosure being formed of an electrically conductive material the enclosure being grounded.

2. Apparatus according to claim 1 wherein the rotor is a hollow cylindrical rotor, the electromagnets being affixed to the inner cylindrical surface of the rotor.

3. Apparatus according to claim 1 wherein the solenoids are connected in parallel circuit relationship.

4. Apparatus for demonstrating magnetic phenomena comprising:
- a frame;
- a cylindrical rotor;
- a shaft journalled on the frame and supporting the rotor for rotation about its longitudinal axis;
- a plurality of electro magnets, each of which is an identical solenoid having a core formed of a material having a high magnetic permeability, the electro magnets being fixedly mounted on the rotor with each electro magnet extending parallel to the axis of rotation thereof,
- means to energize the solenoids of the electro magnets from a direct current source, the solenoids being energized so as to maintain a uniform polar orientation;
- an enclosure surrounding the frame and the rotor, the enclosure being formed of an electrically conductive material, the enclosure being grounded; and
- means surrounding at least a portion of the enclosure to detect and measure the electric field generated during rotation of the energized rotor.

5. Apparatus for demonstrating magnetic phenomena, comprising:
- a U-shaped yoke of highly permeable magnetic material;
- a pair of permanent magnets mounted in axial alignment between the ends of the yoke, one magnet being mounted to each leg of the yoke;
- an electrically conductive non-magnetic rod extending axially through the magnets;
- a stiff conductor mounted at one end to the rod for rotation relative to the yoke in a plane perpendicular to the rod and intermediate the magnets, the conductor extending a sufficient distance beyond the magnets so that its other end is located at a point where the magnetic field from the magnets falls to approximately zero intensity;
- a galvanometer; and
- circuit means connecting the ends of the conductor to the galvanometer to measure current flow through the conductor.

6. Apparatus according to claim 5 wherein the magnets are rotatably mounted to the yoke for rotation about the axis of the rod, and where the magnets are axially magnetized and adjacent faces are of opposite polarity.

* * * * *

APPENDIX III

A CONDITIONAL CRITERION FOR IDENTITY, LEADING TO A FOURTH LAW OF LOGIC

Summary

If logic is regarded as a set of perceptual operations, then logic has a chronotopology (time structure). Identity or nonidentity then results as a decision from an algorithm — a set of perceptual operations and comparisons — in which case the nature of a particular identity is conditional upon the nature of the set of perceptual operations comprising the algorithm.

Ordinary logic does not account for the temporal aspects of perception, merely accounting for the spatial aspects.

In other words, Aristotlean logic is a synthesis of primitive observation, fitted to the partial (spatial) reality emerging from spacetime after the imposition of the monocular (one-at-a-time) photon interaction with matter.

In quantum mechanics, time is a parameter, not an observable. Hence measurement/detection (of observables) deals with primitive observation and Aristotlean logic (topology).

Total reality includes nonprimitive observation — hence, non-Aristotlean logic (chronotopology) — as shown in Young's two-slit experiment.

By applying temporal accounting to each perceptual operation, Aristotle's three laws can be shown to be self-contradictory and incomplete as written. That is, they are topolological, not chronotopological.

A simple derivation of a fourth law is shown and an application rule given which itself may be regarded as a fifth law of logic.

A proof of the fourth law by demonstration is given.

The resulting four-law logic is chronotopological. The application rule states that either Aristotle's three laws apply explicitly and the fourth law is implicit, or the fourth law applies explicitly and Aristotle's three laws are implicit.

The four-law chronotopological logic is theoretically capable of resolving every present three-law paradox.

Aristotle's Laws and the Paradox of Change

Aristotle's three laws of logic, on which foundation rests all mathematical, physical, and rational thinking, can ordinarily be stated as shown in Table 1.

Table 1. Aristotle's three laws of logical thought

1. $A \equiv A$

2. $A \not\equiv \overline{A}$

3. $A \vee \overline{A}$

A variety of arguments can easily be produced to show that these laws are incomplete; i.e., they do not specify all reality, for parts of reality can be shown to contradict one or more of Aristotle's laws.

Indeed, all "observed" reality can be shown to violate all three laws.

E.g., the most direct violation is posed by the problem of change, a problem originally propounded by Heraclitus about 500 B.C., and unsolved to this day. Heraclitus pointed out that, for a thing to change, it must turn into something else, and then asked how a thing could be something other than itself?

We may think of a thing — say, α —some feature A of which is said to change. If A changes, it turns into $\overline{A}$, thus violating logic laws one and two. Further, we are considering A as the "changed thing, $\overline{A}$," i.e., something which is somehow both A and $\overline{A}$, so logic law three is violated as well.

Thus, if Aristotle's laws are taken to be all the fundamental laws of logic, then logically there can be no change whatsoever, because change negates all three laws. I.e., either change does not exist or it is totally illogical.

Since all measurements, detections, thoughts, and perceptions are simply changes, then it follows that these operations logically cannot exist. Or, if we assume the "operations" to exist, their outputs cannot exist. If the operations do not exist, then again their outputs do not exist.

So if the products or outputs cannot exist, then by this reasoning no perceived, detected, measured, conceived thing exists. If we then insist that such things do indeed exist, then all is paradoxical and illogical. This is essentially the nature of the paradox posed by Heraclitus.

Heraclitus's change paradox has not been satisfactorily resolved to this day, and rigorously all the rational science of the Western world, being based on paradoxical change (detection, perception, observation) is itself totally illogical by its own logical standards.

Resolving the Paradox of Change

However, the conditions necessary to resolve the problem of change can be stated simply by inspection of the problem as follows: (1) Aristotle's three laws must specify or apply to only that which is not changing, since change violates or negates all three laws; (2) If change is to logically exist, there must exist at least a fourth law of logic, one which applies to change; (3) This fourth law must contain the negations of each of the first three laws, since change negates them; (4) To be consistent, in any particular logical case, either the three laws explicitly apply or the fourth law explicitly applies (i.e., either change explicitly exists in that particular case or it does not); (5) Since all four laws must apply at all times, then when the three laws apply explicitly, the fourth law must be implicit — and when the fourth law applies explicitly, the three laws must be implicit.

With the five stated conditions, a fourth axiom of logic can be written simply by writing down the negations of Aristotle's three laws, and synthesizing these negations into a single fourth law, as shown in Table 2.

Table 2. Negations to Aristotle's laws.

Aristotle's law	Negation	of negation*
$A \equiv A$	$A \not\equiv A$	$A \equiv \overline{A}$
$A \not\equiv \overline{A}$	$A \equiv \overline{A}$	$A \equiv \overline{A}$
$A \vee \overline{A}$	$A \wedge \overline{A}$	$A \equiv \overline{A}$ or $[A,\overline{A}]$

However, even though we can synthesize the negation into a single law — the old "identity of opposites" idea — we still have the problem of understanding such a law. Though at first glance the negations and the synthesized fourth law seem bewildering, we can readily comprehend them if we carefully consider the temporal nature of the process that occurs in logical thinking.

The Importance of Time

Specifically, a finite interval of time is required to perceive, think, detect, or observe an entity — regardless of whether we refer to "physical" or "mental" detection, because both physical and mental processes are temporal. Indeed, we flatly state without further discussion that ultimately the identifying or mapping of physical and mental operations onto each other is what time is *a priori.*

At any rate, we now carefully account for each individual time interval required to think, conceive, detect, perceive, or observe any entity — whether that entity is physical or mental — and we also account for the finite time interval required to perform a logical operation. So we rewrite Aristotle's three laws as shown in Table 3, with subscripted numbers indicating the separate time intervals in each law.

*These negations mean that A and $\overline{A}$ are totally undifferentiated.

Table 3. Temporally accounted laws and negations.

	Aristotle's law	Negation
1.	$A_1 \equiv_3 A_2$	$A_1 \equiv_3 \overline{A}_2$ or $A_1 \not\equiv_3 A_2$
2.	$A_1 \not\equiv_3 \overline{A}_2$	$A_1 \equiv_3 \overline{A}_2$
3.	$A_1 \vee_3 \overline{A}_2$	$A_1 \wedge_3 \overline{A}_2$ or $[A_1, \overline{A}_2]_3$

The resolution to the entire mystery so long inherent in these axioms of logic now stands simply revealed: Whether one of Aristotle's laws holds or its negation holds is determined solely by the nature of the logical operation in time interval three.[1]

I.e., the operation in interval three may be regarded as an *algorithm* comprised of subsidiary (assumed) operations in separate time subintervals that, taken together, comprise the overall operation implied by the logic symbol.

Thus in the first law, if temporal tags (time snapshots) are not accounted (i,e., if they do not apply), then Aristotle's laws hold, for the snapshot 1 of A is not differentiated in algorithm 3 from snapshot 2 of A. This then rigorously holds for spatial (L^3) entities, but not for spacetime entities. The snapshots in this case for Aristotle's first law (and the others as well) are *spatial* snapshots. On the other hand, if snapshots 1 and 2 of A are themselves temporally differentiated in algorithm 3, then the negation of Aristotle's law applies, because the *spacetime* snapshots A_1 and A_2 are different. This is immediately apparent, e.g., in a Minkowski geometry representation, where the second snapshot of A will have a time coordinate different from the time coordinate of snapshot 1. This is represented as shown in figure 1, where "A" is taken as a simple magnitude, in this case 5.

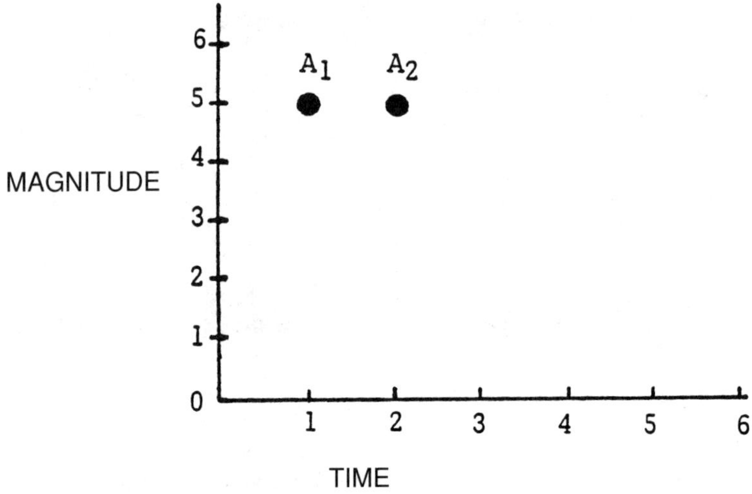

Figure 1. Spatial snapshots of spatiotemporal A differ.

As can be seen from figure 1, 5_1 is not identical to 5_2 *unless we imply the operator* $\partial / \partial t$ *in the time interval three algorithm.*

The negation of the second law may also be simply understood if we use temporal accounting. E.g., suppose we take $A_1 = +1$, $\overline{A}_2 = -1$ and then pose the absolute value operator $|\,|$ for potential use in algorithm 3. If $|\,|$ is not used, then

$$(+1)_1 \not\equiv_3 (-1)_2$$

and Aristotle's second law holds. If $|\,|$ is used, then

$$\left| (+1)_1 \right|_3 \equiv_3 \left| (-1)_2 \right|_3$$

and in that case

$$A_1 \equiv_3 \overline{A}_2$$

Note we are taking the view that there is nothing "absolute" or "inherent" about identity or non-identity; instead, each is a conditional result that can only be established by some logical, comparative set of operations. If the suboperations comprising the decision algorithm for the identity/non-identity determination are changed, the finding of the algorithm (the decision) may often change. Specifically, one can have the cases

$$\equiv_1 \not\equiv_3 \equiv_2$$

$$\not\equiv_1 \not\equiv_3 \not\equiv_2$$

Thus we advance a *conditional identity criterion* to be incorporated into formal logic: "Identity" or "non-identity" is defined by a decision made as a result of applying an operational algorithm; changing the internal operator components assumed inherent in the algorithm can change the decision. We are stating a fundamental principle that "identity" and "non-identity" are conditional and only conditional; they are never absolute.

Primitive Observation and "Reality"

With these points made, we now turn to the third law. From Table 2, on examination it can be seen that the third law actually is a statement for *monocular* perception, detection, observation, thought, or conception. Indeed, this law says that only a single thing at a time can be perceived, detected, observed, thought, or conceived.

As we pointed out in a previous paper[2] , there is a very good reason for this "law." Primitive man lived almost exclusively in a reality detected by light, by the photon interaction. Even in the absence of visible light, all bodies have temperature, and man is immersed in a "sea" of continual electromagnetic photon with interactions. The photon interaction is monocular - - only one at a time interacts with a particle of mass. Further, photon interaction constitutes the operator $\partial/\partial T$ invoked upon L^3T spacetime. Photon emission carries away time (the photon is made of ($\Delta E\ \Delta T$), leaving behind an L^3 *spatial* reality, as we have previously pointed out.[3]

So all our primitive concepts, ideas, and notions about reality have come from over four million years of hominid and human experience in the photon-detected partial reality ("physical," "objective," or "spatial" reality) that remains when the time "dimension" (fundamental variable) is destroyed from L^3T spacetime, leaving only L^3 space behind. Specifically, our observed macroscopic reality consists of large temporal (mental) aggregates of such spatial results, where we cannot distinguish the tiny temporal separations of the pieces. Thus all our observed/perceived entities are spatial, and further, each perception/observation snapshot results in a frozen, unchanging spatial entity (resulting — in physical detection — from the so-called "collapse of the wave function." The loss of a wave function is simply the loss of time.) We vaguely sense "time" and "change" as the relation between these snapshots — i.e., by causality, or the ordering of the spatial changes — much as we see "movement" in movie frames rapidly projected onto a screen one-at-a-time.

Thus our primitive observations, from which have painfully been formed our relational concepts and ideas, are monocular, unchanging, and spatial. Aristotle's three laws of logic — which indeed may be taken to be only a simple synthesis of our primitive observation and corresponding relational concepts — then exhibit the same characteristics; they are monocular, unchanging, 3-dimensional, spatial, non-temporal relational statements. Any statement that is temporal, changing, or 4-dimensional will thus appear as a logical paradox to this logical shorthand.

But from Young's two-slit experiment, we already know that reality and relationships between its parts are quite different if the photon interaction is not invoked — i.e., if $\partial/\partial T$ is not invoked. Classical reality (as prescribed by Aristotle's laws) is directly violated by an electron in the two-slit experiment, e.g., if and only if photon interaction with the electron is not invoked. Again, this has been simply explained by the present author[4], and Charles Musès as early as 1957 pointed out the absence of any mystery in Young's experiment if the chronotopological aspects were considered.[5]

The Conscious Mind is Fitted to the Photon Interaction

However, what is normally referred to as the "conscious, thinking mind" is simply a functioning temporal (rigorously, chronotopological) mechanism that is painfully built up in the individual's awareness (his mind in the greater sense of both thought and awareness, whether monocular or multiocular) by training, conditioning and experience. Its functioning is largely conditioned by one's 90% or so attention to visual stimuli (to the partial reality remaining after photon interaction has been invoked, and to the memory-collated ordering of vast numbers of such photon interactions) and by one's cultural conditioning — which itself has been almost exclusively conditioned and shaped by the monocular photon interaction at base root.

Thus, since the beginning of man, his conscious, rational mind has been trained and constructed to function almost exclusively in basic correspondence with the photon interaction, and his experiential reality consists of the partial reality stripped from fundamental reality by photon interaction.

All "perceived differences," e.g., are created by this deep mindset. As has been previously pointed out, [6] the solitary human problem responsible for all man's inhumanity to his fellow man is directly dependent upon man's almost exclusive detection, observation, perception, and conception of "difference" between humans, these "differences" being due exclusively and totally to the fitting of men's conscious minds to the photon interaction's monocular separation of spatial reality from nonspatial reality, i.e., to

$$\partial/\partial T\,(L^3T) \Rightarrow L^3$$

Such well-nigh total devotion to, and enslavement by, photon interaction also is responsible for the scientist's well-nigh total devotion to, and enslavement by, the present imperfect and incomplete three laws of logic, as presented by Aristotle. The depth of that devotion and enslavement is evidenced by the fact that the resolution of such paradoxes as Heraclitus's problem of change have eluded the best minds of humanity for several thousands of years. Indeed, these paradoxes cannot be resolved by the conscious, rational mind in its present state, for it has been most firmly constructed and fitted to function in accordance with the photon interaction.[7] One cannot hope to resolve any logical paradox by using only those same logical methods that found the situation to be paradoxical in the first place!

Dimensionality

That we need not be constrained by such universal delusion is already shown by binocular vision. Specifically, in viewing a three-dimensional object, each eye never detects a "third dimension," but detects only an L^2 2-dimensional picture. By taking two slightly different 2-dimension snapshots and superposing them, the third dimension is gained. One then essentially sees the resultant superposed pictures as "almost the same but not quite." I.e., the Aristotlean identity algorithm, if satisfied, yields "no difference, hence one object," and if not satisfied, yields "difference, hence multiple (extended) object(s)." So if the two snapshots are almost Aristotlean-identical but not quite, we get an extended-two-dimensional (three-dimensional) object. Otherwise we see two separate, two-dimensional snapshots blurred together (the reader is urged to try this and see).

The point is, "dimensionality" and the identity algorithm are directly related, and geometrically one follows from the other.

Awareness of Time

In very similar manner, we can only gain cognizance of awareness of "time" (as a fourth dimension) by the superposing of two slightly differing (Aristotlean-wise) 3-dimensional snapshots. As is well known, e.g., time is not an "observable" in quantum mechanics; it is a "parameter." Rigorously, the only place such snapshots — each of which is "past" (spatially separated by the annihilation of time in the collapse of the wave function) — can multiply exist is in the "mind" in its most general sense. In a rigorous sense, mind and time can be taken as identical, and the "flow of time" can be taken as the "flow of mind connections or superpositions" of its spatial components. I.e., measured/detected/observed "physical phenomena" are a priori 3-dimensional and spatial, while a mind is four-dimensional and hyperspatial. [8] Spacetime exists mentally but not observably. Time is logically implicit, not explicit.

Temporal Aspects of Logic

Now we return to the temporal aspects of logic. Each perceptual part of each Aristotlean law is fitted to the photon interaction, hence monocular. The logic operation, inherent in the logic symbol in each statement, involves temporal superposition or comparison of spatial perceptual objects. Hence the logic operation is hyperdimensionally a function of mind and injects mind/time into the statement. Yet these laws, being fitted to or synthesizing photon interaction, attempt to prescribe the absence of time, even though writing down the logic operation rigorously invokes time. They are thus totally contradictory, since as written they implicitly violate themselves.

Table 4 summarizes the operations now to be permitted in the time-three algorithm, in developing a new four-law logic:

Table 4. Conditional identity rules.

1. $\boxed{S_1, S_2}_{\,3} = (\text{zero})_3 \;\Rightarrow\; (\text{identity})_3$

2. $\boxed{S_1, S_2}_{\,3} = (\text{nonzero})_3 \;\Rightarrow\; (\text{non-identity})_3$

3. $\boxed{S}_{\,3} = \boxed{\boxed{S}_{1}, \boxed{S}_{2}}_{\,3}$ $\Rightarrow$ monocular separation, differentiation internally

4. $\overset{S}{\sqcap}_{3} = \overset{S}{\sqcap}_{3}$ $\Rightarrow$ nonseparation, no differentiation internally

Rules one and two simply state that, when snapshots 1 and 2 are superimposed (subtracted) in time interval 3, the resultant snapshot 3 may be zero or nonzero. If zero, snapshots 1 and 2 are said to be identical, and if snapshot 1 is to be labeled A, then snapshot 2 is to be labeled A. If snapshot 3 is nonzero, snapshots 1 and 2 are said to be nonidentical; if snapshot 1 is labeled A, then snapshot 2 is labeled $\bar{A}$.

Rule 3 says that snapshot 3 is a "memory" snapshot, and it may be particulately examined to monocularly separate snapshots 1 and 2.

Rule 4 states that snapshot 3 is not a "memory snapshot" and may not be further separated.

Note that in logic we repeatedly apply these rules in combination, serially or compositely. Note further that Rule 1 must serially apply both rules 3 and 4, as must rule 2 also.

If we take $4\big|_3$ to mean "rule 4 applied conditional to rule 3 also being applied," and $4\big|_{\bar{3}}$ to mean "rule 4 applied conditional to rule 3 not also being applied," we may write Table 5:

Table 5. Conditional identity, non-identity, and oneness.

$$4\,\Big|_{\bar{3}} \wedge 1 = \text{identity}\,(S_1, S_2)$$

$$4\,\Big|_{\bar{3}} \wedge 2 = \text{non-identity}\,(S_1, S_2)$$

$4\,\Big|_{\bar{3}}$ = oneness without separate-ones; oneness, extraordinary and unperceivable; thing-in-itself

$4\,\Big|_{3}$ = "ordinary" one, perceivable separation, "thing-as-separate-from-others"

As can be seen, this type of reasoning also sheds a great deal of light on the long-standing problem of the "thing-in-itself," but that is beyond the scope of this paper.

The Fourth Law of Logic

Now we write the fourth law of logic as follows:

$$4.\ \ (A_1\,, \overline{A}_2\,)_3 \ \Rightarrow\ A_1 \equiv_3 \overline{A}_2$$

where all we have said is that, by rule 4, in snapshot 3 no memory process <u>is</u> allowed, and no separation/differentiation whatsoever of A_1 and $\overline{A}_2$ is permitted. Under these operational conditions for identity, what had previously been called A_1 in snapshot 1 and what had been called $\overline{A}_2$ in snapshot 2 are indistinguishable, hence identical.

Figure 2 shows this concretely, and may be taken as a proof of the fourth law by demonstration.

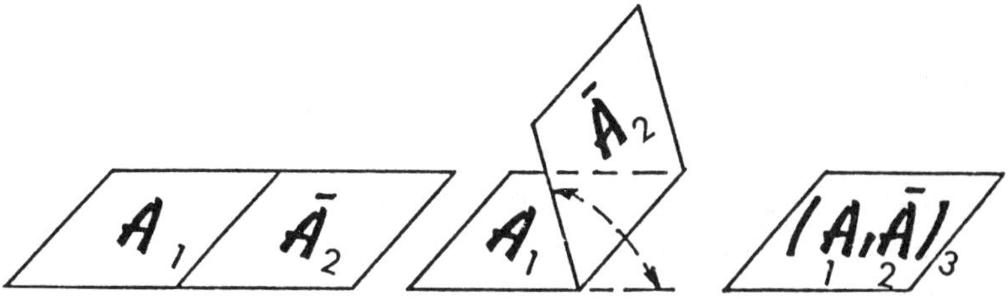

Figure 2. Proof that two opposites can be identified. What was separately perceived as A_1 in time snapshot 1 and what was separately perceived as $\overline{A}_2$ in time snapshot 2, cannot be distinguished in time snapshot 3.

Thus the age-old philosophical dilemma posed by the illogical identity of opposites has a simple resolution if one considers temporal aspects, and introduces temporal conditions for identity or nonidentity decisions.

We now write the new four law conditional identity logic as shown in Table 6:

1. $A_1 \equiv_3 A_2$
2. $A \not\equiv_3 \overline{A}_2$
3. $A_1 \vee_3 \overline{A}_2$
4. $A_1 \equiv_3 \overline{A}_2$

Further, we point out that all four laws now apply. Laws 1, 2, and 3 are the laws of explicit monocular perception, with implicit binocular perception. Law four is the law of explicit binocular perception, with implicit monocular perception. Both monocular and binocular perceptions must be and are used in each law. So in any situation, either the triad applies explicitly and the fourth law applies implicitly, or the fourth law applies explicitly and the triad applies implicitly.

Indeed, one can even take the view that we have prescribed a five-law logic, the fifth law being taken as shown in Table 7:

Table 7. A possible fifth law of logic.

$$5.\ [1,2,3,\ \wedge (4\ )]\ \vee\ [4\ \wedge (1,2,3,)]\ \text{where } () \Rightarrow \text{ implicit}$$

In a previous paper[9], the author has already presented methods to apply this new logic to resolve present paradoxes. At least hypothetically, every present paradox should be simply a statement of the explicit fourth law, and it should be resolvable by explicit application of that law[10].

NOTES AND REFERENCES

1. Specifically, by whether or not exclusivity applies. I.e., we may read Law 1 as "In snapshot (time interval) 3, what was A in snapshot 1 is exclusively identical to (unseparated from) what was A in snapshot 2." Law 2 may be read as "In snapshot 3, what was A in snapshot 1 is exclusively not identical to (is exclusively separated from) what was not-A in snapshot 2." Law 3 reads, "In snapshot 3, what was A in snapshot 1 and what was not-A in snapshot two are exclusively separated." Thus it can be seen that the three laws simply are statements involving whether or not two former perceptions are to be separated in a third perception. These three statements presently prescribe the total separation of the two previous perceptions and prohibit any admixture of the two — the so-called "excluded middle." Thus the three laws prescribe monocular, one-at-a-time perception.

   What we call a "wave" exists in time and is considered to contain an admixture of timeless, static spatial states (such as "wavelengths.") The prohibiting of admixtures thus represents the "collapse of the wave function" and corresponding loss of time. This defines "observation" and explains why all "measurement" and "detection" and "observation" — requiring a collapse of said wave function — are spatial and not spatiotemporal. That is why time is a parameter in quantum mechanics, not an observable.

   Relativity, being constrained by such logic, obviously can find nothing "physical" (observed, spatial, timeless thing frozen by the collapse of the wave function as engendered by or fitted to the photon interaction) that is traveling faster than light — i.e., that violates the conditions implied by the "observing/detecting agent."

That reality need not at all be so constrained is clearly shown by Young's two-slit experiment, the heart of all quantum mechanics. In this experiment, "classical' reality is violated if and only if the photon interaction is not invoked. Classical reality is obeyed if the photon interaction is invoked.
With appropriate change to logic to fit "reality that has not been interacted with by photons" and therefore is spatiotemporal, a new physics becomes possible.

2. Thomas E. Bearden, "Solution of the Fundamental Problem of Quantum Mechanics," January 3, 1977, Defense Documentation Center.

3. Bearden, "Photon Quenching of the Paranormal (Time) Channel: A Brief Note," 20 April 1977, Defense Documentation Center.

4. Bearden, "Virtual State Engineering and Its Implications," 1979, Defense Documentation Center.

5. With the possible exception of Kozyrev — whose more technical works on time remain undisclosed to open science — no other person known to this author seems to have grasped the implications of a dynamic structure of time as penetratingly as has Charles Musès. The importance of the time interaction explaining the two-slit experiment (i.e., in explaining wave-particle duality) was noted as early as 1957 by Musès. See, e.g., Musès' introduction to Jerome Rothstein's **Communication, Organization, and Science**, The Falcon's Wing Press, Indian Hills, Colorado, 1958, p. lxii, where Musès pointed out that the celebrated wave-particle paradox remains a paradox only so long as the chronotopological (his word) phases of the phenomena are left unrealized in the analysis. The entire foreword by Musès is a remarkable document which analyzes the structure of time itself. With his hypernumbers Musès can describe the nested structure of time, which is what is actually

being carried by the photon. Further, he can theoretically predict mechanisms by means of which these structures can be orthorotated. It would appear that practical devices should be constructable on the principles elucidated by Musès, and it is little short of astonishing that fundamental work of such importance and application has been thus far little used by theorists, though it is already recognized in the standard literature; e.g., the profound summary paper "Hypernumbers II" in the January 1978 issue of the journal **Applied Mathematics and Computation**, published by Elsevier.

6. Bearden, "The One Human Problem Its Solution, and Its Relation to UFO Phenomena," Defense Documentation Center, January 3, 1977.

7. Which is why a Zen master often gives the student a koan to confound and overwhelm this automatic, robotic mindset and functioning that has been constructed as the student's "conscious mind."

8. Specifically, consciousness/life involves a seven dimensional body/being in an infinite-dimensional universe. See Thomas E. Bearden, "A Mind/Brain/Matter Model Consistent with Quantum Physics and UFO Phenomena," prepared for the 1979 MUFON Annual Symposium, available in the **Proceedings**, MUFON, 103 Oldtown Road, Sequin, Texas 78155.

9. Bearden, "The Fourth Law of Logic," **Specula**, Journal of the American Association of Meta-Science, P.O. Box 1182, Huntsville, Alabama 35807, Vol. 2, No.1, January-March 1979, pp. 30-40; also in publication in Defense Documentation Center. (The journal **Specula** is no longer pulished).

10. No consideration of the foundations of logic and mathematics is complete until one has read Morris Kline, **Mathematics: The Loss of Certainty,** Oxford University Press, New York, 1980.

APPENDIX IV

LIST OF SELECTED INCIDENTS

Author's note: In 1985-1987 a series of anomalous missile and space failures swept the U.S. and the West. These incidents were not unique, as many think, but were actually only a portion of thousands of related incidents showing the Soviet testing of advanced weapons throughout the world. This listing will show the types of incidents referred to.

The listing is not intended to be complete at all, but only representative. Hundreds of incidents of weather engineering, giant cloud radials and grids, suspicious light incidents, etc. could easily be added, were there time and room. No attempt has been made to exhaustively map the "aerial booms" that have blanketed the U.S., Europe, and other parts of the world. The light and "maybe it's UFO's" reports alone would add thousands of incidents to the list.

Our message is succinct: The Soviet Union has developed a new science and weaponized it, since at least the latter 1940's. It has utilized that science — energetics — to develop superweapons and supervehicles. Because of the danger from accidental initiation of nuclear weapons and materials, it is exceedingly difficult and dangerous for the Soviets to make extensive use of these weapons. Accordingly, a biological warfare strike — AIDS — has been utilized to deliver what is to be the knockout blow to the West.

DATE, INCIDENT, LOCATION, REMARKS

Early spring 1966 - Malstrom AFB Montana.
UFO sighting coincident with simultaneous problems in 10 strategic missiles in launch site associated with Malstrom AFB, Montana. *Similar event in Mar 1967 also. (Source:* ***Clear Intent.).***

20 Mar 67 - Malstrom AFB Montana.
Flight of 10 strategic missiles in launch site associated with Malstrom AFB, Montana experienced problems with guidance and control system. UFO in area and confirmed on radar. Jet fighters scrambled, results unknown. *Similar event one year earlier.* (Source: **Clear Intent.**).

1972 - Prague.
At a secret meeting of European communist leaders in Prague, Brezhnev lays out firm statement of Soviet intent to be able to dominate the world by 1985. Stated would control the oceans, 90% of the land, and the air and space above. *Notice he said control, not invade and conquer.*

Aug 73 - Over ocean.
USAF Minuteman ICBM is launched from Vandenberg AFB, aimed for Kwajalein missile range. Unidentified object appears and is tracked next to the ICBM's nose cone. Crossed the RV's trajectory. Object about 10 ft long. Seen by 2 separate radars. Three other identical objects were seen in the vicinity. *Probable Soviet advanced flying vehicles. Also a deliberate stimulus to see if U.S. knows of the technology, and how the U.S. reacts. (Source:* ***Clear Intent.****).*

18 Oct 73 - Near Mansfield, Ohio.
U.S. Army helicopter is intercepted by glowing red object that converged on it with terrific speed. Object placed some sort of "tractor beam" on helicopter. Object was gray metallic structure, 50-60 ft long. Helicopter was stopped in mid air. Radio blacked out. Official report filed by pilot. *Probable advanced Soviet flying vehicle. Also a deliberate stimulus to see if U.S. knows of the technology, and how the U.S. reacts.*

21 Oct 73 - Near St. Joe, Indiana.
20 or 30 lights sighted circling in the sky near St. Joe, Indiana near a woods fire, by firemen. *Probable Soviet holographic tests to stimulate UFO reports.*

1973 to date - Bennett Island.
Bennett Is. exhaust plumes detected by U.S. weather satellites. *Well over 100. spotted so far. Weirdly, 5 islands and part of the continental Alaskan area are in process of being secretly given to the USSR; Bennett Island is one of them.*

May 1974 - Lake Michigan.
Blue-green glowing ball of light seen to fall into Lake Michigan. *Soviet scalar EM testing.*

8 July 74 - Lake Okeechobee, Florida and Atlantic Ocean.
Orange red ball of light lights up sky over south Florida. Crashes in area of Lake Okeechobee. Was accompanied by a large boom. Several other booms 5-7 min. after "object crashed." Pilots also saw object plummeting in from over Atlantic. *Probable Soviet scalar EM weapons testing and calibration.*

Nov. 74 - Saryshagan. USSR.
Construction of Tora facility begins at Soviets' Saryshagan test facility. Believed to be directed energy facility. *Probably connected with Soviet scalar EM weapons systems development.*

Oct? 74 - Antarctic.
Ozone hole over Antarctic first detected. Did not appear in measurements from 1957-1973. Note did not appear until exhaust plumes noted from and around Bennett Island, with substantial activity. *Looms over the continent every Oct. Diminishes through Mar. More severe each year since 1974.*

1975 - USSR.
Soviet article in **International Life** speaks of weather war, changing the nature of lightning, increasing the power of lightning, and directing electric charges of tremendous power against specified targets. "Atmospheric electricity" can be used to suppress mental activity of large groups of people. *Tip of the iceberg. Unclassified reference to Soviet's scalar EM (energetics) weapon program. Note involvement of "lightning" in destruction of U.S. missiles a decade later.*

16 Feb 75 - Caribbean.
R.M.S. Carmania (UK) observes bright white circular light appear and rise to 20 degrees, leaving comet-like trail, circle and disappear. Repeated four more times at exact hourly intervals. *Soviet scalar EM weapons tests. May have been a shipborne device.*

13 June 75 - Kremlin.
Brezhnev calls for ban on frightful weapons of mass destruction. *Major speech. Repeated proposals to U.S. Senators.*

2 Jul 75 - Kremlin.
Brezhnev repeats his proposed ban on development of frightful new weapons, to a group of U.S. Senators. *To visiting U.S. Senators. No one knew what he was talking about.*

Aug. 1975 - Kremlin.
Ponomarev calls for ban on frightful new weapons of mass destruction. *To visiting Congressmen.*

23 Sep 1975 - United Nations.
Gromyko presents draft agreement to UN General assembly, for banning development of frightful new weapons. *30th session of UN Gen. Assy. No one knew what the Soviets meant.*

Oct - Dec 75 - Satellite, over the Indian Ocean.
U.S. satellites illuminated or "blinded" over the Indian ocean. *Source 10-1,000 times as strong as natural sources. 5 incidents. One 4 hrs. long. Soviets wasted no time after Sep. fiasco.*

28 Oct to 11 Nov 75 - Mid-U.S. and Canada.
Series of "UFO's" seen at Malstrom AFB, Montana; Loring AFB, Maine; Minot AFB, North Dakota; Wurtsmith AFB, Michigan and Canadian Forces Station, Falconbridge, Ontario, Canada by reliable military personnel. Reported to NORAD. Some objects seemed like helicopters. Radar tracked objects. One object at 72,000 ft. was 100-ft sphere, with seeming "craters" around it.
Malstrom F-106's scrambled on one object but could not close on it in darkness and low altitude. Efforts by Air Guard helicopters, SAC helicopters and NORAD F-106's were fruitless. Probable Soviet activity in and around the SAC bases and Canadian radar site. (Source: **Clear Intent**.).

30 Oct 75 - Wurtsmith AFB, Michigan.
UFO's and "unidentified helicopters" sighted (multiple incidents) at or near Wurtsmith Air Force Base, Michigan. Helicopter hovered over the weapons storage area. Radar reported low-flying objects. Returning KC-135 tanker a/c diverted to intercept one UFO. Observed two objects, unable to close. Visual and radar contacts. Low on fuel, KC-135 returned to base to land, again seeing lights over the weapons storage area. (Source: **Clear Intent.**) *Soviet Activity.*

7 Nov 75 - Near Lewiston, Montana.
Giant glowing disc, football field sized, hovered over Minuteman missile launch site K-7, just south of Lewiston, Montana. When it rose to 1,000 ft., NORAD radar picked it up. Two F-106's were scrambled. UFO rose to 200,000 ft. and disappeared from NORAD radars. *Probable advanced Soviet flying vehicle, using antigravity propulsion system.* (Source: **Clear Intent.).**

Nov 75 - Semipalatinsk, USSR.
Large amounts of gaseous hydrogen with traces of tritium begin to be detected by USAF/TRW early warning satellites.
Nuclear debris apparently related to nuclear facility at Semipalatinsk labelled PNUTS (possible nuclear underground test site.) Probable large scalar EM development and test site.

Jan 76 - Cannon AFB, New Mexico.
Two UFO's reported near flight line at Cannon AFB, New Mexico. 25 yards in dia., gold or silver in color with blue light on top, hole in the middle and red light on bottom. Observed and reported by security police. (Source: **Clear Intent.**). *Probable Soviet activity.*

31 Jan 76 - Eglin AFB, Florida.
MG Lane, CG, Armament and Development Test Center, Eglin AFB, Florida reported a UFO sighting near an Air Force Radar site from 0430 to 0600 Eastern Standard Time. Photographs were taken. Later press release called it "building lights." (Source: **Clear Intent.**) *Probable Soviet Scalar EM activity.*

1976 - U.S. Embassy, Moscow.
State Dept. declares U.S. Embassy in Moscow an unhealthful post. Installs Aluminum window screens against Soviet microwave radiation, which has been underway since 1950's.
Provided 20% pay extra differential. Embassy radiated with weak microwave radiation since 1950's. Two U.S. Ambassadors died, Stoessel ill with strange leukemia-like malady. Soviet stimulus to see if we knew about scalar electromagnetics, phase conjugate waves, and EM disease induction. (Stoessel died recently of cancer).

1976 - U.S.
Soviet nuclear scientist named Rudakov visits U.S., proposes cooperative effort in some areas of fusion research. Showed work he had

been doing and results obtained. U.S. officials reacted drastically, classified his talk as top secret, even ripped off blackboard and carried it away.*Very strange incident. Soviet open, public scientific work considered Top Secret by the U.S. One wonders why.*

30 Mar 76 - Netherlands.
Huge atmospheric boom occurs over northern part of Netherlands. *Through 1983, in 10 years 7 events took place.*

22 Jun 1976 - North Atlantic.
Expanding white sphere of light developed for about 10 min. then faded. Other associated light phenomena observed. *Seen and logged by passing ship.*

4 Jul 76 - Soviet Union.
Giant Soviet Woodpecker transmitters activated. *3-30 MHz band. Worldwide interference with communications.*

30 Jul 76 - Fort Ritchie, Maryland.
Several UFO's sighted in and around Ft. Ritchie, Maryland. One hovered over the ammunition storage area. Reported. *Temperature inversion at the time provided a convenient pseudoexplanation. Could not have caused the incidents.* (Source: **Clear Intent.**)

10 Sep 76 - Lithuania.
European Airways flight 831, Moscow to London, at 31,000 ft over Lithuania sees blinding single ball source of light at constant altitude about 5-6,000 ft. below them and above a lower cloud. *Pilot contacted Soviet authorities. Received negative response and suggestions he should not ask questions. Probable deliberate stimulus of flight so, from reports to British authorities, could ascertain whether Britain knew anything about scalar EM weaponry.*

19 Sep 76 - Near Teheran, Iran.
In early morning hours, UFOs were spotted north of Teheran, Iran. Two F-4's attempted to intercept. The first lost all communications and instrumentation at 25 miles distance. When the F-4 turned away, equipment was restored to functioning. Second F-4 acquired radar lock at 27 nm. and attempted to close. Object moved to stay at 25 nm distance. Second object came out of it, headed straight for the F-4. F-4 attempted to fire AIM-9 missile and at that instant weapons

control panel and communications went off. F-4 took evasive action. A third object was seen to emerge from first. The F-4 returned to base. Each time it passed through 150 degrees magnetic bearing, it lost communications and INS fluttered 30 to 50 degrees. A civilian airliner also experienced loss of communications in the vicinity. *Signatures of scalar electromagnetic weapons and antigravity.*

1976 - Soviet Union, Sweden.
Swedish national authorities detect anomalous radionuclides — similar to those from nuclear explosions — over Sweden. No accompanying seismic activity. Correlated with known Soviet activity at Semipalatinsk. *In other words, nuclear explosions were occurring, but they did not shake the earth. Total anomaly. Indicates transformation of the explosive energy. Positive signature.*

1976 - Philadelphia.
Legionnaires Disease precipitously strikes Legionnaires attending convention in downtown Philadelphia. Kills 34, makes 187 others seriously ill. Similar malady struck Odd Fellows convention at same hotel in 1974. *Odd person with apparent transmitter and antenna was expelled. Informed members: "It's too late! You are all dead!" Probable scalar EM conditioning of convention with an immune suppression pattern for the disease.*

21 Jan 77 - Columbia.
Columbia A/L Avianca night flight. Instruments went haywire. Saw enormous, zigzagging glowing light, traveled at fantastic speed back and forth. Blinked landing lights, UFO responded. Sped away at incredible speed. *Probable Soviet advanced performance antigravity flying vehicle. Such have been widely sighted over South America.*

3 Mar 77 - Columbia.
Columbia A/L Avianca night flight. Pilot abruptly changed course to circle a huge, glowing UFO. Object had cigar-shaped fuselage and was twice as big as the aircraft. Blinked lights, UFO responded. Sped away. Air traffic control radar tracked object at ten times the speed of normal aircraft.
Probable Soviet advanced performance antigravity flying vehicle. Such have been widely sighted in South America.

24 Mar 77 - Off coast of Spanish Sahara, Africa.
M.V. Kinpurnie Castle, off coast of Spanish Sahara, Africa, observes complex, dynamic light phenomena. Third phenomenon was the formation of a semi-circular area of moderate luminosity, a hemisphere of light. Took 3 min to form about a previous luminous patch. Then another luminous patch formed over the hemisphere. After about 7 min., phenomena dispersed. *Soviet test of Tesla shield and globes.*

11 Jun 77 - Moscow, USSR.
Soviet biophysicist hands Robert Toth, Los Angeles Times journalist, a report containing proof that certain particles existed in cells, carried information, and were radiated. Both seized by KGB and charged with possessing Soviet state secrets. Interrogated, released. *Neither knew what they actually had. Soviet Academician I.M. Mikhailov pronounced secret such phrases as "micro-organism self-radiation... by means of vacuum particles in space." Use of such particles was discussed, and was secret. Paper contained basis of Soviet energetics use in biology. Positive connection of Soviet classification to mitogenetic radiation and scalar EM waves ("vacuum particles" indicate virtual flux structuring).*

13 July 77 - New York.
Massive electrical blackout strikes New York City. Affects 8 million persons. Staggering series of "natural" electrical shocks, mechanical failures, and human errors occurred. Anomalous "lightning strokes" supposedly initiated the collapse of the power grid. *Probable Soviet test.*

1977 - Ocean off Yugoslavia.
M.V. Dolphin, between Yugoslavia and Israel, observed extensive light balls and repeated phenomena, appearing and disappearing. Men were disoriented. Compass was disrupted. Okay after the phenomena dispersed. *Probable Soviet test. Stimulus to see if Britain recognized the weaponry and knew anything about it.*

13-14 Dec 1977 - Leitchville, Australia.
Large aerial light plus 3 smaller ones observed for four hours by multiple persons. Lights simulated activity of a "mother ship" and smaller craft assigned. Changed colors. Then a shower of orange

lights occurred. *Probable Soviet test. Part of deception plan, to create "UFO" phenomena to hide weapons testing. TR wave holography.*

Dec 77 to Jan 78 - Off East U.S. Coast.
Mysterious atmospheric explosions occur off U.S. Atlantic Coast. *Some accompanied by light phenomena. Soviet tests and calibration (registering the long-range artillery, so to speak.)*

13-14 Dec 77 - Leitchville, Australia.
Large arrays of light phenomena sighted by multiple witnesses. *Probable Soviet creation. Reported as "UFO" phenomena. Holographic creation of "UFO" phenomena as part of deception plan to disguise tests of the weapons worldwide. TR wave holography.*

1977-78 - North Pacific Ocean.
Two huge hot spots in North Pacific ocean, 2,000 mi by 1,200 mi. *May have caused El Nino and one of most severe winters on record. May have been caused by Soviets as a weather experiment.*

27 Jan 78 - U.S. East Coast.
Boeing 727 off east U.S. coast experiences engines failing, 1 at a time, in all three engines. A/c plunges 8,000 feet; engines restart one at a time. *First time ever that all three engines on a 727 had failed. Probable Soviet test.*

Feb 78 - Rocky Mtns. NW of Las Vegas.
Four aircraft crash in a 6-day period in the rugged Rockies, NW of Las Vegas. *Connected with a crashed military a/c from Nellis AF Base. Should be further investigated.*

Feb 78 - Texas coast. Nova Scotia. Charleston, SC.
Atmospheric booms occur. *Multiple booms in Charleston. Soviet tests. Scalar EM weapons.*

2 Apr 78 - Bell Island, Nova Scotia.
Mysterious fireball, explosion accompanied by anomalous electrical effects. *Small bldgs blown apart, trees scorched, fireballs seen. Probable Soviet test. Apparently even registered on U.S. satellite.*

10 May 78 - Off Florida.
Women pilots in race experience anomalous "time loss" on their watches from Fort Myers to Freeport (Bahamas). *39 pilots. Watches synchronized. Up to 3 min. lost. Definitely not normal EM effect. Probably due to sporadic natural scalar interferometry and time-reversed waves generated in area from time to time. "Bermuda Triangle" mechanism?*

May 78 - Florida.
Unexplained lighted objects sighted in sky over remote sector of Florida. Tracked on radar at a Navy EW center. Naval personnel also observed them through binoculars. *Probable Soviet advanced flying vehicles, or tests of intense holograms with energy sufficient to ionize air and reflect radar.*

18 May 78 - England.
Several atmospheric explosions shake houses over a wide area in Hull, Scunthorpe, Holderness coast, and Brough and Grimsby. *Probable Soviet weapon testing and calibration.*

Jun 78 - Indiana.
Large ball of light streaks across sky, stops, hovers, then explodes with a large boom. *Possible test. Standard Soviet incident to generate deception.*

7 Sep 78 - Netherlands.
Large acoustical event (boom) occurs over the Netherlands. *Soviet scalar EM weapons testing and calibration.*

Sep 78 - Tabas, Iran.
Anomalous Richter 7.4 earthquake strikes Tabas, Iran, killing 25,000. No aftershocks. Anomalous depth. Soviets needed to relieve pressure in rocks at nearby Askhabad on the Soviet/Iran border, else lose the city to a large earthquake. *36 hrs. earlier, Soviets exploded monstrous 10 Megaton underground nuclear explosion, to disguise what caused the earthquake. Almost definitely a Soviet- induced earthquake.*

Oct. 78 - USSR.
U.S. DOD weather satellite purportedly photographs a semi-rectangular object climbing out of atmosphere at 4,000 to 4,500 mph.

Object was over the Soviet Union. *Probable Soviet advanced flying vehicle, using antigravity propulsion system, if photograph is real.*

31 Oct 78 - Fairbanks, Alaska & Lake Ontario.
Red and yellow flash seen descending through sky S. of Fairbanks, Alaska by multiple observers. One minute later, U. of Alaska seismograph registered a tremor 1.5-2.0 on Richter scale. Ten days prior, a similar phenomenon was observed over Lake Ontario and a photo taken of the light. *Probable Soviet scalar EM wpns testing calibration.*

Nov 78 - Kuwait.
Large flying vehicle lands at Umm. Alaish oil pumping sta., Kuwait. Disrupts elect. comm, and pumping activities. Leaves after 7 min. *Probable antigravity propulsion system. Soviet vehicle. One of a series of "UFO" sightings in oil fields of Kuwait. Positive scalar electromagnetics and time-reversed wave signatures.*

Nov - Dec 1978 - Kuwait.
Series of "UFO" incidents over Kuwaiti oil fields occur. Kuwait Gov't. investigates, makes official report. *U.S. Pentagon noted incidents. Probable Soviet-induced incidents.*

1979 - British Columbia & Caspian Sea.
Ariel 6 satellite experiences anomalous turnoff of two power supplies. *Over British Columbia and Caspian Sea, when sun is shining. Probable Soviet stimulus.*

Jun 79 - Vienna.
Pres. Carter signs SALT II agreement in Vienna. After that, his acts and speech are erratic and he seems to be in a depressed state. *Suggestive of exposure to EM behavior modification. Soviets had possessed the LIDA technology for 29 years.*

Sep 1979 - USSR.
Strange giant semicircular light phenomena observed in USSR, toward Saryshagan. Observed several times. Source: London **Times.** *Observed from Afghanistan by British cameraman Nick Downie. Definitely Soviet tests of a Tesla globe and / or shield.*

22 Sep 79 - South Atlantic.
U.S. Vela satellites detect anomalous flash over South Atlantic, as if from a nuclear event. *U.S. Govt Agencies still disagree as to whether this was a nuclear event or not. May have been a Soviet test, or a test of a scalar EM weapon by another nonhostile country.*

25 Dec 79 - Afghanistan.
Soviets invade Afghanistan. *This is the Soviet "Spanish Civil War," where wpns, training, and the state of their ready reserves are tested. It is not primarily the regulars who are fighting there. Some scalar weapons -- e.g. Smirch death ray -- are tested also.*

1980 - Afghanistan.
Soviets kill 225 women and children in a village in the province of Maiden, near Kabul, Afghanistan. A month and a half later, bodies still undecayed. Bodies were also shot, to try to deceive Mujaheddin as to cause of death. *Bodies perfectly preserved. No smell, no bugs, no scavengers had eaten them. Probable Soviet test of a "death ray." Definitely scalar electromagnetic weapon signature.*

Feb 1980 - Duncanville, Texas.
About 100 startlings suddenly start falling from flight, instantly dead. *One of several such anomalous bird falls. Connected with very high frequency components added to Woodpecker signals for sharp localization. Birds entering such an area are killed.*

May 1980 - Seminole, Florida.
Start of mysterious plague of assorted illnesses striking healthy persons in a 20-block section of Seminole, Florida. Animals affected also. Lack friendly bacteria in their intestines. *Signatures of EM induction of disease and kill of intestinal bacteria. The lack of friendly bacteria is important. May indicate one direction of biological warfare planned by Soviets.*

June 1980 - USSR.
Huge, luminous hemisphere of light seen within Soviet Union, from Kuwait. Probably over Caucasus region of USSR. Source: personal communication from observer. *Tesla shield. A definite test, unequivocal.*

July 1980 - U.S. and Canada.
Richter 5.1 quake centered in northern Kentucky rumbles through 14 states and into Canada. *No known fault. Was predicted two wks in advanced by an associate.*

7 Nov 80 - Applegate Valley, Oregon.
Mysterious explosion, earth rumbling, brilliant light turns night into day in Southern Oregon. *Associated with subsequent earthquake next day?*

8 Nov 80 - California.
Richter 7.5 earthquake off coast of Southern California. Shakes CA and Southern Oregon. *Note anomalous phenomena in S. Oregon the preceding day.*

Dec 1980 - South Atlantic.
U.S. Vela satellites detect another anomalous nuclear-like flash over the South Atlantic. *In infrared only. Obviously not a normal nuclear wpn.*

28 Dec 80 - South Atlantic.
Great bluish-white flash over the South Atlantic. Clear sky except 2 or 3 small cumulus clouds, one about 600 ft. above ship. *Possibly connected with the second Vela flash detection, or generated by the same system. One of many such incidents.*

1 Jan 81 - Somerset, Pennsylvania.
Pilots of two a/c report the descent of a bright, shiny object with fiery tail over Pennsylvania. Large boom rumbles across most of Western PA. *Possible Soviet scalar EM testing. Part of deception plan.*

Jan 81 - Minnesoto, Wisconsin, South Dakota.
Great skyflashes and rumbling noises occur around Morris, Minnesoto and Wisconsin and South Dakota. *Possible Soviet scalar EM testing. Part of deception plan.*

Feb 81 - San Jose California.
Two pilots menaced by 10 ft. dia. light which flew directly at aircraft over San Jose, CA airport. Plane climbed, light followed, then sped away. *Totally consistent with exercise of the Soviet Launch Phase*

Anti-bomber system's real-time holography aspects of the Woodpecker OTH radars.

6 May 81 - Fredericksburg, Maryland.
EC-135 a/c crashed near Fredericksburg, MD. Severe nose-down from 29,000 ft. Apparent loss of all power. At 5,000 ft., either fire or minor explosion occurred. At 1,500 large explosion destroyed the aircraft. *Possible Soviet test of OTH radar anti-bomber weapon system?*

Mid-81 - Afghanistan.
Soviet helicopters use mysterious, highly lethal agent in Afghanistan. Causes death so quickly victims do not have time to make the slightest move. Rpt by Jane's Defense weekly. Referred to as Smirch gas or Smert gas. *Probable test of a Soviet scalar EM "death ray."*

20-23 Jan., 1982 - Gander, Newfoundland.
"Object with red, green and yellow lights sighted in the Gander, Newfoundland area more than 36 times. Alternately hovered and darted in a complex "flight" pattern. *Possible real-time holographic phenomena produced by Soviet scalar EM weapons as part of the worldwide deception plan. Gander is a major "registration point."*

3 Feb 82 - Newfoundland.
Red and green flashing lights travelling across the horizon at 2,000 mph reported by 3 Armed Forces officers at Gander, Newfoundland. *Possible real-time holographic phenomena produced by Soviet scalar EM weapons as part of the worldwide deception plan. Possible major "registration point."*

Feb 82 - Ankasaray, Turkey.
Cluster of high, multiple lights pass over Turkish town of Ankasaray, 200 km. from Ankara. Dogs were disturbed also. *Possible real-time holographic phenomena produced by Soviet scalar EM weapons as part of the worldwide deception of plan. Gander is a major "registration point."*

Sep 82 - Ankara, Turkey.
Cluster of 10-14 high, multiple lights pass over Ankara, Turkey in clear night sky. Dogs were also disturbed. *Possible real-time holographic phenomena produced by Soviet scalar EM weapons as part of the worldwide deception plan.*

Early 82 - St. Petersburg, Florida.
Extended series of booms occur off coast of Florida, near St. Petersburg. *Continued lengthy period of time. Years of Soviet scalar EM interference grid adjustments have been registered in Florida and off St. Petersburg. Booms are so numerous that meetings of civil defense, federal, and state officials have been held.*

June 82 - Washington/Canada border and off-shore.
Extended series of booms occur over Pacific Ocean, centered about Port Angeles and Sequim near Washington state/Canadian border. *Persisted for several weeks. As many as 10 blasts per day. Fireballs and lights also seen. Soviet extended scalar EM tests.*

18 June 82 - Northern Pacific Ocean.
Two JAL flight crews observe large, yellowish-white globe of light over the North Pacific Ocean 700 mi. east of Hokkaido, Japan. Covered one fourth of the sky. Light gradually dimmed and disappeared. *Tesla globe. Definitely a Soviet weapons test.*

June 1982 - Red China.
Several Red Chinese giant light hemisphere and globe incidents. In one instance, a/c electrical power systems began to fail in several Red Chinese fighter a/c when encountering a huge hemisphere of glowing light. *Tesla globes. Tesla shields. Balls of light. Definitely Soviet weapons tests.*

24 Sep 82 - Maryland, New Jersey.
Anomalous airquakes off the coast of Cape May and Northern Maryland, and Atlantic City, New Jersey. *Adjustment of Woodpecker grid. Soviet tests. 3 weeks later also.*

14 Oct 82 - Maryland, New Jersey.
Anomalous airquakes off the coast of Cape May and Northern Maryland, and Atlantic City, New Jersey. *Adjustment of Woodpecker grid. Soviet tests. 3 weeks earlier also.*

16 Nov 82 - Delaware, New Jersey.
Five mysterious booms rock Sussex county, Delaware and southern New Jersey. *Adjustment of Woodpecker grid. Soviet tests.*

1983 - Loma Linda, California.
Photos and information about the Soviet LIDA machine released. 40 MHz carrier, complex waveforms. Induces catatonic state in humans and animals. *Shows consciousness can be affected by EM means. Was used on U.S. prisoners of war in Korea. Suggests similar capabilities are possible for Woodpecker. U.S. scientific community had said impossible. President Carter affected in Jun. 79?*

Early 1983 - Bennett Island.
Large exhaust plume detected coming from Bennett Island and vicinity, one on-shore and two offshore. Plume was 6 mi. wide, 155 mi. long and reached 23,000 ft in height. *U.S. weather satellites detected it. Nearly horiz. jet, 155 mi. long. Definitely not natural. At angle of perhaps 1.5 degree above horizontal.*

27 Sep 83 - England.
British RAF/Panavia Tornado aircraft loses all electrical power and crashes. *Possible Test? Tornado system is triplexed.*

22 Oct 83 - Off Okinawa.
Two a/c operating off U.S.S. Midway apparently lost w/o trace, about 127 mi. E. of Okinawa, under anomalous conditions. *Causes unknown. Additional data needed.*

8 Nov 83 - Western Europe.
Anomalous earthquake occurs in Western Europe. All foreshocks and aftershocks were missing. Called the "Leige" earthquake. Definite symptoms of manmade (Soviet) origin. *Large boom occurred over Netherlands the next day over 35,000 sq. km. area. Soviet scalar EM weapon testing.*

9 Nov 83 - Netherlands.
Large acoustic event occurs over Netherlands. Detected over 35,000 sq. km. First mistaken as a Dutch quake. *One day after the anomalous Leige quake. Soviet wpn testing.*

Dec 83 - Alma Ata.
Stored munitions exploded at Dolon (Soviet) airfield. 150 km south of Alma Ata. One of six that mysteriously exploded in 7 months. *May be evidence that another nation also has Scalar EM wpns, and*

is checking the Soviets. If so, probably was warning that Soviets also would suffer if they moved.

1984 - Novaya Zemlya.
First mysterious plume detected from Novaya Zemlya by U.S. weather satellites. Sometimes plumes are 200 mi. long. *Novaya Zemlya contains Soviet atomic facilities including weapon facilities.*

1984
Senior Soviet physicist G. Yu. Bogoslovsky publishes paper, "Generalization of Einstein's Relativity theory for the anisotropic space-time." Such Russian research published regularly. Would be impossible in U.S., where similar attempts meet discredit, humiliation, and rejection by leading U.S. physics journals and departments. *The West has decreed that general relativity must not be local, and above all must not be lab-bench experimental. Open Soviet publication indicative of experimental development of local space-time curvature technology.*

1982 - 84 - Florida (& elsewhere).
Airquakes, booms (hundreds). *16 counties, near coast.*

28 Jan 84 - Pennsylvania, New Jersey.
Bright orange light streaks across sky from Pa. to N.J.'s Cape May. Similar "fireball" explodes in Clementon. Two other sky explosions observed. *Possible Soviet activity. TR wave holography and pulses. Part of Soviet deception plan.*

Feb 84 - in space.
All three payloads of the Challenger flight fail. *2 commication satillites, 1 balloon.*

10 Feb 84 - Netherlands.
Large atmospheric boom occurs over Netherlands. *7 others thru 1983.*

29 Mar 84 - Bennett Island.
Bennett Island exhaust plume detected by U.S. weather satellite. *Over 100 such anomalous exhaust plumes detected there.*

9 Apr. 84 - S. of Kurils toward USSR.
Giant rapid cloud tower rose, then faded. Small semicir. halo of light replaced it. Halo expanded to full circle of light. Expanded to giant globe then faded. *Cloud 60,000 ft in 2 min. Light globe expanded to about 380 mi. dia. and center over 200 mi. high. Source:* ***Science*** *Journal. Definitely a Soviet test of multiple weapon modes.*

26 Apr. 84 - Bennett Island.
Bennett Island exhaust plume detected by U.S. weather satellite. *Over 100 such anomalous exhaust plumes detected there.*

May 84 - S.E. U.S.
Series of devastating storms breaks out over S.E. U.S. in early May. Tornadoes, large hail, downbursts. Some loss of life. Persisted through night into early morning hours. Several instances of rapid thunderstorm top warming were observed in satellite photography. Occurred near downbursts. Very heavy plume activity at Bennett Is. noted in Apr. and May, 1984. *Warming of tops of thunderstorms can produce downbursts. In literature. Note that Soviet scalar EM wpns can perform such top-warming of thunderstorm anvils, and induce downbursts on command.*

13 May 84 - Severomorsk, USSR.
Soviet missile storage facility at Severomorsk Naval Base on the Kola Peninsula 1450 km north of Moscow blows up in a series of vast explosions. Over 200 wounded. Soviet North Fleet lost about 1/3 of its missiles. Speculation of an "electromagnetic cause, possibly by reflection of radio waves from ionosphere." Detected by satellites; first thought to be nuclear explosion. *One of six such explosions of Soviet ammunition storage sites in a period of seven months. Definitely not accidental. Probably use of scalar EM weapons by another nation, not hostile to U.S., to warn the Soviets that they also will suffer if they move.*

15 May 84 - Bobrwjk Airfield.
Major blast occurs at Bobrwjk Airfield, 138 km SE of Minsk and the base of a Badger-equipped air-to-surface missile regiment of the Smolensk Air Army. 10 of the 11 ammo storage bldgs blow up and admin. and access control bldgs. are destroyed. Note that fires and explosions were still raging at Severomorsk, from 13 May event. *Same note as above.*

25 Jun 84 - Schuerin, East Germany.
Explosion occurs at an ammunition depot at Schuerin, south of Wismar in East Germany. Windows blown out within 10 mi. radius of depot. *Same note as above.*

27 Jul 84 - Kuril Islands.
Slowly expanding ball of light seen by Boeing 747 crew near the Kuril Islands. Expanded for 10 min. Shell was sharply defined. Light semi-transparent and nearly perfect half-circle. *Tesla globe. Bennett Is. exhaust plumes detected by U.S. weather satellite. Definitely a Soviet test. Related to 9 Apr. 84 incidents S. of Kurils.*

29 Aug 84 - Edwards AFB, California.
B-1 bomber prototype crashes in flight test about 10 mi. NE of Edwards AF Base.

1983-84 - Ireland.
For two years, freak lightning terrorizes villages of West Donegal, Ireland. Roofs stripped off, windows smashed, pipelines wrecked, telephones and TV's blown up. *No known cause for the anomalous lightning. Shows natural potential in area is disrupted.*

25 Dec 84 - Ireland.
Freak lightning continues in West Donegal, Ireland. Causes 3-day power blackout. *Extensive plume activity at Bennett Island.*

1985 - Worldwide.
After years of a superb safety record, airline industry suffers a series of disastrous crashes. 20 major air crashes occur worldwide, with more than 2,150 lives lost.

Early 85 - Worldwide.
KGB begins a worldwide campaign to blame the U.S. for starting the AIDS epidemic. *Effort continues. Disinformation; is believed in 3rd world.*

Jan 85 - San Diego, California.
U.S. Navy chaff caught by wind, blown in over San Diego. Power knocked out to 60,000 homes. *Symptoms of presence of Soviet scalar EM grid in San Diego area.*

7 Jan 85 - Cantrell, Alaska.
Cantrell, Alaska. Blinding white light passes in sky overhead, lights up sky and mountain range for 30-40 seconds for 16 mi. Est. 3-mi. altitude. *Probable Soviet test. Note that plume activity at Bennett Is. is heavy in Jan. 85.*

Feb 85 - Zimbabwe.
Zimbabwe suffering worst electrical storm season in history. Death toll up to 116. 21 persons killed by a single bolt in one case. *Anomalous lightning. Shows natural potential in area disrupted.*

17 & 18 Feb 1985 - Anchorage, Eklutna Flats, Northway, Alaska.
Several anomalous lights and sky booms incidents in Alaska. Skyflashes, balls of light, booms, etc. Seen both from ground and by pilots of aircraft. *Probable Soviet realtime holography tests as part of worldwide deception plan.*

19 Feb 85 - Out from San Francisco, California.
China Airlines Flight 006 Boeing 747 enroute to Los Angeles. Engines fail. A/c falls 32,000 ft. in 2 min. Restarts engines, lands at San Francisco. *Note previous incidents over Alaska on 17 & 18 Feb. Probable Soviet test of launch phase anti-bomber system capability of woodpecker transmitters.*

10 Mar 85 - Tblisi & Tallin, USSR.
Soviet Academy of Sciences announces an Aeroflot a/c had been followed by a UFO for 800 mi. *Soviets occasionally produce light phenomena in their own territory and near Soviet a / c as part of their deception plan. They do not wish to appear different.*

1 May 85 - Near Nashville (monitoring station).
In and around May Day 1985, the Soviet Union held a giant exercise of all its strategic scalar EM weapons. 27 "power taps" into the earth — each two frequencies 12 KHz apart — were activated. The earth was thus in forced gravitational resonance beneath our feet on 54 frequencies. Each tap estimated to power up to six of the giant weapons; thus over 100 major strategic scalar EM weapon transmitters were activated. Frequency bands were filled with scalar EM transmissions, command and control, including to subs on station underwater. *Frank Golden monitored this startling giant exercise, which was probably held for Gorbachev, and this author observed it by courtesy of Golden's special detection equipment. Thus the Soviets*

met the 1985 timetable established by Brezhnev in 1972 at a secret meeting in Prague of European Communist leaders. Western nations do not appear to have the equipment to monitor scalar EM emissions, and so Western intelligence agencies are believed to have totally missed this giant exercise and its significance. At conclusion, two power taps (four frequencies) were left in the earth to power "ready firing batteries," so to speak.

11 Jun 85 - Lanzhou, China.
China B747 crew encounters a huge, expanding yellowish glow of light, with very intense spot at center. *Probable Soviet test.*

11 Jun 85 - Mongolia.
Chinese jumbo jet, Peking to Paris flight, encounters giant "UFO" light form over Mongolia. 10 km. wide. Lit sky for 50 km. Extremely bright spot at center. Paced aircraft for 2 minutes. *Probable Soviet test. Soviet operator tracked a / c exhaust with long range antibomber system. Added giant light form for deception, and to create UFO reports, which are largely ignored.*

23 Jun 85 - Iowa, Nebraska, Kansas, Illinois, Kentucky.
Thunderstorms over Iowa, Nebraska and Kansas organized into single circular pattern rainstorm 200,000 sq. km. in area. Declined until dawn, then rejuvenated to unleash severe weather over Illinois and Kentucky. *Such organization never before had been seen. Now called "mesoscale convective complex." Shows unique new weather pattern involving giant organization.*

2 Aug 85 - Dallas/Ft. Worth, Texas.
Delta Airlines flight 191, a Lockheed L-1011, encounters microburst while approaching runway at Dallas/Ft. Worth International Airport. Crashes and kills 134 of the 163 persons on board. *While such microbursts occur in nature, this was during a period of intense Soviet scalar EM activity. Note that warming the tops of thunderstorm anvil causes a downburst. May have been just accident. May have been test.*

23 Aug 85 - Italy, Adriatic Coast.
More than 28 "UFO" sightings reported along Italy's Adriatic coast soon after midnight. Light phenomena. *Probable Soviet test. Part of deception plan. Scalar EM holography (real-time).*

28 AUG 85 - Vandenberg AFB, California.
Titan B fails after launch at Vandenberg AFB, California. Believed to have carried sensitive U.S. satellite. *Suspicious.*

Sep 85 - Kourou.
Ariane rocket explodes at Kourou. 3rd stage engine failed to ignite properly, forcing loss of power. Destruct then ordered. *French officials suspect Soviet sabotage. Probable Soviet test.*

Sep/Oct 85 - Cape Canaveral, Florida.
Anomalies observed on two U.S. shuttle launches by NASA. *No action taken; NASA does not recognize scalar EM weapons capabilities nor testing over its Cape Canaveral launch site. Nor does it connect the mysterious "booms" that have rocked the Florida coast for several years with the Soviets or with the anomalies noted on its two shuttle launches, such as giant booms.*

2 Sep 85 - Mexico City, Mexico.
Worst hailstorm in 50 yrs. strikes Mexico City, leaving some streets more than a foot deep in ice. 1-hr pelting. 25 bldgs collapsed. 4,000 roofs heavily damaged. 1 killed, 185 injured. Power blacked out . *May have been due to extensive Soviet long range weather engineering. 17 days prior to suspicious giant Mexican earthquake.*

5 Sep 85 - Australia.
Premier Wran, Australia, along with Minister of Agriculture Hallam, observe a brigh spherical "UFO" from their government jet. It was photographed. Radar contact showed object at 100,000 ft. *Probably Soviet advanced performance antigravity flying vehicle.*

18 Sep 85 7:15 p.m. - Catalina Is. Channel Is.
Cookman observes giant cloud radial, awesome to behold, between Catalina and Channel Islands, off California coast.
18 "funnel" strobes, dynamically boiling. Activity indicates great energy poured into earth and atmosphere. Mexican quake the next morning. Indicator of Soviet scalar EM connected to quake.

19 Sep 85 7:18 a.m. - Mexico City, Mexico.
Large earthquake strikes Mexico City, causing great damage. Largest of several. *Preceded wks earlier by giant anomalous hailstorm. Evening before, giant radials showed extensive Soviet power*

transmission activity. Positive indications of Soviet test.

8-9 Nov 85 - Ventura County, California.
Highly anomalous power blackout in Carlisle Canyon, Ventura County, Calif. Accompanied by severe electrical anomalies totally beyond normal electromagnetics. *Investigated and reported by engineer Ron Cole, who lives in the area. TV, light, phone, electrical anomalies plus intermittent 29 Hz signals.*

Nov- Dec 85 - California.
Mysterious hum continues to baffle people at Pacific Heights, Calif. and Marina district on San Francisco Bay. Previously had had same hum. Note such hum in England persisting over long period. Note 8-9 Nov 29 Hz. anomalous elec. signal at Carlisle Canyon, Ventura County, CA. *Possible indications of Soviet scalar EM activity. Area appears to be one of Soviet register / test points.*

26 Nov 85 - Cape Canaveral, Florida.
Launch of space shuttle Atlantis from Cape Canaveral, Florida is accompanied with high anomalies. (1) Seconds before launch, Bob Gladwin inadvertently photographs nearby strike of what appears to be an electromagnetic missile, probably of Soviet origin. (2) Anomalous light is hanging in the sky, near the launch site: a marker beacon, placed there by the Soviet scalar EM weapon system being tested. Seen by hundreds of persons, and photographed by George Suchary. Printed in Fort Pierce **Tribune.** (3) 12 minutes after shuttle is launched, when it is well down range, a tremendous rumbling atmospheric boom occurs, heard 600 mi. up and down the East Coast. Marker beacon then slewed away by distant Soviet operator at high speed. *With offset EM missile strike, Soviets tested the weapon to be used on the Arrow DC-8 two weeks later at Gander AFB, Nfld. Marker beacon used in precise registration. Note it was evidenced again above the explosion of the Titan on 18 Apr. 86 at Vandenberg AFB. Boom is from energy induced over a large area; which can catch multiple missiles being launched, a large Naval task force at sea, or a whole flight of airborne bombers, fighters, or helicopters. Also can catch an entire organization on the ground, or an installation — wiping out all electronics, exploding explosives and ordnance, stunning or killing personnel, etc.*
Again hundreds of NASA engineers and scientists did not recognize what was happening at the site and over their own heads.

12 Dec 1985 - Gander, Newfoundland.
Arrow DC-8 crashes immediately after takeoff at Gander AFB, Newfoundland. Lost power just after takeoff; engines "rumbling" abnormally rather than roaring, according to eyewitness whom the a/c flew directly over, 100 ft up. Aircraft seen by three eyewitnesses to have an orange glow on it. Symptoms of negative energy introduced into engines, cancelling some of heat energy of the engines and seriously interfering with combustion process, causing loss of power. Glow may have been steady, small electromagnetic ball of energy against the aircraft, causing it to electrically charge and exhibit corona. Anomalous hole in right fuselage, just ahead of engines, as if from internal explosion; however, no explosive residue (it was tested). One other anomalous hole found. Wild swings of some instruments recording just at/after liftoff — ignored by investigation. *Note previous 36 light incidents in and around Gander, Jan. 1982. Gander Airport is major stopover for Soviets, and a major "registration point" for scalar EM weapons. Note anomalies in shuttle launch 2 wks earlier, and apparent actual test of the small EM missile then, offset so as not to destroy that shuttle.*

Aircraft crew one of Arrow's best. Aircraft should have flown okay, if not interfered with. Serious indications that the DC-8, with over 250 U.S. soldiers and air crew, was deliberately destroyed by test of a Soviet launch-phase antibomber system.

Note metal-softening Soviet signal detected on 1 Jan 86 by Frank Golden may actually have been on the Woodpecker transmissions on Dec 12, 1985. This metal-softening signal probably played a part in the destruction of the Challenger on 28 Jan 86.

1 Jan 86 - Near Nashville, Tennessee.
Frank Golden discovers a metal-softening signal on the Soviet Woodpecker interference grid. Performs experiments to verify the metal-softening ability of the signal. *Signal is of such a nature that only Golden's instrumentation could have detected it. He then scalarly cancelled the signal to totally prove it.*

24 Jan 86 - Ventura, California.
Engineer Ron Cole observes and sketches a giant grid cloud pattern over Ventura, Calif. at 11:45 p.m. PST. Giant cloud fingers, separated from each other, formed the crossed-grid pattern. *Shows Woodpecker scalar EM power very high and active.*

26 Jan 86 - Northern California.
Strong quake hits Northern Calif. 5.5 on Richter scale. Hollister area, about 120 mi. south of San Francisco. Several power outages in southern Bay area, where quake knocked out transformers, downed 21,000 V. power line, and set off burglar alarms. *May have been induced by Soviet scalar EM transmitters.*

26 Jan 86 - Los Angeles, California.
In greater Los Angeles area, Margaret Wilson observes 3 classic giant radial clouds form at 10 min. intervals: 1:15, 1:25, and 1:35 p.m. Appeared one after the other, till all three were there. Last one lasted about two hours, gradually distorting. *Shows a great amount of structuring to capture and turn the jetstream, to direct cold weather to the Florida Panhandle and catch the Challenger before its impending launch, exposing it to drastic cold conditions. Definitely Soviet engineered.*

27 Jan 86 - Santa Monica, California.
On evening prior to the Challenger disaster, Al Matthews photographs a strange bar-grid cloud formation, absolutely rectangular bars, from the Los Angeles freeway. Pattern approx. over Santa Monica Bay, due north of Catalina Island. Edges and ends very straight, as if drawn in sky by a giant draftsman. *Shows severe high frequency content, and fine-point localization of Soviet scalar EM transmitters, in preparation for forthcoming launch of the ill-fated Challenger.*

27 Jan 86 - Florida Panhandle.
Avalanche of freezing air temperatures to record lows across the Southeast. Low temperature records set all across the South. Jetstream bent far south, across Florida Panhandle. *Definitely caused by Soviet weather engineering. Preceeded by giant radial cloud signatures in "hinge" areas of Los Angeles and Huntsville, Alabama, showing steering of jetstream.*

28 Jan 86 - Cape Canaveral, Florida.
Low temperature records shattered all across the South. Into 30's in Florida and into teens elsewhere. *Definitely result of Soviet weather engineering, and definitely directed against the Challenger rocket on the launch pad.*

28 Jan 86 - Off Florida Coast.
About 4 hr. before the launch of the Challenger, all Soviet ships off-coast, which normally monitor shuttle launches, suddenly depart at high speed. *Soviets do not want any suggestion that the ships' radars and transmitters may have interfered with the Challenger launch. Total anomaly. Unprecented event.*

28 Jan 86 - Cape Canaveral, Florida.
National radio and TV newsmen comment on the highly unusual fact that no birds are flying in the launch area. *Reason: For severe localization, high frequency content of the scalar EM signals had been drastically increased. A bird's brain will detect and resonate to this energy, if the wavelength approaches the diameter of its brain. This resonance will cause great pain and / or death of the bird. Thus the birds flee the area when this begins to occur — or they die. When birds accidentally fly into such a high frequency scalar EM signal, their nervous systems are instantly jammed. They die and fall from the sky.*

28 Jan 86 - Cape Canaveral, Florida.
Space shuttle Challenger, launched from Cape Canaveral after exposure to cold weather conditions, disastrously explodes. Booster seal problem. Encounters air turbulence during launch, at most critical altitude. *Soviet metal-softening signal has been added to grid. Extreme localization in area because of high frequency content added; shown by birds having vacated the area. Anomalous departure of Soviet ships off shore, 4 hrs. earlier. Three previous tests of the weaponry in that exact launch area, against the three previous shuttle launches. Kill of the Arrow DC-8 about 6-1/2 weeks earlier. Actual celebration by the KGB of perfect success of their active measures against the Challenger! U.S. space program crippled and set back severely.*

29 Jan 86 - Moscow.
At KGB headquarters in Moscow, the KGB holds a jubilant party to celebrate the perfect success of their active measures against the Challenger. *Note that Soviet scalar EM weapons — development, deployment, and use — are under the control of the KGB rather than the regular Soviet armed forces.*

31 Jan 86 - Mid-U.S.
Richter 5.0, Earthquake rattles 9 states and Great Lakes. *Possible test of weapon that killed the Challenger, in the earth transmission / earthquake induction mode.*

2-4 Feb 86 - Birmingham, Alabama.
In Birmingham, Alabama dead birds plummet from the air to the ground for three days. Blackbirds, cardinals, sparrows, bluebirds, etc. No trace of poison in carcasses. *Only a few days after kill of the Challenger. To divert the jetstream further south and hit Florida, the Soviets had moved the normal "hinge pin"—where scalar EM energy, either positive or negative, is focussed—from Huntsville to Birmingham. Hinge pin area was still activated. The high frequencies used for extreme localization against the Challenger were lethal to birds. Therefore birds that inadvertently flew into this zone were instantly killed and dropped from the sky.*

10 Feb. 86 - Europe.
Super Frelon (French) helicopter crashes, with 11 killed. Aeronautique Navale aircraft. Part of a spate of crashes of French military aircraft in four months (through June 86). *Defense Minister Andre Giraud launched a special investigation.*

23 Feb 1986 - Irish Sea.
Over the Irish Sea in an airplane, England's Prince Charles sights a brilliantly glowing, red object hovering near them. His pilot reports the object to air traffic control. Four other aircraft traveling through that area radioed similar reports. *Probably either a Soviet craft or a Soviet holographic scalar EM demonstration as part of the overall deception plan, and / or a stimulus to a member of the Royal Family to observe what action is taken by British Ministry of Defense. By actions, could ascertain whether or not Britain knew what was going on.*

30 Mar 86 - Ventura, California.
Engineer Ron Cole in Ventura CA observes significant cloud patterns, positively correlated with his measurements of the Soviet woodpecker transmissions. *Cloud pattern changes were directly correlated to signal changes on the Woodpecker. Shows cloud signatures can be indications of specific Woodpecker activity.*

31 Mar 86 - San Francisco, California.
Strong earthquake, Richter 5.3, rocks San Francisco Bay area. Third in region in 3 days. Three aftershocks within minutes. *Note correlation of Woodpecker activity previous day.*

31 Mar 86 - San Francisco, California.
Crew error on Delta flight accidentally shuts down engines after normal takeoff from San Francisco. Engines restarted. *Definitely a crew error. Possible human effects from earthquake energy in area. Same type incident on Jun. 30, 1987.*

3 Apr. 86 - Florida.
Loud boom shakes houses and rattles windows over Brevard County, Florida. One of a whole series over the years. Not far from Kennedy Space Center. *Soviet adjustment of scalar EM grid.*

Apr 86 - France.
French Armee de L'Air has lost two Jaguars and two Alphajets in April 86. Part of a spate of losses in 4 months, leading Defense Minister Giraud to launch a special investigation.

7 Apr 86 - Sacramento, California.
Charlotte King of Sacramento calls UPI and predicts a major earthquake will strike in Canada, Alaska, Aleutians, or Japan. She had predicted eruption of Mt. St. Helens in 1980. On Apr. 27th, she predicted quake that shook Mexico three days later.
Note that human brain is a scalar EM interferometer, capable of transmitting and receiving scalar EM waves. Unfortunately, not conscious — output of system is in deep unconscious. Some persons are more sensitive than others, and can detect the scalar activity from the increasing stress in rocks that is leading toward an earthquake. Charlotte King is such a person, having over an 80% accuracy of prediction of quakes. She will be able to detect the increasing stress in rocks, whether naturally or artificially induced.

9 Apr. 86 - Aleutian Islands.
Three quakes rock the Aleutian Islands. Predicted by Charlotte King on Apr. 7. *Documented prediction.*

18 Apr. 86 - Huntsville, Alabama; Thousand Oaks, California.
T.E. Bearden sees and photographs remnants of a giant radial cloud

in Huntsville, Alabama. Extensive Soviet woodpecker grid activity noted over Thousand Oaks, California by Engineer Ron Cole. *Both show increased scalar EM activity in the interference grid.*

18 Apr 86 - Vandenberg AFB, California.
USAF Titan 34-D rocket explodes nine seconds after launch from Vandenberg AFB, California. Video captured the Soviet marker beacon **(Aviation Week & Space Technology).** Engineer Ron Cole and team study video of the explosion frame by frame and verify the anomalous beacon light is present, is separate from the explosion, and moves away separately after the explosion. *Sensitive satellite believed on board the rocket. U.S. Space surveillance program crippled. Probable Soviet kill. TR wave adjunct with Woodpecker.*

25 Apr 86 - New Mexico.
NASA research rocket misfires over the New Mexico desert. No public announcement made at the time. Was first failure in 25 consecutive missions of the Nike-Orion rocket. Said NASA spokesman Kukowski: "It looks like we're snakebit."
Possible Soviet test kill.

25 Apr 86 - California; Chernobyl, USSR.
Bill Bise detects the sudden loss of the East-West Soviet woodpecker transmitter he is monitoring in the field, leaving the North-South transmitter. The failed transmitter was about 20-30 km. from Chernobyl.*The Soviet transmitter sites safety circuits go-in full, trying desperately to hold back the giant scalar EM standing-wave potential that has been built up, and slowly and safely drain it away into the earth. In alarm, Soviets shut down nearby reactors at Chernobyl. Any "flash discharge" escape as a flash-over pulse of the scalar EM potential will produce a giant EGP pulse into the earth. When this EGP pulse reaches the four reactors, they will violently explode, full-up nuclear, like giant hydrogen bombs — perhaps 1200 megatons equivalent. Later the Soviets will claim that the operators shut the plant down to do some "unauthorized experiments."*

26 Apr 86 - Chernobyl, USSR.
With the giant scalar EM standing wave almost all drained away, the safety circuits finally fail, dumping a small EGP into the earth. The nearest reactor at Chernobyl gets it, and the uranium fuel rods

suddenly go half-decayed, instantly heating and blowing out the reactor, destroying it. Nuclear radiation fallout spreads over much of Europe.

3 May 86 - Florida.
Delta 178-rocket destroyed by range safety officer at T + 91 after two anomalous power surges occurred in the rocket, causing premature shutdown of 1st stage Rocketdyne RS-27 engine 71 sec. into the flight, and rocket to go aerodynamically unstable. Previous 43 launches had been successful. Since 1960, 177 launches 94% successful. One of most reliable rockets ever built. *Soviet weapons test. One of a series. TR wave adjunct with Woodpecker.*

7 May 86 - Aleutian Islands.
Great earthquake measuring 7.7 Richter strikes Aleutian Islands. Centered about 100 miles SE of the island of Adak. Tsunami alert issued for the North Pacific, but no major waves ever materialize. Thousands evacuate coastal areas. *A U.S. researcher known to this author used a powerful scalar interferometer to block the tsunami. The researcher must remained unnamed.*

9 May 86 - Redstone Arsenal, Alabama.
All power on Redstone Arsenal, Alabama suddenly and mysteriously fails all at once. *Similar related incident on May 12. No explanation.*

12 May 86 - Huntsville, Alabama.
In Huntsville, Alabama — adjacent to Redstone Arsenal — on local radio program Feedback, public radio discussed the mysterious failure of all power on Redstone Arsenal on Fri., May 9, 1986 and requested that , if anyone knew why all circuits would go off at once, to please get in touch. *Immediately the station's radio transmitter went off the air! (Almost as if "Big Brother's listening to you!")*

18 May 86 - Dijbouti.
French Breuguet Atlantic aircraft crashes in Dijbouti, killing 19. *Part of spate of crashes of French military aircraft in 4 months that leads French Defense Minister to open special investigation.*

19 May 86 - Brazil.
Brazilian fighter jets are sent to chase multi-colored "ping- pong ball sized" UFO's in skies over Brazil. 4 jets, two Mirages and 2 F-5's

chased them at speeds of 840 mph. Tracked on radars. Chase lasted 3 hrs. Planes could not catch them; ran low on fuel and returned. Discussed on TV by Brazil's Air Force Minister Brig. Gen. Otavio Moreira Lima. *Soviet scalar EM holographic production; distant Soviet operators having fun and games as part of the deception plan, generating UFO incidents and reports?*

22 May 86 - California.
High-speed orange "X" object with lights seen above Sonoma CA before dawn. At one time the object slowed and hovered.

29 May 86 - Huntsville, Alabama.
Huntsville and Madison County, Alabama electrical power dipped momentarily and mysteriously, causing a seconds-long outage in businesses and homes, playing havoc with traffic signals and computer centers throughout the area. Some traffic signals continued to malfunction for 30-45 min. after power was restored, then mysteriously resumed normal functioning. Some phones also went out inexplicably, and many battery-powered radios went off, and were awry for seconds or minutes before recovering. *Obviously this was not caused by any kind of ordinary electromagnetics. Shows anomalous and high activity (pulsed) in the Soviet scalar EM grid (Huntsville AL. is a pivot point).*

30 May 86 - French Guinea.
Ariane 2 rocket fails because of a faulty ignition system for the third stage engine. Rocket destroyed by ground command 4-1/2 min. after launch from Kourou, French Guinea. The third stage has failed 3 times since start of Ariane's operations in 1979.
Possible Soviet test.

Tad Szulc, Washington journalist, implies that French Defense Minister Andre Giraud may have discussed the possibility of Soviet sabotage of the rocket with Washington.

May? 1986 - Straits of Gibralter.
USS Atlanta nuclear sub runs aground in Straits of Gibralter and suffers "serious damage," according to reports in Madrid. A hole was made in one ballast tank and the sonar wrecked.
Another U.S. nuclear sub ran aground within a month or so (earlier?) of this incident. Could something have interfered with their navigation systems underwater? Continued Soviet Scalar EM tests?

11-12 July - California.
Secret USAF crashes approx. 14 mi. NE of Bakersfield, CA along the Kern River. Site secured. Possible Stealth fighter. Crippled aircraft in trouble seen and photographed by Andy Hoyt, who turned photos over to USAF (properly so). Aircraft not on fire when came down. Did not explode in the air. *No information as to whether any Soviet scalar EM hanky-panky involved or not. Suspicious because follows a series of anomalous missile failures. Woodpeckers definitely have good anti-stealth capability.*

11 July 86 - Tennessee and Georgia.
Moderate quake with sonic boom shakes SE Tennessee and Northern Georgia. 3.7 on Richter scale. Centered just east of Chattanooga Tennessee on the TN/GA line.

12 July 86 - Michigan, Ohio, and Kentucky.
Mild quake in Michigan, Ohio, and Kentucky. 4.0 on Richter scale.

18 July 86 - Los Angeles, California.
Sharp aerial boom rattles Los Angeles Basin at about 0930 hrs. FAA and USAF unable to identify a potential source from an aircraft.

Aug 86 - Soviet Union.
Two huge new Soviet "radars" discovered on Western Soviet border by U.S. intelligence. One near Skrunda, on Lithuanian border. Other near Mukachevo, on the Czech border. *With phase conjugate adjuncts, represent significant strategic weapon system deployments.*

2 Sep 86 - Baltic Sea.
Finnish ferry Scandinavia in Baltic Sea observes a strong light rise from the sea near the Finnish Coast. After 3 to 4 seconds, a giant mushroom reached 500 feet into the sky and covered the moon. *Probable Soviet test.*

12 Sep 86 - Dallas, Texas.
Mysterious, powerful "explosion" rocks South Dallas. No source found or explained. No supersonic jets in area.

15 Sep 86 - Australia.
Katherine, Australia. Object with flaming orange tail moved from sky toward ground at 45 degree angle. Katherine's electrical power suddenly cut off and phone lines in the town disrupted. *Probable Soviet scalar EM generated.*

Oct-Nov 86 - Los Angeles, California.
Giant radial clouds observed in Los Angeles area.

Oct 86 - Reykjavik, Iceland.
Gorbachev and Reagan meet at Reykjavik, Iceland. Gorbachev proposes "zero option." *Seeks to get nuclear missiles removed, since they constitute "dead man fuzing" because of nuclear warheads, and severely limit pulse use of Soviet scalar EM weapons. Adamantly insists on bottling up SDI — because if space laser is converted to scalar EM laser, its power (effective) goes up about* 10^{20} *times, and single shot could devastate Russia.*

10 Oct 86 - Vandenberg AFB, California.
U.S. forced to scrub another missile launch when a USAF Scout satellite malfunctions during final countdown at Vandenberg AFB, Calif. *The booster's gyro system failed a checkout sequence at about T-5 hr. Scalar EM can inertially interfere also.*

13 Oct 86 - ABC News.
On Peter Jennings' ABC News show, Gennadi Gerasimov, Soviet spokesman, indicated that SDI as presently designed was of no concern to Soviets. Real concern is that U.S. will make a "great technical breakthrough" and deploy new, modified devices, presenting an unacceptable threat to the Soviet Union. *Here he is thinking of changing the laser to a scalar EM laser.*

6 Nov 86 - Albuquerque and Phoenix.
Power failures at Albuquerque air traffic control tower and a radar station near Phoenix, Arizona occur. Radar controlling high altitude air traffic from Texas Panhandle to southern California was knocked out for 40 min. First such incident in Albuquerque center. The Arizona radar was out for 59 hrs. *Note similar incident at Montreal on Nov. 11, 1986.*

10 Nov 86 - Huntsville, Alabama.
Three giant radial cloud formations in Huntsville, Alabama photographed by T.E. Bearden. One is a twin giant radial. *Shows heavy activity in scalar EM interference grid.*

10 Nov 86 - SE U.S.
Red glowing light with tail flares across sky in Southeast about sunset. Seen over parts of TN, AL, GA, MS. Ground searches conducted in several areas for possible crash. *Probable Soviet scalar EM activity. Note heightened activity in grid same day.*

10 Nov 86 - Near Nashville, Alabama: Hemet, California.
Frank Golden measures scalar EG field of earth — highly agitated and dynamic, about half as much as when Soviets induce earthquakes. Anomalous winter storm in progress. Cold records broken in Mid-U.S. Heat records broken in Florida. Storm penetrates very deeply southward. *Soviet weather engineering.*

11 Nov 86 - Canada.
Air traffic control radar in Montreal, Canada region broken down. Backup system employed. *Note similar occurrences to Albuquerque and Phoenix on Nov. 6, 1986.*

12 Nov 86 - Atlanta, Georgia.
Stationary arc (dome) of clouds sighted over Atlanta. Well defined lower edge. Upper edge irregular. Multiple witnesses. Clouds moved into top of dome and flowed around it. Very strange sight. *Probable Soviet "gentle test" of placing a suppressive covering over a distant U.S. city. Performed at night, at minimal level (no glow) so no great notice would be taken. Dome was stable against 20 mph winds and other moving clouds that collided with it.*

13 Nov 86 - Huntsville, Alabama.
Twin giant radial cloud observed moving over Huntsville, Alabama by T.E. Bearden. West to East. At nearly noon. At dusk, single giant radial cloud was also spotted over Huntsville.
Significant scalar EM activity in grid.

17 Nov 86 - off Alaska.
JAL Flight 1628 observes giant UFO while enroute from Reykjavik, Iceland on mid-leg of Europe to Tokyo. Crossed Beaufort Sea off

Alaska's north coast. Sighted flashing lights which moved alongside the aircraft. Pilot descended, so did light. Glimpsed craft in profile, twice as big as aircraft carrier. On board radar located it. USAF and civilian controllers reported brief radar echoes, but tapes did not show it. Approaching Fairbanks, Alaska. Pilot made 360 degree circle, object stayed with him. Finally disappeared as he was approaching Anchorage. *Probable Soviet test as part of deception plan. TR wave holography.*

27 Nov 86 - Fort Pierce, Florida.
Flash of light in sky and sonic boom occurred vicinity of Fort Pierce, Florida. *Probable Soviet EM test. Note that a classified payload was scheduled for launch in near future at Cape Canaveral nearby.*

4 Dec 86 - Huntsville, Alabama; Hemet, California.
Twin giant radials seen and photographed over Huntsville AL. Large radial cloud seen in skies over Hemet, Calif. and photo printed in **The Press Enterprise,** Hemet, CA 5 Dec 86.

4 Dec 86 - Cape Canaveral, Florida
Atlas/Centaur rocket successfully launched at Cape Canaveral, orbits a communications satellite for DOD. *The Soviets had to allow one or two of the missiles to succeed, else even the lethargic U.S. bureaucracy would have caught on. Grid activity indicates they probably just tracked it without the other goodies.*

5 Dec 86 - Vandenberg AFB, California.
MX ICBM launched from Vandenberg AFB. Two of RV's did not deploy although all impacted within the Kwajalein Missile Test Range. *Note: Soviets let one go from Vandenberg.*

21 Dec 86 - Huntsville, Alabama.
Twin giant radial photographed over Huntsville Alabama.

23 Dec 86 - Huntsville, Alabama.
Small flash in lower sky over Huntsville, Alabama observed by T.E. Bearden. Followed by faint boom. Momentary loss of power occurred in large area of Huntsville. Positive correlation between the aerial flash/boom and the loss of the power. *Soviet test.*

7 - 21 Jan 1987 - Florida.
Several giant radial clouds seen in vicinity of Fort Lauderdale, Florida. *Indicates substantial action in scalar EM grid.*

20 Jan 87 - U.S.
Highly unusual bend in jetstream. Completely down West Coast, curving east under Texas, NE along SE USA. *Shows great action in scalar EM grid. Significant weather engineering.*

20 Jan 87 - Vandenberg, AFB, California.
Minuteman missile destroyed in launch. *Note substantial action in scalar EM grid.*

23 Jan 87 - Huntsville, Alabama.
Bearden photographs twin giant radial over Huntsville AL. Cloud fades with great and unusual rapidity. A private-type jet, similar to a Learjet, continually circled under the strange twin radial cloud, as if observing and/or photographing it. *Perhaps someone in the U.S. system wised up.*

28 Jan 87 - Vandenberg AFB, California.
Minuteman missile successfully launched from Vandenberg AFB. Note: *Anniversary of the Challenger disaster.*

7 Feb 87 - Alabama - Tennessee border.
Loud aerial boom or explosion shakes area from Tennessee, New Market, Monte Sano through Huntsville Alabama area.

10 Feb 87 - Huntsville, Alabama.
Bearden photographs twin radial cloud in Huntsville, AL. Cloud stayed fixed, although winds present and other clouds moved. Note big storm in NE - Cape Cod, etc. *Associated with weather engineering.*

11 Feb 87 - Huntsville, Alabama.
Bearden photographs another twin giant radial in Huntsville, Alabama. *Shows activity in Woodpecker grid.*

Feb 87 - Vandenberg AFB, California.
USAF Titan launched from Vandenberg AFB, Calif.

12 Feb 87 - California.
Blue Angel F-18 a/c crashed near Brawley, CA. Fourth military air crash in the Imperial Valley since October. *Note Woodpecker grid activity on previous day.*

26 Feb 87 - Cape Canaveral, Florida.
GOES-H weather satellite launched from Cape Canaveral on a DELTA rocket.

26 Mar 87 - Cape Canaveral, Florida.
Stunning failure of an Atlas/Centaur rocket launched from Cape Canaveral. May have been hit by lightning. Failed suddenly 51 sec. after liftoff. Veered out of control and destroyed. *Note: Possible Soviet scalar EM involvement. Much to do later about multiple lightning strikes; very suspicious.*

June 1987 - Vandenberg AFB, California.
Minuteman 3 missile fired from Vandenberg AFB, Calif. is aborted and destroyed in flight. *Note similar incident in July.*

12 Jun 87 - Cape Canaveral, Florida.
Trident III launched successfully from flat pad.

21 Jun 87 - Alaska.
Three strong earthquakes shake parts of remote Alaskan Peninsula.

30 Jun 87 - Los Angeles, California.
Delta 767 flight 810 crew inadvertently shuts down engines shortly after takeoff from Los Angeles. Starts to fall, restarts engines and recovers. *Definitely crew error. Similar incident on Mar. 31, 1986 after takeoff from San Francisco.*

12 July 87 - Over Pacific Ocean.
Minuteman missile is destroyed in flight over the Pacific Ocean because of a problem in flight. Launched from Vandenberg. *Note similar incident the previous month.*

16 Jul 87 - Huntsville, Alabama.
Anomalous large "boom" occurs at Huntsville, Alabama.

17 Jul 87 - Huntsville, Alabama.
Another anomalous, large "boom" occurs at Huntsville, Alabama. *Note that Huntsville is a pivot point on the Soviet grid. Adjustments in the grid often "spill out" energy, causing such a boom. It causes a sharp boom if pinpoint spillage occurs. It causes a more general quaking, rumbling sound of longer duration if spillage occurs over an area.*

20 July 87 - Cape Canaveral, Florida.
Tident III successfully launched from flat pad.

14 Oct. 87 - Nellis Air Force Gunnery range.
Top secret plane crashes; possible stealth fighter. *Did the Soviets kill another one?*

9 Nov. 87 - Vandenberg, AFB, California.
Minuteman II missile is destroyed seconds after launch. *Unnamed anomalies cited. Did the Soviets interfere?*

4 Jan. 88 - Madison and Huntsville, Alabama.
Giant radial sighted for several hours. Three mysterious booms rattle Huntsville. *Soviet scalar EM activity continues.*

APPENDIX V

*DEAD MAN FUZING**
THE REAL MEANING OF THE REYKJAVIK SUMMIT

Soviet Foreign Minister spokesman, Gennadi Gerasimov, following failure of the Iceland Summit, said in a radio interview that SDI (U.S. Strategic Defense Initiative), as presently designed, is of no concern to the Soviet Union. The real Soviet concern, he indicated, is that the U.S. would make a great technical breakthrough and deploy new devices in space as a modification to SDI presenting an unacceptable threat to the Soviet Union.

Peter Jennings' ABC News Show, Los Angeles, CA
13 October 1986.

Gerasimov let the cat out of the bag!

With their deployed scalar electromagnetic weapons, the Soviets would immediately hold the winning hand–if these weapons could be unrestrainedly brought to bear.

As pointed out in **Fer-de-Lance: A Briefing On Soviet Scalar Electromagnetic Weapons,** Tesla Book, Co., 1986, the use of massive Soviet scalar EM weapons can only be gingerly applied. Activation and use of the Soviet scalar EM weapons is fraught with grave danger to the entire earth and to the whole human species because of the presence of nuclear facilities in the desired target area, and because of the "backlash" potential against the Soviet Union's own nuclear weapons and facilities.

The explosion at Chernobyl was apparently caused by the accidental failure of a nearby scalar EM transmitter, and the eventual impulsive loss of part of the electrogravitational potential built up by the transmitter before it failed. The resulting electrogravitational pulse (EGP) in the earth "pulsed" the nearest nuclear material ... feul rods in the reactor at Chernobyl.

Had the EGP not been depleted prior to its escape, all four reactors at Chernobyl would have exploded with the same intensity as if

*The term "Dead Man Fuzing," means that, even though your opponent kills you, a weapon or effect of your own will inevitably result which will then kill your opponent.

they had been "triggered" by a fission explosion.

In short, if unrestrainedly used, the EGPs from the Soviet scalar EM weapons would initiate most of the nuclear weapons where they are in the targeted area-in storage, in silos, in aircraft, etc. Target area nuclear reactors and nuclear wastes would also be violently initiated into nuclear explosion. The resulting vast megatonnage of nuclear explosions, much of them "in the dirt, " would provide an unthinkable holocaust. The effects of these giant explosions, deadly fallout and dense clouds of smoke and dirt, would blanket the earth with nuclear effects greater than is presently expected from an all out nuclear war, in which many of the weapons are expected to be destroyed or lost without being exploded nuclearly. Deadly nuclear radiation would blanket the globe, contaminating it for thousands of years. From the covering of the earth by dense smoke and dirt clouds, a new and deeply bitter global ice age–not just a "nuclear winter"–would almost certainly be initiated. In 1960 Khrushchev appropriately characterized these fantastic weapons by stating that they could wipe out all life on earth if unrestrainedly used.

A country's nuclear weapons and facilities, then, become its inadvertent "dead man fuzing" to prevent any substantial employment of large scalar EM weapons against it. So long as nuclear "dead man fuzing" is in place in a country, its adversary can only utilize scalar EM superweapons against it with great difficulty, and then only sparingly. At present, both the U.S. and its NATO allies are "dead man fuzed" by the presence of Western nuclear weapons–and to some extent, by the presence of nuclear reactors and stored nuclear wastes.

Obviously the Soviet Union's task of world domination–and the mind-rending risks it must take in employing large scalar EM weapons–would be greatly expedited if the obstacle of "deployed U.S. and NATO nuclear weapons and facilities" could be eliminated or minimized.

Also, Gorbachev must be acutely aware that the U.S. is finally beginning to look at the possibility of scalar EM weaponry. He would assume that either the U.S. is already on the way to acquiring scalar EM weaponry of its own, or else the time is imminent when it will do so. If this happened, and the U.S. then were to deploy SDI **scalar** EM lasers in space, the effects of each laser would be enormously increased by the electrogravitational amplification factor. Reasonable gain increases of the yield of each laser shot might approach, for example, on the order of 10^{20}. In that case, each laser could suddenly devastate a whole state or region with one or two shots, instead of just being able to destroy one little missile. The Soviets know that Reagan's Star Wars weapons–if modified to the "improved" kind and deployed in space–could deliver a surprise first strike in seconds, and devastate Russia before all the Star Wars space weapons could be knocked out by Soviet ground-based scalar EM beams.

The Soviets also know that it is not too difficult to modify lasers to become such powerful scalar EM lasers.

This means that Gorbachev needs to insure that the Star Wars weaponry is not actually tested in space. Testing in space requires developing at least prototype "space deployment" SDI weapons, to get them up in space to test them from there in the first place. And even such "prototype" SDI weapons would be sufficient to devastate the Soviet Union, given that the prototypes employed the technological breakthrough represented by scalar EM weapons. This is what Gerasimov was really referring to!

Thus Gorbachev simply cannot allow such space testing of SDI weapons, if he hopes to be able to safely seize the opportunity to employ his own already-deployed, massive scalar EM weapons during the "window of time" that would be provided by dismantling of U.S., NATO, and Soviet nuclear weapons.

And–given that he gets agreement and implementation of the "zero option"–Gorbachev knows he will only have a narrow "window" of time in which he can hope to achieve world domination. It can be only a short time until the U.S. produces results in scalar EM weapons, and promptly develops such weapons of its own. Faced with that eventuality, Gorbachev would then have no choice but to turn away from the Communist dream of world domination, and reach a mutually agreed accommodation with the West. Both the West and the Soviets then would have to take immediate and drastic measures to prevent the rapid development and spread of the relatively cheap scalar EM weaponry throughout other nations, particularly those motivated from fanatical beliefs and quite capable of "blowing up the earth" deliberately.

Thus, before the U.S. becomes aware of scalar EM weapons and builds its own, Gorbachev desperately needs to get rid of the "dead man fuzing" problem posed by the nuclear weapons and facilities possessed by the U.S. and its Nato allies, so that he can utilize his superweapons to dominate the world without destroying it.

And he needs to block any chance that the U.S. would be able to have space-tested high energy laser prototypes which could be quickly modified to scalar EM weapons, fired into space, and used to counter Soviet aggression or even destroy the Soviet Union in retaliation.

In short, today the paramount and almost desperate need of the Soviet Union is to reduce American dead-man fuzing and keep the SDI space laser genie bottled up in the lab on the ground.

Accordingly, in Iceland, in what appeared to be a stunning concession on nuclear arms, Gorbachev suddenly offered Reagan a complete dismantling of all nuclear weapons–Reagan's "zero option." Actually this move had been planned by Gorbachev from the beginning; it was not a spur-of-the-moment offer. The reason was simple: If the U.S. could only be persuaded to quickly get rid of its nuclear weaponry, the Soviets would hold an absolutely winning hand. Their massive, deployed, operational scalar EM weapons could then be unleashed with minimal restraint. The extremely delicate and incredibly dangerous problem of bringing the large scalar EM "continent-buster" weapons to bear, without inadvertently causing world destruction, would be vastly eased if only the ordinary U.S. nuclear facilities such as nuclear power plants and radioactive wastes had to be reckoned with.

Fortunately, Ronald Reagan fervently believes in defense .

He made the right decision, whether or not it was for the right reasons.

Indeed, he probably knew in advance that SDI was to be targeted in Iceland by the Soviets, and that sweeping concessions might be offered by them for that purpose. According to one report (" 'Blinded' Satellites," Rowland Evans and Robert Novak, **Washington Post,** Oct. 29, 1986), just before Reykjavik the CIA-sent a report to Reagan with the warning that "the sole reason for Gorbachev's wanting the Iceland summit was to offer unprecendented inducements for Reagan to drop SDI."

Fortunately, Reagan rejected Gorbachev's proposal, because he does not wish to give up what he truly regards as a potential defense against incoming Soviet missiles.

Apparently neither Reagan nor his advisors were aware of the real reason for Gorbachev's unexpected and breathtaking proposal for what would essentially be near-total nuclear disarmament.

The Soviet ground-based scalar EM lasers could sweep the

heavens of the presently conceived SDI weapons, as Gerasimov obliquely implied. However, this would not change the barrier represented by U.S. nuclear dead man fuzing, unless the nuclear weapons had been removed.

Meanwhile, Gorbachev's chess game to remove the dead man fuzing is certainly not over. The Soviets have mounted an intense propaganda campaign urging nuclear disarmament and cancellation or restraint of SDI. With a Democratic Senate now in, and with the approaching end of Reagan's term in office, the Soviet effort to clear the U.S. nukes–and the dead man fuzing–out of the way for Soviet deployed superweapons, while keeping the SDI genie in its laboratory bottle, can only be intensified. Already the Soviets are beating every drum to get substantial antinuclear segments of the U.S. scientific, congressional, political, and pacifist communities aroused to oppose SDI and urge a quick zero nuclear option.

The treaty for dismantling certain missiles in Europe has already been signed by the President, and its ratification by the U.S. Senate appears imminent. More is yet to come, and quickly.

In its aching desire for peace, if an unsuspecting America falls into Gorbachev's trap, shackles SDI and removes its dead-man fuzing, the Soviet Union will be free to enforce its will wherever and whenever it wishes.* If that happens, our beloved stars and stripes will be replaced with the atheistic hammer and sickle. And the noblest experiment of all–freedom for the common person—will have come to an ignoble end.

*Just as Brezhnev forecast for 1985, at a secret meeting in 1972 of the communist party leaders of Europe.

Other Books by Thomas E. Bearden

FER-DE-LANCE: A Briefing on Soviet Scalar Electromagnetic Weapons

SOLUTIONS TO TESLA'S SECRETS AND THE SOVIET TESLA WEAPONS AND REFERENCE ARTICLES FOR SOLUTIONS TO TESLA'S SECRETS (with John T Ratzlaff)

TOWARD A NEW ELECTROMAGNETICS (PART III): Clarifying the Vector Principle

TOWARD A NEW ELECTROMAGNETICS (PART IV): Vectors and Mechanisms Clarified

STAR WARS NOW! The Bohm–Aharanov Effect, Scalar Interferometry, and Soviet Weaponization

THE NEW TESLA ELECTROMAGNETICS AND THE SECRETS OF ELECTRICAL FREE ENERGY—PROOF OF FREE ENERGY DEVICES AND SUPPORTING DATA (with Dr. Rolf Schaffranke)

EXCALIBUR BRIEFING: Explaining Paranormal Phenomena

And Two Video Tapes

SOLUTIONS TO TESLA'S SECRETS & THE SOVIET TESLA WEAPONS

SOVIET WEATHER ENGINEERING OVER NORTH AMERICA

Please note that all of Bearden's books are available from:

TESLA BOOK COMPANY
P.O. Box 1649
Greenville, Texas 75401

TESLA BOOK COMPANY
P. O. BOX 121873
CHULA VISTA, CA 91912